# Birds in Bhutan

## Status and Distribution

# Birds in Bhutan
## Status and Distribution

Peter Spierenburg

ORIENTAL BIRD CLUB

Published 2005 by the Oriental Bird Club, P.O. Box 324, Bedford MK42 0WG, UK.
Registered Charity No. 297242

ISBN 0-9529545-1-6

A CIP catalogue record for this book is available from the British Library.

This book uses paper produced with elemental chlorine-free pulp, harvested from managed sustainable forests.

www.orientalbirdclub.org

Typeset and designed by Fluke Art, Cornwall

Printed and bound in China on behalf of Compass Press Ltd.

10 9 8 7 6 5 4 3 2 1

Front cover: Ward's Trogon by Jan Wilczur
Back cover: Wedge-billed Wren Babbler by Ren Hathway
Title page: Slender-billed Scimitar Babbler by Phil Jones

# Contents

Acknowledgements ............................................................................................ 6

Foreword ............................................................................................................ 7

Maps .................................................................................................................. 8

1.  Introduction .............................................................................................. 9

2.  Methodology ............................................................................................ 10

    2.1. Approach ........................................................................................ 10

    2.2. Preparing the dataset ..................................................................... 10

    2.3. Analysis of distribution patterns ..................................................... 11

    2.4. Data presentation ........................................................................... 12

    2.5. Completeness .................................................................................. 14

3.  History of bird study in Bhutan ............................................................. 17

4.  Habitats ................................................................................................... 19

    4.1. Biodiversity in the Eastern Himalayas ............................................ 19

    4.2. General distribution patterns .......................................................... 19

    4.3. Habitats and birds in the subtropical zone ...................................... 20

    4.4. Habitats and birds in the temperate zone ........................................ 21

        4.4.1. The lower montane zone ....................................................... 21

        4.4.2. The middle montane zone ..................................................... 22

        4.4.3. The upper montane zone ...................................................... 22

    4.5. The alpine zone ............................................................................... 23

5.  Migration and seasonality ....................................................................... 24

    5.1. Residents ......................................................................................... 25

    5.2. Altitudinal migrants ........................................................................ 25

    5.3. Summer visitors .............................................................................. 26

    5.4. Winter visitors and passage migrants .............................................. 26

6.  Threats and conservation ........................................................................ 28

    6.1. Historical habitat changes ............................................................... 28

    6.2. The development process ................................................................. 29

    6.3. Conservation ethics ........................................................................ 30

    6.4. The protected areas system ............................................................. 30

    6.5. Challenges for bird conservation ..................................................... 31

7.  Glossary ................................................................................................... 32

8.  Species accounts ...................................................................................... 33

9.  Update to 2004 ........................................................................................ 357

10. Birding sites in Bhutan ........................................................................... 358

11. References ................................................................................................ 361

    11.1 Literature sources .......................................................................... 361

    11.2 Primary data .................................................................................. 363

Index of scientific names ................................................................................. 369

Index of English names .................................................................................... 376

# Acknowledgements

Being able to work in Bhutan for several years is special in itself, but even more so if you are posted amidst beautiful forests with birds everywhere, as I was in Zhemgang and the Jigme Singye Wangchuck National Park. Frequent travel enabled me to visit even more great birding sites. It was in the field that the idea for this book germinated, gradually developing into a project of such magnitude that the book could not have been completed without the support of the many people mentioned below.

Firstly, I thank my colleagues at the Nature Conservation Division (NCD) and the National Parks. They provided me with the opportunity but, through their commitment to conservation, also with the motive: increased knowledge of Bhutanese birds will enhance the conservation of the country's unique biodiversity. The Joint Director of the NCD, Dr Sangay Wangchuk, has supported the idea of this book from the start, and has facilitated the use of unpublished field data and the production of the distribution maps. In Sherub, Ornithologist at the NCD, I found a sparring partner, whose enthusiasm and knowledge greatly helped the idea take off in the initial stages. Dasho Sangay Thinley, Secretary of the Department of Forests, kindly agreed to provide a foreword to the book.

A special word of thanks must go to the Oriental Bird Club. None of the initial impetus would have found its course, but for the Club kindly supporting the project and generously providing funds to publish the book. I am particularly grateful to Nigel Redman for his enthusiasm in managing the project and for his personal support. I also thank Guy Kirwan for his considerable editing skills, Nigel Collar for his expert proof-reading, and Julie Dando for skillfully adapting my maps and graphs, and transforming the whole thing into an attractive and stylish book.

I am also strongly indebted to Carol and Tim Inskipp, for their untiring encouragement and advice throughout. This book builds on the foundations they have laid, particularly the bibliography and collection of reports they have compiled, as well as the field data they shared. Their knowledge of the region's avifauna was crucial in shaping my ideas concerning distribution patterns. They generously reviewed the draft text and invested much time in it, even gently drawing attention to sentence structures that too obviously reflected my non-Anglophone background. David Farrow also took an important share in reviewing the species accounts.

Ren Hathway made a great contribution to the book by volunteering to coordinate the artwork. He and Dan Cole contributed many excellent illustrations, covering a broad selection of bird species, including a good number of Bhutan's specialities. Jan Wilczur, Phil Jones, Mike Langman and Chris Orgill also kindly contributed original artwork. Further illustrations are reproduced from previously published books with kind permission of the publishers, Christopher Helm. The artists concerned are Norman Arlott, Clive Byers, Lawrence Chappell, John Cox, Carl D'Silva, Brin Edwards, Alan Harris, Peter Hayman, Dan Powell, Craig Robson and Tim Worfolk. Finally, I am especially grateful to Jan Wilczur for his breathtaking cover painting of Ward's Trogon.

Among the many people who generously shared their field data I must make specific mention of the leaders of the various bird tour groups and their companies. David Bishop (Victor Emanuel Nature Tours), David Farrow (Birdquest), Paul Holt (Sunbird), Krys Kazmierczak (Sunbird/Peregrine Holidays) and Ben King (KingBird Tours) all granted me unrestricted access to the wealth of data they have collected over the years. This represents a fine example of bird tourism making a significant contribution to our collective knowledge of birds and their habitats, and thereby to conservation. I am grateful to all of them for their support and inspiration. In the field, I was often in the good company of various birding friends: Dr Adam Pain, Richard Pickering, Rebecca Pradhan, Sherub, Durga Devi Sharma, Tshering Phuntsho, Ruth Urban, Ab Steenvoorden, Ferry Bleumink and Bert van der Geest. I owe them a great deal for putting me on track with regard to the Bhutanese avifauna, providing fresh views and their many unpublished data.

Finally, I thank all of the other people who have kindly shared their field data, including Robert and Sue Armstrong, Lhap Dorji, Sangay Dorji, Bjarne O. Jensen, Brian Fletcher, Jan Ove Gershaug, Steve Madge, Lyn Mair, Herman Matthijsen, Arend van Riessen, Nigel Redman, Rinchen Singye, John Sparks, Tom and Margot Sutherland, Dago Tshering, Sharap Wangchuk and Rob van Westrienen.

# Foreword

Birds are intricately linked to the landscape of Bhutan. Whether one is in a village, in the capital or walking in the forests, birds and their songs are part of the scenery. To live in an environment with an astonishing diversity of birds is nothing out of the ordinary for the Bhutanese. Yet there is a growing realisation that the avifaunal richness is a valuable asset to the country. None of the animal taxa are as conspicuous and, in many cases, of such brilliant appearance as birds. They are one of the most visible manifestations of the unique condition of Bhutan's environment. The bare facts of over 70% forest cover, 26% of the country designated as National Parks and an additional 9% as Biological Corridors become profoundly tangible at the sight of a hornbill gliding down a densely forested slope. Birds are true ambassadors of conservation.

The overwhelming richness of Bhutan's avifauna has drawn international attention for over three decades now. Many acknowledged ornithologists have visited the country. Interest is still growing and the audience is widening. Bhutan holds a unique attraction to tourists and birds are increasingly becoming part of what the country has to offer. This growing attention is the fruit of the perseverance and dedication of a few pioneers in Bhutan. These people have long taken up bird study as a serious pursuit, if not a way of life. Their efforts have not only rooted bird conservation firmly in the country's policies and legislation, but have also inspired others. They now see their ranks enhanced with a new generation of promising, young bird experts.

This book comes at just the right moment. It does justice to the wealth of information that has already been gathered on birds in Bhutan but, equally as important, it is full of challenges for the future; challenges for conservation in the first place, as Bhutan's forests constitute a vital resource for a large number of species that are threatened on a world scale, but, secondly, there is also the challenge to learn more about the complex patterns of distribution of birds in a rich and diverse mountain environment. It is hoped that this book will mark another step forward in the development of our knowledge of birds in Bhutan, and will also add to the appreciation of the richness of our avifauna and the beautiful environment in which it is allowed to flourish.

Dasho Sangay Thinley
Secretary of the Department of Forests

# Maps

Roads

Bhutan: districts, towns and roads

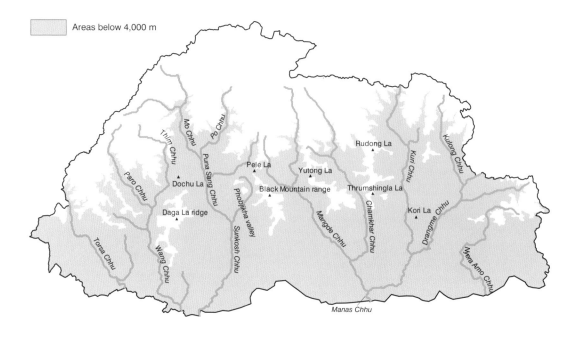

Areas below 4,000 m

Bhutan: physical features

# 1. Introduction

Bhutan is extraordinarily rich in birdlife. Its location in the extremely biodiverse Eastern Himalayas, the existence of vast areas of relatively undisturbed natural habitats, and the country's progressive conservation policies have placed it at the centre of regional conservation efforts. In particular, the vast expanses of old-growth subtropical and temperate forests have become unique in the Himalayas, providing habitat for birds now rare elsewhere, such as Rufous-necked Hornbill *Aceros nipalensis*, White-bellied Heron *Ardea insignis* and Beautiful Nuthatch *Sitta formosa*. Perhaps the best-known feature of the Bhutanese avifauna is the wintering Black-necked Cranes *Grus nigricollis*, their presence being closely intertwined with the rich local culture. A total of 645 species has been confirmed from Bhutan, including 19 species listed by BirdLife International as globally threatened and 12 as Near Threatened.

This rich avifauna has been brought to light progressively, through the efforts of many. Various ornithological expeditions, surveys of the country's protected areas, winter counts of Black-necked Cranes and regular visits by bird tour groups, have all served to draw increasing attention to the magnificent birdlife that can still be encountered. The present work is a further step in this direction, attempting to bring together the wealth of knowledge accumulated over the years. It is intended as a snapshot of what we know now, in the hope that it will encourage further studies and research. Despite its size, the main conclusion of this book should be that we are still in the initial stages of understanding avian distributions in a highly diverse montane environment such as that found in Bhutan.

My objective is to describe the distributions of birds in Bhutan, in relation to their ecology. For this, an effort has been made to collate data from as many sources as possible in a standardised dataset so as to permit systematic analysis. The results of this analysis have been interpreted from an ecological perspective, linking bird distributions to season, habitats and behaviour. The main body of the work is the 643 species accounts detailing occurrence by season and altitude, as well as providing other information such as numbers and breeding records (Chapter 8). The book commences with several introductory chapters contextualising bird study in Bhutan (Chapters 2–6). These include an account of the history of bird study in the country, the habitats and their birdlife, and migration patterns. Finally, there is a discussion of issues relevant to bird conservation such as historical changes in the avifauna, the development process, conservation ethics, the protected areas system and future challenges. Chapter 9 gives a brief update on new information that has become available up to 2004, and Chapter 10 gives an overview of birding sites in Bhutan. Chapter 11 lists the primary data and literature sources used.

# 2. Methodology

## 2.1. Approach

The objective of this book is to describe distribution patterns of birds in Bhutan, in relation to their ecology. Through the efforts of professional ornithologists, local and expatriate birders, and bird tour groups, a vast amount of data on birds in Bhutan has been collected. This represents an impressive dataset, culled from both high-quality ornithological surveys and carefully recorded observations by individual birders and bird groups. However, because of the variety of sources, they do not form a systematic dataset as such, which could readily be used to analyse distribution patterns. The data were gathered by a variety of methods, with unequal coverage of different seasons and parts of the country. Also, among the observers there was variation in identification skills, as well as in the quality of identification guides and optical equipment at their disposal. Field methods include incidental observations, day and/or locality lists, trip lists, systematic surveys (e.g. Inskipp and Inskipp 1993b), collections, tape playback, migration counts, waterfowl counts and breeding bird inventories. The methodology employed was therefore designed to make optimal use of the available records, utilising as many sources as possible.

## 2.2. Preparing the dataset

The first step was to collect publications and unpublished trip reports and species lists from Bhutan. In this endeavour, the bibliography maintained by Tim Inskipp (Inskipp 2001) was invaluable, as was the generous data-sharing by the various bird tour companies and numerous individuals. Based on these, a standard database was established placing each record into a standard format: species name, (approximate) date of observation, locality, altitude and any additional information. All records that combined species name with any of the other parameters were considered relevant to the analysis or parts of it. Use of such varied records made it essential to accept relatively high error margins concerning localities, dates and altitudes. Records for which date was imprecisely known were estimated with an error margin of two weeks. Localities were transposed to 5′ x 5′ grid squares ($\approx$ 10km-square), with an error margin of one square. In this way, records made, for example, 'between Namling and Yonkhola' could be utilised. Secondly, localities were linked to the biogeographic units described below, whereby even less precise records, for example, 'between Gedu and Thimphu', also could be included in the analysis. Altitude was the most problematic parameter to standardise, particularly because of the scarcity of readings and their unreliability. Many observers also provided data for a range of altitudes, for example during the course of a day's trek. At the same time, the altitude of many frequently visited sites is known and others can relatively easily be estimated if relating to points along the national highway, because its Indian engineers in the 1960s designed the road network with remarkably constant slopes, most high passes being approached in a 5% ascent, so as to permit the passage of heavy traffic. To generate sufficient altitudinal records for analysis, an error margin of 250 m was used. If no altitude or range was reported but the approximate altitude of the birding site was known, an estimated altitude was assigned to the record. In the same way, reported altitudes were cross-checked against known points and corrected if deviating by more than 250 m. Errors in field identification, in record reporting and in data entry were eliminated, as far as possible, by double-checking aberrant data against the original source and, if possible, with the observer. Records considered doubtful were eliminated from the analysis without prejudice that they may prove valid in future. Species only reported in the 19th century (Blue-eared Kingfisher *Alcedo meninting*, Pallid Harrier *Circus macrourus*, Changeable Hawk Eagle *Spizaetus cirrhatus*) were not included, as it is generally difficult to ascertain whether the birds were actually collected in present-day Bhutan. A decision was made not to provide a detailed rationale concerning the non-inclusion of such records, as it was thought that this would significantly lengthen the species accounts and, moreover, would enter the domain of any rarities committee that might be established in the future.

These various procedures resulted in a database containing over 91,000 records for 640 species, which were suitable for further analysis at different levels. Some of the potential data sources could not be accessed and thus the dataset covers an estimated 90% of those records potentially available. The database covers records up to June 2002. Details of new species added to the country's list have been included up to 2004. This has resulted in a total of 645 species covered.

# 2.3. Analysis of distribution patterns

Analysis of distribution patterns relies on several basic assumptions. The first is that the principal ecological variation in the Eastern Himalayas is related to altitude, with climate and habitat as underlying factors. The distribution of a given bird species is therefore circumscribed primarily by its altitudinal range. For birds with marked altitudinal migrations it is important to distinguish summer and winter ranges. Altitudinal ranges were derived through a standardised analysis, taking 90% of all altitude records to represent the species' regular altitudinal range, rounded to 200 m intervals. The 5% of records above and below this range were considered to represent more occasional or exceptional occurrence. Here, a second basic assumption is that the species' altitudinal range has a normal distribution from a statistical standpoint. This assumption appears generally valid, but may be more problematic in the case of those species continuously distributed from the southern border northwards or from the alpine zone southwards, particularly as the northern and southern zones of the country are under-represented in the dataset. Also, irruptive presence in a higher or lower altitudinal zone in some years complicates analysis, as does the presence of migrants passing through higher or lower zones to reach their regular range. Therefore, in such cases, the altitudinal range derived from the standardised analysis was interpreted cautiously. The highest and lowest reported altitudes have been double-checked against the original reports to reduce the effect of possible errors in data entry.

Another assumption is that altitudinal movements are subject to distinct seasons in which birds are, for instance, in their summer and winter ranges. For each species cut-off points were determined whereby the majority of the population was considered to be in the summer range. This was performed visually, based on figures plotting altitude against season. For species with an extensive period during which they are en route between their winter and summer ranges the results were not always satisfactory, leading to suggested summer and winter altitudinal ranges that were too broad. In these cases, priority was given to delimiting a reliable summer range, taking the period when the species had almost entirely departed from lower elevations.

A major assumption in the analysis was that, for the majority of species, the north–south ridges between the major river valleys constitute dispersal barriers, leading to patterns of west–east gradients in their distributions. In the high Himalayas and in the foothills, on the other hand, these barriers are less important. The concept of biogeographic units was used to describe these patterns. The following division is adapted from MacKinnon (1991), adjusting the unit limits to those of the main forest types in the *Flora of Bhutan* (Grierson and Long 1983).

- The Himalayan or alpine zone, located along the main Himalayan range above 4,000 m, is subdivided into eastern and western components separated by the Kuri Chhu valley, referred to as the **high west** and **high east** hereafter.
- The temperate zone may be considered as a central belt from west to east between 1,000 and 4,000 m. It is divided into western, central-western, central-eastern and eastern components, separated by the Daga La ridge/Dochu La, the Black Mountain range and the Thrumshing La range, respectively. These four units are referred to as the **western valleys**, the **Sunkosh Valley**, the **central valleys** and the **eastern valleys**.
- The subtropical zone starts at the southern border, reaching up to 1,000 m in the foothills and 500 m in the main river valleys. It is divided into western, central and eastern components by the large Sunkosh Chhu and Manas Chhu. These three units are referred to as the **western foothills**, the **central foothills** and the **eastern foothills**.

The biogeographic units are shown in Fig. 1.

As observer effort varied considerably between the various biogeographic units, the data were standardised to guide interpretation of east–west distribution patterns. For this, the relative presence of each species per biogeographic unit was calculated, i.e. the number of records of the species as a percentage of the total number of records.

The description of distribution patterns does not take into account changes over time, and records from the 1930s to the present were treated equally. This approach appears to be justified by the fact that Bhutan has mostly been spared large-scale landscape changes, and by the observation that many species still occur at the same sites where they were reported in the 1930s. Possible declines or changes in distribution of a species are dealt with in the relevant accounts.

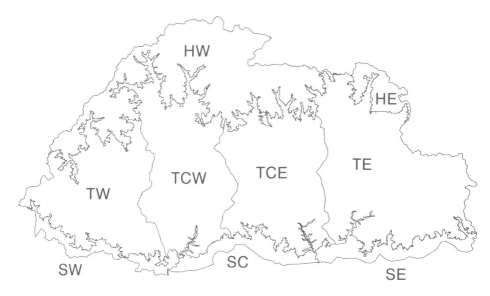

**Figure 1**: Biogeographic units

HW: high west    HE: high east
TW: western valleys    TCW: Sunkosh valley    TCE: central valleys    TE: eastern valleys
SW: western foothills    SC: central foothills    SE: eastern foothills

# 2.4. Data presentation

The taxonomy, nomenclature and sequence of the species follow Inskipp *et al.* (1996). New taxonomic information is taken into account if two or more forms of a (proposed) species complex occur in Bhutan, which is only the case for Golden-spectacled Warbler (Alström and Olsson, 1999).

Each account commences with a short summary of the species's range and status in the region or worldwide, along with some generalities concerning habitat choice and behaviour. This introduction is based on Ali and Ripley (1983), BirdLife International (2001), Grimmett *et al.* (1998), Hagemeijer and Blair (1997) and Robson (2000), and such references are not mentioned in the text.

The distribution of most species is presented on a graph and a map. The keys for these are explained in Figures 2 and 3. Graphs and maps are included for all species with more than ten records in Bhutan, as well as for species listed by BirdLife International as threatened or Near Threatened with more than three records. The graph presents altitudinal and seasonal distribution. All suitable records are plotted against month on the x-axis and altitude on the y-axis (see Figure 2), providing an immediate overview of altitudes and season of occurrence of the species in Bhutan. The map presents geographical distribution (see Figure 3). The maps include one or more elements:

**Confirmed records per grid square.** This is included in all maps as black dots.

**Main river systems.** This is added as a background in a minority of cases, replacing the probable distribution range (see below). It is only used for species closely associated with wetland habitats, for which a distribution range based on altitude would not make sense.

**Probable distribution range.** This element is added for all other species with more than ten records in Bhutan. Depending on the status of the species as a summer visitor, altitudinal migrant, winter visitor or resident, the map may include one to three shades of green representing summer, winter and all-year range. The basis for mapping is the species's altitudinal range and its occurrence in the nine biogeographic units. The altitudinal range is mapped for those biogeographical units where regular occurrence of the species is expected, that is when three or more records exist (note: not necessarily sites) from this unit. As the foothills and the alpine zone are under-represented in the dataset, a single record was considered sufficient to include these units within the species's mapped distribution. The dots representing confirmed records will largely correspond to the mapped range, but may include isolated records from outside this range as well. In some cases, where the probable distributional range does not accord with the confirmed records, a further level of detail is included, by mapping only suitable habitat in the species's altitudinal range. This is applied to some species associated with (a) agricultural areas and (b) warm broadleaf forest. Where this filter has been used, it is indicated in the altitude summary in the species heading, e.g. R 400-2000 (broadleaf forest).

The status and abundance of each species was assessed systematically, using a classification modified from Inskipp and Inskipp (1995). Based on the seasonal and altitudinal patterns, and status elsewhere in the Indian subcontinent, species were classified as follows: resident, altitudinal migrant, summer visitor, winter visitor, passage migrant or vagrant. To determine relative abundance, the percentage of records of a given species in the entire dataset was calculated. A weighting factor was applied for records from different altitudinal zones, in order to correct for observer effort (under-representation of species at high and low elevations) and differences in species-richness (decreasing at higher elevations). Species were subsequently ranked and the lower 10% were considered 'rare', the next 10–50% 'uncommon', the middle 50–75% 'frequent', the following 75–90% 'common' and the uppermost 10% 'abundant'.

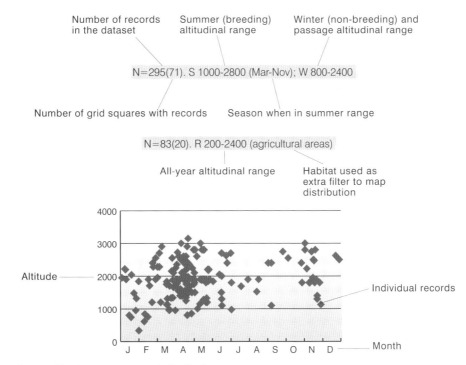

Figure 2: Key to altitudinal and seasonal distribution

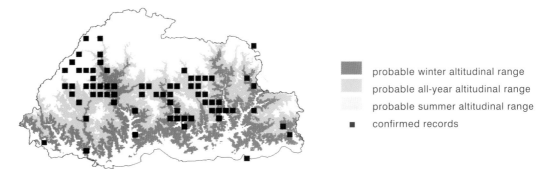

Figure 3: Key to the distribution maps

Discussion of breeding status follows the terminology of the *EBCC Atlas of European breeding birds* (Hagemeijer and Blair 1997), distinguishing possible, probable and confirmed breeding.

**Possible breeding**
1. Species observed in breeding season in possible nesting habitat
2. Singing male(s) present (or breeding calls heard) in breeding season

**Probable breeding**
3. Pair observed in suitable nesting habitat in breeding season
4. Permanent territory presumed through registration of territorial behaviour (song, etc.) on at least two different days, a week or more apart, at the same place.
5. Courtship and display
6. Visiting probable nest-site
7. Agitated behaviour or anxiety calls from adults
8. Brood-patch on adult examined in the hand
9. Nest-building or excavating nest-hole

**Confirmed breeding**
10. Distraction-display or injury-feigning
11. Used nest or eggshells found
12. Recently fledged young (nidicolous species) or downy young (nidifugous species)
13. Adults entering or leaving nest-site in circumstances indicating occupied nest (including high nests or nest-holes, the contents of which cannot be seen) or adult seen incubating
14. Adult carrying faecal sac or food for young
15. Nest containing eggs
16. Nest with young seen or heard

In the text, references to primary data have been added, for various significant records such as high- and low-altitude records, late and early records, and breeding records.

## 2.5. Completeness

It goes without saying that a dataset based on records resulting from a variety of field methods and largely collected unsystematically leaves many gaps. Its strength lies in the various sources being complementary. Figure 4 shows the number of records provided by different categories of birders. Bird tour groups are the largest providers, with 46% of the records. As they tend to visit the same localities over multiple years, their data stand out due to the completeness of the species lists for certain localities. At the same time, they also attempt to cover a broad altitudinal range to witness as much of the avifauna as possible. As a result, the altitudinal range between 200 m and 3,500 m has been well sampled, albeit with some emphasis on mid-elevations, where

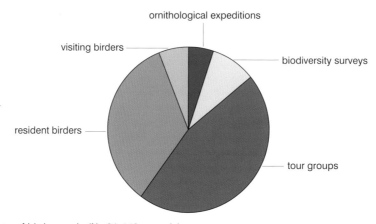

**Figure 4:** Sources of bird records (N=91,449 records)

the lateral highway passes. Resident birders, both local and expatriate (including the author), provided 34% of the records, constituting an essential complement to the data of the bird tour groups, particularly in records from outside the spring period and from areas less easily accessible to tourists. The systematic work of the ornithological surveys, and biodiversity surveys of protected areas, again add significantly to the geographical coverage and to the completeness of the species lists. Finally, the data of visiting individuals represent a valuable contribution to the dataset, particularly in records from outside the spring season.

Overall, data are available for 213 5′ x 5′ grid squares, representing 36% of all such squares (Fig. 5). In the pattern of sampled squares the national road network is clearly discernible, as are the main high-altitude treks, whilst the foothills and the alpine zone are under-represented. Due to problems of accessibility, few birders have been able to visit these zones, particularly outside the favourable spring and autumn seasons (Fig. 6). During the monsoon bad road conditions inhibit good coverage of the country. Summer records are thus largely confined to those areas with resident local birders and, as a result, between 1,500 m and 2,500 m. More subtle gaps lie in the degree of coverage of the various biogeographic units, with particular gaps in the lower parts of the western, Sunkosh and eastern valleys. While the vast stretches of warm broadleaf forest stand out due to their high species diversity, and their host of rare and critical species, these have not yet been surveyed intensively. In particular, those areas between the Trongsa–Gelephu and Trashigang–Samdrup Jongkha highways and on either side of the Thimphu–Phuntsholing highway are still largely unexplored. Considering the number of records per square, the country's favoured birding spots clearly stand out, with concentrated records from around Thimphu, Punakha/Wangdue Phodrang, Zhemgang, the forests between Sengor and Yonkhola, Mongar district, and the Deothang area, Samdrup Jongkha district. The number of records per square varies considerably, and the number of species found in each increases with observer effort, the curve flattening off only after 500 records (Fig. 7). In consequence, only 16% of the 213 squares can be considered to have been adequately surveyed. For these, between 147 and 328 species have been confirmed, with a mean of 218 species in each. The maximum number was found in a square located within the bird-rich forests between Namling and Yonkhola, in Mongar district.

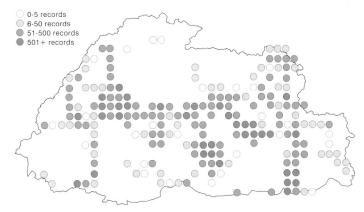

Figure 5: Geographical coverage of the available data

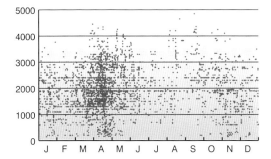

Figure 6: Distribution of records by season and altitude (N=6,051; 10% sample from the dataset)

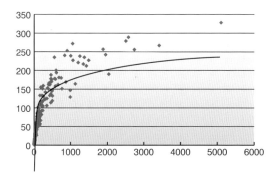

**Figure 7:** Number of species confirmed from a 5' x 5' square as a function of the total number of records (N=211 squares; 1 square with 10,110 records not presented)

Aside of the limited geographical coverage, the data also show a strong bias towards spring (Fig. 8). This relates in the first place to greater birding activity at this season, particularly with the presence of the bird tour groups, which have contributed the bulk of the spring records. However, spring is also when viewing conditions for birds are best; many species are defending breeding territories and high-altitude species migrate through accessible elevations. The arrival of summer migrants overlaps with the passage of many winter migrants, making it possible to observe more than 100 species on any day in spring, and over 300 in a three-week intensive birding trip. Finally, this is also the season with the best weather conditions, whilst from July to September many mornings are marred by rain. Records reveal March to June to be the period with most records per morning, while September to November is a period relatively poor in records (Fig. 9).

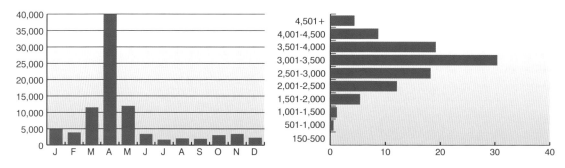

**Figure 8:** Number of records per month and per altitude class (N=91,449 records)

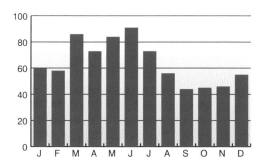

**Figure 9:** Records per birding morning (N=21,054)

# 3. History of bird study in Bhutan

The first ornithological records for Bhutan date from the 19th century. In 1837–1838, Captain R. B. Pemberton made an official visit to the court of Bhutan. Starting from Gauhati in December 1837, he travelled to Deothang, Trashi Yangtse and then west to Punakha, returning south to the Buxa Duars in May 1838. With the assistance of, amongst others, Dr William Griffith, a botanist, he collected bird specimens, which numbered at least 350, according to Ludlow (1937). His mention of the 'sarus of Bengal', which he shot in the 'valleys of Boomdungtung, Jugur and Jaeesah', between 2,500 m and 2,900 m, according to Ali *et al.* (1996) can be considered the first record of Black-necked Crane in Bhutan. The place names refer to the Bumthang Valley, amongst others Gyetsa, which is still a known wintering site for the species. Thereafter, based on specimens taken in Bhutan, Delessert, Blyth and Gray described several species and subspecies new to science, including Greater Rufous-headed Parrotbill *Paradoxornis ruficeps* (Blyth), Grey-headed Parrotbill *P. gularis* (Gray), Striated Laughingthrush *Garrulax striatus* (Blyth) and Black-billed Magpie *Pica pica bottanensis* (Delessert). Subsequently, a few specimens were collected by the taxidermist accompanying the Hon. Ashley Eden's Mission in 1864, and by Lieutenant Colonel F. M. Bailey in 1922, but the expeditions of Frank Ludlow in the 1930s were the first serious ornithological work in Bhutan (Sherub 2000b).

Frank Ludlow and Mr Sherriff first visited Bhutan in 1933, at the invitation of the second King of Bhutan, Jigme Wangchuck. Between mid-April and August they travelled from Gangtok to Ha and via Paro east to Trashi Yangtse, crossing into Tibet at Singye Dzong. Following this first successful tour, in which they were particularly pleased by the richness of the avifauna in east Bhutan, they planned a series of expeditions systematically to explore the avifauna and flora of the Eastern Himalayas, from Bhutan to the Tsangpo Valley. This again took them to east Bhutan in 1934 (June–early July and late August to mid-November), 1936 (February–March, October–November) and 1938 (November), travelling from Deothang north to the Trashi Yangtse Valley and the passes to Tibet, as well as traversing the Sakten area. Ludlow collected over 1,800 specimens of 316 species in Bhutan, including extensive series of the little-known wren babblers and tesias. Diagnosis of these collections by N. B. Kinnear established Ludlow's (White-browed) Fulvetta *Alcippe vinipectus chumbiensis* as a subspecies new to science. To date, Ludlow's work represents a landmark in our knowledge of birds in Bhutan. In particular, those records from high elevations in summer are still unique and hardly matched by recent work.

The next major study of the country's avifauna was initiated by the third King of Bhutan, Jigme Dorji Wangchuck, who had an earnest wish to create a well-illustrated field guide to the birds of Bhutan, especially for his royal guests, nature lovers and visiting foreign tourists. Between 1966 and 1973 a research programme was conducted by the Bombay Natural History Society, the Smithsonian Institution (Washington D.C., USA) and the Zoological Survey of India (Calcutta), during which nine expeditions were undertaken, led by Salim Ali, S. Dillon Ripley and B. Biswas. They travelled the country, primarily in the period October–March, following the new road network under construction, and trekking to higher elevations in west and central Bhutan. A total of 3,218 specimens was collected, of 481 species. Subsequently, the *Field guide to the birds of the Eastern Himalayas* was published in 1977, followed by the *Birds of Bhutan* in 1996, the latter providing a full account of the survey work. The work of Ali, Ripley and Biswas drew international attention to the richness of Bhutan's avifauna. At that time 516 species were confirmed from the country and at least 100 more were suspected to occur. In recent years research and museum collecting has been taken up again, in a collaborative effort between the Nature Conservation Division of the Forestry Services Division and the Field Museum of Natural History, Chicago, USA.

In the late 1980s the wintering population of Black-necked Cranes and the protection of their habitat attracted much attention, primarily through the efforts of Dasho Peljor J. Dorji. As a result, several papers on the cranes were published in international journals. In 1989, the first winter count was organised in collaboration with the International Crane Foundation (ICF), which confirmed that wintering areas in Bhutan hold internationally significant numbers. Crane counts have since been repeated annually, through a collaborative effort between the Royal Society for Protection of Nature (RSPN) and the ICF. In 1998 this sparked the first satellite-tracking research project in Bhutan, with a transmitter attached to a crane from Phobjikha Valley and three others banded. The Black-necked Cranes have become central to the work of the RSPN, and they now constitute a flagship for bird conservation efforts in the country, having a central role in public awareness campaigns at national level and in mobilising communities around conservation and development activities in the Phobjikha Valley.

Around the same time a group of local bird enthusiasts started to appear in Bhutan. Rebecca Pradhan, a dedicated and experienced field biologist, was the focal point in this. Perhaps most importantly, she encouraged a young generation to acquire an interest in birds and field biology in general. Under the auspices of the RSPN the first bird club was formed. Pradhan also collected extensive field data on globally threatened birds. One of the most significant records concerned a flock of 21 Beautiful Nuthatches she observed in a remote part of Zhemgang district. In 1999, together with Tandin Wangdi, she published a booklet, *Threatened birds in Bhutan*, aimed particularly at making the Bhutanese youth acquainted with the country's unique avifauna.

Local birders have always been augmented by numbers of expatriates residing in the country for periods of up to several years. These have often brought with them birding experience from around the globe, and have made a valuable input into bird study in Bhutan. The first expatriate birder was J. R. S. Holmes, who was employed by the Bank of Bhutan in Phuntsholing in the 1960s. He was in close contact with the ornithological surveys working at that time, and he contributed many records from south-west Bhutan. He tragically died in a traffic accident in 1970. The particular contribution of expatriate birders lies in the opportunity they possess, either through their assignments or privately, to visit areas off the beaten track and outside the best birding season. Their records have greatly enhanced our knowledge of the distribution of birds in Bhutan.

Birders visiting the country on birdwatching trips have become relatively commonplace since the late 1980s. In particular, the first visitors were in a position to travel widely and make many interesting discoveries, regularly adding new species to the Bhutanese list and reporting their findings in international journals, drawing increased attention to the country's avifauna. The first Naturetrek group visited Bhutan in 1988, and since 1994–1996 a number of established companies have operated annual spring tours to Bhutan. The most regular of these are Victor Emanuel Nature Tours (led by David Bishop), Birdquest (David Farrow), Sunbird (Paul Holt) and KingBird Tours (Ben King). The highly skilled birders leading these groups have, over the years, developed extensive expertise with Bhutanese birds, using tape playback amongst other techniques. This has resulted in the discovery of several new and rare species for the country, with sites for Wedge-billed *Sphenocichla humei* and Long-billed Wren Babblers *Rimator malacoptilus* amongst some of the recent thrilling finds. David Bishop published an account of new records of rare species in *Forktail*, and also drew attention in the *Oriental Bird Club Bulletin* to the outstanding birding opportunities on the road between Ura and Lingmethang. April is considered the best month for birding in Bhutan and brings the largest number of groups, which generally follow an itinerary covering the national highways, from Paro to Samdrup Jongkha, whilst recently Zhemgang is developing as a newer tour destination.

Among the first foreign birders to visit the country in the late 1980s and early 1990s were Tim and Carol Inskipp, authorities on the avifauna of the Indian subcontinent. They subsequently became involved in a series of missions for WWF-Bhutan and the Nature Conservation Section (NCS) of the Forestry Services Division, which assisted in ornithological surveys of the newly established protected areas. Between 1993 and 2000 they made four visits during which they trained NCS and National Parks staff in field survey work. A similar mission was organised in 1994, led by Scott Connop. These missions yielded a vast dataset, added several species to the national list and resulted in a number of publications in *Forktail*. The Inskipps also compiled *An introduction to birdwatching in Bhutan*, published by WWF-Bhutan, which included a first checklist for the country that listed over 580 species. In addition, these missions provided a basis for the NCS, now upgraded to divisional status, as well as the National Parks, to develop a capacity for bird survey work. This culminated in the appointment of an ornithologist to the Division in 1999. The person concerned, Sherub, has led various ornithological surveys to the remotest parts of the protected areas.

Meanwhile, the identification literature available to birders in Bhutan made an enormous leap forward with the appearance of Scott Connop's tape, *Bird sounds of the Himalayas* and the publication, in 1998, of the *Birds of the Indian subcontinent* by Richard Grimmett, Carol Inskipp and Tim Inskipp, who also compiled a field guide edition of this work specifically for Bhutan, which was published as *A field guide to the birds of Bhutan* in November 1999, commemorating His Majesty, Jigme Singye Wangchuck's 25 years on the throne (Sherub 2000b). Other field guides for the region and adjacent areas have since followed.

Today, the number of birds confirmed to occur in Bhutan stands at 645, with further additions being made annually. However, quality is even more significant than quantity in this case. Bhutan offers opportunities to observe and undertake research on several rare and spectacular birds that are often hard to find elsewhere. It is the combined effort of professional ornithologists, local and expatriate birders, and bird tour groups that has unveiled some of the richness of the avifauna, although much more unquestionably remains to be discovered.

# 4. Habitats

## 4.1. Biodiversity in the Eastern Himalayas

The Eastern Himalayas stretch from east Nepal to Arunachal Pradesh and include the hills of north-east India and adjacent parts of Myanmar (Burma) and south-west China. Originally rich in biodiversity the area still harbours large tracts of well-preserved habitats. In particular, the wet lowland and montane rainforest zones are of great importance to birds. These zones have been identified by BirdLife International as Endemic Bird Areas (EBAs; 130 Eastern Himalayas and 131 Assam plains), defined as a place where two or more species of restricted range (i.e. with global distributions of less than 50,000 km²) occur together. Twenty-four species have their world range restricted to EBA 130. Bhutan is in a key position in the Eastern Himalayas from a conservation standpoint, as the country has a large area of relatively undisturbed forest. The vast tracts of temperate and subtropical broadleaf forests constitute a unique feature that has become rare elsewhere in the region.

Species richness in the Eastern Himalayas results from a combination of factors. Firstly, it is an area of overlap between two biogeographic regions, the Indo-Malayan (south and south-east Asia) and the Palearctic realms (Europe and north Asia), and therefore its avifauna is derived from both. South and south-east Asia, in general, has the greatest avian diversity in the world, after South America. This diversity has originated, to a large extent, from historical interaction between geographical and climatic factors. During Pleistocene glacial periods the diverse geography, with its complex arrangement of mountain chains, provided multiple refugia to which vegetation formations and associated avifaunas withdrew. This led to successive isolation and expansion of bird populations, and thereby speciation. In addition, these glacial periods created corridors of temperate conditions through the mountains via which species from the East Palearctic were able to reach south and south-east Asia and further differentiate. The Eastern Himalayas therefore lie not only at the crossroads between the Palearctic and Indo-Malayan realms, but have also periodically formed a highway between the two (Ali 1983).

Another important factor affecting species richness is habitat diversity, ranging from tropical forests and grasslands, in the Assam plains, to glaciers and permanent snowfields along the high peaks of the Himalayas, within a distance of just 150 km. In addition, the Eastern Himalayas possess a relatively wet climate, permitting the formation of diverse broadleaf forests in the subtropical and temperate zones. These forests are extremely rich in species composition and structure, offering a variety of ecological niches for many bird species. Their multiple vegetation layers are also spatially diversified, forming a patchwork of assemblages varying according to slope, aspect and history of human utilisation.

Finally, in Bhutan the Eastern Himalayas have largely escaped the large-scale destruction of natural habitats that has accompanied the development process elsewhere in the region. This destruction was most severe in the 20th century, during which Bhutan was relatively spared because of difficult access due to both geographical and political factors, as well as a low population density and prevailing traditional conservation ethics. These factors have produced a rich heritage of vast natural and relatively undisturbed habitats in Bhutan, whilst holding a promise for its future. In the last 20 years the country has been building a firm foundation for future conservation of its rich biodiversity, through exploring possibilities for sustainable development, the further development of conservation ethics and by setting aside an important and representative part of the country's forest, and other natural habitats, as protected areas and biological corridors.

## 4.2. General distribution patterns

Ranging in altitude from 150 m to close to 8,000 m, Bhutan harbours a wide variety of landscapes and habitats. For the purpose of this book, the country's three main landscapes are defined as the subtropical zone, ranging from 150 m to 1,000 m, the temperate zone, ranging from 1,000 m to 4,000 m and the alpine zone above 4,000 m. The distributions of birds follow these principal divisions in broad terms, with species of Palearctic origin dominating the alpine zone, for example accentors and rosefinches, and those with an Indo-Malayan distribution in the subtropical zone, for example hornbills. The temperate zone forms a melting pot where the Palearctic and Indo-Malayan mix extensively. More subtle distribution patterns are superimposed on this broad canvas, such as west–east gradients in species composition. The distribution of various natural and man-made habitats within each zone forms another, more complex, pattern.

West–east gradients have been noted for certain plant groups, for example the genus *Quercus* (oaks), with several different species in the western Bhutanese valleys compared to the eastern (MacKinnon 1991). In colonising the area, species have dispersed along the main south–north-oriented river valleys. The principal montane ridges separating these valleys constitute dispersal barriers, separating populations of different species and taxa. In the subtropical zone it is the larger rivers that constitute barriers, particularly for certain mammals. Thus, biogeographical units can be identified that coincide with the three main landscapes described above, but with a number of subdivisions from west to east. These units also appear to be applicable for birds, despite the greater mobility of the latter. The high ridges above their normal altitudinal ranges constitute dispersal barriers for many species. The Black-billed Magpie *Pica pica*, which has an established population in the Bumthang Valley, known since the initial avifaunal explorations of the 19th century, is probably the best example of this. Whilst suitable habitat is available in adjacent valleys, the species has been unable to spread there, with passes of over 3,500 m apparently constituting a major barrier. Differences in the avifauna of the west and the east of the country exist particularly in the temperate zone. This is most apparent amongst babblers, where closely related taxa occupy complementary ranges, separated by one of the main ridges. For example, White-browed Fulvetta is found from the western valleys to the Kuri Chhu, whilst Ludlow's Fulvetta assumes the same niche in the east part of the eastern valleys. In others, for example barwings, a retreating altitudinal range accompanies the approach of a species' distributional limit, sometimes with a closely related species gradually replacing it. Another distinct east–west pattern is the increasing scarcity in the western valleys of bird species that meet their westernmost global limits in east Nepal.

However, most details in avian distributions can be explained by different species' associations with certain habitats within the three main landscapes. The occurrence of various forest types is largely determined by altitude, which is thus a dominant factor in the distribution of birds, with closely related species of similar ecological niches occupying complementary altitudinal ranges. This is evident in many families, particularly flycatchers and babblers. A second important factor determining forest type and species composition is humidity, which depends much on slope aspect. West- and north-facing slopes are more humid than east- and south-facing ones, resulting in differences in species composition or even entirely different forest types. This is definitely an important factor in the distribution of many bird species but is, in most cases, beyond the 'resolution' of the dataset available here. The same is true of other more detailed patterns, for example those related to the degree of habitat disturbance. However, in some cases, a comparison of habitat preferences between closely related species occupying similar ecological niches provides interesting insights. For example, the altitudinal ranges of Grey-hooded *Seicercus xanthoschistos* and Grey-cheeked Warblers *S. poliogenys* largely overlap, but closer inspection reveals a stronger association with mature, undisturbed forests in the latter species. Three low-altitude, similar-sized drongos have overlapping altitudinal ranges but are segregated through their preference for, respectively, the forest canopy (Lesser Racket-tailed Drongo *Dicrurus remifer*), mid-storey (Bronzed Drongo *D. aeneus*) and understorey (Crow-billed Drongo *D. annectans*).

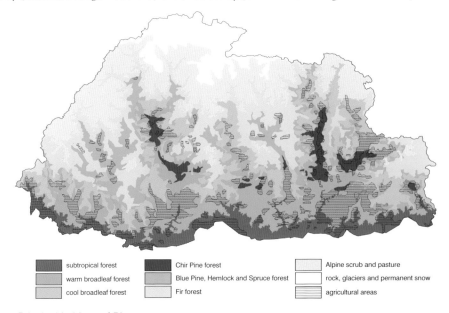

| | | |
|---|---|---|
| subtropical forest | Chir Pine forest | Alpine scrub and pasture |
| warm broadleaf forest | Blue Pine, Hemlock and Spruce forest | rock, glaciers and permanent snow |
| cool broadleaf forest | Fir forest | agricultural areas |

Figure 10: Principal habitats of Bhutan

In the following sections a short description is given of various habitats in the subtropical, temperate and alpine zones, and their related avifaunas, largely following the vegetation classifications of the *Flora of Bhutan* (Grierson and Long 1983).

# 4.3. Habitats and birds in the subtropical zone

In Bhutan, the subtropical zone constitutes a narrow strip of plains, often absent, which rises to a range of low foothills, reaching 1,000 m. Many large rivers and smaller streams dissect these, plunging into the plains in wide stony riverbeds. The major rivers Sunkosh and Manas form the divide between the western, central and eastern foothills.

The *Flora of Bhutan* identifies a single forest type in the wet subtropical zone below 1,000 m. Subtropical forest is characterised by species such as *Bombax ceiba*, *Gmelina arborea*, *Shorea robusta* (Sal) and is often relatively open with a well-developed scrub layer. Bird species typical of this habitat are Great Hornbill *Buceros bicornis*, Wreathed Hornbill *Aceros undulatus*, Asian Fairy Bluebird *Irena puella*, Golden-fronted Leafbird *Chloropsis aurifrons*, Plain Flowerpecker *Dicaeum concolor* and White-rumped Shama *Copsychus malabaricus*. Flowering trees constitute an important seasonal source of food, at which drongos, bulbuls, Streaked Spiderhunter *Arachnothera magna*, leafbirds and sunbirds congregate. In winter, scrub constitutes an important habitat for migrants from higher elevations, particularly various flycatchers. Stands of old-growth forest in this zone have been little explored in Bhutan, and their extent is largely unknown, although Phibsoo Wildlife Sanctuary, in particular, is thought still to harbour important stretches. Species indicative of undisturbed tall forest such as Great Slaty Woodpecker *Mulleripicus pulverulentus* and Himalayan Flameback *Dinopium shorii* have not yet been found in Bhutan in significant numbers.

Tall grassland subject to seasonal flooding is a characteristic and highly endangered habitat of the plains along the Himalayan foothills. These grasslands hardly penetrate Bhutanese territory, and owing to limited ornithological exploration, characteristic and rare species such as Bengal Florican *Houbaropsis bengalensis* have yet to be discovered there.

Stony riverbeds constitute important wetland sites, providing potential habitat for resident and wintering waterbirds. Their actual importance, particularly for wintering waterbirds, requires further assessment. Various bird species have been recorded in this habitat, including Pallas's Fish Eagle *Haliaeetus leucoryphus*, Ruddy Shelduck *Tadorna ferruginea*, Little Cormorant *Phalacrocorax niger*, Small Pratincole *Glareola lactea* and Eurasian Thick-knee *Burhinus oedicnemus*.

The subtropical zone has been extensively developed for agriculture and industry, both in the semi-urbanised areas around border towns and in rural areas like Samtse and Sarpang-Gelephu. The avifauna of these areas is characterised by common residents of the adjacent Indian rural plains, particularly mynas, parakeets, Indian Roller *Coracias benghalensis* and Eurasian Collared Dove *Streptopelia decaocto*.

# 4.4. Habitats and birds in the temperate zone

The temperate zone covers the mid-mountains at altitudes of 1,000–4,000 m. It is dissected by an extensive system of streams and rivers. From west to east lie the Torsa Chhu and Wang Chhu valleys (the western valleys), the Sunkosh Chhu valley, and the Mangde Chhu and Chamkhar Chhu (central valleys). Finally there is the Manas watershed with the Kuri Chhu and Drangme Chhu as major tributaries, which together with the upper Nyera Amo Chhu valley forms the eastern valleys. The mountain ranges separating these valleys are, from west to east, the Daga La (between the western and Sunkosh valleys), the Black Mountain range (between the Sunkosh and central valleys) and the Thrumshing La (between the central and eastern valleys).

The temperate zone is largely forest-covered and represents the country's main timber resource, as well as a uniquely preserved biodiversity hotspot. A variety of forest types are present. A short description of each forest type and its avifauna is given below, using a subdivision into lower montane (referred to as 'dry subtropical' in the *Flora of Bhutan*), mid-montane and upper montane/subalpine zones, respectively lying at 1,000–2,000 m, 2,000–3,000 m and 3,000–4,000 m.

## 4.4.1. The lower montane zone

At lower elevations the alternation of dry, rocky slopes with wetter ones creates a mosaic of species-poor Chir Pine and species-rich warm broadleaf forest. **Chir Pine forest** is found at 900–1,800 m, with *Pinus roxburghii* (Chir Pine), *Euphorbia royleana* and *Ziziphus incurva* amongst the characteristic species. It is a savanna-type vegetation, with relatively spaced trees and a well-developed grass layer. It has expanded locally under former regimes of frequent forest fires. The avifauna of this habitat is particularly poor, but has several characteristic species such as Striated Prinia *Prinia criniger*, Himalayan Bulbul *Pycnonotus leucogenys* and Slender-billed Oriole *Oriolus tenuirostris*.

**Warm broadleaf forest** presents a sharp contrast to the adjacent Chir Pine forest, being highly structured and the forest type richest in bird species. It ranges from 1,000 m to 2,000 m, with *Castanopsis indica*, *Schima wallichii* and *Engelhardtia spicata* as some of the characteristic tree species. Various cane species are found, creating thick impenetrable jungles. In old-growth forest, particularly at higher levels, there is a well-defined top canopy with branches thickly covered with epiphytes, the domain of the Beautiful Nuthatch *Sitta formosa*. Landslides and fallen trees create gaps in the canopy where bamboo thickets can develop, harbouring specialists such as Greater Rufous-headed Parrotbill *Paradoxornis ruficeps* and Coral-billed Scimitar Babbler *Pomatorhinus ferruginosus*. A seemingly limitless variety of warblers, babblers, woodpeckers and barbets breed in this habitat, their numbers reinforced in winter by altitudinal migrants. At the latter season mixed-species flocks of babblers and warblers roam these forests and can include up to 20 different species in a single flock. Large stretches of old-growth forest harbour thriving populations of the spectacular and globally threatened Rufous-necked Hornbill *Aceros nipalensis*. Streams and rivers with heavily forested banks are another unique feature and harbour the critically endangered White-bellied Heron *Ardea insignis*, along with breeding Pallas's Fish Eagle and Tawny Fish Owl *Ketupa flavipes*. Broader, open stretches of river in the Sunkosh Chhu valley constitute an important wetland site, with a large winter concentration of Ruddy Shelducks, and various passage migrants staging there in spring and autumn.

The lower montane zone offers favourable conditions for agriculture and warm broadleaf forest is extensively broken by settlements and agricultural fields. Vast agricultural areas with limited tree cover dominate the middle Sunkosh Chhu, Mangde Chhu, Kuri Chhu and Drangme Chhu valleys. Characteristic species of such habitat are Crested Bunting *Melophus lathami*, Striated Prinia, Spotted Dove *Streptopelia chinensis*, and the regular commensals such as Common Myna *Acridotheres tristis* and Eurasian Tree Sparrow *Passer montanus*. Shifting cultivation dominates historically more remote areas south of the main towns, particularly in Pemagatshel and Zhemgang dzongkhag, creating a mosaic of fields, secondary scrub and forest. Here, both the species characteristic of agricultural areas and some forest species occur, although diversity amongst the latter is reduced, particularly in areas where pressure on the land is highest.

## 4.4.2. The middle montane zone

Above 2,000 m, warm broadleaf forest grades into **cool broadleaf forest**, which occurs to 2,900 m. The divide is more than arbitrary and bears considerable ecological significance, as many bird species appear to reach their upper or lower limits around this altitude. The cool broadleaf forest has an equally rich structure as the warm broadleaf forest, with *Acer* spp., *Elatostema monandrum* and *Betula alnoides* amongst characteristic tree species. Partial altitudinal migrants start to dominate the avifauna, with various flycatchers, warblers and babblers present. Black-headed Shrike Babbler *Pteruthius rufiventer* is one of the rare, but characteristic, bird species of this zone.

On drier slopes above 1,800 m Chir Pine forest gives way to **evergreen oak forests**, which are found up to 2,600 m. *Symplocos lucida*, *Castanopsis histrix* and *Quercus lamellosa* are some of the characteristic trees. Bird species found primarily in oak forest include the rare Ward's Trogon *Harpactes wardi* and Rufous-throated Wren Babbler *Spelaeornis caudatus*, the common Grey-winged Blackbird *Turdus boulboul* and Eurasian Jay *Garrulus glandarius*, and the extremely common Rufous Sibia *Heterophasia capistrata*. There is, however, a large overlap in species composition with the warm and cool broadleaf forests, with which it shares a well-developed structure. On the other hand, there appears to be a specific preference for oak forest in many species, as they reach their lower altitudinal limit, either in their summer or winter ranges, at *c*.1,500 m, which coincides with the lower limit of evergreen oak occurrence.

Still higher, dry slopes may hold stands of **Blue Pine** or **spruce** forest, at altitudes of 2,100–3,000 m and 2,700–3,200 m, respectively. Blue Pine forest is relatively poor in tree species being almost entirely composed of Blue Pine *Pinus wallichiana*, with an extensive scrub understorey of *Berberis asiatica*, *Rosa sericea* and *Rhododendron arboreum*. Spruce forest has a greater variety, with *Picea* spp., *Acer* spp. and *Larix griffithiana*. Some characteristic birds of Blue Pine forest are Indian Blue Robin *Luscinia brunnea*, Ultramarine Flycatcher *Ficedula superciliaris* and White-collared Blackbird *Turdus albocinctus*. In winter it harbours mixed flocks of tits and warblers, as well as other altitudinal migrants such as Spotted Laughingthrush *Garrulax ocellatus*.

Important wetlands occur in the mid-montane zone in the form of upland marshes in broad glacial valleys, particularly in the Phobjikha, Kotokha and Bumthang valleys. These are traditional winter sites for the rare

Black-necked Crane *Grus nigricollis*. Smaller wetlands and forest marshes also occur, providing winter habitat for Solitary Snipe *Gallinago solitaria* and Wood Snipe *G. nemoricola*.

Part of the upland valleys in the middle montane zone has been converted for large-scale agriculture, whilst towns such as Paro, Thimphu and Jakar have also grown up. With extensive Blue Pine forest surrounding these valleys, characteristic species include Eurasian Hobby *Falco subbuteo*, Oriental Turtle Dove *Streptopelia orientalis*, White Wagtail *Motacilla alba* and Russet Sparrow *Passer rutilans*.

## 4.4.3. The upper montane zone

On wetter slopes in the upper montane zone **hemlock forest** gradually replaces cool broadleaf forest, from 2,800 m to 3,300 m. Mixed stands of hemlock and broadleaf forest often occur here. Characteristic tree and scrub species include *Tsuga dumosa* (hemlock), *Betula utilis*, *Magnolia globosa* and *Daphne bholua*. The forest has a rich structure, whilst becoming gradually more open, affording greater opportunities for bamboo and rhododendron thickets to develop in the forest understorey. Bird species with a preference for such forest include the rare Bar-winged Wren Babbler *Spelaeornis troglodytoides* and the spectacular Satyr Tragopan *Tragopan satyra*. The presence of various *Phylloscopus* warblers and flycatchers is largely seasonal, the majority of birds departing in winter.

Above 3,100 m **fir forest** replaces the hemlock and spruce forest, reaching up to the treeline at *c.*3,800 m. Characteristic species are *Abies densa* (silver fir), *Rhododendron* spp. and *Betula utilis*. Fir forest is subject to a life cycle of abrupt and massive colonisation, growth and degradation. In the prolonged stage of gradual degradation the mature fir forest becomes very open, allowing extensive colonisation by bamboos, which form dense stands. The latter are the domain of various parrotbills and other bamboo specialists such as Slender-billed Scimitar Babbler *Xiphirhynchus superciliaris*. Other species typical of fir forest are Blood Pheasant *Ithaginis cruentus* and Coal Tit *Parus ater*. Blood Pheasant is among the few hardy species that use this habitat in winter.

Towards the treeline and on dry, exposed slopes, fir forest gives way to **juniper–rhododendron scrub**. This vegetation type is found between 3,700 m and 4,200 m, with *Juniperus* spp. and *Rhododendron lepidotum* characteristic. Generally, it forms a mosaic with patches of fir forest and open pasture. Some of the birds associated with this habitat are Himalayan Monal *Lophophorus impejanus*, Fire-tailed Sunbird *Aethopyga ignicauda*, Rufous-vented Tit *Parus rubidiventris*, White-winged Grosbeak *Mycerobas carnipes* and White-browed Rosefinch *Carpodacus thura*.

The occurrence of wetlands in the upper montane/subalpine zone is limited to forest marshes, which so far have been little studied. These are the probable breeding quarters of the enigmatic Wood Snipe.

As conditions are too harsh for large-scale agriculture, the main man-made habitat of this zone is extensive pasture, where trees and shrubs have largely been removed. These open areas support few bird species, among which there are few specialists. Red-billed Chough *Pyrrhocorax pyrrhocorax*, Common Buzzard *Buteo buteo* and Oriental Skylark *Alauda gulgula* are some of the species regularly encountered here.

# 4.5. The alpine zone

Alpine landscape starts above the treeline, at *c.*4,000 m. A single vegetation type has been identified in the *Flora of Bhutan*, **dry alpine scrub**, which ranges from 4,000 m to 4,600 m. Some of the characteristic plant species are *Rhododendron anthopogon*, *Salix lindleyana* (dwarf willow) and *Aconitum* spp. The avifauna is characterised by high-elevation pheasants such as Tibetan Snowcock *Tetraogallus tibetanus* and Snow Partridge *Lerwa lerwa*, as well as rosefinches and altitudinal migrants such as Blue-fronted Redstart *Phoenicurus frontalis* and Rufous-breasted Accentor *Prunella strophiata*. Furthermore, rugged country above the treeline is the domain of Golden Eagle *Aquila chrysaetos* and Lammergeier *Gypaetus barbatus*. Above 4,600 m there is little or no vegetation, the landscape being dominated by rocks, glaciers and permanent snowfields. Even so, there is birdlife, with Grandala *Grandala coelicolor*, Red-fronted Rosefinch *Carpodacus puniceus* and, in summer, Alpine Accentor *Prunella collaris* and Rosy Pipit *Anthus roseatus* occurring here. The permanent snowline is located at 4,800–5,000 m, and more or less marks the limit of bird occurrence. As a whole the alpine zone has been insufficiently surveyed and the upper altitudinal limits of many birds are unclear. Most data are available from the favourable trekking months of April and October, with birders rarely reaching above 4,500 m.

Wetlands are limited to alpine lakes and 'white' wetlands in the form of permanent snow and ice. These are of little or no importance to waterbirds, with only the remote alpine lakes supporting a breeding population of Ruddy Shelduck. Human activities have modified little of the natural landscape of the alpine zone, although yak grazing maintains a mosaic of pasture and scrub.

# 5. Migration and seasonality

Birds in Bhutan are confronted by two major seasons. The summer monsoon sweeps over Bhutan between June and September, bringing heavy rains, rising water levels in streams and rivers, and an outburst of plant and insect life. Rains are heaviest at lower elevations, where humid air from the Gulf of Bengal sheds much of its moisture. As a result, annual rainfall across Bhutan varies enormously, from 5,500 mm in the south to 300 mm in the north. From October to April there is a relatively dry winter season. There is occasional snowfall, particularly in January–March, creating inhospitable conditions for birds at higher elevations. Snowfall is regular above 3,500 m and becomes gradually more incidental down to 2,000 m, with significant annual variations. Aside from snowfall, it is the fall in temperatures and the halt in biological activity that force some birds to vacate higher elevations. Nocturnal frosts are regular above 2,000 m, becoming increasingly severe with altitude. Whilst many bird species tolerate winter conditions prevalent in cool broadleaf forest, the alpine zone and higher-altitude conifer forests become largely devoid of birdlife, with only the hardiest species remaining. Temperatures rise again by March. Spring then gradually spreads from lower elevations into the mountains, and plant and insect life increases again, permitting birds to return. Below 2,000 m, in the warm broadleaf and subtropical forests, birds experience a less drastic drop in food supply in winter, as temperatures remain moderate. Various tree species continue to flower and fruit, providing continuous foraging opportunities throughout the year. Flowering trees are an important source of food for many bird species, not only because of the flower nectar but also the insects they attract.

In response to these changing conditions over the course of the year, birds undertake seasonal movements. As the montane environment supports different habitats within a short distance, such movements are often relatively small-scale, but equally include long-distance migrations by species that are only present in Bhutan for part of the year. In the following sections seasonal occurrence and behaviour are described for four categories of birds (Fig. 11).

a)  Residents: birds remaining in the same altitudinal range year-round. Although only a few species may be truly sedentary (e.g. Tawny Owl *Strix aluco*), the available data provide insufficient detail to describe potential movements within the same altitudinal range. So, for example, birds which are more numerous in the lower parts of their ranges in winter, but do not descend below the lower limit of their summer range, are classified here as resident.

b)  Altitudinal migrants: birds shifting between summer and winter altitudinal ranges, whether partial (only part of the population moving) or complete.

c)  Summer visitors: birds that occur in Bhutan in spring and summer, and almost completely vacate the country in favour of south and south-east Asian or African wintering grounds. Species for which part of the population remains in Bhutan in winter are classified as altitudinal migrants.

d)  Winter visitors and passage migrants: birds usually originating from areas north of the Himalayas that occur in Bhutan in winter and/or on migration.

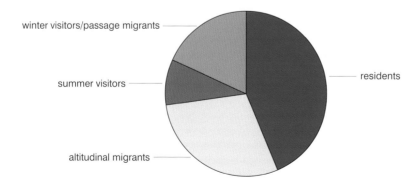

Figure 11: Composition of the Bhutan avifauna (N=476, excluding rare species)

# 5.1. Residents

Residents make up the largest part of the Bhutan avifauna, comprising 43% of all species. They are dominant in warm broadleaf forest and below, where the food supply is predictable, even in winter. At higher elevations sedentary birds are mostly ground feeders with a largely vegetarian diet, such as Blood Pheasant *Ithaginis cruentus* and Red-fronted Rosefinch *Carpodacus puniceus*. Many sedentary species flock outside the breeding season, a strategy with various advantages, such as better protection against predators and efficient exploitation of food resources that become scarcer and more local in winter (e.g. fruiting trees). Certain groups, such as babblers, warblers and tits, form mixed flocks. The largest concentrations generally occur in late winter, when food resources reach their lowest levels. At a certain point in spring the flocks separate into pairs and breeding territories are established. Post-breeding, birds may move around for some time in family groups, before again aggregating in larger flocks, normally as food resources decrease. This is the basic seasonal pattern of sedentary birds, which of course has many variations. Some species are extremely gregarious, e.g. Striated Yuhina *Yuhina castaniceps* and Nepal House Martin *Delichon nipalensis*, and occur in flocks year-round. Others are largely solitary, such as most birds of prey. Also, there is variation in the timing of breeding, with some raptors starting as early as December, most insectivores in April–May, and seedeaters in July–August. Timing is generally dictated by the need for the young to fledge when there is abundant food.

# 5.2. Altitudinal migrants

Altitudinal migrants comprise 29% of the species known from Bhutan and dominate at higher elevations. The basic seasonal pattern of residents and altitudinal migrants is similar, with the main difference being that birds or flocks move (somewhat) further from their breeding grounds. The simplest form of altitudinal migration involves dispersal of part of the population, which descends to lower elevations in the non-breeding season. In such cases, some birds remain at their upper altitudinal limit throughout the year, as is the case for Stripe-throated Yuhina *Yuhina gularis*, for example. The reverse also occurs, with birds remaining in the lower part of their ranges and also spreading to higher elevations in the breeding season. Species possessing such behaviour include Black Bulbul *Hypsipetes leucocephalus*, Coal Tit *Parus ater* and Yellow-vented Warbler *Phylloscopus cantator*. Birds at higher elevations exhibit the most pronounced altitudinal movements, often completely vacating their summer ranges. For example, in *Ficedula* flycatchers, the winter range of high-altitude species is often below that of related species breeding at lower altitudes. The latter show less pronounced altitudinal movements and occupy a winter zone partially overlapping with or just below their summer range. This has been described for other migratory birds as a 'leapfrog' pattern, the birds breeding at highest latitudes or, in this case, altitudes, being forced to 'leap' over areas already occupied by populations or related species at lower latitudes/altitudes. Among birds covering the longest distances, breeding in alpine scrub and wintering in tall grassland in the plains, are rare species such as Chestnut-crowned Bush Warbler *Cettia major*, Gould's Shortwing *Brachypteryx stellata* and White-bellied Redstart *Hodgsonius phaenicuroides*.

In most cases, altitudinal movements appear to be rather gradual, with migrating birds covering short distances each day. Such movements have been noted, for example, for Grey-headed Canary Flycatcher *Culicicapa ceylonensis* and Long-tailed Minivet *Pericrocotus ethologus*. This results in a widespread presence between the winter and summer ranges during the migration season, as in the case of Grey-sided Bush Warbler *Cettia brunnifrons*. In some cases, the scarcity of records at intermediate altitudes, or rapid vacation of the winter area, suggests that birds move in direct flight. Sight records of actively moving migrants are, however, rare and limited to a few species such as raptors, Rosy Pipit *Anthus roseatus* and Olive-backed Pipit *A. hodgsoni*.

For some species, altitudinal movements are visibly related to variation in food availability. Stripe-throated Yuhina, Rufous-vented Yuhina *Yuhina occipitalis* and Fire-tailed Myzornis *Myzornis pyrrhoura* follow the flowering season of rhododendrons, which commences at progressively higher elevations over the course of spring. Great Hornbill *Buceros bicornis* and Hill Myna *Gracula religiosa* exhibit occasional movements to higher altitudes in autumn, when certain tree species are fruiting in the temperate zone. Brown Dipper *Cinclus pallasii*, Ibisbill *Ibidorhyncha struthersii* and Crested Kingfisher *Megaceryle lugubris* have an early breeding season and move to smaller streams and higher elevations as water levels rise in late spring and foraging opportunities deteriorate. Pallas's Fish Eagle *Haliaeetus leucoryphus* takes this strategy to the extreme, breeding early in the year and then departing Bhutan to summer further north. For some species, the extent of altitudinal movement depends largely on conditions in the wintering area. Accentors, bush chats, Plain-backed Thrush *Zoothera mollissima*, rosefinches and other birds wintering at high elevations descend to lower altitudes following heavy snowfall.

# 5.3. Summer visitors

Summer visitors form a minority of Bhutan's avifauna, comprising just 9% of the species. They reach Bhutan from a variety of destinations. The longest distance is covered by Lesser Cuckoo *Cuculus poliocephalus*, which has its main winter quarters in East Africa. Another long-distance destination is south-east Asia, from the Malay Peninsula through Indonesia to New Guinea. Oriental Cuckoo *Cuculus saturatus*, White-throated Needletail *Hirundapus caudacutus* and Ferruginous Flycatcher *Muscicapa ferruginea* winter in this area. Arrival of long-distance migrants is generally marked by a 'sharp' front, the majority of birds reaching the breeding areas more or less simultaneously over a period of weeks, with rare early records and very few from outside the regular altitudinal ranges. This is the case for Eurasian Cuckoo *Cuculus canorus* and White-throated Needletail, for example. The migration routes of (suspected) long-distance migrants from south-east Asia are still imperfectly known, and the winter areas of populations breeding in Bhutan require further investigation.

Within the Indian subcontinent, the humid hills of south-west India and Sri Lanka form an important winter area for insectivores, for example, Large-billed Leaf Warbler *Phylloscopus magnirostris*. Birds from the drier Western Himalayas migrate west–east along the Himalayan foothills to winter in the more humid Eastern Himalayas and hills of north-east India. These movements are relatively difficult to discern in Bhutan, as part of these species' populations may winter as far west as this. Although east–west migration may be prevalent in many songbirds in the Himalayas, in Bhutan it is only visibly manifested by the spring presence of Orange-headed Thrush *Zoothera citrina* and Tickell's Thrush *Turdus unicolor*.

Seasonal movements of birds in the northern Indian subcontinent may lead to the occurrence of vagrants in Bhutan during summer. In the early monsoon season, once water levels rise, various waterbirds occupy their breeding areas. They may be swept off course, particularly during heavy rainstorms from the south, and end up in the mountains of Bhutan, where no breeding habitat is available. This pattern has been noted for species such as Cinnamon Bittern *Ixobrychus cinnamomeus*, Indian Pond Heron *Ardeola grayii* and Bronze-winged Jacana *Metopidius indicus*, which have occurred in Bhutan between April and July.

# 5.4. Winter visitors and passage migrants

Winter visitors and passage migrants comprise 17% of the species occurring in Bhutan. The Indian subcontinent receives a large number of winter visitors from various parts of Eurasia, although the main Himalayan range provides a major obstacle to the migration routes of these migrants. There is little direct evidence of birds crossing the Himalayas. In Nepal, mainly large birds, like Bar-headed Goose *Anser indicus* and Steppe Eagle *Aquila nipalensis*, have been noted migrating over the high mountains, but the main migration routes apparently circumvent higher parts of the Himalayas, instead following the deeply incised, broad valleys of the Indus and Brahmaputra. Migratory movements on the south side of the Himalayas can therefore be expected to possess an important east–west component, with birds radiating from the Indus and Brahmaputra valleys in winter and being channelled back to these areas in spring. In addition, a more diffuse, broad-front crossing may occur between these two valleys (Inskipp and Inskipp 1995).

The seasonality of birds in Bhutan suggests a direct Himalayan crossing for large numbers of birds, including songbirds. For many species, high-altitude records are concentrated during arrival to, and departure from, Bhutan, suggesting that they cross the Himalayas on a broad front. Concurrently, migration is channelled through the main river valleys, like those of the Sunkosh Chhu, Mangde Chhu and Kuri Chhu, with the latter, in particular, providing a relatively low-elevation passage to the Tibetan Plateau.

Raptors are amongst the most visible passage migrants, with regular observations of active migration. In Nepal a westward movement of *Aquila* eagles and several other large to medium-sized birds of prey has been noted in autumn (see Inskipp and Inskipp 1995, de Roder 1989). This movement is also discernible in Bhutan in autumn, with a more visible westward migration in spring. The main species involved are Steppe Eagle, Himalayan Griffon *Gyps himalayensis* and Common Buzzard *Buteo buteo*. Mountain ridges probably provide favourable migration features, with multiple steep cliffs where thermals occur. Passage appears concentrated at particular sites such as low passes and areas with strong thermals, but it is unclear where these birds eventually cross the main Himalayan ridge. The main direction of passage is north–south, through the river valleys, for birds of prey that are less dependent on thermals, such as Eurasian Hobby *Falco subbuteo*, Black Kite *Milvus migrans* and Osprey *Pandion haliaetus*. These species probably cross the Himalayas via the main river valleys. Large-scale migration of Black Kites was noted by Ludlow, who reported hundreds descending from the Tibetan Plateau via the Kuri Chhu valley. Raptor migration is evident August–November and March–May, with peaks in March and October.

Another group of relatively conspicuous migrants are the waterbirds including ducks, geese, waders and gulls. Flocks of migrating geese, mostly unidentified, have been observed flying north in early morning and heard at night. Most waterbirds show a concentration of records in spring and only few or none in autumn, even allowing for the larger number of birders active in spring. One factor affecting this is the more favourable staging conditions in spring (low water levels), but loop migration probably also occurs. In this, birds would make a gradual descent through the Brahmaputra Valley in autumn, utilising favourable habitat en route, while in spring they take a direct route to their breeding areas. Presence in spring depends much on weather conditions in the Himalayas, with bad weather delaying birds at staging sites in Bhutan, and sometimes leading to large concentrations of waterbirds, particularly on the Puna Sang Chhu between Punakha and Wangdue Phodrang, especially in early March. For Pallas's Gull *Larus ichthyaetus*, the presence of larger flocks is entirely dependent on bad weather. Peak duck numbers appear in the first half of March, which is somewhat later than reported for Kosi Barrage, Nepal, where numbers are highest around mid-February (Inskipp and Inskipp 1985). For waders the period is similar to that in Nepal, with most records in March–April. Autumn migration of waterbirds occurs September–November.

There is no evidence of direct Himalayan passage for songbirds but for most species there are numerous records at higher elevations than their normal winter range. In Nepal (Inskipp and Inskipp 1995), it is suspected that some birds skirt the Himalayas in the west through the Indus Valley (Dark-throated Thrush *Turdus ruficollis atrogularis*, Blyth's Reed Warbler *Acrocephalus dumetorum*, Dusky Warbler *Phylloscopus fuscatus*), or in the east through the Brahmaputra Valley (Siberian Rubythroat *Luscinia calliope*, Red-throated Flycatcher *Ficedula parva*, Brown Shrike *Lanius cristatus*). For other species, direct Himalayan passage is confirmed (Black Redstart *Phoenicurus ochruros*, Tickell's Leaf Warbler *Phylloscopus affinis*, White Wagtail *Motacilla alba*). Apparently, it is particularly long-range migrants from Siberian breeding grounds that channel through the Indus and Brahmaputra valleys, whilst birds breeding on the Tibetan Plateau pass the Himalayas on a broad front. If high-altitude records are an indication for direct Himalayan passage, this appears to be the principal strategy of Palearctic migrants passing through Bhutan. Common Stonechat *Saxicola torquatus* is one songbird with many high-altitude records during the migration season and which is therefore likely to cross the Himalayas on a broad front. Red-throated Flycatcher and Siberian Rubythroat, on the other hand, appear to move laterally along the base of the Himalayas, circumventing the main range, with no records above 2,000 m. April–May and September–October are the main seasons of passerine migration.

A particular migration phenomenon observed in Bhutan is the irruptions of thrushes. In recent years, the winters of 1994/1995, 1997/1998 and 1999/2000 appear to have brought large numbers to Bhutan. The origin of these irruptions may lie across the Himalayas in the north-east or more to the north-west, depending on the year. They are probably induced by severe weather conditions in the normal winter range of these thrushes, and they usually coincide with periods of heavy snowfall within Bhutan. Dark-throated Thrush is the most abundant and conspicuous species involved in these irruptions, but Rufous-bellied Bush Robin *Tarsiger hyperythrus*, White-throated Redstart *Phoenicurus schisticeps* and possibly other Turdinae have also appeared in larger numbers in these years. Irruptions become evident from December and reach their peak in March, with the last birds leaving the country in April. The 1999/2000 irruption was also widely noted in south-east Asia.

Aside from Palearctic migrants, Bhutan receives small numbers of winter visitors from the plains of India. These are birds that disperse from their Indian breeding grounds in the dry season. Pied Kingfisher *Ceryle rudis* is one example of a species that regularly disperses to the mountains in winter.

# 6. Threats and conservation

## 6.1. Historical habitat changes

Like most areas in the world, the landscapes of Bhutan have been profoundly influenced by human activities. The habitats and their avifaunas that we see today are the result of a long interaction between man and the natural environment. Bhutan is rather unique in that these interactions have left much original biodiversity intact. With more than 75% of the country forested, mostly in the species-rich temperate zone, habitats still exist at a scale where natural ecological processes can take their course. Also, corridors between various habitats are still largely intact, resulting in continuous corridors from the subtropical to the alpine zones. Although the quality of these habitats is varied, the presence of significant areas of relatively untouched old-growth forest indicates that Bhutan has avoided much of the massive destruction that often accompanies man's presence.

At the same time, human activities have negatively impacted the country's modern landscape. Bhutan has a long settlement history. Historical sources point to the presence of a thriving society since the fourth century. The country's warm broadleaf forests have thus been influenced by shifting cultivation for one or more millennia, particularly in the centre and east of the country, which are the traditional areas of those ethnic groups with the longest history, the Khengpa and Sarchogpa (Pelgen and Rigden 1999). In long-settled areas, for example around the villages of Kikhar and Buli, Zhemgang district, in the core of the Kheng area, present old-growth forests may well have been cultivated in the past. Small patches of banana trees within forest are observed here, probably indicating the locations of former homesteads. Traditional shifting cultivation, by its relatively small scale and long fallow periods, may not have overly damaged original forest, and possibly has enriched it. Over time, in various areas under different demographic and economic circumstances, the shifting cultivation system appears to have crossed a threshold whereby old-growth forest has disappeared. The landscape has thus become dominated by fields, scrub and young secondary forests. High pressure on the land has considerably reduced forest stands, resulting in relatively bird-poor agricultural areas, particularly in eastern districts. Nevertheless, the conversion of warm broadleaf forest to agricultural land is far from the level seen elsewhere in the Eastern Himalayas, and bird distribution reflects this. Many birds characteristic of rural areas of the north Indian plains, such as Common Iora *Aegithina tiphia*, Pied Bushchat *Saxicola caprata*, House Crow *Corvus splendens* and parakeets do not extend beyond the subtropical zone, whilst in neighbouring Nepal their upper altitudinal limit appears to be considerably higher, over most of the warm broadleaf forest zone.

A feature of the Bhutanese landscape, which struck Ludlow on his expeditions in the 1930s, is the dry and barren aspect of the middle parts of the main river valleys, for example around Punakha/Wangdue Phodrang, Kuenga Rabten, Lhuntse and Trashigang. The principal explanation of this phenomenon is that these areas lie in the rainshadow of the main north–south ridges, sheltering them from the south-west monsoon. In addition, these are the traditional political and economic centres of the country with important population concentrations. Whilst at first sight nothing appears to survive in these areas but Chir Pine, the original vegetation must have been more species-rich broadleaf forest (Miehe and Miehe 1998). The areas concerned were probably stripped of their original forests centuries ago, almost certainly under the influence of shifting cultivation, grazing and fire. Indeed, photographs taken in the early 20th century (Aris 1995) show Chir Pine vegetation to be even thinner than at present. Over the course of the 20th century, the original land use on the steep slopes lost its economic rationale and forest cover appears to have grown back gradually, partially through plantations and part naturally. Remarkably, the presence of these inhospitable habitats in the middle river valleys appears to have consequences for the distribution of some bird species of warm broadleaf forest. The Wangdue Phodrang/Punakha Valley is a good example of this. As the agricultural and Chir Pine areas reach the upper distributional limit of the warm broadleaf forest zone, they form an effective barrier for critical species like Rufous-necked Hornbill *Aceros nipalensis* as well as the relatively common Bronzed Drongo *Dicrurus aeneus*. These species have the same upper distributional limit, c.2,000 m. In apparently suitable habitat north of the Wangdue Phodrang/Punakha area these species are absent or uncommon, presumably as a result of isolation from the main population. A similar pattern emerges in the east, where certain species of subtropical and warm broadleaf forests, such as Red-faced Liocichla *Liocichla phoenicea* and Long-tailed Sibia *Heterophasia picaoides*, are confined to southern parts of the eastern valleys. In agricultural areas of Trashigang district, broadleaf forest within their altitudinal range is fragmented by Chir Pine and cultivation, and neither species occurs.

A similar process has occurred in the upland valleys of Paro, Thimphu, Phobjikha, the Pele La to Trongsa area, and the Bumthang Valley, albeit with a less-marked effect. Relatively small patches of cool broadleaf and evergreen oak forests remain in the upper Thimphu and Paro valleys, and these lack certain species expected in this altitudinal range. *Pangzhing* was historically a dominant land-use system in these areas. Under this system pastureland is cropped in a long rotational cycle of around ten years. This is, however, sufficient to reduce forest and scrub growth over vast areas, particularly as fire was extensively used to clear land and improve pasture. During the 20th century, but particularly in the 1950s and 1960s, the agricultural use of these areas was gradually abandoned. An additional factor was the first Forest Act of 1969 that restricted forest fires. As a result, rapid colonisation of some of these areas by Blue Pine forest has occurred, giving the upland valleys their present face. Photographs taken in the early 20th century (Aris 1995) show much larger agricultural areas around Jakar dzong than exist at present. A sharp and irregular boundary between the Blue Pine and higher fir forest visible today also points to this regeneration process. In the larger, more open pastures such as around Pele La, where the former *pangzhing* terraces are clearly visible, this regeneration process has been less marked. One factor could be the presence of a dense mat of dwarf bamboo, maintained by intensive grazing mainly by yaks, which suppresses tree growth.

Finally, the main change that has occurred in the Bhutanese landscape is the opening of the country to a road network in the 1960s and early 1970s. This has fundamentally changed the economy of rural areas and triggered a process whereby pressure on natural resources is increasingly concentrated in accessible areas, whilst being reduced in more remote areas. Urbanisation goes hand in hand with this. In the distributions of birds, these processes are noticeable as some of the rarer species become increasingly difficult to find close to roads, and some typical urban specialists, like House Crow and House Sparrow *Passer domesticus*, hesitantly arrive. Nevertheless, Bhutan is still unique in terms of the possibility of encountering rare and difficult-to-observe birds in forest directly adjacent to the country's main highway. This is perhaps one of the biggest attractions to bird tours and constitutes a valuable asset in the future development of tourism.

## 6.2. The development process

Since the 1960s, with the first of the five-year plans and the construction of the main roads, Bhutan has begun a rapid modernisation process. Its potential effect on natural habitats is profound. Whilst Bhutan has already deployed remarkable effort in maintaining biodiversity in this process, it is also in a position to move further along this path, using the multiple opportunities of current development trends.

The road network and the urbanisation process have drastically changed economic and social realities in rural areas. Traditional land-use types, depending on extensive use of resources over vast areas of forest, such as shifting cultivation and forest grazing, are gradually losing their economic rationale. The result is a sharper divide between accessible production areas on the one hand and regenerating forest (both in area and in structure) in more remote areas on the other. Agricultural and forestry policies greatly enhance this process. In the long term this will place Bhutan in a strong position to conserve old-growth forests and their related avifauna, provided that intensification of land use and development of a protection regime for regenerating forests go hand in hand.

A major drawback of the above development will be that more birds will not necessarily be easier to find, as they are increasingly restricted to remote areas. This may to some extent limit the future development of ecotourism. A visible manifestation of a landscape with a sharper divide between production and conservation areas is the spread of urban constructions, and the environmental effects of further expansion and maintenance of the road network. For example, in Thimphu, small wetland sites within the built-up area where, amongst others, the globally threatened Wood Snipe *Gallinago nemoricola* is found, are being gradually lost. Thus, urban planning and environmentally friendly road construction and maintenance will determine, to a large extent, the future avifauna of Bhutan: rare birds in remote areas or just nearby for everybody to see.

Timber and other forest products continue to be important in facilitating the country's development process. Timber extraction has left its mark on Bhutan's forests, particularly as the process is often concentrated in particular areas, as a relatively small percentage of forest is earmarked for economic exploitation. Often timber extraction areas overlap with those of abundant birdlife. For example, the large population of Mongar and Trashigang districts is largely dependent for timber on the Kharung La, Kori La and Lingmethang areas, which are also among the richest (accessible) bird sites in these districts. Opportunities rest in the extensive areas of conifer forest, for which sustainable management systems have been successfully developed. In broadleaf forest there is still the risk of significant negative impacts of forestry practices on birds. Whilst these forests support the highest bird species diversity, and the lion's share of globally threatened species, sustainable management systems are still largely in the research stage. A further important opportunity for forest conservation lies in the development of Bhutan's hydroelectric power potential. Although this may have severe local impacts, for example, the clearance of forest for power lines, it provides a strong reason for maintaining forest cover within the catchment areas of such schemes.

# 6.3. Conservation ethics

Bhutan has not been dragged into a turmoil of development activities with merely economic and social aspects in mind. Environment and culture have been important considerations in carefully shaping the modernisation process. This is reflected, amongst others, in the country's 'middle path' policy, seeking development that does not compromise Bhutan's rich cultural and natural heritage. These strong conservation ethics are rooted in traditional Buddhist values. Concern for environment is deeply embedded in Bhutanese beliefs and day-to-day activities, giving a special turn to the modernisation process, with the environment possessing a much more central role than in many countries.

> **Buddhism and environment** (source: Biodiversity Action Plan, MoA, 2002)
> Buddhism teaches that all life forms are interdependent. In the continuous cycle of birth and death, there is no single being that has not been, at one point in time one's mother. Therefore, the Buddha taught respect for all life forms in the manner that one respects one's mother. Additionally, the purity that one seeks within oneself is linked to the purity of one's environment, as the elements of the physical form of life, earth, water, fire and air are directly linked to those in nature. Furthermore, nature's wilderness is considered to provide inspiration for growth of the human mind and the pursuit of wisdom. In everyday life the Bhutanese worship and evoke deities such as *Lha* (deities of the heaven above), *Tsen* (deities of the mountains), *Lu* (beings of the underneath world) and *Sadag* (deities of the land). There is a fervent belief that if people pollute heaven, the mountain in-between and the land below, man is bound to suffer the wrath of his respective deities.

# 6.4. The protected areas system

Since the modernisation process started to gain momentum, from the late 1980s, Bhutan has taken important steps to maintain its biodiversity and lay a foundation for its future conservation. The first Forestry Act of 1969, and its successor the Forestry and Nature Conservation Act of 2000, provided the legal framework for this, at the same time as environmental legislation was gradually being developed. A very important step was the declaration by His Majesty the King of Bhutan to keep 60% of the country forested at all times to come. In 1993 the original wildlife protection zones on the northern and southern borders were revised in a fully fledged protected areas system, covering 26% of the country and harbouring the complete range of natural habitats found in Bhutan. In particular, the creation of large protected areas in the temperate zone was a major step, greatly enhancing prospects for conservation of the rich biodiversity of the Eastern Himalayas at landscape level. Finally, an additional 9% of the country was declared 'biological corridors' in 2000, using existing corridors of natural habitat to safeguard connections between all protected areas. The Nature Conservation Division of the Department of Forestry Services is the key agency in the management of the protected areas system and the biological corridors, and at present is gradually building its capacity, including expertise in bird surveys and conservation.

The protected areas system has a central place in the conservation of the avifauna of Bhutan, with important parts of the ranges of various globally threatened or Near Threatened species lying within these areas (see map on p.359).

**Royal Manas National Park** (1,023 km²) is the oldest protected area and harbours vast stretches of subtropical and warm broadleaf forest, with Great Hornbill *Buceros bicornis*, Rufous-necked Hornbill, Pallas's Fish Eagle *Haliaeetus leucoryphus*, Beautiful Nuthatch *Sitta formosa* and Blyth's Kingfisher *Alcedo hercules* amongst significant bird species. In particular, the south of the park has not yet been extensively surveyed and could hold rare birds characteristic of the transition zone between the plains and foothills.

**Jigme Dorji National Park** (4,349 km²) is the largest protected area, holding vast areas of alpine habitats and temperate forests, including some warm broadleaf forest in the Mo Chhu valley. Satyr Tragopan *Tragopan satyra* and other high-altitude species are characteristic of this park, along with several rare birds associated with rivers in warm broadleaf forest, e.g. White-bellied Heron *Ardea insignis*, Pallas's Fish Eagle and Tawny Fish Owl *Ketupa flavipes*.

**Jigme Singye Wangchuck National Park** (1,400 km²) was formerly known as Black Mountain National Park and is the largest park in the temperate zone, harbouring vast stretches of warm and cool broadleaf forests, as well as relatively undisturbed high-altitude fir forest. It has an extremely varied avifauna, including threatened and Near Threatened species such as Rufous-necked Hornbill, White-bellied Heron and Satyr Tragopan.

**Thrumshingla National Park** (768 km²) is a smaller equivalent of Jigme Singye Wangchuck National Park, with similar habitats and avifauna. The national highway traversing the heart of the park, through prime fir and cool broadleaf forest, provides excellent opportunities for birdwatching. Threatened and Near Threatened species found here include various wren babblers, Ward's Trogon *Harpactes wardi*, Rufous-necked Hornbill and Beautiful Nuthatch.

**Bumdeling Wildlife Sanctuary** (1,487 km²) was originally created because of its wintering Black-necked Cranes, but equally harbours vast stretches of well-preserved alpine and forest habitats, over a similar altitudinal range as Jigme Dorji National Park. The rare Gould's Shortwing *Brachypteryx stellata* has been found here, along with various threatened and Near Threatened species such as Pallas's Fish Eagle, Rufous-necked Hornbill and Yellow-rumped Honeyguide *Indicator xanthonotus*.

For **Phibsoo Wildlife Sanctuary** (278 km²), **Sakten Wildlife Sanctuary** (650 km²), **Khaling Wildlife Sanctuary** (273 km²) and **Torsa Strict Nature Reserve** (651 km²) detailed biodiversity data are not yet available and bird species richness in these areas remains unknown. Phibsoo Wildlife Sanctuary covers forests in the subtropical zone and is known to possess a rich mammal fauna. Khaling Wildlife Sanctuary covers similar habitat in the east. Torsa Strict Nature Reserve holds largely untouched alpine habitats. Sakten Wildlife Sanctuary covers the entire range from warm broadleaf to alpine zones, and is expected to be important for the rare Blyth's Tragopan *Tragopan blythii*.

# 6.5. Challenges for bird conservation

With its rich avifauna, vast stretches of well-preserved habitats and progressive conservation policies, Bhutan bears a particular responsibility for conservation in the Eastern Himalayas. This combined with a rapid modernisation process creates a situation of multiple challenges.

In the past ten years it is particularly the Black-necked Crane that has attracted bird conservation attention. Through surveys, an annual festival, awareness raising and mobilisation of local communities, particularly in Phobjikha Valley, the place of the cranes in the future of the area has been largely secured. The Royal Society for the Protection of Nature has played a central role in this. At the same time, the Nature Conservation Division of the Department of Forestry Services has organised ornithological surveys of protected areas. With more information now available, threatened and Near Threatened birds are gradually emerging in protected area management plans as target species for specific conservation measures.

A first, and probably most important, challenge for bird conservation in Bhutan lies in survey and research. The present work is a first attempt to collate available knowledge on the distribution and ecology of birds in Bhutan. In so doing, it is the numerous gaps in knowledge that particularly catch the eye and which provide equally abundant opportunities for follow-up research. For example, the distribution of birds in relation to habitats is an area open to future study. Further studies could take various forms, ranging from data collection on distribution to fully fledged ecological research. Good-quality distributional data are now available from a variety of sources: local birders and organisations, bird tour groups and professional ornithologists. The challenge lies in finding axes of collaboration between them, for example through newsletters and groups, a central database and bird clubs, which have already partly been initiated. The birding scene in Bhutan is still young but can already rely on impressive, country-specific expertise.

Ecological research is primarily the domain of government agencies in Bhutan. Obvious challenges lie in developing our understanding of the ecology of threatened and Near Threatened species for which Bhutan may harbour internationally important populations. Such knowledge, in combination with well-targeted surveys, may yield reliable population estimates of, for example, Rufous-necked Hornbill, Pallas's Fish Eagle, White-bellied Heron and Beautiful Nuthatch, and guide future habitat management. At the same time, research could target certain bird groups critical in their habitat choice, such as hornbills, woodpeckers and wren babblers. Their occurrence might provide important indications of habitat quality and, thereby, management ideas for protected areas.

Despite the attention given to Black-necked Cranes, wetlands and waterbirds appear to be relatively under-represented in bird conservation efforts, primarily because potentially important wetland sites are located outside currently protected areas. In addition to the annual crane counts, midwinter waterbird surveys were started in 2000 and are now annual. Better protection for wetlands, for example concerning sand and boulder extraction from riverbeds, need to be developed.

It is now clear that Bhutan shoulders particular responsibility for the conservation of three bird species: Beautiful Nuthatch, Rufous-necked Hornbill and White-bellied Heron, which are globally threatened and dependent on large areas of old-growth forest in the warm broadleaf forest zone. They all have specific habitat requirements and the threats perhaps facing these species in Bhutan are of a hidden, long-term nature, and lie in the possible loss of old-growth forest at lower elevations, particularly of corridors linking populations in the protected areas. Here, forest grazing and timber extraction may alter forest composition and structure, leading to the effective loss of the old-growth character of these forests, eventually fragmenting bird populations and placing them on the road to extinction. Development of sustainable forest management practices outside protected areas is crucial to counteract this process.

Presently available information shows that isolation effects threatening bird populations are far from hypothetical, even in Bhutan's case. The dry and extensively cultivated middle parts of the main river valleys constitute dispersal barriers to many forest bird species, including Rufous-necked Hornbill. This underlines the importance of biological corridors, whilst demonstrating the need to ensure these corridors remain ecologically functional. In an area like Punakha/Wangdue Phodrang this could mean that corridor management may need to address long-term restoration of continuous forest cover, allowing hornbills to 'migrate' through these areas.

Finally, an overall conservation challenge, with particular relevance to birds, exists in managing the modernisation process, for example, to use the opportunities to preserve high-quality habitats far from roads, whilst not completely foregoing the continued presence of such habitats and their avifaunas in more accessible areas. Bhutan can then continue to be what it is today, a paradise for birds but also for people to enjoy their presence.

# 7. Glossary

**Chhu:** river.

**Chorten (stupa):** Buddhist monument.

**Dzong:** traditional building, housing government and religious bodies; often an old monumental fortress.

**Dzongkhag:** district.

**Geog:** block – the lowest administrative level in the Bhutan government structure.

**La:** mountain pass.

**Pangzhing:** an historical land-use system where pastureland is cropped in a long rotational cycle of around ten years.

**Terai:** the undulating alluvial, often marshy, strip of land 25–45 km wide, north of the Ganges plain, extending from Uttar Pradesh through Nepal and northern West Bengal to Assam; naturally supports tall elephant grass interspersed with dense forest, but large areas have been drained and converted to cultivation.

# Snow Partridge
## *Lerwa lerwa*

N=17(3). R 3800-4200

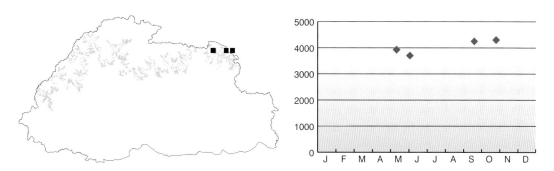

The Snow Partridge occurs in the high-altitude zone of the Himalayas, from Afghanistan to Arunachal Pradesh, and north of the main Himalayan range in southern Tibet and western China. It is among the highest-ranging phasianids in the region, always being found close to the snowline.

In Bhutan the Snow Partridge has been recorded on only a few occasions, reflecting the generally limited coverage of high-altitude areas. It has been found in the west and east of the country, at 3,800–4,200 m. Records in the west have not been mapped due to imprecise localities being reported. The species is an apparently uncommon resident of rather erratic occurrence or it is largely overlooked. However, it appears to breed in Bhutan as evidenced by a flock of 20 including eight juveniles encountered at 4,250 m on 18 September[49].

# Tibetan Snowcock
## *Tetraogallus tibetanus*

N=15(9). R 4000-4600

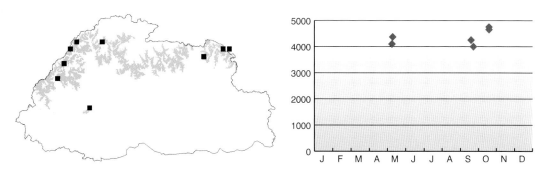

The Tibetan Snowcock occurs on the Tibetan Plateau, extending through the Himalayan main range locally between Himachal Pradesh and Arunachal Pradesh. It is a bird of rocky slopes and ridges in the alpine zone.

In Bhutan this snowcock has been found in the west and east, just reaching the temperate zone in the western valleys. Generally an uncommon resident, all records are from altitudes of 4,000–4,600 m. The species is usually encountered on the slopes of the highest passes, over 4,500 m, along high-altitude treks, such as the Snowman Trek. A record from the Daga La ridge, south of Thimphu, at 4,000 m[43], is remarkable, as it suggests the presence of a population separate from the Himalayan main range by c.50 km and over passes as low as 3,100 m. Available records are from March, May, September and October, i.e. the period favourable for high-altitude trekking. An observation of a covey of seven including four juveniles, at 4,250 m on 18 September[49], is the only evidence of breeding in Bhutan. Four pairs on the western ascent of the Yari La, at 4,000–4,700 m in March[2], suggest that, at least locally, it may be not uncommon, but the species is often under-recorded due to the physical remoteness of its range.

# Black Francolin
*Francolinus francolinus*                                                    N=1(1)

The Black Francolin occurs from Turkey and the Middle East to South Asia, reaching its easternmost limit in north-east India. It is a bird of cultivated areas and their fringes, where there is sufficient ground cover and plentiful water.

In Bhutan the Black Francolin is rare, in contrast to its common occurrence in Nepal. It has been found once, at Manas, at 350 m in April[22].

# Tibetan Partridge
*Perdix hodgsoniae*                                            N=20(4). R 4000-4200

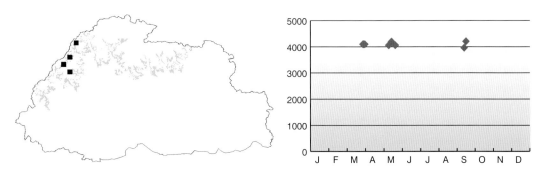

The Tibetan Partridge is a bird of high-elevation desert areas on the Tibetan Plateau. In a few places its range extends south of the main Himalayan range.

In Bhutan this partridge only occurs in the high west, at the headwaters of the Sunkosh Chhu and Wang Chhus, in the narrow altitudinal band between 4,000 m and 4,200 m. Encountered singly or in pairs, on 15 September a female and a fledgling were collected at 4,200 m[1], which confirms breeding in Bhutan.

# Common Quail
*Coturnix coturnix*                             N=10(5). W 1200-3000 (agricultural areas)

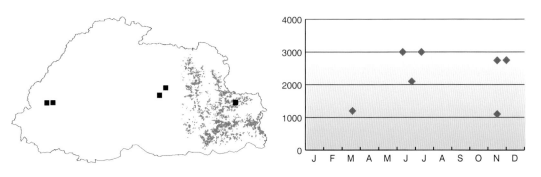

The Common Quail is a widespread breeder from Western Europe and north-west Africa east to Lake Baikal, where it is replaced by the closely related Japanese Quail. It winters from West Africa, through Arabia to India. Most reach the Indian subcontinent via the Indus Valley, from where it spreads into northern and western parts. Numbers vary greatly between years, but have clearly declined. It is also a local breeder in the northern subcontinent.

The status of this quail in Bhutan is difficult to assess, as in many cases it is indistinguishable from the Japanese Quail in the field. Definite identification is only possible in the breeding season, by its distinctive call or by observation of a male in typical breeding plumage. To further complicate matters, some specimens taken in Bhutan appear intermediate between the two species. Thus, their distributions must be described with caution.

During his surveys in the 1930s, Ludlow found Common Quail breeding commonly in the Ha, Paro and Bumthang valleys, at 2,200–3,050 m, in June and July. He collected a nest with eggs from Gyetsa, Bumthang, at 3,050 m on 9 June[31]. In mid-March birds appeared in paddy stubble in the Gamri Chhu valley, Trashigang. However, a specimen taken there was intermediate between Common and Japanese Quail[31]. Subsequently, a single was collected at Jakar, Bumthang in November 1973[1], indicating the possibility of a wintering population. Since then, there have been no definite records and its present status is unclear. Possibly some or all winter records of quail might refer to this species. Unidentified quails have been seen in winter in the Gamri Chhu valley[45], the Bumthang valleys[16] and at Phobjikha[43,52] (1,200–3,000 m). Common Quail appears to have disappeared as a breeder, as none has been heard recently at previously occupied sites. Remarkably, in summer the Bumthang valleys are now occupied by Japanese Quail.

# Japanese Quail
## *Coturnix japonica*

N = 16(4). S 2800-3000 (agricultural areas)

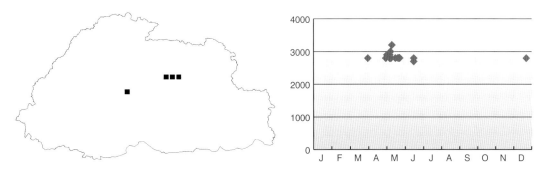

The Japanese Quail replaces the Common Quail east of Lake Baikal to Japan. It winters south to southern China and mainland south-east Asia, reaching Assam in the Indian subcontinent. In the Indian subcontinent it has been found as a summer visitor as well, in Bhutan and Assam.

In Bhutan the status of Japanese Quail is difficult to assess because of the difficulty of distinguishing it from Common Quail. Some collected in Bhutan in the 19th and 20th centuries possess features intermediate between the two species[1]. Indeed, there are no typical Japanese Quail specimens, which is in stark contrast to the regular field observations from recent years. Since 1993 it has been commonly found in Phobjikha Valley[10,22,52,55] and the Bumthang valleys (Tang and Chamkhar)[10,52] at 2,800–3,000 m. They are identified by their characteristic call and have been noted late April until at least mid-June. The species uses wheat and buckwheat fields, with probably several tens of territories in the three valleys. Wintering quails seen in December and March in the Phobjikha Valley[43,52] might be Japanese Quail, but confusion with Common Quail cannot be excluded. I tentatively consider Japanese Quail to be an uncommon summer visitor. Generally, the distribution of both quails matches their reputations as unpredictable species, and is complicated by the difficulties in distinguishing them.

Japanese Quail
*Ren Hathway*

# Common Hill Partridge
## *Arborophila torqueola*

N=380(67). S 1600-3600 (mid-Mar-Oct); W 1800-3000

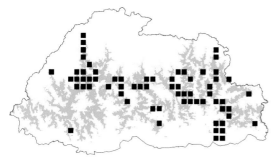

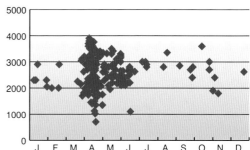

The Common Hill Partridge occurs in the Himalayas from Himachal Pradesh in the west and Arunachal Pradesh in the east. Its range extends into south-east Tibet in the north and northern Vietnam in the east. Of the three *Arborophila* species in Bhutan it has the highest altitudinal range, and inhabits ravines and slopes in evergreen broadleaf forest, especially oak.

In Bhutan the species is abundant throughout the temperate belt, with a few records in the high west and eastern foothills. It shows some altitudinal movement, in summer occurring at 1,600–3,600 m, retreating below 3,000 m in winter. It is more occasional to 700 m[19] and 3,900 m[52]. Below 2,000 m it seems relatively scarce and thus its main range is above those of other *Arborophila*. However, care is needed to interpretate altitudinal distributions, as almost all records concern calling birds, with relatively few records from the non-breeding period. Some identification errors may be involved, given the similarity of *Arborophila* vocalisations and that few records have been documented with sound-recordings. Calling birds are heard mostly from the second half of March to June, occasionally until September. The species is found in cool broadleaf forest, more occasionally in fir, Blue Pine, hemlock

Common Hill Partridge
*Dan Cole*

and mixed forest. Here its far-carrying call is among the common background sounds of spring, with often up to ten heard in an early-morning trip. No confirmed breeding records exist for Bhutan, which is unsurprising as sight records of all of the hill partridges are rare.

# Rufous-throated Partridge
## *Arborophila rufogularis*

N=406(47). R 600-2000

The Rufous-throated Partridge occurs in the Himalayas from Himachal Pradesh to Arunachal Pradesh, and in the hills of north-east India, Bangladesh, Myanmar and east to south-west China and north Vietnam. Within this range it occupies lower altitudes than Common Hill Partridge and inhabits dense undergrowth in warm broadleaf and subtropical forest, including second growth.

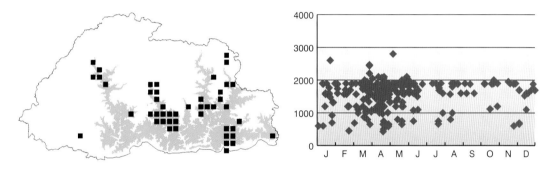

In Bhutan Rufous-throated Partridge is found throughout the temperate belt and in the central and eastern foothills. It is a common resident, but concentrated in the east, being particularly uncommon in the western and Sunkosh valleys. Mainly found at 600–2,000 m, immediately below Common Hill Partridge. The lowest record is from 400 m[19] and the highest 2,800 m[49]. Almost all records involve calling birds, which are heard year-round, peaking January–May. A mean density of 2.5 breeding territories per km was found near Zhemgang, at 1,600–1,900 m[52]. With the exception of calling birds holding territories, there is no confirmation of breeding in Bhutan.

# Chestnut-breasted Partridge
## *Arborophila mandellii*

N = 75(13). R 1600-2000

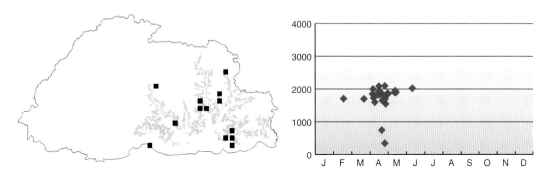

The Chestnut-breasted Partridge is the rarest *Arborophila* in the region and the least known. It occurs in the Himalayas from West Bengal east to Arunachal Pradesh, and is considered globally threatened, being classified by BirdLife International as Vulnerable, because of its small population which is increasingly fragmented by habitat loss. Inhabits dense undergrowth in evergreen broadleaf forest, often with bamboo thickets. Over much of its range the integrity of this habitat is threatened by shifting cultivation and forest clearance.

In Bhutan this partridge is an uncommon resident, confined to the central and eastern valleys, with one record from the central foothills[1]. It is localised, having been found at around seven sites until the present. There are reports from several other sites, but these need confirmation given the difficulties in identification, which relies on experience with its vocalisations. It appears to occupy a narrow altitudinal band, at 1,600–2,000 m, roughly between the ranges of Common Hill Partridge and Rufous-throated Partridge, and appears to replace these species, particulary in moist mature broadleaf forest on north- or west-facing slopes. Presence to 250 m appears occasional. Calling birds are heard mid-March to June, mostly in April, when it is annually located at a few regular sites. The maximum number heard at a site in any year ranges between one and eight, with most found either side of the Kuri Chhu valley[28,49], in old-growth forest within Thrumshingla National Park and Bumdeling Wildlife Sanctuary. Other than the territorial call and the observation of a duetting pair[5], there are no clear breeding records for Bhutan.

# Blood Pheasant
*Ithaginis cruentus*

N=124(45). R 2800-4200

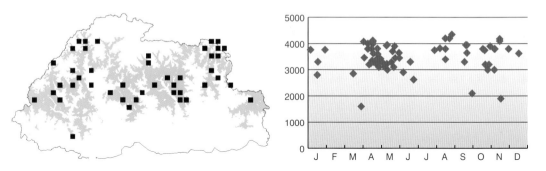

The Blood Pheasant occurs in the Himalayas from western Nepal to Arunachal Pradesh, its range continuing into Tibet and montane western China. Two subspecies occur in Bhutan, *cruentus* in the west and *tibetanus* in the east, the divide suspected to be the Black Mountain range, although few data are available to confirm this. Its habitat is open fir and rhododendron forest, showing a preference for bamboo thickets.

In Bhutan this pheasant is a common resident, found throughout temperate and alpine zones. It is the most common pheasant on high-altitude treks. Its regular range is 2,800–4,200 m, which it appears to occupy year-round. Stray birds are occasionally seen lower down in cool broadleaf forest, with an exceptionally low record from 1,600 m in March[44]. It appears closely associated with relatively undisturbed fir forest, with particularly large numbers in mature forests around the Thrumshing La pass, in the core of the National Park. Several tens are regularly encountered here, with a maximum of over 50[28]. In October–April it is regularly found in flocks of up to ten or more. Pairs form during April, with sightings of pairs or small groups usual from late April. A nest with eggs was found at 3,650 m on 30 May[49] and fledglings at 3,300 m on 17 June[31].

# Satyr Tragopan
*Tragopan satyra*

N=169(43). R 2000-3600

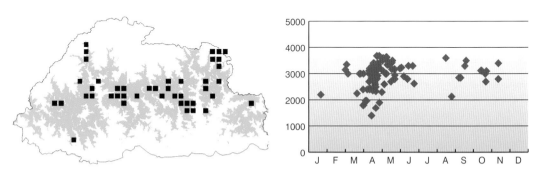

The Satyr Tragopan is distributed along the Himalayas from Uttar Pradesh to western Arunachal Pradesh. It is considered Near Threatened by BirdLife International and has declined particularly in the western part of its range due to forest loss and hunting pressure. Habitat consists of moist oak and rhododendron forest, with dense undergrowth and bamboo clumps.

In Bhutan this tragopan is a frequent resident, found throughout the alpine and temperate zones. Its altitudinal range is from 2,000 m to 3,600 m, more occasionally to 1,400 m[14] and 3,800 m[22]. There are few winter records, but it appears to remain in this altitudinal range year-round. The species is mostly noted March–May, when males are calling. Peak vocal activity is from mid-April to mid-May. A max. 5 birds have been heard at a single site[6,28]. In undisturbed habitat considerable densities appear to occur, as demonstrated by a total of ten between Gasa and Laya in a single afternoon[22]. As most birding activity is concentrated along the road the species is probably under-recorded. Even so, the frequency of sightings (often concerning several birds) leaves no doubt as to the presence of a healthy population. Further west similar densities are exceptional and confined to well-protected sites, such as Pipar in the Annapurna Conservation Area, Nepal (Kaul and Shakya 2001, Inskipp and Inskipp pers. comm.). In Bhutan the vast areas of continuous forest habitat and overall low hunting pressure are favourable factors in the species's conservation. Jigme Dorji National Park, Thrumshingla National Park, Jigme Singye Wangchuck National Park and Bumdeling Wildlife Sanctuary each hold significant populations, which appear to be still connected, given widespread occurrence of tragopans outside these protected areas. Thus, management of biological corridors is of particular relevance to the conservation of this species in Bhutan.

Satyr Tragopan
*Dan Cole*

# Blyth's Tragopan
## *Tragopan blythii*

N=5(3)

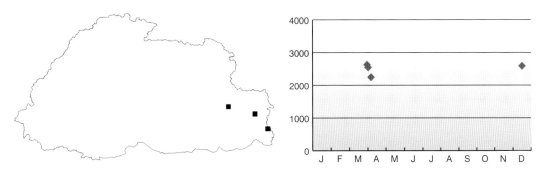

Blyth's Tragopan is rare and local in the Himalayas of eastern Bhutan, Arunachal Pradesh and south-east Tibet, as well as north-east India and further east in Myanmar. It is globally threatened, being listed by BirdLife International as Vulnerable, because of its small fragmented population, which is declining through loss of forest habitat and hunting pressure. It inhabits dense undergrowth and bamboo thickets in moist broadleaf forest, presumably at lower elevations than Satyr Tragopan. However, records from elsewhere in its range are inconclusive of its altitudinal range, the species having been found at the winter snowline, at 2,500 m and 2,800 m in Myanmar (King 2001), as well as breeding at 1,400 m in Nagaland in June (Choudhury 2001).

In Bhutan Blyth's Tragopan is a rare resident, confined to the eastern valleys. It is primarily known from specimens collected at Shinkhar Louri[1,31] and Yonpu La[31], Trashigang district, at *c.*2,600 m, in the 1930s and 1960s/1970s. These localities are within the same belt of broadleaf forest south of the high-elevation areas of Merak-Sakten, *c.*40 km apart. In recent years it has been observed again close to the Shinkhar Louri area in Serthig geog[44], Samdrup Jongkha district, in dense bamboo. A possible record of this elusive species is of a female tragopan crossing the road between Wamrong and Deothang, at 2,250 m[6] and relatively close to the collection sites. Unfortunately, identification could not be ascertained. Obviously, its status in Bhutan requires clarification through field surveys, in order to obtain data on its altitudinal range and the extent of its distribution in the extreme east. In particular, the potential importance of Merak-Sakten Wildlife Sanctuary to the species must be assessed.

# Himalayan Monal
## *Lophophorus impejanus*

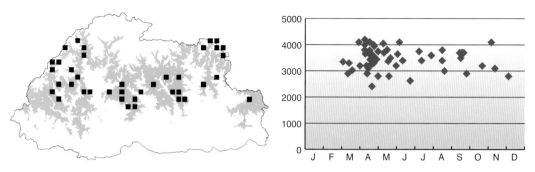

The Himalayan Monal is distributed through the Himalayas from Afghanistan to Arunachal Pradesh, reaching northern Myanmar in the east. It is a species of high altitudes, summering in the alpine zone, descending to winter in forests lower down.

Himalayan Monal
*Ren Hathway*

In Bhutan the monal is a common resident throughout the temperate and alpine zones. It has been found at 2,800–4,200 m, occupying a similar altitudinal range to Blood Pheasant. It occurs in a wider range of habitats, including alpine scrub, and regularly feeds in open areas. A single male at 2,400 m in April is the lowest record[19]. Whilst overall frequent, it becomes gradually scarcer in the east, where it approaches the species's easternmost limit. This is reflected in its altitudinal range, which is increasingly confined to the alpine zone in this region, with relatively few records from temperate parts of the central and eastern valleys. Whilst regularly found to 2,800 m in the west, in the eastern valleys the lowest records are from 3,300 m. The species mostly occurs singly or in small groups of up to three. In suitable habitat it can reach considerable densities as witnessed by the observation of 12 males and several females at 3,800–4,100 m above Phajoding, Thimphu district, in early April[52,53], when males were displaying. In the high east a nest with eggs was found on 5 June at 4,100 m[49] and the first juveniles were reported in late July[31]. In August–September family parties of up to five are encountered[49,52]. Winter records are few and birds may keep to the cover of high-altitude coniferous forest in this period, as demonstrated by observations in this habitat in November–December[52,53].

# Red Junglefowl
## *Gallus gallus*

The Red Junglefowl occurs in the northern and eastern Indian subcontinent, in the Himalayas from Kashmir to Arunachal Pradesh, in eastern and north-east India, and in Bangladesh. Further east its range extends to Vietnam and south through the Malay Peninsula. Its habitat is a mosaic of agricultural fields, scrub and moist forest. As the ancestor of the domestic chicken, part of the population may comprise feral birds.

In Bhutan the junglefowl is an occasionally recorded resident, found throughout the subtropical zone and in adjacent parts of the central valleys. There are single records from the western[44] and eastern valleys[25],

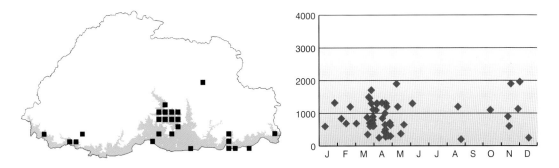

the latter involving one in the Kuri Chhu valley, far from its regular range, that was possibly feral. Whilst it occurs in foothills to 800 m, in the Mangde Chhu valley the species is regular to 1,800 m and occasional to 2,000 m. Mostly noted mid-February to mid-May when males are most vocal. Groups tend to be small, with no records of more than three together. Frequently encountered in scrub near villages, venturing into fields to feed. A female with chicks was seen at c.1,300 m on 20 April[52]. It is unclear to what extent there is interbreeding between wild and domestic populations, although there are no visible signs of this in wild birds.

# Kalij Pheasant
## *Lophura leucomelanos*

N=295(71). S 1000-2800 (Mar-Nov); W 800-2400

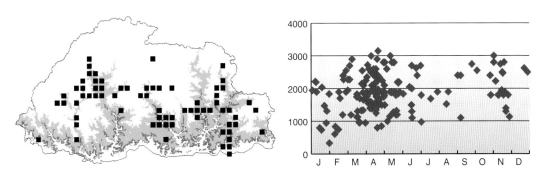

The Kalij Pheasant occurs in the Himalayas from Pakistan to Arunachal Pradesh and north-east India, its range extending further east to Myanmar. Three subspecies occur in Bhutan, *melanota* in the west, *moffitti* in the centre and *lathami* in the east. It inhabits a variety of forest habitats, provided there is dense undergrowth.

In Bhutan the Kalij is found throughout the temperate belt, with occasional records from the eastern, central and western foothills. The distribution of the three subspecies appears complex. Western *melanota* is found in the Wang Chhu valley and the northern Sunkosh Chhu valley. *Lathami* occurs from the Mangde Chhu valley eastwards. However, in the lower Mangde Chhu valley the two subspecies appear to intergrade, with multiple specimens collected in the 1960s and 1970s deemed to be intermediate[1]. In the adjacent Sunkosh Chhu valley, east of the river, the rare subspecies *moffitti* has been found[7,22]. There is also an intermediate *melanota/lathami* specimen from this area, collected close to Nobding, Wangdue Phodrang (along the Pe Chhu)[1]. Obviously, the subspecific status of those in the Sunkosh Chhu and Mangde Chhu valleys requires further study.

Kalij Pheasant is one of the few Phasianidae in the country that shows noticeable altitudinal movement. The summer range is from 1,000 m to 2,800 m, with occasional records to 3,000 m. In December–February it retreats below 2,400 m and is noted to 800 m, occasionally reaching 400 m[1]. Most of the year birds are encountered singly or in small flocks, but in September–February larger, usually single-sex flocks, of c.7 birds are occasionally seen. The largest flock consisted of 20[44]. The breeding season appears quite prolonged. A pair with chicks (*moffitti*) was seen at 1,300 m on 16 May[22], and a male with a small chick (*lathami*) at 1,700 m on 17 July[52]. Densities within its breeding range appear low, with fewer than 0.5 pairs per km[52].

Kalij Pheasant
*Ren Hathway*

# Grey Peacock Pheasant
## *Polyplectron bicalcaratum*

N=43(16). R 400-1400 (broadleaf forest)

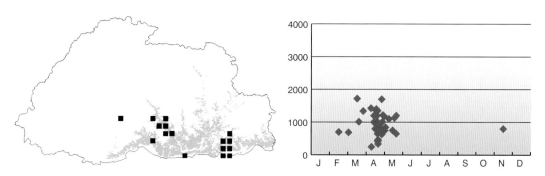

The Grey Peacock Pheasant occurs in the Himalayan foothills from Sikkim to Arunachal Pradesh, and in the hills of north-east India east to Vietnam. It is an extremely secretive bird of dense undergrowth in tropical and subtropical forest.

In Bhutan this pheasant is an uncommon resident of central and eastern valleys and foothills. There is one record from the Sunkosh Valley[22], which is close to the westernmost limit of its range. It has been noted at 400–1,400 m, with occasional sightings to 200 m[19] and 1,700 m[14]. It does not penetrate far into the eastern valleys, probably because cultivation and Chir Pine plantations have fragmented its broadleaf forest habitat. Almost all records are in spring (mid-February to mid-May) when males are vocalising. The only November record is of two specimens collected by Ludlow[31]. It occurs annually in April–May between Samdrup Jongkha and Deothang, with a maximum of six calling birds present at one site[5].

# Indian Peafowl
## *Pavo cristatus*

N=5(4)

The Indian Peafowl occurs over most of the Indian subcontinent, except the north-west and parts of the north-east. It inhabits undergrowth in deciduous forest near streams.

In Bhutan the species is a rare resident in the foothills. It has been found in western, central and eastern parts, with records from Samtse[44], Manas[22] and near Samdrup Jongkha[44,45]. Whilst common in adjacent India it does not penetrate deep into Bhutan, being unknown in the country above 400 m.

# Fulvous Whistling-duck
## Dendrocygna bicolor
N=1(1)

The Fulvous Whistling-duck has a discontinuous global distribution, in parts of South America, Central and East Africa, and the Indian subcontinent, where it occurs mainly in north-east India and Bangladesh, although it was formerly more widespread and appears to have declined. A bird of marshes and shallow lakes with extensive vegetation, including partially submerged trees in which it breeds.

In Bhutan this species has been recorded once, on 9 May 1998 at the fishponds near Gelephu, when five were present[24]. Although it is locally common in Assam, in Bhutan suitable habitat for this bird is largely absent.

# Greylag Goose
## Anser anser
N=5(3)

The Greylag Goose breeds in the temperate zone from northern Europe through Central Asia to Kamchatka. In the Indian subcontinent it is a winter visitor, particularly to the north-west, where birds follow the Indus Valley on migration. In the north and east it is more patchily distributed, through the Gangetic plains and Brahmaputra Valley.

In Bhutan the Greylag Goose is a rare passage migrant. All five records are from the second half of February and first half of March. Two involve flyover migrants (at Zhemgang[52] and Deothang[31]). Unidentified geese also have been seen in the early morning migrating high over the Mangde Chhu valley and eastern foothills[14]. There are two records of birds resting by day near Punakha at 1,400 m, respectively of 1[52] and 15 birds[40]. That most birds have been observed in flight is indicative of the rapid spring migration, from its winter quarters in the Assam plains and apparently crossing the Himalayas via the shortest route to their breeding grounds. There are no autumn records, suggesting that birds follow a different route at this season, possibly along the Brahmaputra River.

# Bar-headed Goose
## Anser indicus
N=29(6). W 1400-2400

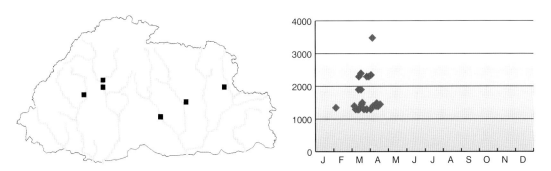

The Bar-headed Goose breeds on high-altitude lakes of the Tibetan Plateau, in the Central Asian republics and Mongolia. It is a common winter visitor to the Indian subcontinent, and is more widespread than the Greylag Goose.

This goose is an uncommon migrant in Bhutan. Like Greylag Goose, passage is confined to spring, and is noted early March to mid-April. An exceptionally early record is from 3 February[29], whilst the latest was on 16 April[5]. Most records concern staging birds, primarily in the Puna Sang Chhu valley, between Wangdue Phodrang and Punakha (1,300 m), where it occurs almost annually. More occasionally it appears at the sewage ponds at Babesa, Thimphu district (2,300 m)[14,24,52]. Away from these sites there are records of birds in flight over Thimphu Valley[43], the west side of Thrumshing La (3,400 m)[5] and Zhemgang (1,900 m)[52], the latter involving birds heard at night. Staging birds may pause several days, particularly if weather conditions for crossing the Himalayas are unfavourable. Maxima recorded in the Puna Sang Chhu were 20 on 26 March 1995[5] and 21 on 10 March 2000[49,57], both records coinciding with bad weather that held up large numbers of waterbirds.

# Ruddy Shelduck
## *Tadorna ferruginea*

N=178(23). S 4000-4600 (mid-May-Sep); W 1000-2800

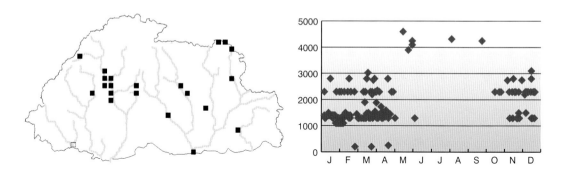

The Ruddy Shelduck breeds from southern Europe through Turkey, the Central Asian steppes to the Tibetan Plateau and Mongolia. It is a common breeder on high-altitude lakes in Tibet, and a winter visitor to lowlands of the Indian subcontinent, where it utilises large rivers and lakes with extensive sandbanks.

The species is mainly recorded during winter in Bhutan. The main wintering site is Bajo, Wangdue Phodrang (1,300 m), and the adjacent stretch of the Puna Sang Chhu below Punakha, and (in small numbers) down to Kamechu[49]. Other regular winter sites are the sewage ponds at Babesa, Thimphu district (2,300 m), the Torsa Chhu near Phuntsholing (200 m). The first record at Babesa concerned three in 1996/1997[49] since when the numbers have gradually grown to c.40 in 2001/2002[42,52]. A winter population also appears to be established in the Phobjikha Valley (2,800 m), with birds present since winter 1999/2000[47]. There are isolated winter records from recent years at Paro[53] and the Ura Valley[50]. A gradual increase has also occurred at Bajo, where numbers reached c.420 during the midwinter count of January 2002[42,52], approaching 1% of the estimated Central Asian population (Wetlands International 2002). These sites are relatively high compared to other wintering areas in the subcontinent. In addition, Manas is probably a wintering area. To date, there are few records from many of these sites, as birders have not frequently visited them. Birds arrive from mid-October, reaching their largest numbers in the last week of November. The first Babesa birds appear a few weeks earlier than those at Bajo, probably because high water levels persist through October at the latter. Most leave in the first half of March, with the last birds noted in late April. In 2002 one stayed at Bajo until at least June[52]. Passage of birds wintering further south is evidenced by records from outside the wintering areas in October and March. In particular, the Mangde Chhu and Chamkhar Chhu valleys appear to form a migration corridor, possibly involving birds from Manas. Breeding in Bhutan was recently confirmed from alpine lakes at 4,000–4,400 m in the east. Birds were present at three different lakes and in one a pair with young was observed on 3 August[49]. In the high west breeding is probable as birds have been observed at alpine lakes in May[5,44], with the highest record from 4,600 m[34].

# Common Shelduck
## *Tadorna tadorna*

N=12(2). W 1400-2400

The Common Shelduck is a mainly coastal breeder in Europe, but is found further east on the saline lakes of Central Asia, east to Mongolia and the Tibetan Plateau. In the Indian subcontinent it is an irregular winter visitor, appearing on large rivers and lakes in variable numbers.

Common Shelduck is mainly a rare spring passage migrant. It passes through in March and occurs less than annually at Bajo, Wangdue Phodrang district (1,300 m), during this period. It mostly occurs in flocks of at least ten, 32 being the maximum counted[5]. In June there are regular records of 1–4 moulting birds at the sewage ponds at Babesa, Thimphu district[42,52].

# Mandarin Duck
## *Aix galericulata*

The Mandarin's range comprises Japan, Korea, south-east Siberia and China. It occurs in the Indian subcontinent as a vagrant.

In Bhutan Mandarin Duck is a vagrant found twice in March 2002, both records probably of the same bird. A male in full breeding plumage was first present on 4 March, at Bajo, at 1,300 m[53] and was observed again at the same site on 25 March[52,53].

# Gadwall
## *Anas strepera*

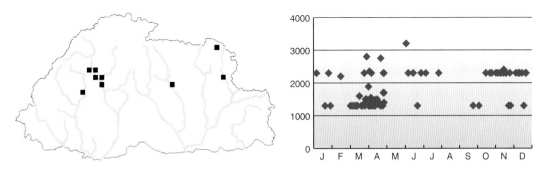

The Gadwall breeds in the temperate zone from Europe through Central Asia to Kamchatka, and in North America. In the Indian subcontinent it is a widespread winter visitor to freshwater marshes and lakes with abundant aquatic vegetation.

In Bhutan this duck is a frequent passage migrant, normally forming the bulk of flocks of migratory ducks. Spring passage is noted particularly along the Puna Sang Chhu and Mo Chhu between Wangdue Phodrang and Tashithang (1,300–1,600 m), from the first week of March to late April. It is then regular in flocks of up to 20, with a max. 50 reported[5]. Peak passage is in the second half of March. During this period and in April it occasionally appears in other areas, e.g. Bumdeling in Trashi Yangtse district (1,900 m)[49], the Bumthang Valley (2,800 m) and the sewage ponds at Babesa, Thimphu district (2,300 m). Autumn migration mostly lasts mid-October to the first week of December, with the earliest on 22 September[29], when it is usually found at the sewage ponds at Babesa and occasionally on the Puna Sang Chhu. Maximum at Babesa was 41 on 16 November 1997[52]. Wintering is rare, with a few present in January–February 1998 and 2002, along the Puna Sang Chhu and Babesa, and a single at Paro in 2000[49,52]. In contrast, oversummering appears regular, both at the sewage ponds and along the Puna Sang Chhu. In June–July small numbers are present which are moulting their primaries. Max. 15 in June 1999 at Bajo[52]. In the same period it has been noted at alpine lakes in the east[49].

# Falcated Duck
## *Anas falcata*

The Falcated Duck breeds in boreal north-east Asia. Its winter quarters lie in eastern China, Japan and south to northern Myanmar. It occurs in the Indian subcontinent as a rare but regular winter visitor.

In Bhutan Falcated Duck is a vagrant which has been recorded twice. On 14 March 2000 a male was present at Bajo, Wangdue Phodrang district[14], during a period when many waterbirds were delayed on their Himalayan passage because of bad weather. Another was noted at Paro, on 17 March 2001[32].

# Eurasian Wigeon
## *Anas penelope*
N=90(12). W 1400-2400

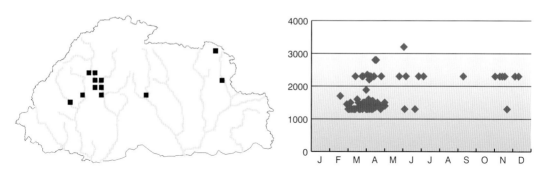

The Eurasian Wigeon breeds across a broad swathe of Europe to eastern Asia, in the boreal and arctic zone. In the Indian subcontinent the species is a widespread winter visitor to lowlands. Its preferred winter habitat is open lakes and rivers.

In Bhutan the wigeon is a frequent passage migrant, principally recorded at two regular sites, the Puna Sang Chhu and Mo Chhu between Wangdue Phodrang and Tashithang (1,300–1,600 m), and the sewage ponds at Babesa, Thimphu district (2,300 m). Like Gadwall, spring records are mostly from the Puna Sang Chhu, with occasional records in April from the sewage ponds at Babesa, Paro[14,19], Bumthang Valley[14,28] and Bumdeling, Trashi Yangtse district[49]. Spring migration is in March–April, with an early record on 17 February[49,52]. In March up to 10–50 birds are present daily, with generally lower numbers in April. Fluctuating numbers indicate high turnover. The largest concentration was 86 on 13 March 2000, when passage was delayed by bad weather. The species's regular presence in spring contrasts with its weak autumn passage, suggesting a loop migration in which birds bypass Bhutan at the latter season, instead reaching the Indian subcontinent via the Brahmaputra and Indus valleys. The few autumn records are mostly from the frequently visited sewage ponds, with isolated records from the Puna Sang Chhu, mostly of singles. The earliest autumn record is 8 September[52], the last 10 December[53]. Whilst none winters, summering is regular, with a few remaining until at least July at Bajo, Wangdue Phodrang and Babesa. A max. 13 were present at Bajo in June 1999[52]. During the same period the species has been noted at alpine lakes in the east[49].

# Mallard
## *Anas platyrhynchos*
N=85(17). W 1400-2400

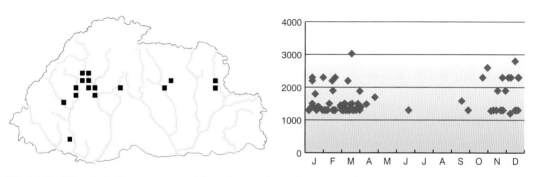

The Mallard breeds in the temperate and boreal zones throughout the Holarctic. In Asia its distribution extends south over the Tibetan Plateau, with small breeding populations in the Himalayas, in Nepal and Kashmir. It is a winter visitor to the north-west and north subcontinent.

In Bhutan the species is a frequent winter visitor and passage migrant. It winters annually at a handful of sites: the Puna Sang Chhu and Mo Chhu between Baso Chhu, Wangdue Phodrang and Tashithang (1,200–1,600 m), near Amseling in the Thimphu Valley and in the Paro Valley. At Bajo, on the Puna Sang Chhu, the wintering flock numbers 70–90 birds and has been stable in recent years. Up to 5–20 have been recorded at Paro and Thimphu. Those wintering at Bajo roost during the day and forage at night along the riverbanks and paddyfield stubbles. In autumn the first records are in mid-September[1]. However, migration is evident from the second half of October, with records at the sewage ponds near Thimphu and in the Bumthang valleys. Passage continues here until mid-December. The wintering flock at Bajo increases from late October and reaches full strength by mid-December. Numbers remain stable until late February, after which spring migration brings peak numbers to Bajo in the first half of March, with a max. 296 in this period[19]. By the end of March practically all have gone, with few remaining until April and the last recorded on 25 April[39]. There is one summer record, a single male at Bajo on 20 June[52]. In common with most wildfowl, spring passage is significantly more pronounced than in autumn and, in the case of Mallard, entirely concentrated in the Puna Sang Chhu area. The Sunkosh Chhu valley constitutes a major migration corridor, the availability of suitable stopover habitat probably being an important factor.

# Spot-billed Duck
## *Anas poecilorhyncha*

N=25(2). W 1400

The nominate subspecies of the Spot-billed Duck is a widespread resident in the western and northern Indian peninsula. Two other subspecies occur in northern south-east Asia, east from Assam (*haringtoni*) and in eastern China north to Manchuria and Japan (*zonorhyncha*). Whereas *haringtoni* is resident in east Assam, *zonorhyncha* is a rare winter visitor to the north-east Indian subcontinent.

In Bhutan this duck is an uncommon winter visitor and very local passage migrant. Its single wintering site is Bajo, Wangdue Phodrang district, where it is annual from mid-November to late March. Typically 5–7 are present January–February. In March numbers rise to 10–15 birds, with a max. 19 counted[14], indicating some passage occurs. All appear to be *zonorhyncha*[52,53]. The latest spring record is 24 April[28]. The earliest autumn record concerns a passage bird at sewage ponds near Thimphu on 21 October[52].

# Northern Shoveler
## *Anas clypeata*

N=18(7). W 1400-2400

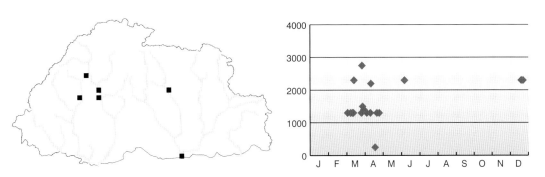

The Northern Shoveler breeds throughout the Holarctic in temperate and boreal zones, in Asia far north of the Tibetan Plateau (45°N). The species is a widespread and common winter visitor to the Indian subcontinent.

In Bhutan this species is an uncommon spring migrant. Regular sites are the Puna Sang Chhu and Mo Chhu between Wangdue Phodrang and Tashithang (1,300–1,600 m), and the sewage ponds at Babesa, Thimphu district (2,300 m), with single records from Manas (200 m)[22], Bumthang (2,800 m)[26] and Paro (2,200 m)[14]. Passage occupies early March to at least late April. A male at the sewage ponds on 5 June[43,52] was probably a late migrant, as the species is amongst the last ducks to leave its winter quarters in India. There is one winter record from the sewage ponds, on 20 December[43,52]. The largest number recorded is 30 at Manas[22].

# Northern Pintail
## *Anas acuta*

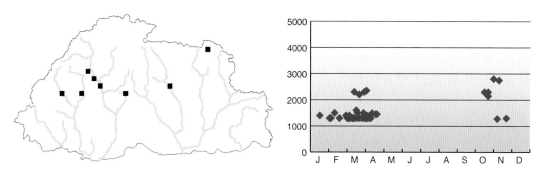

The Northern Pintail breeds throughout the Holarctic, from the temperate to the arctic zones. In India it is a widespread winter visitor, migrating particularly through the Indus Valley, from where it spreads throughout the peninsula.

Northern Pintail is mainly an uncommon migrant in Bhutan. Autumn passage commences mid-October, with records from localities in the western, Sunkosh and central valleys at 1,300–2,800 m. Broad-front passage continues until mid-November. Winter records are scarce, with 1–5 present along the Puna Sang Chhu and Mo Chhu between Wangdue Phodrang and Tashithang some winters. Spring migration is manifest from March, with peak numbers in the first half and smaller numbers until mid-April. Latest spring record 19 April[12]. Peak numbers are associated with spells of bad weather that prevent passage over the Himalayas, with maxima of 112 in March 2000[14] and 43 in March 1995[19]. As with the Mallard, spring migration is primarily through the Sunkosh Chhu valley. Spring records from other valleys are almost entirely lacking, with a few records of singles from the sewage ponds at Babesa[14,52] and from Paro[10] in late March–early April. Only during bad weather in March 2000 did larger numbers appear at Babesa[14], although the flock of ten observed fell short of numbers along the Puna Sang Chhu in the same period.

# Garganey
## *Anas querquedula*

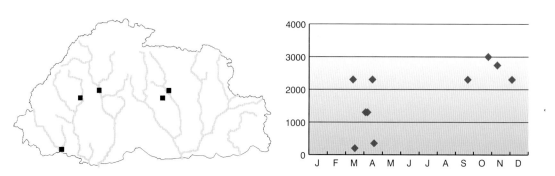

The Garganey breeds in the boreal and temperate zone, from W Europe east to Kamchatka. In India it is one of the commonest wintering ducks and amongst the earliest to arrive in autumn.

In Bhutan Garganey is a rare migrant and somewhat atypical in its occurrence compared to most other ducks. Records are evenly distributed between spring and autumn, and are not concentrated in the Sunkosh Chu valley. Moreover, given the large wintering population in India, records are remarkably scarce. Thus, numbers in Bhutan represent a small percentage of those passing the Himalayan main range on a broad front. Noted in autumn from mid-September[52] to early December[53], with the largest flock being 17[52]. Spring passage is relatively short, mid-March to mid-April, with flocks of up to ten. At both seasons, noted from varied localities, from the Torsa Chhu at Phuntsholing[20,22] to the Bumthang Valley[1], at 200–2,800 m.

# Baikal Teal
## *Anas formosa*
N=1(1)

The breeding range of the Baikal Teal lies in eastern Siberia, from the Yenisey River to the Sakhalin peninsula, and south to Lake Baikal. It winters in China, S Korea and Japan, and is a rare winter visitor to the northern Indian subcontinent. Listed by BirdLife International as globally Vulnerable, its population is rapidly declining due to destruction of wetlands and hunting pressure.

In Bhutan the Baikal Teal is a vagrant, with one record. On 7 November 2001 an immature male was present along the Thim Chhu at Babesa, Thimphu district, at 2,300 m, with a small flock of Common Teal[17,52].

# Common Teal
## *Anas crecca*
N=86(14). W 1400-2400

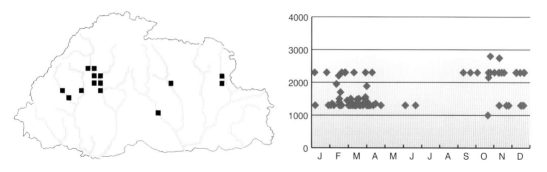

The Common Teal breeds from the extreme west to extreme eastern Eurasia, as well as in North America, mostly in the temperate and boreal zone. In the Indian subcontinent the species is a widespread winter visitor to a range of freshwater habitats.

In Bhutan this teal is an occasional passage migrant, and winter visitor. Earliest autumn records are in September from the sewage ponds near Thimphu. Peak migration appears to be late October to mid-November, when there are also records from the Bumthang Valley, Paro[22] and a small stream near Zhemgang[52]. Numbers are small with a max. 9. The main wintering site is at Bajo, Wangdue Phodrang (1,300 m), with a population of c.100. The birds roost during the day on the shingle banks, probably feeding nocturnally on stubble in the surrounding rice fields. Amongst wildfowl it is the most widespread winter visitor, with records from the sewage ponds at Babesa, the Thimphu Valley, Paro Valley, and the Mo Chhu and Po Chhu in Punakha district (1,300–2,300 m), where individuals or small flocks (max. 10) rest on the boulder-strewn riverbanks. Mostly inhabits broader river valleys, but sometimes also occurs on smaller fast-flowing streams, and is always easily overlooked. The wintering flock increases in November, with the full complement reached by mid-December. During February spring migration is apparent with a gradual decrease in numbers, followed by an influx in March from southern sites. Given the fluctuating numbers, it can be assumed that turnover of passage birds is high. A spell of bad weather in the first half of March 2000 delayed migrants for a longer period, with a max. 300 being reached[57]. Passage continues until mid-April, with the latest spring record 24 April, whilst numbers fall from several tens to only a few. Occasionally remains into summer as evidenced by records in June 1999 and 2002[52].

# Red-crested Pochard
## Rhodonessa rufina

N=27(4). W 1400-2400

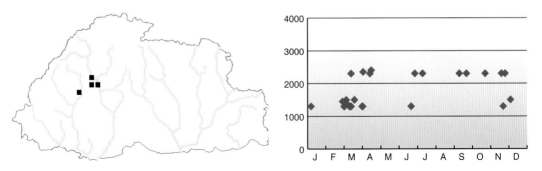

The Red-crested Pochard's main breeding area is the Central Asian steppe, from the Ukraine to Kyrgyzstan, with smaller populations further west in Europe. In the Indian subcontinent the species is a winter visitor, mostly to the north-west. It is a diving duck, which prefers open water with extensive submerged vegetation.

In Bhutan this pochard is an uncommon passage migrant. From September to early December small numbers are encountered annually on the sewage ponds at Babesa, Thimphu district (2,300 m), at Bajo, Wangdue Phodrang district, and further north along the Mo Chhu, Punakha (1,300–1,600 m). There are relatively few autumn records, with the earliest on 8 September at the sewage ponds[52], and the latest at the end of November. There is one winter record, from the mild winter of 2000/2001, when a male was observed at Bajo[52,53]. Spring migration is evident from the first week of March and continues until mid-April.

Red-crested Pochard
*Chris Orgill*

Whereas numbers are usually small at both seasons (fewer than five at a site), an exceptional concentration occurred in early March 2000, when migrants were delayed at Bajo by bad weather. Numbers built up to 139 birds during this period[57], demonstrating that considerable numbers typically cross Bhutan in nonstop flights. One or two regularly summer at Babesa or Bajo, with records from June and July[52].

# Common Pochard
## Aythya ferina

N=35(4). W 1400-2400

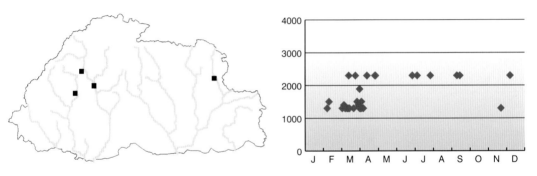

The Common Pochard breeds in temperate Europe east to Lake Baikal. It is a winter visitor to open waters of the Indian subcontinent, where it feeds mainly by diving.

Common Pochard is an uncommon passage migrant through Bhutan, recorded at the sewage ponds near Thimphu, at Bajo, Wangdue Phodrang district, and further north along the Mo Chhu, Punakha district. There are few autumn records, all between September and early December. Spring migration is more predictable, from the first week of March to late April. Numbers are invariably small, with fewer than five per season. However, in early March 2000, c.20 were present on the Puna Sang Chhu between Punakha and Wangdue Phodrang[40] among the concentrations of passage waterbirds held up by bad weather. A female wintered along the Puna Sang Chhu in 2000/2001[52]. Summering is equally rare but occurred at the sewage ponds in June–September 1997 and 1999, when 1–2 birds were present[52].

# Ferruginous Pochard
## Aythya nyroca

N=9(3)

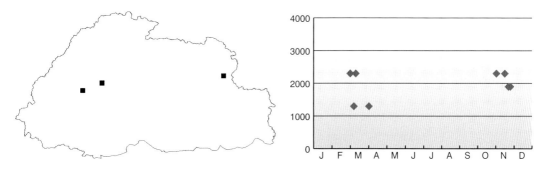

The Ferruginous Pochard breeds from Eastern Europe through the Central Asian steppes and the Tibetan Plateau. It is a widespread and locally common winter visitor to the Indian subcontinent, but is listed as Near Threatened by BirdLife International, because of a serious population decline in recent decades, with loss of wetland habitat and hunting pressure as underlying factors. It is less associated with open water than the commoner Aythya species, frequenting pools with extensive marginal and aquatic vegetation.

In Bhutan this duck is a rare passage migrant, with six clusters of records. Found twice on autumn passage, in November, at the sewage ponds at Babesa, Thimphu district (2,300 m)[52], and at Bumdeling, Trashi Yangtse district (1,900 m)[49]. In both cases singles were present for at least 3–4 days. Spring records concern mostly singles at Bajo, Wangdue Phodrang district (1,300 m), in March to early April[26,42,49,57]. During the bad weather in the first half of March 2000, a total of

Ferruginous Pochard
Phil Jones

six was present at Babesa[15] and at Bajo[49,57] among the concentrations of waterbirds. Almost all records concern males, suggesting that females are possibly overlooked among Tufted Ducks.

# Baer's Pochard
## Aythya baeri

N=2(2.0)

Baer's Pochard is much the rarest of the Aythya ducks recorded in the region. It breeds east of Lake Baikal to the Amur region. In the Indian subcontinent it is a rare winter visitor, mostly to the north-east. The species is considered Vulnerable by BirdLife International, because of its small, declining population, which is subject to habitat loss through degradation of wetlands, as well as hunting pressure.

In Bhutan Baer's Pochard is a vagrant which has been recorded twice. Singles were found among migrant waterfowl staging on the Mo Chhu and Puna Sang Chhu, in the Punakha/Wangdue Phodrang area, respectively: a male on 26 March 1994[5] and a female on 11 April 1998[19].

Baer's Pochard
*Jan Wilczur*

# Tufted Duck
*Aythya fuligula*

N=30(5). W 1400-2400

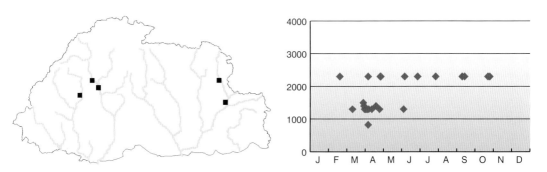

Among the *Aythya* diving ducks, the Tufted Duck is the most extensively distributed in Eurasia, breeding from the extreme west to the extreme east, in the temperate and boreal zones. In the Indian subcontinent it is a widespread winter visitor. On spring migration it has been found at high-altitude lakes up to 5,000 m.

Like other *Aythya*, Tufted Duck occurs in Bhutan mainly as an uncommon passage migrant. Probably there is no suitable habitat that would permit longer stays, although feeding birds have been observed at Bajo, Wangdue Phodrang. The species has been observed at the sewage ponds near Thimphu (2,300 m) and at Bajo, Wangdue Phodrang (1,300 m), with isolated records in the central and eastern valleys[19,28]. The record in the central valleys has not been mapped due to an imprecise locality being reported. Numbers are invariably low, with never more than six together. Remarkably, only one was present amongst the migrant waterfowl delayed by bad weather in March 2000[57], suggesting that Bhutan is not on a main migration route of this species. Spring passage is from March to late April, with an early record, on 18 February[49,52], of a female at the merganser roost on the sewage ponds at Babesa, Thimphu district. Summering appears quite regular with 1–3 noted near annually at Babesa and Bajo, in June to late October[52].

# Common Merganser (Goosander)
*Mergus merganser*

N=193(22). W 600-2400

The Common Merganser breeds in North America and in the boreal zone of Eurasia from Europe east to Sakhalin, with a separate population, of the subspecies *orientalis*, breeding at high altitudes from Afghanistan east to Tibet. The latter is a winter visitor to the Indian subcontinent, particularly to the north-east. Its habitat consists of lakes and rivers, including fast-flowing streams.

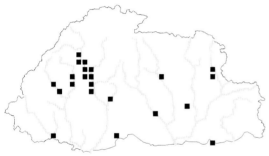

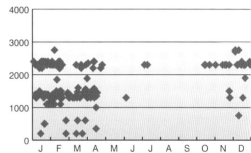

In Bhutan the merganser is a frequent winter visitor, being widespread on all main rivers, 200–2,800 m. Regular sites include the Torsa Chhu near Phuntsholing, the Paro and Thimphu valleys, and the Puna Sang Chhu and Mo Chhu between Wangdue Phodrang and Tashithang. In an extensive count in February 2000 it was found to be distributed very regularly at a density of 1.2 birds per km in the Paro, Thimphu and Wangdue Phodrang/Punakha valleys[49,52]. It arrives in mid-October and leaves by mid-April, with the latest spring record on 25 April[52]. Singles are occasionally noted in summer, at Babesa and Bajo, Wangdue Phodrang district, with records in June–July[43,52]. There is no evidence of passage, probably because only small numbers reach the Assam plains. It feeds by day, often in groups hunting cooperatively for fish, as can be observed early morning near Tashichho Dzong, Thimphu[49]. At night it gathers at roosts, with large movements noted early morning and evening. Birds

Common Merganser
Mike Langman

feeding along the Thim Chhu, from Dechencholing to the confluence with the Paro Chhu, gather to roost at the sewage ponds at Babesa, Thimphu district[49,52]. A max. 89 was counted in January 2002[42,52], which represents c.1% of the estimated Central Asian population of *orientalis* (Wetlands International 2002). Considering the species's regular distribution along large stretches of river, Bhutan may host internationally significant numbers of wintering mergansers.

# Yellow-legged Buttonquail
## *Turnix tanki*
N=4(3)

The Yellow-legged Buttonquail is widespread in the Indian subcontinent, including the Himalayan foothills, from Nepal eastwards, but is generally uncommon. Its wider range includes south-east Asia south to Thailand and Vietnam, north through eastern China to south-east Siberia, in grassland and cultivated fields.

In Bhutan this buttonquail is a rare resident in the eastern valleys[28,29,49] at altitudes around 1,200 m. All records are from the period February–June.

# Barred Buttonquail
## *Turnix suscitator*
N=3(2)

The Barred Buttonquail is found almost throughout the Indian subcontinent, except the north-west. Further east its range includes much of south-east Asia, from Japan south to Indonesia. The species inhabits open country with grassland and shrubs, as well as deciduous forest.

In Bhutan, Barred Buttonquail is a rare resident or perhaps a vagrant, with three records from the central and eastern valleys. On 19 February 1936 one was collected at Deothang at 600 m[31]. In April 1998 two were noted along the road between Trashigang and Narphung[14]. Most recently, on 21 July 2001 one was observed at 1,850 m near Zhemgang, in a roadside drain in humid broadleaf forest, apparently outside its regular habitat[52].

# Yellow-rumped Honeyguide
## *Indicator xanthonotus*

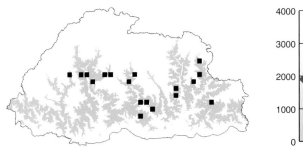

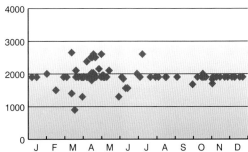

The Yellow-rumped Honeyguide is a rare and local resident of the Himalayas, from Pakistan to Arunachal Pradesh, north-east India, and into Myanmar, and is listed as Near Threatened by BirdLife International. Its habitat consists of forest around cliffs with Rock Bee *Apis dorsata* hives. It feeds on bees' wax and insects caught on the wing. Males defend a large honeycomb as territory and mate with females visiting the comb. The species probably breeds in tree holes, although the nest has never been found.

In Bhutan the honeyguide is an occasionally recorded resident, known from a few traditional sites. As the species is easily overlooked, it can be assumed to be more widespread than is known. All localities are within a relatively narrow altitudinal range, 1,400–2,600 m, with the lowest record 900 m[10]. The best-known site is Bubja, near Trongsa (1,900 m), where it was initially located in the 1960s and during subsequent research in the 1970s[1,21]. More recently, the species has been found in the western valleys (one site), the Sunkosh Valley (three sites), the central valleys (three sites) and eastern valleys (five sites), and in the central foothills (one site). At most of these, in spring one or occasionally up to four males are present, defending a honeycomb. At Bubja it is recorded year-round, with most records in mid-March to late April, when 1–3 territorial males are present, and occasionally a female is seen. At other seasons the species's occurrence is less predictable, with never more than one present. Although it is entirely probable that the species is being overlooked in this period, an alternative explanation could be migration to, and concentration at sites in, the south, which might explain the large numbers noted in October/November in the 1970s at Honey Rocks, Sarpang district[1,21]. Occurrence at Zhemgang also suggests this, as birds are only seen in autumn (July–October). On 13 May 2000, a male was observed visiting a possible nest site at 2,100 m near Namling, Mongar, in the midstorey of a huge broadleaf tree above a small stream[6]. This is the first possible breeding record of a bird whose nesting habits are otherwise unknown.

Although new sites are now being discovered, the species was apparently more widespread in the 1960s–mid-1980s, when the bird was known from several areas from which there are no recent observations. There appears to have been a serious decline in the 1980s and early 1990s, coinciding with a reduction in the number of Rock Bee colonies (Spierenburg 2000b). The presence of 27 birds at Honey Rocks, Sarpang district, and nine nearby at Batase in October/November1973[1] is unmatched by present totals. As recently as March 1986, one observer recorded a minimum ten birds from at least five different sites within a week[10]. It should be noted that sites in the south have not been visited in autumn in recent years, and any influx of migrants will thus have been missed. Presently, there are indications that Rock Bee and honeyguide populations are again increasing, although it is unclear to what extent this can be attributed to greater attention being paid to the species and increased birding activity. At Bubja the number of hives in winter/spring increased from 30 in 1999/2000 to 50 in 2000/2001 and 60 in 2001/2002[52]. Obviously the extreme specialisation on sites near Rock Bee hives makes the bird sensitive to disturbance. Territories defended by males include the largest combs (more than 75 cm diameter), which have been built the previous year and abandoned the subsequent spring. Destruction of hives for their honey therefore constitutes a threat, especially considering the localised occurrence of Rock Bee colonies. Although honey collection is not practised at any of the known sites, vigilance is important to the conservation of the species.

# Eurasian Wryneck
## *Jynx torquilla*

N=6(5)

The Eurasian Wryneck breeds in temperate Eurasia from Western Europe to Manchuria, with an isolated population in the Western Himalayas. It is a winter visitor to the northern Indian subcontinent, in open country.

In Bhutan this species is a rare passage migrant, recorded in spring from the central and eastern valleys, the western foothills and the high west. Spring passage is concentrated in the second half of April[1,14,22,28], with early records on 26 March[52,53] and 25 February[19]. The latter is from Phuntsholing, at 300 m, and might have involved a wintering bird. A record from 3,800 m[22] suggests that birds cross the main Himalayan range. All sightings concern singles.

Eurasian Wryneck
*Dan Powell*

# Speckled Piculet
## *Picumnus innominatus*

N=95(3). R 400-2000

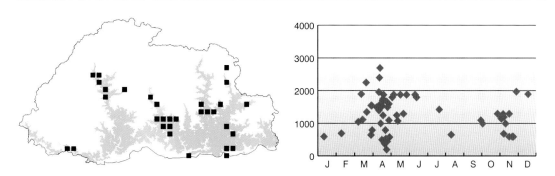

The Speckled Piculet occurs in the Himalayas from Pakistan to Arunachal Pradesh and north-east India, with disjunct populations in eastern and south-west India. Further east it extends through much of south-east Asia, from southern China south to Sumatra and Borneo. Its habitat consists of bushes and bamboo undergrowth in broadleaf forest.

In Bhutan this piculet is frequent throughout the temperate zone and in the western and eastern foothills. It is relatively scarce in the western valleys, but may have been overlooked due to insufficient surveys. Resident at 400–2,000 m, with occasional records to 200 m and 2,700 m[19], from July to March singles are usually found in mixed flocks, with small babblers and warblers. In late March through June the species is mostly found in pairs and breeding territories are defended by drumming and calling. Copulation has been observed on 29 March[19] and 6 April[5], both at 1,500 m, but with no further evidence of breeding. Specimens comprise an important percentage of records outside the breeding season, demonstrating that it is easily overlooked.

# White-browed Piculet
## *Sasia ochracea*

N=64(24). R 400-2000

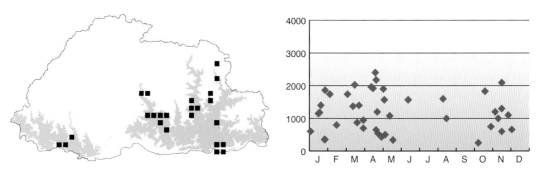

The White-browed Piculet is found in the Himalayas from central Nepal to Arunachal Pradesh and in the hills of north-east India. Further east its range extends to Vietnam. It is a bird of dense undergrowth in broadleaf forest, with a preference for bamboo. The nest hole is excavated in a large decaying bamboo stem.

In Bhutan the White-browed Piculet is frequently recorded but has a scattered distribution. It is found over most of the temperate and subtropical zones, but remarkably is absent from the Sunkosh Valley and the central foothills, although the latter might be attributed to insufficient coverage. It is resident over much the same altitudinal range as the Speckled Piculet, 400–2,000 m, more occasionally to 200 m and 2,400 m[19]. Compared to Speckled Piculet it appears to be more associated with bamboo in the breeding season and shrubbery at other seasons. The scarcity of records suggests that it is easily overlooked. Outside the breeding season, in August–March, it is almost invariably found in mixed flocks with small warblers and babblers, always singly. Other than drumming on bamboo stalks in February–March[52], there is no evidence of breeding in Bhutan.

# Grey-capped Pygmy Woodpecker
## *Dendrocopos canicapillus*

N=75(20). R 200-1200

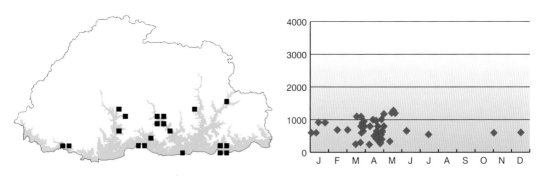

The Grey-capped Pygmy Woodpecker is distributed along the Himalayas from Pakistan to Arunachal Pradesh and in the hills of north-east India. Outside the subcontinent it is widespread in eastern and south-east Asia, from Ussuriland south to Sumatra and Borneo. This woodpecker is a bird of relatively dry forest, in open as well as denser habitats.

In Bhutan the Grey-capped Pygmy Woodpecker is primarily found in the foothills, becoming gradually more common to the east. In the temperate belt it occurs from the Sunkosh Valley eastwards. The species is a frequently recorded resident at 200–1,200 m. Year-round it regularly aggregates in loose flocks of up to five. In winter these are often found on isolated trees in cultivated land and thus easily located. An observation of 5–10 birds in one such area in winter[52] suggests that it is locally common. There are no indications of breeding other than observations of pairs in the breeding season.

# Fulvous-breasted Woodpecker
## *Dendrocopos macei*
N=34(19). R 200-2000

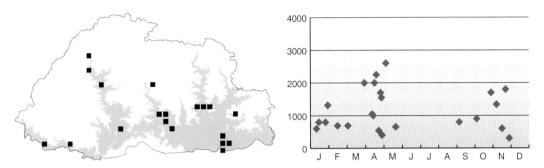

The Fulvous-breasted Woodpecker occurs in the Himalayas from Pakistan to Arunachal Pradesh and the hills of north-east and eastern India, Bangladesh and the Andamans. Further east it occurs in much of south-east Asia south to Java. It is a bird of forest edges and open forest at lower elevations.

In Bhutan this woodpecker is an uncommon resident. It has been found from the Sunkosh Valley eastwards and in the western and eastern foothills, although it is everywhere sparse. The scarcity of records and risk of misidentifications make it difficult to assess the species's altitudinal range, but this mainly appears to be 400–2,000 m, with the lowest record from 300 m[1] and the highest at 2,600 m[55]. In the breeding season it is found singly or in pairs, but in September–February it may gather in small flocks of up to five[52]. There is no evidence of breeding other than observations of pairs in the breeding season.

# Rufous-bellied Woodpecker
## *Dendrocopos hyperythrus*
N=213(52). R 1600-3000

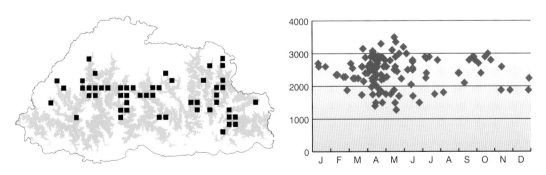

The Rufous-bellied Woodpecker is distributed along the Himalayas from Himachal Pradesh to Arunachal Pradesh and north-east India. Further east it is widespread in east and south-east Asia, from Ussuriland south to Cambodia. Its habitat is mainly temperate forest, occurring in broadleaf as well as conifer forest.

In Bhutan the Rufous-bellied Woodpecker is a frequently recorded resident throughout the temperate belt. It is found between 1,600 and 3,000 m, with occasional records to 1,300 m[19] and 3,500 m[52]. Altitudinal movements are somewhat unclear, but the species appears to retreat below 3,000 m from September until the second half of March. Occurrence below 2,000 m is linked to oak forest on relatively dry slopes. The breeding season is March–May, with apparently some variation in timing. Displaying males have been seen at *c*.2,600 m on 7 March[19], a pair drilling a nest hole at 2,200 m on 28 April[22] and a male transporting food at 1,900 m on 15 May[49]. Numbers encountered are generally low, although five or more can be present at a site.

# Crimson-breasted Woodpecker
## *Dendrocopos cathpharius*

N=194(45). R 1400-2600

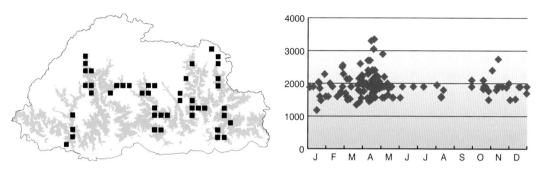

The Crimson-breasted Woodpecker occurs in the Indian subcontinent in the Himalayas from central Nepal to Arunachal Pradesh and the hills of north-east India. Further east its range reaches central China and northern Vietnam. It is found in moist broadleaf forest, particularly with oak and rhododendron.

In Bhutan this woodpecker is frequent throughout the temperate zone, with an isolated record from the central foothills[1]. It clearly becomes gradually more common further east, and is resident at 1,400–2,600 m, with occasional records to 1,200 m[22] and 3,400 m[19]. Pairs have been seen excavating nest holes on 30 January and 3 February, both at 1,600 m[43,52]. Both holes were 10–20 cm from the top of an exposed branch, around 15 cm in diameter, in a dead tree c.10–15 m high. Drumming occurs early March to mid-April. A juvenile was seen on 7 July[52]. Breeding pairs are well spaced out, with a density of 0.5 pairs per km recorded at Zhemgang between 1,600 m and 1,900 m[52]. In November–December it occasionally associates with mixed flocks of small babblers and warblers.

# Darjeeling Woodpecker
## *Dendrocopos darjellensis*

N=196(50). R 1600-3200

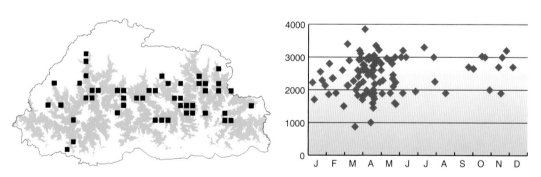

In the Indian subcontinent the Darjeeling Woodpecker has a similar distribution to the Crimson-breasted Woodpecker, occurring in the Himalayas from central Nepal east, in north-east India, and further east to south-west China and northern Vietnam. Among Bhutan's woodpeckers it reaches the highest elevations and occurs in broadleaf as well as coniferous forest, where it forages on mossy branches and on decaying tree trunks on the forest floor.

In Bhutan the Darjeeling Woodpecker is frequent throughout the temperate belt, with a few records from the eastern foothills. It is resident at 1,600–3,200 m, with occasional records to 900 m[5] and 3,800 m, at the treeline[2]. No marked altitudinal movements, but possibly withdraws below 3,000 m in winter. Pairs have been observed displaying at 2,600 m on 22 March and at 2,100 m on 20 May[22]. A pair was seen excavating a nest hole on 28 April at 2,200 m[22]. Found in a range of forest types, from warm broadleaf and cool broadleaf forests to hemlock and fir forest at higher elevations. Densities generally low, with rarely more than four seen in a day.

# Rufous Woodpecker
## *Celeus brachyurus*

N=65(23). R 200-1600

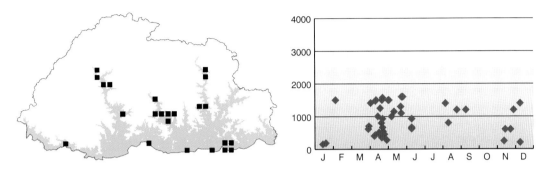

The Rufous Woodpecker's main range is the Indian subcontinent, where it occurs along the Himalayas from Uttar Pradesh to Arunachal Pradesh and north-east India, extending into Bangladesh and eastern India. It is also found in the south-west and on Sri Lanka. Elsewhere, the species is found over much of south-east Asia, south to the Greater Sundas. It feeds primarily on ants that construct papier-mâché-type nests in trees, and it excavates its hole in these nests. Its habitat is broadleaf forest including second growth.

In Bhutan the Rufous Woodpecker is a frequent resident, being found throughout the subtropical zone and in the temperate belt from the Sunkosh Valley east. It is resident from 200 m to 1,600 m. There are no confirmed breeding records. Outside the breeding season it is occasionally found in loose aggregations of up to six. The species is regularly encountered in abandoned shifting cultivation fields with *Castanopsis* regrowth.

# Lesser Yellownape
## *Picus chlorolophus*

N=189(40). R 400-2000

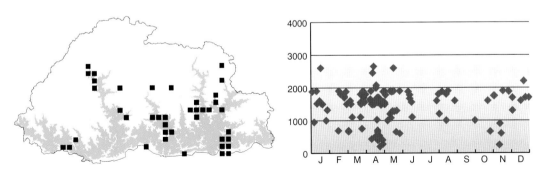

In the Indian subcontinent the Lesser Yellownape occurs along the Himalayas from Himachal Pradesh eastwards, in north-east, eastern, south and south-west India, and Sri Lanka. Further east its range extends over much of mainland south-east Asia. It is a versatile woodpecker, occurring in a variety of broadleaf forest habitats.

In Bhutan this is a frequently recorded resident, found throughout the temperate and subtropical zones. It is resident at 400–2,000 m, with occasional records to 200 m[1] and 2,800 m[19]. The Sunkosh and central valleys appear to be strongholds, with relatively more records, and all observations above 2,000 m are from these areas. Year-round it is found mostly singly or in pairs. In January–March it occasionally joins mixed flocks, particularly with larger babblers such as White-browed Shrike Babbler. Evidence of breeding includes a pair excavating a nest hole at 1,500 m on 9 April[5] and copulation on 16 May at 1,900 m[52]. Breeders are well separated, with 0.5 pairs per km near Zhemgang at 1,600–1,900 m[52].

# Greater Yellownape
## Picus flavinucha

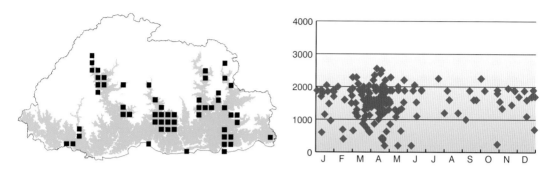

The Greater Yellownape is widespread in south-east Asia, reaching its westernmost limit in the Himalayas east to Uttar Pradesh, in north-east India and locally in eastern India. Habitat is broadleaf forest.

In Bhutan the Greater Yellownape is a common resident throughout the temperate and subtropical zones. It is, however, relatively uncommon in the western valleys. The species's altitudinal range largely overlaps with that of the Lesser Yellownape and Grey-headed Woodpecker, at 400–2,200 m. Occasionally, it reaches 200 m and 2,600 m. Whilst their altitudinal ranges and habitats overlap, the ecological segregation between the three 'green' *Picus* woodpeckers appears to rest in their feeding habits. Greater Yellownape feeds more on the trunk and larger branches than Lesser Yellownape, which is often encountered in shrubs. Grey-headed Woodpecker is primarily a ground feeder. Drumming birds have been noted in March[52]. The breeding season apparently varies with altitude, with one excavating a nest hole on 26 May at 1,900 m[22] and fledglings observed on 7 June at 200 m[20]. Breeders are well separated, with a density of 0.8 pairs per km near Zhemgang at 1,600–1,900 m. Year-round it is found mostly in pairs or individually, although up to three have been seen together on occasion. The species is only rarely seen in mixed flocks.

# Streak-throated Woodpecker
## Picus xanthopygaeus

The Streak-throated Woodpecker occurs in the southern and central Indian subcontinent, reaching the Himalayan foothills from Himachal Pradesh east, as well as north-east India. Further east its range continues to southern Vietnam. It is a bird of open broadleaf forest.

In Bhutan the Streak-throated Woodpecker is a vagrant recorded just once. On 14 January 1995 one was seen at 1,500 m in the Mangde Chhu valley[28].

# Grey-headed Woodpecker
## Picus canus

The Grey-headed Woodpecker occurs across a broad swathe of temperate Eurasia, from Central Europe to eastern China, and south to Sumatra. Its range extends into the Indian subcontinent along the Himalayas, west to Pakistan and in north-east and eastern India. It is a bird of moist subtropical and temperate forests, where it feeds mostly on the ground.

In Bhutan the Grey-headed Woodpecker is a common resident throughout the subtropical and part of the temperate zone. In the latter it is absent from the western valleys but becomes gradually more common to the east. The species's altitudinal range is from 400 m to 2,200 m, with some tendency to withdraw from higher areas in winter. There are occasional records to 200 m and an exceptionally high record from Dochu La at 3,100 m[19]. Calling birds are heard mostly in mid-February to mid-May, with a peak in April. At some sites it is

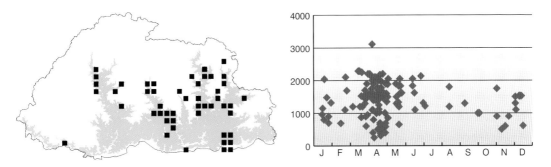

only noted in April, being rather secretive the remainder of the year. A density of 0.5 calling birds per km was noted near Zhemgang at 1,600–1,900 m[52]. Larger numbers, of five or more, at a particular site are noted in October–January. There are no confirmed breeding records.

# Himalayan Flameback
## Dinopium shorii                                                N=9(5)

The Himalayan Flameback occurs patchily in the foothills of the Himalayas from Himachal Pradesh to Arunachal Pradesh and north-east India, and further east in Myanmar. It is a bird of old-growth forest in the foothills and is sensitive to habitat change and deforestation.

In Bhutan the species is an uncommon resident below 400 m in the western[20,44], central[22] and eastern foothills[29]. It is probably under-recorded, as potential sites with old-growth forest in the foothills have not been systematically surveyed. The observation of 1–2 birds on four consecutive days in Royal Manas National Park, in 1993[22], suggests regular occurrence in suitable habitat.

# Greater Flameback
## Chrysocolaptes lucidus                                   N=26(8). R 200-600

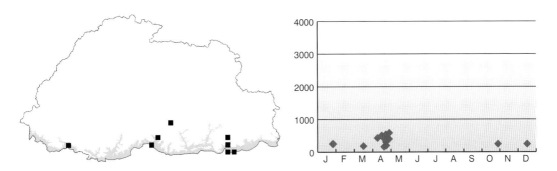

The Greater Flameback is similarly distributed in the Indian subcontinent to the Rufous Woodpecker, occurring along the Himalayan foothills from Himachal Pradesh in the west, through north-east India, Bangladesh to eastern India, as well as south-west India and Bangladesh. It is widespread in south-east Asia, reaching south to the Greater Sundas. Its habitat consists of tropical and subtropical broadleaf forests.

In Bhutan the Greater Flameback is an uncommon resident in the subtropical zone up to 600 m. Its stronghold is the eastern foothills, with almost all recent records from this area. There is another recent, but isolated, record from the central valleys[48]. It has been observed October–May, with a maximum of four in a day[28].

# Pale-headed Woodpecker
*Gecinulus grantia*                                                      N=7(2)

The Pale-headed Woodpecker is an uncommon resident of the Himalayan foothills, from extreme eastern Nepal to Arunachal Pradesh and the hills of north-east India. Its range continues further east to Vietnam. Preferred habitat is bamboo jungle.

In Bhutan this woodpecker is a rare resident, although it is probably overlooked as it keeps to bamboo thickets and the call is rather similar to that of Bay Woodpecker. It is found at 3–4 sites in the central subtropical zone[1], in the central valleys[5,52] and on the lower part of the Trashigang–Samdrup Jongkha road in the east[5,28]. All records are from 600 m to 1,400 m. Pockets of large *Dendrocalamus* bamboos appear to be an essential requirement of this species.

# Bay Woodpecker
*Blythipicus pyrrhotis*                                         N=432(58). R 800-2200

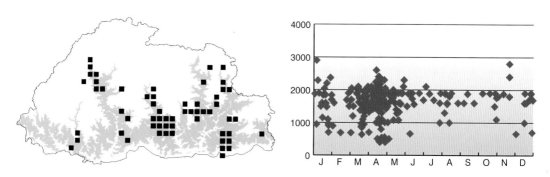

The Bay Woodpecker occurs in the Himalayas from western Nepal to Arunachal Pradesh, reaching north-east India and Bangladesh in the south. It is also found further east to Vietnam. Habitat is mature warm broadleaf forest, where it forages particularly on or near the ground on fallen tree stumps.

In Bhutan the Bay Woodpecker is a common resident throughout the temperate belt and in foothills. It is relatively scarce in the western valleys, becoming gradually more common to the east, and occurs at 800–2,200 m, with occasional records to 400 m and 2,900 m. It is most frequently located by its call, which is given year-round, but most frequently in the breeding season (January–May). It is an early breeder as shown by the observation of a pair feeding two young in the nest on 22 March[46]. The species can reach considerable densities, with on average 1.4 breeding pairs per km near Zhemgang at 1,600–1,900 m[52]. Whilst mostly recorded singly, it occasionally joins mixed flocks of laughingthrushes in winter.

# Great Slaty Woodpecker
*Mulleripicus pulverulentus*                                              N=4(3)

The Great Slaty Woodpecker occurs in the Himalayan foothills from Himachal Pradesh to Arunachal Pradesh and in the hills of north-east India. Further east it is found across much of south-east Asia, reaching the Greater Sundas and the Philippines. It is a bird of mature Sal and tropical broadleaf forest, where it utilises the tallest trees.

In Bhutan this woodpecker is rare. It has been found in the western[44] and central foothills below 400 m[1], with a single record from the central valleys, at c.600 m[48]. Suitable habitat for the species has not been systematically surveyed and, indeed, the extent of such habitat in the country is unclear.

# Great Barbet
## *Megalaima virens*

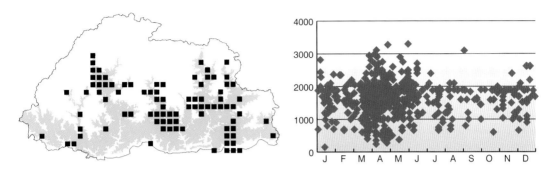

The Great Barbet is found in the Himalayas from Pakistan to Arunachal Pradesh and in the hills of north-east India, and east to Vietnam. Habitat is moist subtropical and temperate forests, where its call dominates the chorus throughout the breeding season. Barbets excavate tree holes for nesting and feed on fruits, particularly figs.

In Bhutan the Great Barbet is an abundant resident throughout the temperate and subtropical zones. Its regular altitudinal range is from 600 m to 2,400 m, with a more occasional presence to 200 m and 3,300 m[52]. Records above 2,800 m are mostly from the Sunkosh Valley in mid-March–September, representing a local seasonal expansion of its range. The species calls year-round, but particularly in April–May. Whilst apparently omnipresent due to its far-carrying call, breeding territories appear somewhat spaced, with 1.9 territories per km near Zhemgang at 1,600–1,900 m[52]. Nevertheless, day totals can reach 30–40, as the species is very widespread. In the breeding season it is generally found in pairs or singly. From late September until January it occasionally gathers in flocks of up to 20 at abundant food sources. The largest concentration, in January 2000, was of approximately 50 in *c*.20 ha with an abundant fruit crop[43,52]. Although common, there are no confirmed breeding records.

# Lineated Barbet
## *Megalaima lineata*

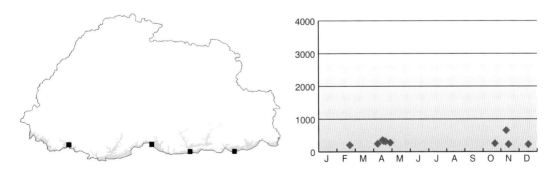

The Lineated Barbet occurs in the Himalayan foothills from Himachal Pradesh to Arunachal Pradesh, as well as north-east India and Bangladesh. Further east it reaches parts of south-east Asia south to Indonesia. It inhabits low elevations, in open forest, gardens and roadside plantations.

In Bhutan this barbet is an uncommon resident of the western, central and eastern foothills, at 200–400 m, with one record from 650 m[22]. Numbers are low with only 1–2 birds reported per sighting.

# Golden-throated Barbet
## *Megalaima franklinii*

N=560(60). R 1000-2200

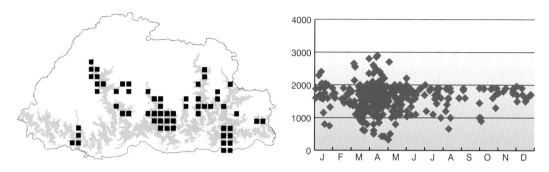

The Golden-throated Barbet's main range is mainland south-east Asia, reaching the Indian subcontinent in north-east India and in the Himalayas west to west-central Nepal. It occurs in moist broadleaf forest in the subtropical and temperate zone.

Golden-throated Barbet
*Dan Cole*

In Bhutan the Golden-throated Barbet is an abundant resident which is found in all major river valleys, and from 1,000 m to 2,200 m, with occasional records to 400 m and 2,800 m[19]. Records above 2,200 m are mostly from the Sunkosh Chhu valley, where it is widespread in spring. Below 1,500 m it is scarce and is replaced by Blue-throated Barbet. Birds vocalise mid-March–September, and occasionally in autumn and late winter. Peak calling activity in the breeding season is mid-April–July. There are few records indicative of breeding, the most significant being a bird excavating a nest hole on 19 April at 1,700 m[22]. Near Zhemgang a mean density of 3.5 breeding pairs per km was found at 1,600–1,900 m, with highest densities towards the lower part of this range[52]. There was also considerable fluctuation between years, from 1.3–3.9 pairs per km in three years at 1,900 m[52], probably reflecting variation in fruit crops between years. Winter flocks are generally small, typically fewer than five, but in winter 1999/2000 a concentration of *c*.30 was encountered[52]. The following breeding season was marked by the lowest density of pairs at the monitoring site at 1,900 m, suggesting that food scarcity may have forced the birds to concentrate at localised food sources.

# Blue-throated Barbet
## *Megalaima asiatica*

N=321(44). R 200-1800

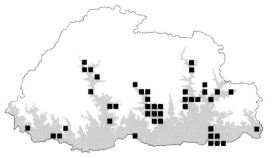

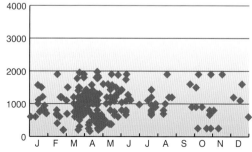

The Blue-throated Barbet is found in the Himalayas from Pakistan to Arunachal Pradesh, generally at lower altitudes than Golden-throated Barbet. Its range extends to Bangladesh and north-east India, reaching north Vietnam in the east. Habitat consists of open deciduous and evergreen forests.

In Bhutan the Blue-throated Barbet is abundant throughout the temperate and subtropical zones in warm broadleaf and subtropical forest. It is resident at 200–1,800 m, with occasional records to 1,900 m. However, overlap with Golden-throated Barbet appears limited, with the divide at c.1,500 m, above which the latter largely outnumbers the present species. Vocalising birds are heard year-round, with a peak in mid-April–July, which is presumably the breeding season. Birds excavating nest holes have been noted on 22 and 27 April[5], the former at 1,100 m[52]. It is more solitary than other barbets, only rarely forming flocks. However, the species is quite common, with up to 15 encountered in spring at one site[28].

# Blue-eared Barbet
## Megalaima australis

N=18(5). R 200-400

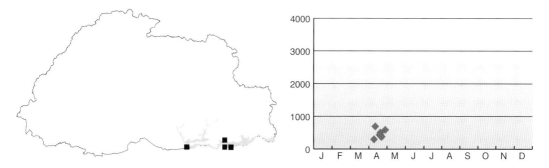

The Blue-eared Barbet occurs in the Himalayan foothills from eastern Nepal to Arunachal Pradesh and the hills of north-east India, ranging widely in south-east Asia south to the Greater Sundas. It is a bird of dense evergreen broadleaf forest.

In Bhutan this barbet is an uncommon resident in the central and eastern foothills. Regular sites are the forests above Samdrup Jongkha and Manas, where it is locally common as demonstrated by annual observations in April above Samdrup Jongkha, with up to six reported at one site[22]. It is found at 200–600 m, the highest record being from 700 m[5].

# Coppersmith Barbet
## Megalaima haemacephala

N=17(6). R 200-400

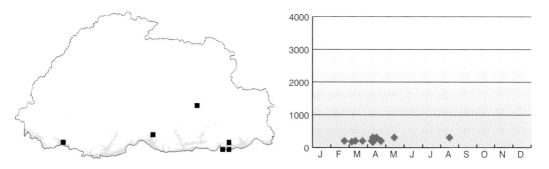

The Coppersmith Barbet occurs throughout much of the Indian subcontinent and is widespread in south-east Asia, reaching the Philippines and much of Indonesia. It frequents open wooded country, often around settlements.

In Bhutan Coppersmith Barbet is an uncommon resident in the western, central and eastern foothills, below 400 m. Most records are from the Phuntsholing area where it is regular and has been found breeding. On 10 April a pair was observed attending a nest hole in the centre of the town[5]. A max. 8 has been reported from this area[44]. Elsewhere its occurrence is more irregular and mostly single birds are reported.

# Great Hornbill
## *Buceros bicornis*

N=89(23). R 400-1400

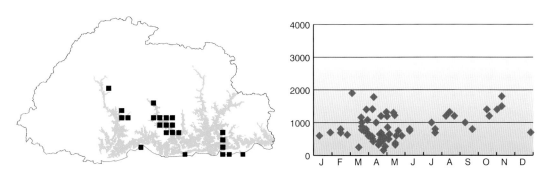

The Great Hornbill occurs patchily in southern and south-east Asia. In the Indian subcontinent disjunct populations are found in the southern hills, in the Himalayas from Kumaon east to Arunachal Pradesh and in the hills of north-east India. Further east its range continues through mainland south-east Asia and south to Sumatra. It is a bird of mature tropical and subtropical forests. It depends on a broad variety of tree species to find fruits throughout the year and for tree holes to nest in. It is listed by BirdLife International as Near Threatened because of habitat loss and its vulnerability to poaching.

In Bhutan this hornbill is a frequently recorded resident, found in the central and eastern foothills, and reaching higher in the central valleys. Its altitudinal range is 400–1,400 m, with occasional records to 200 m and 1,800 m. Higher records are mostly from October to December, when it appears to wander, probably in search of specific tree species fruiting in that season. It feeds in a wide variety of trees, with one observation of a bird that had caught a flying squirrel[52]. The species's stronghold appears to be the Mangde Chhu valley and the Manas area, given the presence of relatively little-disturbed broadleaf forest areas in Zhemgang district, compared to those of Sarpang and Samdrup Jongkha, which have been modified by timber plantations (Pradhan 2000). Overall numbers and frequency of reporting is much lower in the Samdrup Jongkha area and all records are below 600 m. However, there are old records from higher elevations in the eastern valleys. Ludlow observed flocks of 20–30 at 1,500 m and 1,800 m in early November 1934[31]. Whilst this suggests a local decline, there is a clear need to update its presence in the lower Drangme Chhu and Kuri Chhu valleys, in Pemagatshel district and southern Trashigang and Mongar districts. Records from the Sunkosh Chhu valley are all from Wangdue Phodrang district, in Chir Pine forest, suggesting that possibly more important populations exist further south. However, in Bhutan the Great Hornbill is reportedly able to utilise relatively poor habitat with a large Chir Pine component, subsisting particularly on the abundant *Phyllanthus emblica* (Pradhan 2000). The single largest population is in the lower Mangde Chhu valley and adjacent foothills at Manas, largely within the boundaries of Royal Manas and the southern part of Jigme Singye Wangchuck National Parks. At Manas a large roost is present, with a max. 110 Great Hornbills together with 86 Wreathed Hornbills observed[44]. A congregation of 150–200 in the 'south-east Bhutan lowlands' was presumably also from the Manas area[1]. Adjacent to Royal Manas National Park, in the north, a roost of 12 was reported at Tingtibi, Zhemgang district, on 31 March 1967[1]. A total of 11 counted on 30 March 2000, moving to a roost in the same area[52], suggests stable populations in this part of its range. In view of this, Royal Manas and adjacent Jigme Singye Wangchuck National Park will be important for the future conservation of the species, along with its habitat of old-growth forest.

# Rufous-necked Hornbill
## *Aceros nipalensis*

N=432(45). R 600-2000 (broadleaf forest)

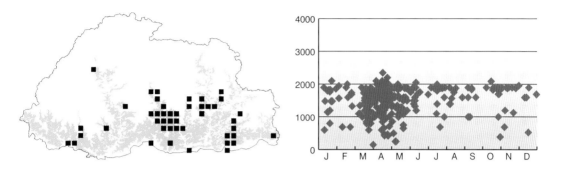

The Rufous-necked Hornbill occurs in the Himalayas from Bhutan to Arunachal Pradesh and in north-east India. Further east it is found in Myanmar, northern Thailand and northern Vietnam. Like Great Hornbill, it is a bird of mature subtropical broadleaf forest, but occupies a somewhat higher altitudinal range. Rufous-necked Hornbill is classified by BirdLife International as Vulnerable, because of habitat destruction due to logging and shifting cultivation, and severe hunting pressure in much of its range. It is now extinct in eastern Nepal and Darjeeling, Bhutan thus constituting the modern westernmost limit.

In Bhutan Rufous-necked Hornbill is a common resident that is widespread in the temperate and subtropical zones. Its apparent abundance relates partly to the special attention it receives from birders and to the fact that it is relatively conspicuous and easily located by its call. On the other hand, Bhutan's forests hold the single largest remaining population of the species (Bishop 1999a), with extensive areas of relatively undisturbed warm broadleaf forest and the near absence of poaching as the main contributory factors. The population is probably in the low thousands (BirdLife International 2001). It occurs at 600–2,000 m, with occasional records to 200 m and 2,400 m. The strongholds are the Mangde Chhu and Kuri Chhu valleys with, amongst others, Thrumshingla National Park, Royal Manas National Park and Jigme Singye Wangchuck National Park also holding significant numbers. Over 30 pairs have been noted on *c*.40 km (200–1,000 m) of trail in Royal Manas National Park and 40 pairs over a 20-km stretch (500–1,500 m) in an adjacent area in Zhemgang dzongkhag[44]. These totals are in the same order of magnitude as the density of 1 breeding pair per km found near Zhemgang at 1,600–1,900 m[52], revealing it to occur at relatively high densities throughout its altitudinal range in Bhutan. The western limit of the current distribution is the Gedu and Chhukha area, and near Phuntsholing. In the Sunkosh Valley it is particularly scarce and virtually absent from apparently suitable habitat along the Mo Chhu near Tashithang, Punakha. Here, habitat fragmentation could be a factor. Below 2,000 m broadleaf forest in the Mo Chhu valley is separated from forested areas lower down by extensive cultivation and degraded Chir Pine forest around Wangdue Phodrang and Punakha. The absence of hornbills from broadleaf forest in Trashi Yangtse and Lhuntse district might similarly be explained (but cf. Pradhan 2000). The breeding season appears to be mid-April–June, when most records concern lone males, as breeding females are incubating or feeding young. A pair was seen excavating a nest hole and in courtship on 19 April 1998 between Namling and Yonkhola, Mongar, at 1,900 m[14]. On 20 April 2001, a male was found attending a nest hole, presumably feeding the female, near Zhemgang, at 1,600 m[5]. Throughout the breeding season small flocks of males and females are observed, possibly of young non-breeders. In winter the species mostly gathers in small flocks at fruiting trees. Larger flocks are encountered gathering to roost, e.g. 16 near Dakpai, Zhemgang district[52], in early April, 24 near Chhukha, in December[53] and 20 near Gedu, in October[1]. The two latter records are from 2000 and 1968, indicating that there has not been a major decline even in the westernmost part of its range. As the species is sensitive to logging in mature warm broadleaf forest, its conservation will depend on protection of mature forest stands in national parks and the corridors linking them, as well as sustainable forest management practices elsewhere.

# Wreathed Hornbill
*Aceros undulatus*                                                  N=48(13). R 200-600

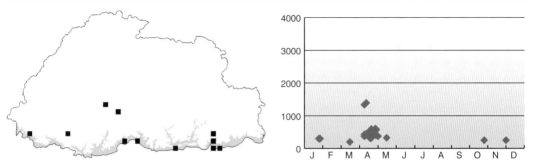

The Wreathed Hornbill occurs in the Himalayan foothills and adjacent plains from West Bengal to Arunachal Pradesh and in north-east India. Further east its range continues through mainland south-east Asia south to the Greater Sundas. It inhabits mature tropical forest.

In Bhutan the Wreathed Hornbill is a frequently recorded resident of foothills, from west to east, at 200–600 m. It penetrates higher only in the Sunkosh Valley, where it reaches 1,300 m[12]. The eastern foothills are a stronghold, with regular sightings in the forests above Samdrup Jongkha, with flocks of up to nine. In Manas, at a regular roost site, 86 have been counted, together with 110 Great Hornbills[44].

# Oriental Pied Hornbill
*Anthracoceros albirostris*                                         N=21(5). R 200-400

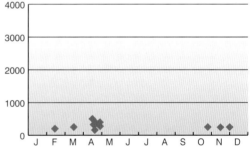

The Oriental Pied Hornbill occurs in the northern and eastern Indian subcontinent, its range continuing south through south-east Asia to the Greater Sundas. It is a bird of open forest.

In Bhutan this hornbill is an uncommon resident in the central and eastern foothills, reaching 400 m. Locally it extends into the deep river gorges further north such as in Tsirang district[44]. Records in this area have not been mapped due to imprecise localities being reported. It is found annually above Samdrup Jongkha, albeit in very small numbers, with a max. 4 reported[28]. The largest flock numbered 17, on 30 November 1967, near Gelephu[1]. Breeding was confirmed by the observation of a male attending a nest hole near Gelephu, at 250 m, on 15 March[10].

Oriental Pied Hornbill
*Phil Jones*

# Common Hoopoe
## *Upupa epops*

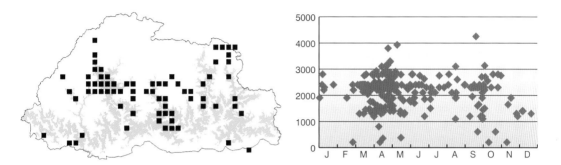

The Common Hoopoe is widespread in Eurasia, from Mediterranean Europe east to eastern Siberia, China and mainland south-east Asia. It occurs throughout the Indian subcontinent, as a resident and winter visitor from across the Himalayas. Its habitat consists of open country with scattered trees and around habitation.

Hoopoes are found in the alpine, temperate and subtropical zones, and are common altitudinal and passage migrants. The species breeds in the higher valleys, with confirmed records from the Thimphu, Phobjikha and Bumthang areas, where it nests mostly under the roofs of houses and in cavities in walls. It is common, with, e.g., three pairs nesting in the eastern wall of Tashichho Dzong on 18 June[52]. Other areas where calling birds and June/July records suggest the presence of breeders are the Wangdue Phodrang/Punakha area and the upper Mangde Chhu valley around Trongsa/Chendebji. Further east there are as yet no indications of breeding, and it may be only a passage migrant in this part of the country. Most appear to breed at 2,000–2,800 m, shunning lower elevations because of higher rainfall and higher elevations due to low temperatures. Vocalising birds are heard from mid-March to July. Adults feeding nestlings are noted from the first week of May to the third week of June, with most pairs breeding later in this period. A recently fledged juvenile was seen on 3 August, at 2,800 m[52]. Spring passage lasts March–May, when singles are widespread. From March to mid-April these involve birds moving to their breeding areas, and during this period they occur at 200–2,800 m. From mid-April to May there appears to be a second wave of migrants, at 200–4,000 m, probably involving trans-Himalayan migrants. In autumn passage appears to be in September–October, with some high-altitude records. The highest record is from 4,250 m[49]. Peak passage is in September, when up to ten have been found at the sewage ponds at Babesa, Thimphu district[52]. Wintering birds are noted mostly at 1,200–2,400 m, albeit rather erratically. The highest winter record is from 2,800 m in January[52].

# Red-headed Trogon
## *Harpactes erythrocephalus*

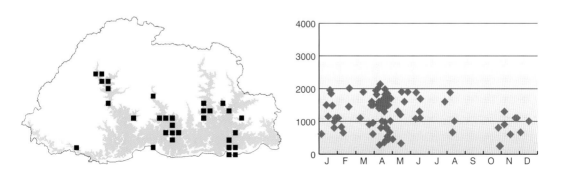

The Red-headed Trogon occurs in the Himalayas from central Nepal to Arunachal Pradesh and the hills of north-east India. Further east its range continues through mainland south-east Asia south to Sumatra. It inhabits dense subtropical broadleaf forest, where it occurs in the midstorey.

In Bhutan this trogon is a frequently recorded resident throughout the subtropical zone and, in the temperate belt, from the Sunkosh Valley east, becoming gradually more common to the east. It occupies an altitudinal range complementary to that of Ward's Trogon, at 400–2,000 m, with only one record above this, from 2,150 m[1]. Indeed, occurrence above 1,600 m is largely known only from the warm spring of 2001, when various species from the warm broadleaf zone were more extensively distributed. Representative of this, a pair held a breeding territory in spring 2001 at 1,900 m, near Zhemgang, having established itself by mid-May[52]. Similarly, winter presence above 1,600 m[1,22,49] is probably rather exceptional and related to mild winters. Calling birds are heard year-round, with a peak early in the presumed breeding season, in March–April. Most records concern singles or pairs, with a few records of three, mostly in January–March. The total number of records only slightly exceeds that for Ward's Trogon, probably because more ornithological attention is devoted to the latter. However, in the field it is noticeably more common than Ward's Trogon. Although they both prefer well-developed forest, the present species appears also to tolerate more degraded forests.

# Ward's Trogon
## *Harpactes wardi*

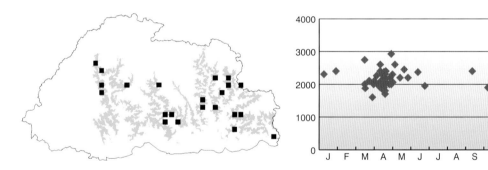

Ward's Trogon is a rare bird of the temperate zone in the Himalayas, from Sikkim to Arunachal Pradesh, and reaching north Myanmar, Yunnan (China) and north Vietnam. BirdLife International classifies the species as Near Threatened, having recently removed it from the globally threatened list on the basis of new information, particularly from Bhutan. Threats include habitat loss due to shifting cultivation and logging. Its habitat is broadleaf forest where it particularly inhabits the lower storey.

In Bhutan Ward's Trogon is an uncommon resident, found in the Sunkosh, central and eastern valleys. It occupies a relatively narrow altitudinal range in the lower cool broadleaf forest zone, at 1,800–2,600 m, occurring occasionally to 1,600 m[44] and 3,200 m[1]. The species is highly specific in its habitat requirements, mature broadleaf forest characterised by the presence of climbers and an intact canopy. It is, for example, absent between Trongsa and Kuenga Rabten. Although the altitude is suitable here, the forest is relatively young, having been heavily affected by road construction in the 1960s. Ward's Trogon also appears to favour wetter, north- or west-facing slopes, occurring at similar sites as another rare speciality, the Chestnut-breasted Partridge. It calls year-round, but activity peaks in April. The large number of records from this

Wards Trogon
*Carl D'Silva*

month is related to this, but also to the presence of bird tour groups, who target this species. Almost all records concern singles or pairs, with sometimes up to five located at one site[14,22,49]. Other than the presence of calling males and pairs, there is no evidence of breeding.

# Indian Roller
## *Coracias benghalensis*

N=33(18). S 200-1200 (mid-Apr-Oct); W 200-400

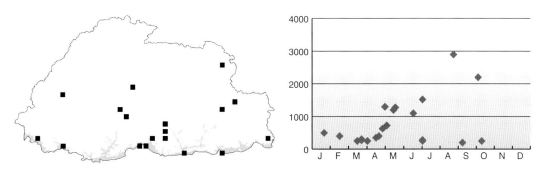

The Indian Roller is widespread in southern Asia, from the Persian Gulf in the west to mainland south-east Asia in the east. It occurs virtually throughout the Indian subcontinent, reaching the Himalayan foothills. It favours open country, often in cultivated areas, where it hunts from a perch for large insects.

In Bhutan this roller is an uncommon altitudinal migrant that is found regularly throughout the foothills up to 400 m. Although it is resident, towards late April it disperses higher into the river valleys. Until August birds have been noted throughout the temperate zone, reaching 2,200 m, with one record at 2,900 m[52]. Such dispersal appears to be related to the end of the breeding season, which in other parts of the region is mostly March–May. Breeding has not been confirmed in Bhutan.

# Dollarbird
## *Eurystomus orientalis*

N=20(12). R 200-800

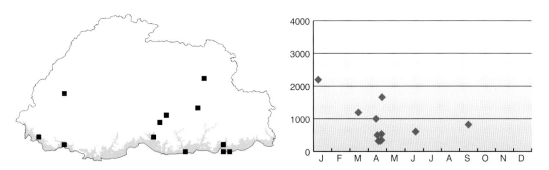

The Dollarbird is found in the Himalayas from Haryana to Arunachal Pradesh, as well as the hills of north-east and south-west India. Its range extends through Myanmar and China north to south-east Siberia and south to Australia. Habitat consists of clearings in tropical broadleaf forest. It is particularly active at dawn and in the evening, when it hawks for insects on the wing.

In Bhutan the Dollarbird occurs throughout the subtropical zone and in the Sunkosh, central and eastern valleys. It is an uncommon resident, ranging from 200 m to 1,600 m. Records above 600 m mostly concern wandering birds, which appear at various sites high in the valleys, without any pattern. The highest record is from 2,200 m in January[13]. A pair entering a possible nest hole at 350 m[1], on 22 April, establishes it as a probable breeder in Bhutan.

# Blyth's Kingfisher
## *Alcedo hercules*

N=26(6). R 400-1200

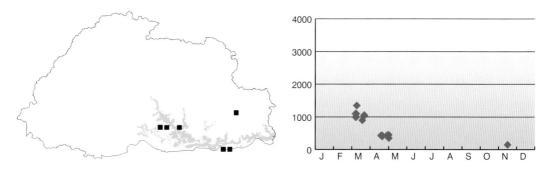

Blyth's Kingfisher is a rare bird, sparsely distributed in the Himalayan foothills from eastern Nepal to Arunachal Pradesh, and in the hills of north-east India and Bangladesh. Further east its range reaches south China and north Vietnam. It is listed as Near Threatened by BirdLife International, due to its small population and disappearing habitat. It inhabits fast-flowing streams in dense tropical and subtropical forests. The inaccessibility of its habitat and its shyness make it difficult to find.

In Bhutan Blyth's Kingfisher is an uncommon resident, which occurs locally in the central and eastern foothills, and adjacent areas of the central and eastern valleys. It is known from five localities: Chapley Khola (Sarpang district)[26], near Subrang (Zhemgang district)[5,40,44,52], between Langdurbi and Dunmang on the lower Chamkhar Chhu (Zhemgang district)[44], at Khaling (Trashigang district)[44] and between Deothang and Samdrup Jongkha. The latter is a well-known site, where 1–2 birds are observed annually. Ludlow collected one from the same area in 1934[31]. Altitudinally it occurs at 200–1,200 m, with the Khaling record from the relatively high altitude of 2,000 m[44]. This record is not included on the graph due to an imprecise date being reported. As suitable habitat appears available, it will probably be discovered at additional sites in the future.

# Common Kingfisher
## *Alcedo atthis*

N=100(19). S 1200-2400 (May-Oct); W 200-2400

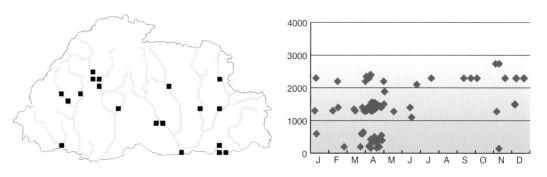

The Common Kingfisher has a vast distribution in the Palearctic and Oriental regions, ranging from Western Europe east to Japan and south to Indonesia, and occurs throughout most of the Indian subcontinent. It frequents pools, rivers and lakes in open country, avoiding dense riverine forest. The nest hole is excavated in a steep riverbank.

In Bhutan this kingfisher is frequent in the temperate belt and the western and eastern foothills, but relatively uncommon in the central and eastern valleys, probably because suitable habitat is scarce. It typically occurs near pools in riverbeds left after the summer floods have retreated, a habitat mainly associated with the broad glacial valleys in the west of the country. Nesting occurs relatively early, from March to mid-May, before water levels rise and feeding habitat is reduced. Breeding was confirmed in a riverbank along the Puna Sang Chhu, near Lobeysa, in mid-March[43]. At this season it occurs at 200–2,400 m, with strongholds in the Sunkosh Valley and in the foothills. After the breeding season the species disperses, becoming more widespread in the central, eastern and western valleys,

Common Kingfisher
*Chris Orgill*

and occasionally reaching 2,800 m. Concurrently, it withdraws from the lower part of its range, below 1,200 m. As water levels fall it occupies its breeding range from November.

# Oriental Dwarf Kingfisher
## *Ceyx erithacus*
N=7(3)

The Oriental Dwarf Kingfisher is widespread in south-east Asia, reaching the Philippines and well into Indonesia. In the Indian subcontinent it occurs in the Himalayan foothills from Sikkim to Arunachal Pradesh, in north-east and south-west India, and Sri Lanka. It frequents small streams in tropical forest, moving to its breeding quarters at the onset of the monsoon.

In Bhutan this tiny kingfisher is a rare summer visitor to the eastern foothills, at altitudes up to 500 m, being found in April–May at Manas[22] and in the forests above Samdrup Jongkha[6,28].

# Ruddy Kingfisher
## *Halcyon coromanda*
N=10(5). R 200-600

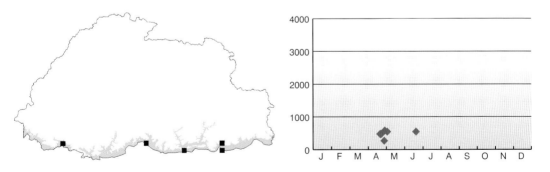

The Ruddy Kingfisher is widespread in eastern and south-east Asia, from north-east China south to Indonesia. Its distribution reaches the north-east Indian subcontinent, where it occurs in the Himalayan foothills from central Nepal to Arunachal Pradesh, and north-east India. Habitat is pools and streams in dense tropical forest.

In Bhutan Ruddy Kingfisher has been reported in the foothills, from west to east, and is generally rare. It is observed in April–June, below 600 m. A pair was observed near Phuntsholing on 19 June 1968[20], but there is no other evidence of breeding.

# White-throated Kingfisher
## Halcyon smyrnensis

N=177(33). R 200-1600

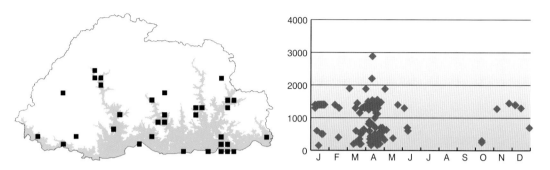

The White-throated Kingfisher is widely distributed in southern and south-east Asia, ranging from Turkey and the Arabian Peninsula east to Taiwan, the Philippines and Java. It occurs virtually throughout the Indian subcontinent, where it occupies diverse habitats, often far from water, including cultivated areas and forest edges, as well as rivers.

In Bhutan White-throated Kingfisher is a common altitudinal migrant recorded throughout the temperate and subtropical zones at 200–1,600 m. Occasional records to 2,200 m are available, and there is an exceptionally high record from c.2,800 m[19]. It is common in the Sunkosh Valley and the foothills. In the higher part of its range the species prefers the vicinity of rivers. From May it moves away from these areas, particularly favouring cultivated areas and forest edges. From June to October it is largely absent from the temperate belt, presumably on the breeding grounds in the foothills and possibly further south into India. There is one definite breeding record, a pair nesting in an agricultural clearing at 400 m in the eastern foothills on 1 May[5]. In November it disperses again to higher elevations, with most records in January–April, at the peak of the dry season in India. In this period it is common, with regularly several present at a site and a max. 15 reported in a day[27].

# Black-capped Kingfisher
## Halcyon pileata

N=1(1)

The Black-capped Kingfisher occurs on coasts and in mangroves around much of the Indian peninsula. Further east it ranges widely through eastern and south-east Asia, from North Korea to Indonesia. It sporadically wanders inland.

This species is a vagrant to Bhutan which has been recorded once: on 27 April 2001, near Gangtey, Wangdue Phodrang district, at 3,300 m[33]. As this is the start of its breeding season on the coast, the record probably concerned a migrant that (severely) overshot its breeding areas.

# Crested Kingfisher
## Megaceryle lugubris

N=195(45). S 1400-2800 (mid-Jun-mid-Nov); W 400-2400

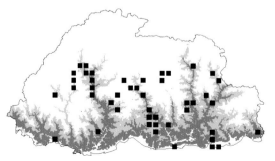
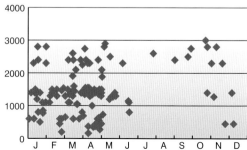

The huge Crested Kingfisher is distributed along the Himalayas from northern Pakistan to Arunachal Pradesh, and in the hills of north-east India. Further east it reaches Vietnam and north to Japan. It is a bird of fast-flowing montane streams and rivers, where it hunts for fish from a rock or branch.

In Bhutan Crested Kingfisher is a common altitudinal migrant throughout the temperate and subtropical zones. It is particularly conspicuous along the Puna Sang Chhu and Mo Chhu between Wangdue Phodrang and Tashithang, Punakha district, with a maximum of six reported[53]. In November–May it is more widespread, at 400–2,400 m, with occasional records to 3,000 m. There are few records in June–October, during and directly after the monsoon, when it withdraws from the lower part of its range, below 1,400 m. At this season it possibly also vacates larger rivers, where feeding is more difficult due to the torrents and the water being muddied by sediment. In moving to smaller streams the species is more likely to escape detection at this season. There are no confirmed breeding records, but the widespread presence of pairs in March–April indicates that it is a regular breeder throughout the altitudinal range.

Crested Kingfisher
*Jan Wilczur*

# Pied Kingfisher
## *Ceryle rudis*

N=19(4). W 200-1200

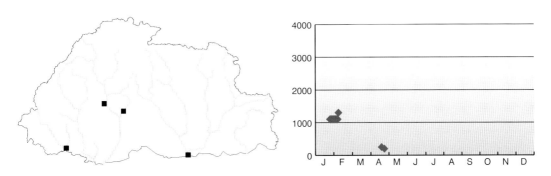

The Pied Kingfisher is widespread in Africa and South Asia, reaching its easternmost limit in mainland south-east Asia. It inhabits slow-flowing rivers, and characteristically hovers above the surface in search of fish, which it catches by steeply diving into the water.

In Bhutan the species is uncommon, with reports from the western[19] and eastern foothills[22] and the Sunkosh Valley[44]. It is mostly encountered at *c*.200 m, but is apparently regular around 1,200 m in the Sunkosh Valley below Wangdue Phodrang. Records fall between January and April, suggesting that occurrence in Bhutan involves dry-season dispersal from the main breeding areas in India.

# Blue-bearded Bee-eater
## Nyctyornis athertoni

N=90(20). R 400-2000 (broadleaf forest)

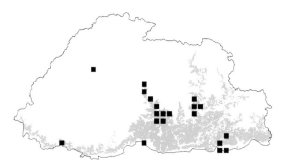

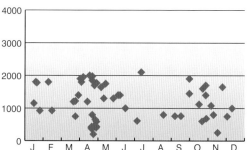

The Blue-bearded Bee-eater has a scattered distribution in highland areas of the Indian subcontinent, including the Himalayas from Himachal Pradesh to Uttar Pradesh, and north-east India. Further east its range continues through much of mainland south-east Asia. Habitat consists of forest edges and clearings in dense moist broadleaf forest. It excavates a nest hole in the steep bank of a ravine.

In Bhutan this bee-eater is an occasionally recorded resident, mainly from the central and eastern valleys and the eastern foothills. Occurrence is more occasional in the western and central foothills, with an isolated record from the Sunkosh Valley. It is resident at 400–2,000 m, with occasional records to 200 m and 2,100 m. The species is apparently absent from upper parts of the eastern valleys, probably because broadleaf forest here is fragmented by cultivation and Chir Pine. Invariably found singly or in pairs, and relatively easily overlooked as it perches quietly in the foliage, the species appears to be rather sparsely distributed, although, for example, it is recorded annually between Namling and Yonkhola, Mongar district. In October–November it is more widespread, indicating some dispersal. The lone record from the Sunkosh Valley was from this period. There is no confirmation of breeding, but a displaying pair was seen on 3 April at 1,800 m[19].

Blue-bearded Bee-eater
*Carl D'Silva*

# Green Bee-eater
## Merops orientalis

N=4(3)

The Green Bee-eater has a vast distribution from sub-Saharan Africa through the Middle East to mainland south-east Asia, including almost the entire Indian subcontinent. It is a bird of open country with scattered trees.

In Bhutan the Green Bee-eater is rare, with four records from the western and central foothills at c.200 m[1,7,19,44]. Records fall in the period October–February, suggesting that it is mainly a winter visitor, dispersing from its main breeding range further south in the dry season.

# Chestnut-headed Bee-eater
## *Merops leschenaulti*

N=21(10). R 200-400

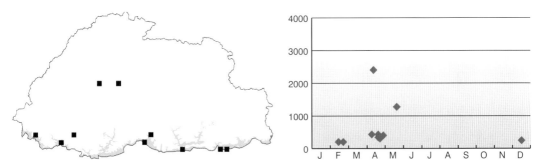

The Chestnut-headed Bee-eater occurs in hills of the Indian subcontinent, including the Himalayan foothills, and adjacent plains from Himachal Pradesh to Arunachal Pradesh. Further east it is widespread in south-east Asia, south and east to Bali. It is found near streams in broadleaf forest.

In Bhutan Chestnut-headed Bee-eater is an uncommon resident in the western, central and eastern foothills below 400 m. Two records exist from higher elevations, both from the Sunkosh Valley, where it has been observed at 1,300 m[55] and 2,400 m[19] in April and May. Apparently resident, with records from winter as well as spring, but as the foothills have been insufficiently explored in summer, the possibility cannot be excluded that the species vacates these areas in the rainy season. It occurs only in small numbers, with a max. 4 birds[19].

# Chestnut-winged Cuckoo
## *Clamator coromandus*

N=37(14). S 400-1600

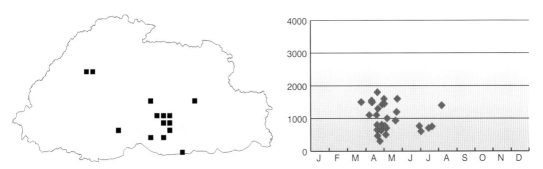

In the Indian subcontinent the Chestnut-winged Cuckoo is a summer visitor to the Himalayas, occurring patchily from northern Uttar Pradesh to Arunachal Pradesh and south to north-east India and Bangladesh. It migrates to southern India, Sri Lanka, Malaysia and Indonesia in winter. Further east, its range continues through mainland south-east Asia south to the Greater Sundas. It is a brood parasite that targets laughingthrushes, particularly Greater and Lesser Necklaced Laughingthrushes.

Chestnut-winged Cuckoo is an uncommon summer visitor to Bhutan, where it occurs in the Sunkosh, central and eastern valleys, as well as the western, central and eastern foothills. Its stronghold appears to be the Mangde Chhu valley, and the adjacent Gelephu plain and Manas area. Here the two necklaced laughingthrushes are relatively common, and the cuckoo occurs over a similar altitudinal range to these, at 400–1,400 m. However, the species's presence is not limited to the range of these laughingthrushes. It is found also in the Mo Chhu valley, at 1,400–1,600 m, where both laughingthrushes are absent, implying that it targets other hosts as well. However, there is no direct information concerning which other species are parasitised. The bulk of the population arrives in the breeding areas in mid-April, the earliest spring record being 24 March[52]. The latest summer record is 5 August[52]. Densities are low, with a max. 3 calling birds at any one site[5].

# Large Hawk Cuckoo
## *Hierococcyx sparverioides*

N=663(84). S 1000-3000

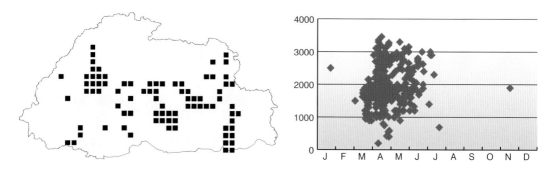

The Large Hawk Cuckoo breeds in the Himalayas from Himachal Pradesh to Arunachal Pradesh and in north-east India. Further east it occurs from central China south to the Greater Sundas and Sulawesi. It is a partial migrant, with winter records available from southern India and Indonesia. Habitat is broadleaf forest, particularly oak. A brood parasite of laughingthrushes and various small songbirds, among which Streaked Spiderhunter and Lesser Shortwing are favoured hosts.

In Bhutan the Large Hawk Cuckoo is an abundant summer visitor throughout the temperate zone, with occasional records in the foothills, where the Common Hawk Cuckoo generally replaces it below 1,000 m. This species's regular altitudinal range is 1,000–3,000 m, with occasional records to 200 m and 3,500 m, and is noted in its breeding quarters in the second half of March, when the first arrivals are heard below 2,000 m. It rapidly spreads throughout its altitudinal range, reaching the upper elevations by early April. The peak calling period is mid-April to mid-May. By the first week of July calling ceases and is no longer noted, the birds possibly departing for their winter quarters. A juvenile was still present on 20 July at 800 m[52]. Considering its elusive behaviour outside the breeding season, it is possible that part of the population is resident in Bhutan, given records in January[28] and early March[31] from the eastern valleys, at 2,500 m and 1,700 m. Near Zhemgang a density of 2.5 territories per km was found at 1,600–1,900 m, and was rather stable between years. There is no information concerning host species in Bhutan.

Large Hawk Cuckoo
*Carl D'Silva*

# Common Hawk Cuckoo
## *Hierococcyx varius*

N=11(8). S 200-2000

The Common Hawk Cuckoo is widespread in the Indian subcontinent, being absent only from parts of the north-west and from the Himalayas above 1,000 m. Further east its range reaches Myanmar. Like the previous species, it is very vocal in the breeding season, sometimes continuing to give its monotonous call throughout

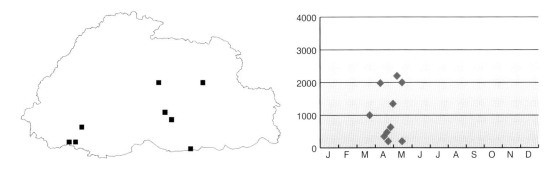

the night. There is many a story of sleepless nights because of these cuckoos. It is a brood parasite of *Turdoides* babblers and laughingthrushes.

In Bhutan the Common Hawk Cuckoo is an uncommon summer visitor, found throughout the foothills, with occasional records in the western, central and eastern valleys, at 200–2,000 m, the highest record being from 2,200 m[15]. However, the species's range may be largely confined to below 600 m and it may have been largely overlooked in the lowlands due to limited ornithological activity at such elevations in late spring. Higher-altitude records may concern strays swept there by the first monsoon rains. Recorded from late March to mid-May, during which period it is easily located by voice. Whether the population in Bhutan is migratory or perhaps resident is unclear due to the lack of records outside the breeding season. There is no information available on its host species in Bhutan.

# Hodgson's Hawk Cuckoo
## *Hierococcyx fugax*

N=246(43). S 800-2800

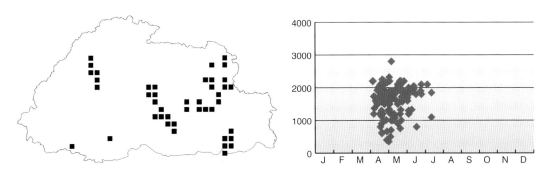

Hodgson's Hawk Cuckoo ranges through much of eastern and south-east Asia, reaching north to Kamchatka and south to Indonesia, and has a number of subspecies. In the west of its range it penetrates the north-east Indian subcontinent, along the Himalayas west to eastern Nepal. However, its distribution in this region is rather unclear. It is thought to be a brood parasite of flycatchers and shortwings, although details for the region are virtually unknown. Similarly, data are lacking concerning migratory status.

In Bhutan the species is a frequently recorded summer visitor throughout the temperate zone, and in the western and eastern foothills. There is only one isolated record from the western valleys, where it approaches its westernmost limit. It becomes gradually more common to the east. There are records at 1,000–2,200 m, with occasional sightings to 300 m and a relatively high-altitude record from 2,800 m[49]. Records below 1,000 m are from early in the season and probably concern migrants rather than breeders. The bulk reaches the breeding quarters in mid-April, the earliest record being 4 April[19]. Almost invariably located by call; sight records are rare. Peak vocal activity is short, May until the first half of June. Singing ceases in early July, with the last record from 11 July[52]. There are no breeding records for Bhutan other than calling birds on territory. A density of 1.4 territories per km was found near Zhemgang, at 1,600–1,900 m[52].

# Indian Cuckoo
*Cuculus micropterus*                     N=258(51). S 600-3000

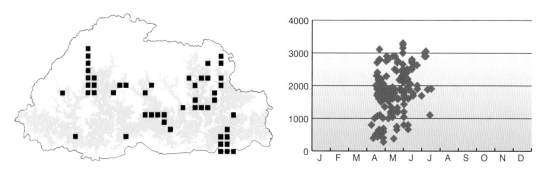

The Indian Cuckoo ranges through much of the eastern Indian peninsula and the Himalayas from Punjab eastwards. Elsewhere in Asia it occurs from the Tibetan Plateau through southern China north to south-east Siberia and south to Indonesia. A bird of forested areas, it usually keeps to the treetops, and is a brood parasite of Black and Ashy Drongos.

In Bhutan the Indian Cuckoo is a common summer visitor throughout the temperate zone and the eastern foothills, at 600–3,000 m and occasionally to 3,300 m[40,52]. The earliest records, around 10 April, are from below 1,000 m and presumably involve passage birds. However from 15 April the species has already spread across its entire altitudinal range. Birds call throughout April–June, and occasionally until mid-July. Earliest spring record 8 April[19], and the latest summer record 16 July[52]. Nothing is known of host species in Bhutan, although its altitudinal range clearly overlaps with that of Ashy Drongo. Indian Cuckoo occurs at relatively low densities, possibly because of its narrow host species specialisation. Near Zhemgang a density of *c*.1.0 territory per km was found at 1,600–1,900 m[52].

# Eurasian Cuckoo
*Cuculus canorus*                     N=358(65). S 1400-3200

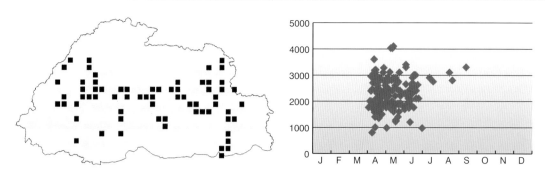

The Eurasian Cuckoo is as a summer visitor to the Himalayas and locally in north and central India. It is widespread in Eurasia, from Europe and North Africa in the west to Japan in the east. Northern populations winter to Africa and south-east Asia. Those from the Himalayas probably also move south, although there are scattered winter records from the subcontinent. It is the least specialised cuckoo, being found in a broad range of habitats and targeting a wide range of hosts, including babblers, warblers and flycatchers. Among cuckoos it is probably the most conspicuous as it often calls from exposed treetops.

In Bhutan the species is a common summer visitor to the temperate zone, with isolated records in the high west and eastern foothills. Regularly recorded at 1,400–3,200 m, and more occasionally to 800 m[19] and 4,100 m[38]. It arrives in the first week of April and immediately spreads throughout its range, suggesting a migratory population arriving following a long-distance flight. In the warm spring of 2001 birds appeared a few days earlier than usual. Peak vocalisation activity is from mid-April to late May, with the last heard in July. The latest autumn date is 11 September[31]. No breeding evidence is available, other than birds maintaining territories in spring. Near Zhemgang a density of 1.5 territories per km was found at 1,600–1,900 m[52]. Given that various cuckoo species are present within the same altitudinal range and, to a large extent, in the same warm and cool broadleaf forests, it is probable that there is strong niche specialisation in terms of hosts. However, it is unclear which hosts the Common Cuckoo targets in Bhutan.

Eurasian Cuckoo
*Chris Orgill*

# Oriental Cuckoo
## *Cuculus saturatus*

N=632(70). S 1000-2800

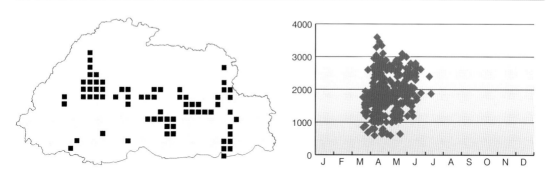

The Oriental Cuckoo is a summer visitor to the Himalayas. Elsewhere in Asia it breeds from the Urals east to Kamchatka and south to Indonesia. Its hosts are *Phylloscopus* and *Seicercus* warblers, and it winters in the Philippines, the Greater Sundas, Wallacea, New Guinea and Australia. It is a forest species, and is normally difficult to spot in the foliage.

In Bhutan this is the commonest cuckoo species and is an abundant summer visitor throughout the temperate zone, with a few records from the high west and the western and eastern foothills. It occurs at 1,000–2,800 m, occasionally to 600 m[52] and 3,600 m[19]. Low-altitude records are mostly early season, indicating passage birds. Arrival is from 20 March[40,52], with calling birds widespread in the first half of April across the entire altitudinal range. Remarkably, it arrives in the Thimphu Valley almost one month later than further east, at the end of April. This might be explained by the more marginal habitat there. In Bhutan its preferred habitat appears to be broadleaf forest, rather than pine, which is dominant in the Thimphu Valley. In suitable habitat it reaches considerable densities, e.g. 3.0 territories per km (or *c*.15 individuals per sq km) at 1,600–1,900 m near Zhemgang[52]. Birds call throughout April–June, rarely into early July. There is no other breeding evidence than calling birds on territory and no indications as to which host species it uses.

# Lesser Cuckoo
## *Cuculus poliocephalus*

N=192(50). S 1000-3200

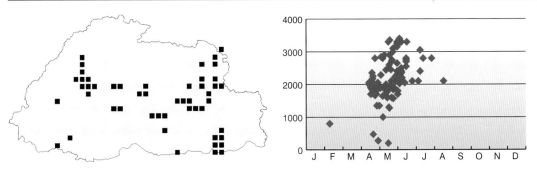

The Lesser Cuckoo is a summer visitor to the Himalayas, from Afghanistan to Arunachal Pradesh. Further east it ranges from northern mainland south-east Asia to Ussuriland. Unlike most other cuckoos, it winters to the south-west, crossing the Indian Ocean to East Africa. It is a forest species that parasites the broods of small ground-nesting birds such as *Phylloscopus* warblers, wren babblers and shortwings.

In Bhutan the Lesser Cuckoo is an occasional summer visitor. It has been found throughout the temperate zone, with scattered records in the western and eastern foothills and the high east, and is among the latest cuckoos to arrive. It mainly occurs at 1,000–3,200 m, occasionally to 200 m[10] and 3,400 m. Records below 1,000 m are from early season and concern passage birds. Arrival is from mid-April, although there is one earlier record, one collected on 8 February at Deothang[1], which perhaps indicates that small numbers winter in the foothills. Most are heard in May, but they call throughout June and, occasionally, until late July. Ludlow collected a juvenile on 15 August at 1,800 m in the eastern valleys[31], which is the latest autumn record and the only indication of breeding, other than the presence of territorial birds. Near Zhemgang a density of 0.8 territories per km was found at 1,600–1,900 m[52]. Such relatively low densities suggest a rather narrow niche specialisation in respect of its host species, much like Indian Cuckoo.

# Banded Bay Cuckoo
## *Cacomantis sonneratii*

N=32(8). S 400-1000

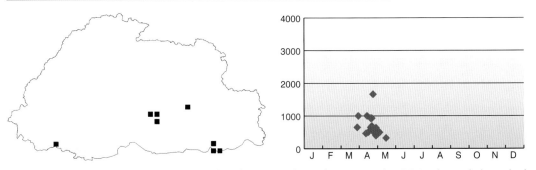

The Banded Bay Cuckoo has a scattered distribution in the Indian peninsula, Sri Lanka and through the Himalayan foothills from Uttar Pradesh to Arunachal Pradesh and north-east India. Further east, it reaches mainland south-east Asia and south to the Greater Sundas. Habitat preferences vary, but it affects dense woodland in the Himalayas in Nepal. It is a brood parasite that targets Common Iora and minivets.

In Bhutan, Banded Bay Cuckoo is uncommon in the eastern foothills and adjacent parts of the central and eastern valleys, with an isolated record from the western foothills[52]. Its altitudinal range is from 400 to 1,000 m, with one record at *c*.1,600 m[28]. It has been recorded from late March to mid-May, but it is unclear whether the species is resident in Bhutan, as elsewhere in the Indian subcontinent. Following the cessation of calling, in late spring, this cuckoo is easily overlooked. Calling birds are sparsely distributed, with a max. 2 at one site.

# Grey-bellied Cuckoo
## *Cacomantis passerinus*

N=16(14). R 400-2200

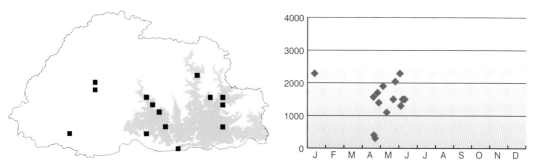

The Grey-bellied Cuckoo is widespread in the Indian subcontinent, but easily overlooked outside the breeding season, when it is silent, thus its status is often unclear. Thought to be resident in some areas and migratory and nomadic elsewhere, in the Himalayas it is a summer visitor that reaches its easternmost limits in Bhutan. This cuckoo is a brood parasite of the genera *Prinia*, *Cisticola* and *Orthotomus*. Habitat is lightly wooded country, including cultivated areas, where its hosts are most abundant.

In Bhutan this cuckoo is uncommon and has been found mostly in the central and eastern valleys and foothills, with scattered records in the western and Sunkosh valleys. It has been observed in April–June at 400–2,200 m, with one winter record from the western valleys at 2,300 m[20], suggesting that the species is resident in Bhutan. Grey-bellied Cuckoo is heard from mid-April to mid-June, and has been found in open areas with scrub near cultivation, as well as in forest clearings. Evidently its altitudinal range and habitat overlaps with that of its probable host species in Bhutan, members of the *Prinia* and Common Tailorbird.

# Plaintive Cuckoo
## *Cacomantis merulinus*

N=52(21). R 400-2000

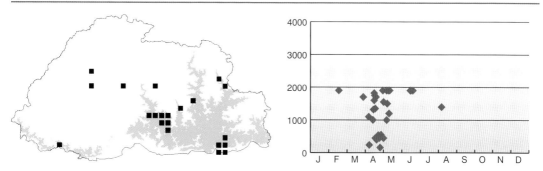

The Plaintive Cuckoo replaces the Grey-bellied Cuckoo from north-east India east through mainland south-east Asia to the Philippines, the Greater Sundas and Sulawesi. Bhutan is at the western limit of its range, where it overlaps with the Grey-bellied Cuckoo. These two species are rather variable both in plumage and song; thus their respective status in the overlap zone must be viewed cautiously, as misidentifications could easily distort our understanding. Habitat choice and hosts are similar to Grey-bellied Cuckoo.

Contrary to earlier opinion, in Bhutan the Plaintive Cuckoo appears to be the more common of the two, although identification errors might be partially responsible for this apparent difference. It is nonetheless uncommon, but quite widespread in the central and eastern valleys, and eastern foothills. There are isolated records from the western foothills[19] and the Sunkosh Valley[5]. It is mainly found at 400–2,000 m, and more occasionally to 200 m. Most records are in April–June when males are calling. Records from February[52], March[26] and August[52] suggest that the species is resident in Bhutan. In suitable habitat several calling birds may be present at a site.

# Asian Emerald Cuckoo
## Chrysococcyx maculatus

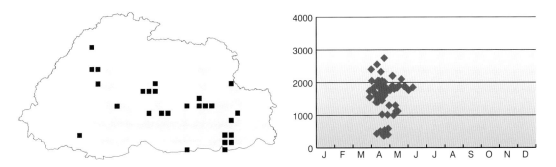

The Asian Emerald Cuckoo is a summer visitor to the hills of north-east India and the Himalayas west to Bhutan, with only scattered records further west, but across south-east Asia it occurs from central China south to Thailand and central Vietnam, in evergreen broadleaf forest. It is a brood parasite, targeting sunbirds and spiderhunters.

In Bhutan the Asian Emerald Cuckoo is a frequent summer visitor to the temperate zone, from the Sunkosh Chhu valley eastward, and in the eastern foothills. There is one record from the western valleys[19]. It is rather sparsely distributed at 400–2,200 m, and is occasionally found to 2,400 m with one record from 2,800 m[22]. Arrival is normally from 10 April, when it immediately occupies its entire altitudinal range. However, in the warm spring of 2001, the first birds were noted from 28 March[19]. The species's presence remains evident throughout April and May, the latest date being 8 June[52]. Near Zhemgang a mean density of 0.3 birds per km was found at 1,600–1,900 m[52], with considerable inter-annual fluctuations. Regular sites are the broadleaf forests between Namling and Yonkhola, Mongar district, and the forests above Samdrup Jongkha, with 1–4 located annually at both.

# Violet Cuckoo
## Chrysococcyx xanthorhynchus

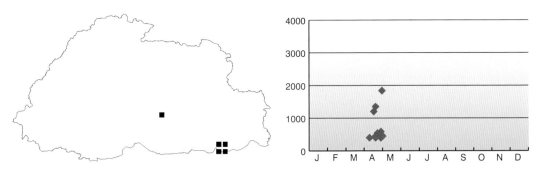

The Violet Cuckoo reaches the westernmost limit of its range in central Bhutan, being found further east in the north-east Indian hills and across much of south-east Asia, south to the Greater Sundas. It occurs in similar habitat as Asian Emerald Cuckoo and probably targets the same host species.

In Bhutan this cuckoo is an uncommon summer visitor that been found primarily in the eastern foothills and in the forests above Samdrup Jongkha, with isolated records from the central[5,52] and eastern valleys[19]. Its altitudinal range is from 200 m to 1,400 m, but mostly below 600 m. A pair at c.1,900 m, near Zhemgang, is the highest record, and the most westerly[52]. All records are in April–May, coinciding with the peak period of ornithological activity in the country. The earliest date is 9 April[19].

# Asian Koel
## *Eudynamys scolopacea*

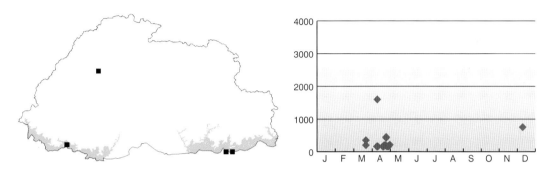

The Asian Koel is widespread over much of the Indian subcontinent and south-east Asia, including Indonesia and New Guinea. It is a bird of open country with scattered trees, often near habitation, and a brood parasite of House and Large-billed Crows.

In Bhutan the koel is uncommon and largely restricted to border towns where House Crow is plentiful. It has been found at Samdrup Jongkha and Phuntsholing, with up to four recorded in a day. Occasionally it wanders higher into the foothills, reaching 800 m[44], with one record of a straggler, in the Sunkosh Valley, at *c*.1,600 m in early April[19]. Most records are in March–April, with one in December[44] suggesting that the species is resident. The rarity of this cuckoo in Bhutan sharply contrasts with its status in Nepal, where it is widespread and common up to 1,800 m.

# Green-billed Malkoha
## *Phaenicophaeus tristis*

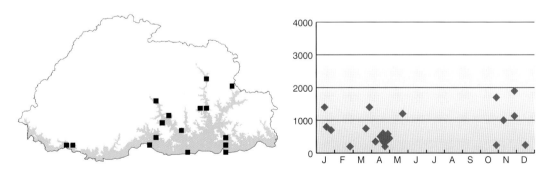

The Green-billed Malkoha occurs patchily in the Indian subcontinent, in north and north-east India, and along the Himalayas west to Uttar Pradesh. Further east, it reaches southern China and south to Sumatra. Habitat is dense thickets at low elevations. Although a member of the cuckoos, it is not a brood parasite.

In Bhutan this malkoha is an uncommon resident throughout the foothills and extending into the central and eastern valleys. There is one record from the western valleys[44], but its stronghold is the eastern valleys and foothills, where the species is recorded annually. A max. of 7 has been reported from this area[28]. Due to its unobtrusive behaviour, it is infrequently recorded and records are thinly spread. Apparently resident at 200–1,400 m, there are occasional records to 1,900 m[52].

# Drongo Cuckoo
## *Surniculus lugubris*

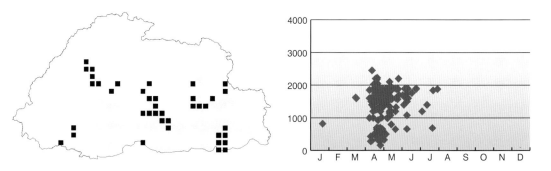

The Drongo Cuckoo is a summer visitor to the Himalayas and much of north-east India. Its distribution becomes patchier west of Bhutan to Uttar Pradesh. Elsewhere in the Indian subcontinent it occurs only in the south, as a resident, and further east almost throughout south-east Asia. It is a lower-elevation cuckoo, favouring forest edge and relatively open habitat. Among its host species is the Nepal Fulvetta, although information on breeding is rather limited.

In Bhutan the Drongo Cuckoo is a common summer visitor throughout the temperate and subtropical zones. There is, however, a clear east–west trend in the frequency of records, with only scattered occurrences in the western foothills and valleys, and the species becomes gradually more common from the Sunkosh Valley eastwards. It ranges from 400 m to 2,000 m, broadly coinciding with the distribution of its presumed host species, the Nepal Fulvetta. The cuckoo is more occasional to 200 m and 2,400 m[19]. Its breeding quarters are occupied from the second week of April, with a few arriving in mid-March, with the earliest record on 15 March[46]. Interestingly, the majority of records prior to 10 April are from the western and Sunkosh valleys, and the western foothills, indicating a west–east trend in arrivals. For the western valleys and foothills there are actually no records later in the season, suggesting that the birds are only transient here. Peak calling occurs from late April to mid-May. In June birds become less vocal, with the last being heard at the end of July. Near Zhemgang a mean density of 1.9 territories per km was found at 1,600–1,900m[52]. There is one winter record, from 20 January, at 800 m in the eastern foothills[20]. No information concerning host species in Bhutan is available.

Greater Coucal
*Phil Jones*

# Greater Coucal
*Centropus sinensis*

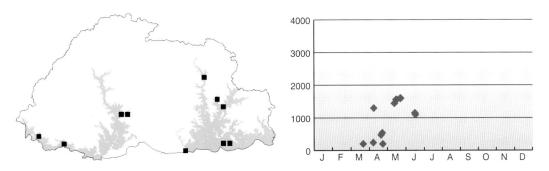

The Greater Coucal occurs throughout most of the Indian subcontinent, including the foothills of the Himalayas, as well as over most of south-east Asia. Its habitat consists of tall grassland, scrub and bamboo, often in cultivated areas. It hunts mostly on the ground, taking a variety of prey, including insects, small mammals, reptiles and birds' eggs.

In Bhutan the Greater Coucal is an uncommon resident with a scattered distribution, having been found in the temperate zone from the Sunkosh Valley eastwards and in the western and eastern foothills, at 200–1,600 m, with one record from 1,800 m[31]. There are records throughout the year, demonstrating the species to be resident.

# Lesser Coucal
*Centropus bengalensis*

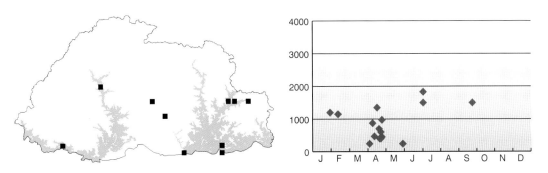

The Lesser Coucal occurs in the Indian subcontinent along the Himalayan foothills from Uttar Pradesh east to Arunachal Pradesh and north-east India, with an isolated population in the hills of southern India. Further east, it reaches eastern China and Taiwan, and south to Indonesia. Its habitat consists of tall grassland and scrub jungle at forest edges.

In Bhutan this coucal is an uncommon resident with a similarly scattered distribution as Greater Coucal. It also occupies the same altitudinal range, having been recorded from the Sunkosh, central and eastern valleys, and in the western and eastern foothills, at 200–1,600 m. Its presence in Bhutan appears to be mostly confined to spring, with most records in March–May, although it has been found at Samtse in autumn[44] and it is probably under-recorded.

# Alexandrine Parakeet
## *Psittacula eupatria*

N=11(2). R 200-400

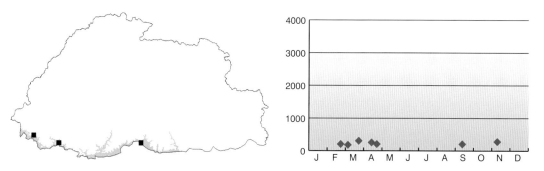

The Alexandrine Parakeet occurs over most of the Indian subcontinent, but is commonest in the north, where it reaches the Himalayan foothills. Further east, its range extends to Vietnam. The species affects a variety of wooded habitats, often close to settlements where it may cause considerable damage to orchards and crops.

In Bhutan the Alexandrine Parakeet occurs in the western and central foothills, principally in the border towns of Phuntsholing and Gelephu, and reaching just 300 m. Numbers are low with a max. 30 reported[19]. There is no direct evidence of breeding in Bhutan, although on 22 April a pair was seen interacting with Jungle Mynas[52,53], apparently competing over a nest hole.

Rose-ringed Parakeet
*Phil Jones*

# Rose-ringed Parakeet
## *Psittacula krameri*

N=9(4). R 200-400

In the Oriental region, the Rose-ringed Parakeet is associated with towns and cities as well as rural areas. It occurs over much of the Indian subcontinent, being particularly common in northern urban areas. Further east its range reaches southern China, and to the west it is widespread in sub-Saharan Africa.

In Bhutan this parakeet occurs in the subtropical zone, reaching 400 m in the foothills. It has been recorded year-round in the border towns of Phuntsholing, Gelephu and Samdrup Jongkha, but the species's occurrences are irregular. Generally numbers are small, but at Gelephu more than 100 were observed in a pre-roosting flight in October[52].

# Slaty-headed Parakeet
## *Psittacula himalayana*
N=4(3)

Among the region's parakeets, the Slaty-headed Parakeet is most associated with forest and reaches higher elevations. Its range is restricted to the Himalayas, from Pakistan eastwards and reaching its easternmost limit in Bhutan.

In Bhutan the Slaty-headed Parakeet is remarkably rare, given that it is common in Nepal, where it is regular to 2,100 m. With only four records, the species is probably best considered a vagrant, and its range has perhaps contracted, as only one of these is recent – from May 1998[4]. It has occurred at Phuntsholing, Gelephu and at Deothang, Samdrup Jongkha district (200–800 m)[31], the easternmost locality. There is only one record from the temperate zone, a specimen collected at 1,800 m in the Mo Chhu valley, Punakha district[1].

# Red-breasted Parakeet
## *Psittacula alexandri*
N=7(6). R 200-600

The Red-breasted Parakeet occurs in the Himalayan foothills from Uttar Pradesh to Arunachal Pradesh, and in north-east India and Bangladesh. Its range reaches further east to parts of mainland south-east Asia and Indonesia. It is a species of open forest and shifting cultivation.

In Bhutan the Red-breasted Parakeet is found in the subtropical zone. Like the other parakeets, it is primarily known from the border towns (Phuntsholing, Gelephu, Samdrup Jongkha), but differs from the other species in its regular presence in rural areas. It is resident and reaches to 600 m in the foothills. Numbers are low, with a max. 7 recorded at Phuntsholing in February[19].

# Himalayan Swiftlet
## *Collocalia brevirostris*
N=437(72). S 600-3000 (mid-Mar-Oct); W 200-1800

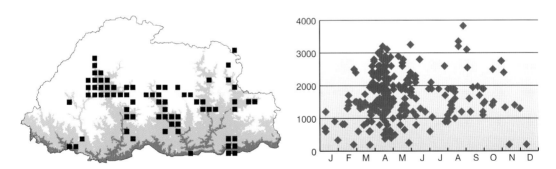

The Himalayan Swiftlet occurs in the Himalayas from Himachal Pradesh to Arunachal Pradesh and north-east India, and east to Myanmar and Thailand. It breeds in colonies in caves, where it glues its nest to the walls. In daytime it forages especially over forested areas.

In Bhutan the Himalayan Swiftlet is an abundant altitudinal migrant, occurring throughout the temperate zone and foothills, with one record in the high east. In summer it is found at 600–3,000 m, but from November to mid-March it retreats to below 1,800 m, reaching 200 m in the foothills. Whilst largely confined below 1,000 m in midwinter, from February the species begins to move upslope gradually, reaching the uppermost part of its range in mid-April. There are occasional records above 2,800 m, the highest being in the high east, at 3,800 m on 26 August[31]. Year-round it occurs in flocks, from several to 200 birds, often associated with other swift species. A breeding colony was located at 2,250 m at Gasa hot springs, where more than 1,000 were present on 18 April[39]. Large flocks of up to 500 over the Mo Chhu valley in the first half of April[5] might be associated with this colony.

# White-throated Needletail
*Hirundapus caudacutus*                                   N=186(62). S 600-3200

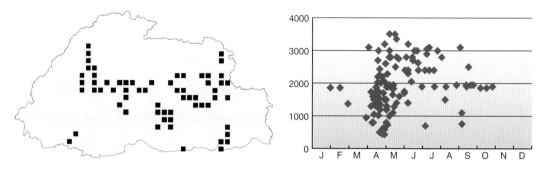

The White-throated Needletail breeds in the Himalayas from north Pakistan east to Arunachal Pradesh, and north-east through western China to Sakhalin. It winters south to New Guinea and Australia, although the winter quarters of those breeding in the Indian subcontinent are unclear. Little is known of the species's breeding behaviour.

In Bhutan the White-throated Needletail is a frequent summer visitor throughout the temperate and subtropical zones, with one record from the high west. Its regular altitudinal range is 600–3,200 m, with occasional records to 400 m and 3,500 m[22,52]. The species is present late March–September, with a few records in February and October. The earliest record is from 1 February[1] and the latest 25 October[52]. Spring passage commences early April, swiftly becoming a massive influx. In the second week of April, thousands have been observed migrating high over the eastern foothills at Deothang[5]. At this time it suddenly becomes widespread in the country and continues to be so until late May. The species has been seen over open fir forest with abundant dead trees in early May, and on two occasions has been observed entering tree holes, at 3,000 m[5] and 3,500 m[22], providing some evidence of probable breeding. Summer presence, from late April to August, might represent a breeding population, presumably in high-altitude conifer forest, with foraging over adjacent valleys down to 2,000 m. Foraging flocks of 5–20 are regular in May–June, e.g. in the Bumthang and Phobjikha valleys. Larger flocks of up to 200 have been reported from July to September[52], the peak rainy season, suggesting that such individuals are reacting opportunistically to food availability, e.g. the swarming of certain insects following a rainstorm. The species's widespread presence in spring suggests that some are en route to more northerly breeding areas. Considering its low presence in the western foothills and valleys, such movements are probably mostly through eastern Bhutan.

# Asian Palm Swift
*Cypsiurus balasiensis*                                   N=66(13). S 200-1600

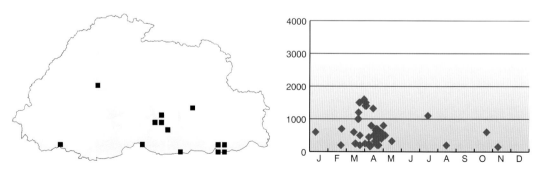

The Asian Palm Swift occurs over much of the Indian subcontinent and is widespread in south-east Asia, reaching the Philippines and the Greater Sundas. It is usually associated with palm trees, in which it roosts and nests. However, the subspecies occurring in north-east India also uses the eaves of thatched roofs in the absence of palm trees.

In Bhutan the Asian Palm Swift is frequent throughout the foothills and in adjacent areas of the eastern and central valleys, at 200–1,600 m. Records are concentrated in spring, from mid-March to mid-May, and autumn and winter records are scarce, suggesting that its occurrence is largely seasonal. However, the species may have been overlooked at low elevations in winter due to limited ornithological activity in these areas at this season. In April, birds have been seen entering the large bamboo poles supporting the roofs of farmhouses, at 1,300 m in the central valleys[52]. Flocks of up to 20 have been observed in April–May in various villages at this altitude[52], and are probably breeding. However, as yet there are no confirmed breeding records in the country.

# Alpine Swift
## Tachymarptis melba

N=1(1)

The Alpine Swift breeds in southern Europe, East Africa and Central Asia east to Pakistan. In the Indian subcontinent it occurs in the Himalayas from Himachal Pradesh to Sikkim, in the south-west and on Sri Lanka. It is unpredictable in its occurrence, breeding on cliffs but covering large distances on foraging flights, and adapting to weather circumstances.

Despite its regular occurrence in Nepal, in Bhutan the Alpine Swift is a vagrant, with only one record, over Wangdue Phodrang on 20 May 1994[55].

# Fork-tailed Swift
## Apus pacificus

N=435(70). S 1000-3000

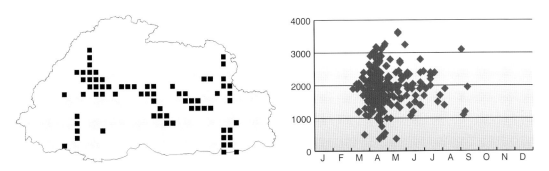

The Fork-tailed Swift breeds in eastern Asia, in a vast area from China and Mongolia north to Sakhalin and south to Vietnam, as well as the Himalayas from Pakistan east, and winters in south-east Asia and Australia, with scattered records at this season in peninsular India. It breeds in colonies in rock fissures.

In Bhutan the Fork-tailed Swift is an abundant summer visitor throughout the temperate zone, more occasionally to the eastern foothills and with single records from the western foothills and the high west. It occurs at 1,000–3,000 m, occasionally to 400 m and 3,600 m[22]. Breeding colonies have been found at 1,600–2,800 m. Records at lower elevations concern passage birds and are mostly early in the season. Arrives in early March, with the earliest record 1 March[52]. Breeding colonies are occupied from late March, as evidenced by birds entering nest holes. Breeding has been confirmed by the observation of young in cliff nests at the end of June[1], with the colonies apparently deserted by early July, although birds probably remain in the breeding areas longer, albeit in much smaller numbers. By late July there is clear evidence of extensive moult[52]. By mid-September all have left, the latest autumn record being 11 September[52]. Throughout, it regularly occurs in flocks numbering several tens, with breeding colonies typically containing 5–20 pairs. Based on the presence of birds near roadside cliffs, a total of six colonies of similar size were located over 80 km at suitable altitudes in the Mangde Chhu valley. The period of arrival, from March to mid-April, is marked by occasional records of larger flocks, with a max. 300 reported in the Mo Chhu valley, Punakha district, on 8 April[19].

# Dark-rumped Swift
## Apus acuticauda

N=33(6). S 400-1400 (broadleaf forest)

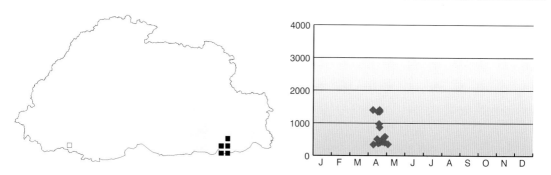

The Dark-rumped Swift is endemic to the Indian subcontinent, being known only from a few localities in the north-east. It has been found breeding in Bhutan, Meghalaya and, probably, Mizoram. It nests in fissures in cliffs, staying close by in the breeding season and disappearing thereafter, its winter quarters being unknown. Considered globally threatened by BirdLife International, the species is listed as Vulnerable, on account of its overall rarity.

In Bhutan the Dark-rumped Swift is primarily known from one site near Samdrup Jongkha in the eastern foothills, where it was initially located in 1996[28]. It has been reported once between Chhukha and Gedu, but this site requires confirmation given the difficulties of identifying the species[15]. At Samdrup Jongkha birds have been noted from early April to mid-May, during the period when most bird tours visit[5,14,19,27,28,32]. A small breeding colony has been located at c.400 m, from where birds spread higher across the valley, reaching 1,400 m. Based on the maximum number of birds observed in the period 1996–2001, it appears that the number of breeding pairs is relatively stable at 4–5, with a minimum of two in 1997 and a maximum of seven in 1999. Birds have been seen entering fissures in the cliffs, which establishes it as a probable breeder in Bhutan.

# House Swift (Little Swift)
## Apus affinis

N=157(30). R 200-2000

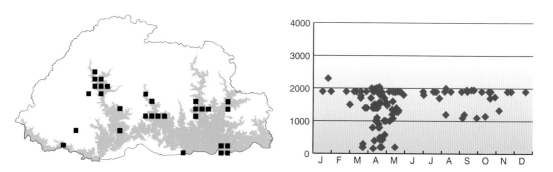

The House Swift occurs over most of the Indian subcontinent, including the Himalayan foothills. It ranges widely in south-east Asia, south to Indonesia, and breeds in fissures of cliffs, as well as in man-made structures.

In Bhutan this swift is a frequent resident throughout the temperate zone and the western and eastern foothills at 200–2,000 m. Like most other swifts, it appears to be relatively scarce in the western valleys. Birds at Zhemgang attend a mixed colony with Nepal House Martin throughout the year, roosting in the cliff nests in winter[52]. Flocks of up to 30 are regular in March–October here and at other potential colonies. However, in November– February only small numbers are present, suggesting that some leave Bhutan in winter, although it is possible that they move only as far as the foothills, where surveys have been limited. Further evidence for largely seasonal occurrence in Bhutan is the larger flocks noted in March and September, apparently coinciding with the migration season. The largest flock of 80 was noted during this period[52]. Compared to Fork-tailed Swift, colonies appear to be more sparsely distributed.

House Swift
*Dan Cole*

# Crested Treeswift
## *Hemiprocne coronata*

N=2(2)

The Crested Treeswift occurs in the eastern Indian peninsula and the Himalayan foothills, extending east to south-west China and central Vietnam. It is a bird of well-forested areas, constructing its tiny nest on a small bare tree branch.

In Bhutan the Crested Treeswift is a rare resident or summer visitor. Singles have been found at Manas (250 m), on 20 April 1993[22], and at Gomphu, Zhemgang district (500 m), on 14 April 1999[52], both localities in Royal Manas National Park.

# Mountain Scops Owl
## *Otus spilocephalus*

N=174(35). R 200-2800

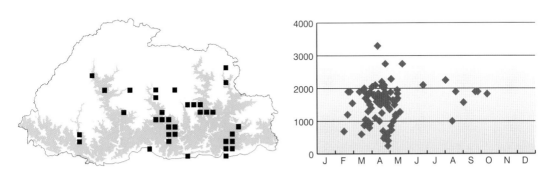

The Mountain Scops Owl has a wide range in south-east Asia. In the Indian subcontinent it occurs in the Himalayas from Pakistan to Arunachal Pradesh and the hills of north-east India and Bangladesh. It is a bird of dense temperate broadleaf forest.

In Bhutan this is the commonest scops owl. It is frequent throughout the temperate zone and in the central and eastern foothills, but scarce in the western and Sunkosh valleys, only gradually becoming commoner further east. The species is mainly found at 600–2,200 m, occasionally to 200 m and 2,800 m, with the highest record at 3,300 m[19]. Despite being common, it is rarely observed and is mostly located by its call, heard both nocturnally and in early mornings. The seasonal pattern of records fully reflects calling activity. In spring the first birds are heard in mid-February and they remain active vocally until September. Up to three may be heard at a single locality. Records from October and December concern specimens[1].

# Oriental Scops Owl
## Otus sunia

N=3(2)

The Oriental Scops Owl has a primarily east Asian distribution, from Sakhalin in the north to central Vietnam in the south. In the Indian subcontinent it occurs in the Himalayas, from Pakistan to Arunachal Pradesh, as well as in north-east and south-west India and Sri Lanka. The species is a bird of tropical and subtropical forests, being regularly noted close to settlements.

In Bhutan the Oriental Scops Owl is a rare resident, having been recorded from Manas at 250 m[22], where it is probably regular, with one record from the eastern valleys at 1,400 m[19]. All records are of vocalising birds in April.

# Collared Scops Owl
## Otus bakkamoena

N=68(25). R 600-2000

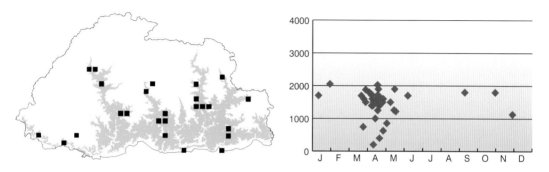

The Collared Scops Owl is widespread in the Indian subcontinent including most of the lower Himalayas. It is, however, absent from parts of the north-west, centre and east. Further east, the species ranges widely across eastern and south-east Asia, from Sakhalin south to the Greater Sundas. It occurs in forest and well-wooded country, including around villages.

In Bhutan the Collared Scops Owl is an uncommon resident of the temperate zone, from the Sunkosh Valley eastwards and throughout the foothills. There is just one record from the western valleys, but the species has probably been overlooked here[44]. It occurs at 600–2,000 m, occasionally to 200 m. It is vocal early in the season, from January until at least early June, but is probably overlooked later in the year. Less common than Mountain Scops Owl, with invariably only singles heard calling at any given site. Autumn records mostly concern specimens[1,31], although it tends to be more visible than Mountain Scops Owl.

# Spot-bellied Eagle Owl
## Bubo nipalensis

N=3(3)

The Spot-bellied Eagle Owl is one of the largest owls in the region, occurring sparsely in dense subtropical and tropical forests along the Himalayan foothills, from northern Uttar Pradesh to Arunachal Pradesh and north-east India. Elsewhere, it is found in south-west India, Sri Lanka and in mainland south-east Asia, east to central Vietnam. It takes prey the size of pheasants and young deer.

In Bhutan the Spot-bellied Eagle Owl is a rare resident, seldom encountered due to its nocturnal behaviour. There are three records from the eastern valleys and foothills. One was collected in May 1966 at Samdrup Jongkha (300 m)[1], whilst in the Lhuntse Valley it has been observed above Ungar in April/May 1989 (1,500 m+)[37] and from approximately the same area at Autsho (c.1,200 m) in November 1991[7].

# Tawny Fish Owl
## *Ketupa flavipes*

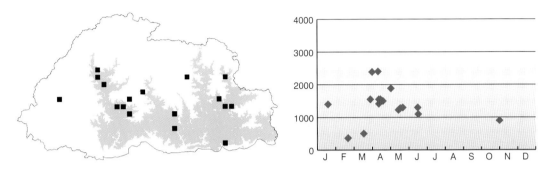

The Tawny Fish Owl is locally distributed in the Himalayas from Himachal Pradesh to Arunachal Pradesh and the hills of north-east India. Its range extends further east to Taiwan and parts of mainland south-east Asia. It is a species of streams and lakes in heavy broadleaf tropical and subtropical forests.

In Bhutan the Tawny Fish Owl is an uncommon resident of the Sunkosh, central and eastern valleys, and the eastern foothills, with one record from the western valleys[40]. It has been found at 400–2,400 m[12,52], with the highest record from 2,800 m[49]. This record is not included on the graph due to an imprecise date being reported. The upper altitudinal limit appears to be higher than previously thought, and a recent record from Arunachal Pradesh of one trapped at 2,450 m confirms that its range may reach the cool broadleaf forest zone (Choudhury 1998). It is found singly or in pairs, mostly in April–May, when ornithological activity is concentrated in the country. The Sunkosh Valley appears to be one of its strongholds, with regular records, particularly in the forested part of the Mo Chhu valley below Tashithang, Punakha district, and in the broadleaf zone of Jigme Dorji National Park, where it shares riverine forest habitat with two very rare species, White-bellied Heron and Pallas's Fish Eagle.

# Brown Wood Owl
## *Strix leptogrammica*

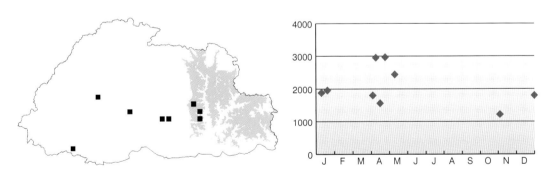

The Brown Wood Owl is a local and uncommon resident of the Himalayas from Kashmir to Arunachal Pradesh, and the hills of north-east, south-west and south-east India and Sri Lanka. Various subspecies occur over much of south-east Asia, from Taiwan south to Java. It is entirely nocturnal, perching concealed in a large tree by day. Its habitat consists of dense broadleaf forest in the subtropical and temperate zones.

In Bhutan the species is a rare resident throughout the temperate zone, but owing to its nocturnal habits and limited knowledge of its vocalisations it is probably overlooked. It appears to be resident at 1,600–3,000 m in cool broadleaf and upper warm broadleaf forests. The lowest record is from 1,200 m, in November, and concerns the only specimen to have been collected in Bhutan[20]. Almost all records concern singles heard at night. Birds have been heard from late December[52] until mid-May[22].

# Tawny Owl
## Strix aluco

N=35(14). R 2000-3000

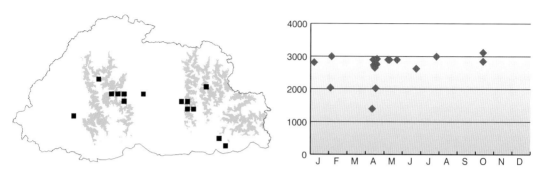

The Tawny Owl's range comprises the temperate forest zone of Eurasia, from Western Europe to Korea, as well as the Himalayas from Pakistan to Arunachal Pradesh and the hills of north-east India. Its habitat consists of temperate broadleaf and conifer forest. It is rarely seen due to its nocturnal habits.

In Bhutan the Tawny Owl is an uncommon resident throughout the temperate zone, from 2,000 m to 3,000 m, with the lowest record at c.1,400 m[14]. At lower elevations it is scarce and outnumbered by Brown Wood Owl. Above 2,600 m Tawny Owl is commoner and, unlike its relative, also occupies conifer forest. Recorded annually in the Sengor area, Mongar. Most records concern singles calling at night or in early morning. Calling birds appear active throughout spring, January–June, and occasionally in autumn, as evidenced by October records[22].

# Collared Owlet
## Glaucidium brodiei

N=434(69). R 800-2800

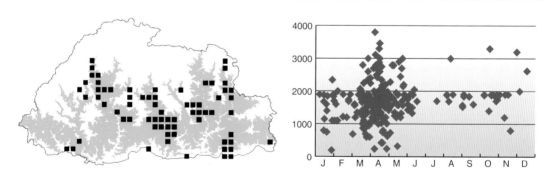

The Collared Owlet occurs along the Himalayas from Pakistan to Arunachal Pradesh and in the hills of north-east India. Further east its range includes much of south-east Asia, from Taiwan to Sumatra and Borneo. Its habitat is warm and cool broadleaf forest, where it mostly hunts small birds.

In Bhutan the Collared Owlet is a common resident throughout the temperate zone and foothills, becoming more common further east. It mainly occurs at 800–2,800 m, in warm and cool broadleaf forests, but with occasional records at 200 m and 3,800 m, and from conifer forest at higher elevations. Calling birds are heard almost year-round, except in winter from mid-November to January. It is, however, most active from mid-March to May, with many records from this period. Despite the presence of territorial birds, there are no confirmed breeding records for Bhutan. A mean 2.3 territories per km was found near Zhemgang at 1,600–1,900 m[52]. The species frequently calls by day, when it may also be located by the mobbing parties of sunbirds, warblers and small babblers that may attend a roosting bird.

# Jungle Owlet
*Glaucidium radiatum*

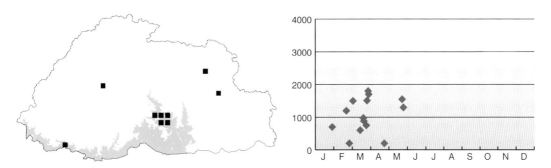

The Jungle Owlet occurs in the central and eastern Indian subcontinent, reaching the Himalayan foothills in the north, from Himachal Pradesh to Arunachal Pradesh, and to north-east India and Myanmar. It is generally found at lower elevations than Collared and Asian Barred Owlets, affecting open forest in the subtropical and tropical zones.

In Bhutan the Jungle Owlet is an uncommon resident and the rarest of the *Glaucidium* owlets. It occurs in the western and central foothills and the Sunkosh, central and eastern valleys, at 200–1,800 m. Its principal stronghold appears to be the Mangde Chhu valley with only sparse records elsewhere. Jungle Owlet is most regular in dry forest near cultivation, occurring in Chir Pine and secondary broadleaf forest. Territorial activity is pronounced in mid-February and March, and most records are from this period. Breeding pairs appear to be well scattered, with a maximum of three territorial birds noted at Tingtibi town, Zhemgang district, in March 2002[52].

# Asian Barred Owlet
*Glaucidium cuculoides*

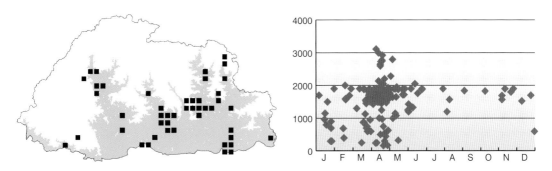

The Asian Barred Owlet is found in the Himalayas from Pakistan to Arunachal Pradesh and in the hills of north-east India, its range reaching east to Vietnam. It occupies generally lower altitudes than Collared Owlet, albeit partly overlapping. Its habitat is broadleaf forest.

In Bhutan the Asian Barred Owlet is a common resident throughout the temperate zone and foothills, and shows a similar east–west trend as Collared Owlet, with scattered records from the western valleys, becoming commoner further east. Its altitudinal range is from 200 m to 2,600 m, with occasional records to 3,100 m[19]. Whilst it overlaps with Collared Owlet, the difference in size presumably permits them to occupy complementary niches over most of their respective altitudinal ranges. Like Collared Owlet, it can be heard most of the year except midwinter, peaking mid-March to May. This owlet is more regularly observed than the previous species, as it often perches conspicuously on an exposed branch. Other than territorial birds, there is no breeding evidence for Bhutan. Near Zhemgang a density of 1.0 territory per km was found at 1,600–1,900 m[52].

Asian Barred Owlet
*Dan Cole*

# Spotted Owlet
## *Athene brama*

N=4(2)

The Spotted Owlet is distributed from eastern Iran throughout the Indian subcontinent, east to mainland south-east Asia. It occurs in the Himalayas in Nepal commonly up to 1,500 m, and is a bird of villages and cultivated areas.

In Bhutan this is a rare resident of the central and eastern foothills, and is confined to altitudes around 200 m. Singles have been noted in March–April in the Gelephu[4,10] and Samdrup Jongkha areas[19], suggesting the presence of a small population along the Indian border.

# Boreal Owl (Tengmalm's Owl)
## *Aegolius funereus*

N=1(1)

The Boreal Owl occurs in North America, Europe and Central Asia, reaching the Himalayas in the south. In the Indian subcontinent there are very few records from the Western Himalayas, but the species is probably overlooked due to its strictly nocturnal habits.

The Boreal Owl has been discovered only recently in Bhutan. A bird was photographed in the Rudong La area, between Bumthang and Lhuntse, in April 2001[49].

# Brown Hawk Owl
## *Ninox scutulata*

N=8(4)

The Brown Hawk Owl has a vast range across southern, south-east and eastern Asia, ranging from south-east Siberia in the north to Indonesia in the south. In the west of its range, it occupies much of the Indian subcontinent, except the north-west, occurring in the Himalayan foothills from Himachal Pradesh eastwards. In our region it is a species of tropical and subtropical forests.

In Bhutan this owl is a rare resident of the eastern foothills[22,28], with isolated records in the western foothills[19] and the eastern valleys[5]. The species appears to be regular at Manas, at 200–600 m, given that it has been heard daily during visits to the area[22]. There is one record from higher altitude, a bird calling in forest between Namling and Yonkhola, Mongar district[6]. All records involve calling birds in April.

# Long-eared Owl
## *Asio otus*

N=1(1)

The Long-eared Owl breeds in North America and from Europe east to Amurland and Japan, mostly in the temperate zone. It is a scarce winter visitor to the north-west Indian subcontinent.

Long-eared Owl is a vagrant to Bhutan, with just one record involving a bird collected near Zhemgang on 30 November 1967[1].

# Short-eared Owl
## *Asio flammeus*

N=1(1)

The Short-eared Owl has a Holarctic distribution, with additional populations in South America and on various islands. In Eurasia it breeds in the temperate, boreal and tundra zones, and occurs throughout the Indian subcontinent as a winter visitor.

In Bhutan the Short-eared Owl is a vagrant recorded just once. On 11 April 1997 a single was observed between Trongsa and Jakar, Bumthang district[28].

# Grey Nightjar
## *Caprimulgus indicus*

N=237(63). S 1000-2800  (Mar-Sep); W 1400-2400

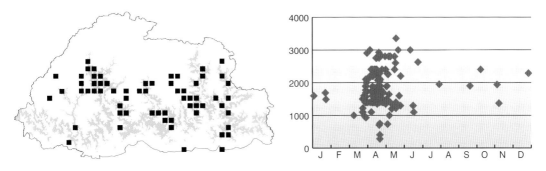

The Grey Nightjar occurs across much of the Indian subcontinent, including the Himalayas from Himachal Pradesh eastwards. Further east its range extends through China to south-east Siberia and north-west of mainland south-east Asia, wintering south to the Philippines and the Greater Sundas. It inhabits openings in forested areas.

In Bhutan the Grey Nightjar is frequent throughout the temperate zone, with occasional records in the western and eastern foothills. Its summer range appears to be 1,000–2,800 m, occasionally to 200 m and 3,400 m[22]. Most records are from the last week of March until late June, when the birds are vocalising and most easily located. However, there are quite a few autumn and winter records, indicating that the population is at least partially resident. Winter records are all below 2,400 m, the species appearing to remain just below the altitude at which serious nocturnal frosts occur in winter. The November specimen collected in the 1960s at Kamji, Chhukha district, was identified as being of the East Asian subspecies *jotaka*[1], suggesting that there is an influx in winter from breeding areas north of Bhutan. There are no confirmed breeding records, but a displaying pair was seen at 900 m on 28 March[52,53]. The species can reach considerable densities, with up to three calling at a given site.

# Large-tailed Nightjar
## *Caprimulgus macrurus*                                                        N=8(6)

The Large-tailed Nightjar occurs in the north and north-east Indian subcontinent, including the Himalayan foothills from Himachal Pradesh eastwards. It is widespread in south-east Asia, south to northern Australia. Its habitat consists of clearings and forest edge in subtropical and tropical forests.

In Bhutan the Large-tailed Nightjar is rare in the foothills, up to 600 m. There is one specimen from the western valleys, collected at 1,200 m[20]. Most records are from spring but a November record[1] suggests the population is resident.

# Savanna Nightjar
## *Caprimulgus affinis*                                                         N=4(4)

The Savanna Nightjar is widespread in the Indian peninsula, and further east in parts of south-east Asia from Taiwan to Indonesia. It also occurs sporadically along the foot of the Himalayas, and is a species of dry open habitat.

In Bhutan this species is rare. The four records are from February to April, suggesting that it reaches the country on dry-season dispersal from its breeding areas further south. Records are from the western and eastern foothills, at 200 m and 300 m, as well as higher in the Sunkosh and central valleys, at 1,400 m and 1,800 m. The latter sites consisted of dry slopes with shrub and Chir Pine vegetation.

# Rock Pigeon
## *Columba livia*                                N=360(52). R 400-3000 (agricultural areas)

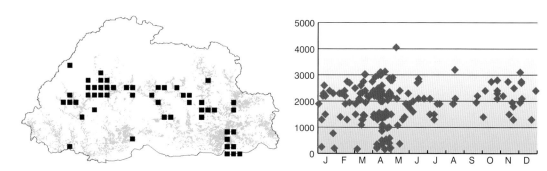

The Rock Pigeon has a vast distribution across Eurasia and Africa, including most of the Indian subcontinent. As the ancestor of domesticated pigeons, its range has increased through the establishment of feral populations in many urban and rural areas, where the birds are often protected and fed by people. Wild populations breed on cliffs and ruins near cultivation. However, wild populations exist alongside feral ones and mix so extensively that it is now arbitrary as to whether classify many populations as 'feral' or 'wild'.

In Bhutan the Rock Pigeon is common in towns, villages and adjacent cultivated areas. In particular, dzongs provide good nesting habitat for the species. There are no records of cliff nesting in Bhutan and the population shows various degrees of cross-breeding with domesticated pigeons. It is a common resident throughout the temperate zone and in the western and eastern foothills, with an isolated record from the high west[22]. It appears to be particularly common in the Paro, Thimphu and the Wangdue Phodrang–Punakha valleys. However, there are few data on numbers, as most birders tend to ignore it. Up to 90 have been counted in a small town like Zhemgang, around the breeding colony in the dzong[52]. In Thimphu hundreds gather in early morning near the clock tower where they are fed[5], whilst flocks of tens are observed in feeding flights further up the valley. In the Paro and Wangdue Phodrang valleys a max. 200 has been observed[14,52]. Its main range is at 400–3,000 m, with no evidence of altitudinal movements, although it is occasionally recorded to 200 m and 3,200 m, and the highest record is from 4,050 m[22]. Birds have been observed nest building in April, at 1,300 m[52], in a small colony in the ceremonial gate near Wangdue Phodrang police checkpoint.

# Hill Pigeon
## Columba rupestris

N=5(3)

The Hill Pigeon occurs from Turkestan to the Lake Baikal region and east to Amurland, reaching the Tibetan Plateau in the south. In the Indian subcontinent it occurs mainly on the dry steppes of the Tibetan Plateau.

In Bhutan the Hill Pigeon was first discovered in 2001, in late March, when two small flocks of c.8 birds in total were observed near Goya and Chebisa, Gasa district, at 3,700–3,900 m[2]. Subsequently c.3 were observed on a cliff near Paro at 2,200 m, where they were possibly nesting[32]. The latter would be an extremely low-altitude record, as the species is usually found well above the range of the Rock Pigeon.

# Snow Pigeon
## Columba leuconota

N=192(49). S 3600-4600 (May-Sep); W 1800-4000

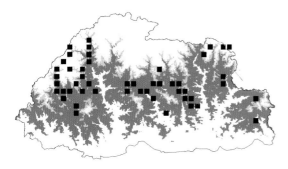

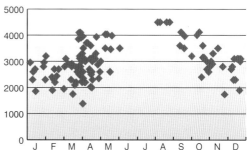

The Snow Pigeon occurs from Central Asia eastwards through the Himalayas to western Arunachal Pradesh, and further north to the mountains of western China and south to northern Myanmar. It is found in rocky terrain in wet mountain areas and nests in colonies on cliffs, feeding on grassy or rocky slopes and in cultivation.

In Bhutan the Snow Pigeon is a common altitudinal migrant throughout the alpine and temperate zones, but tends to be scarcer further east, where it is at the limits of its range. Being a high-altitude breeder, there are few records from the breeding season, but its summer range appears to be 3,400–4,600 m, based on records in June–September. It gradually descends lower from October to mid-November, when it is found at 1,800–4,000 m. However, the species's winter range appears to lie entirely below 3,200 m, where it frequents open pastures and cultivated areas. It is present at these altitudes until March, and in April–May gradually spreads up to 4,000 m again. During winter, it forms large flocks of several tens to 100–200, the largest flock being of 400[20]. In late spring and autumn flocks are smaller, normally fewer

Snow Pigeon
Phil Jones

than ten. However it remains highly gregarious, with observations of singles being rare. Given its high-elevation breeding grounds, it is unsurprising that there are no confirmed breeding records.

# Speckled Wood Pigeon
*Columba hodgsonii*                    N=158(44). S 2200-3400 (May-Nov); W 1400-2800

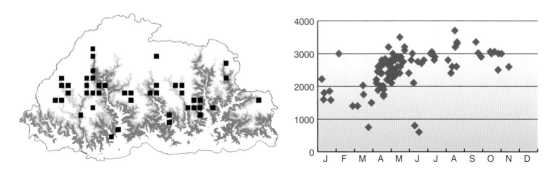

The Speckled Wood Pigeon occurs along the Himalayas, from Pakistan to Arunachal Pradesh, and into north-east India, Myanmar and western China. It occurs in broadleaf forest and feeds largely on fruits, performing nomadic movements in response to food availability.

In Bhutan this pigeon is a frequent altitudinal migrant throughout the temperate zone, being commonest in the western valleys, and occasionally reaching the high west and western foothills. Its summer range lies at 2,200–3,400 m (May–November). In winter and early spring it descends slightly to 1,400–2,800 m, with occasional records down to 600 m. The breeding areas are occupied from mid-May, when winter flocks disband into small groups and pairs. Vocalising birds have been heard in June–July[52], with up to three present at a site. The summer range reaches well into conifer habitat, including fir, hemlock and Blue Pine forests. By late September birds assemble again in flocks, numbering several tens or even more than 200[19]. Occurrence is rather unpredictable outside the breeding season, and it may even be absent in some years at certain sites, e.g. the well-explored forests between Sengor and Yonkhola, and on the east slope of Dochu La. Winters 1994/1995 and 1999/2000 produced peak numbers in the Sunkosh Valley, in both cases followed by a second winter of abundance, albeit involving somewhat lower numbers. In the central and eastern valleys numbers peaked in 1998/1999 and 2001/2002, while in 1996/97 the species was rare throughout. Such fluctuations probably reflect nomadic movements along an east–west axis in the temperate zone of the Himalayas.

# Ashy Wood Pigeon
*Columba pulchricollis*                    N=10(6). R 1200-2200 (broadleaf forest)

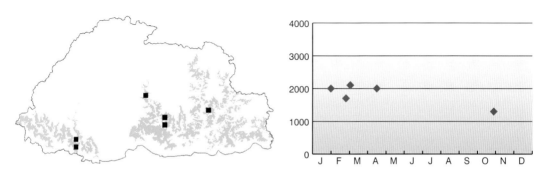

The Ashy Wood Pigeon is a rare and easily overlooked resident of the Himalayas, from central Nepal to Arunachal Pradesh and the hills of north-east India, and further east through Myanmar and northern Laos to Taiwan. It inhabits dense broadleaf forest, feeding in fruit trees.

In Bhutan the Ashy Wood Pigeon is a rare resident of the western, central and eastern valleys, having been found around Gedu, Chhukha district[1,15,29], Trongsa[4], Zhemgang[48,52] and Kori La[11,25,44], with 1–3 records at each of these localities. It occupies a relatively narrow altitudinal range, 1,200–2,200 m, with records in January–April and October. Surprisingly, the species is unknown from the rich forests between Namling and Yonkhola, suggesting that it has highly specific habitat preferences.

# Oriental Turtle Dove
*Streptopelia orientalis*  N=1015(111). S 1200-3200 (Apr-Oct); W 800-2800

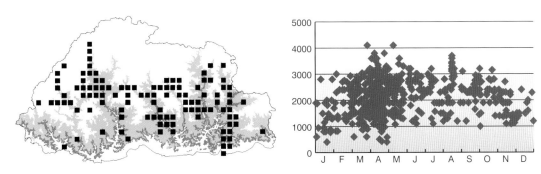

The Oriental Turtle Dove is widespread in central, southern and eastern Asia, through eastern Siberia from the Urals to Sakhalin, and south to Afghanistan, the Indian subcontinent and adjacent Myanmar and Thailand. In the Indian subcontinent it breeds in the Himalayas and in a broad band from central to north-east India. Elsewhere it is a winter visitor, with numbers augmented by migrants from north of the Himalayas. Habitat consists of open forest, generally near settlements, where it feeds in fields on fallen grain and other vegetable matter.

In Bhutan the Oriental Turtle Dove is amongst the most abundant species in all biogeographic units, except the high east. It appears to be commonest in the western and Sunkosh valleys, where its favoured habitat is most frequent, cultivated areas at higher altitudes and adjacent forests. Blue Pine stands are particularly favoured in the breeding season. There is some altitudinal movement, descending from its regular summer range at 1,200–3,200 m, to winter at 800–2,800 m. Records above 3,200 m are sparse and limited to March/April to August, with the highest record from 4,100 m[2] in April. It is occasionally found down to 400 m in January–May. The migration periods are not obvious, but birds move to higher altitudes in March–April, and gradually descend from September into winter. Seasonal occurrence is strongly dictated by local movements according to food supply, and concentrations of several tens occur in areas where rice and other cereals are being harvested. As cropping calendars differ between valleys and according to altitude, such movements are probably quite complex. Although thus concentrated, the species does not form large flocks and is usually encountered as singles or a few together, spread over a larger area or a stretch of road. Several tens in a day are typical, with a day maximum of 175[28]. There is no marked variation in numbers during the year and no evidence of any influx of winter migrants. Birds vocalise year-round, but mostly in March–April when they occupy territories. There are remarkably few breeding records and timing is unclear: one was observed carrying nest material at 2,800 m on 13 June[52] and a pair were feeding a recently fledged young at 2,400 m on 20 June[52].

# Laughing Dove
*Streptopelia senegalensis*  N=4(4)

The Laughing Dove's distribution comprises Africa, the Middle East and south Asia, where it occurs over much of the Indian subcontinent, except the Himalayas and the north-east. Its habitat consists of cultivated areas.

In Bhutan the Laughing Dove is a vagrant that has been recorded four times in April–July, at altitudes up to 2,800 m, in the Thimphu and Bumthang valleys. Given the seasonality and high altitudes where it has been recorded (2,800 m in April[37] and 2,400 m in June[52]), its occurrence is probably related to monsoon storms sweeping birds off course.

# Spotted Dove
## *Streptopelia chinensis*

N=389(62). S 200-2000 (mid-Mar-Oct); W 200-1800

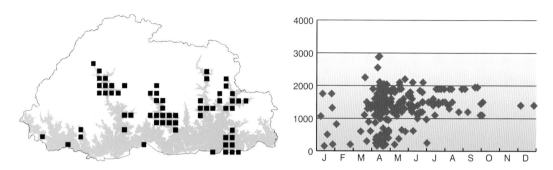

The Spotted Dove is widespread in southern and south-east Asia, with introduced populations elsewhere in the world. Its range extends from mainland south-east Asia well into Indonesia and west over most of the Indian subcontinent, including the Himalayan foothills. It is associated with cultivated areas and settlements, but in wetter and more wooded habitat than Eurasian Collared Dove.

In Bhutan the Spotted Dove is abundant throughout the temperate and subtropical zones, being apparently less common, but probably under-recorded, in the western valleys. It is mostly a summer visitor, with a clear influx from the last week of March, when it becomes common throughout 200–2,000 m, more occasionally higher, up to 2,900 m[19]. By late October most appear to have left., but some remain in the foothills and occasionally in the lower Mangde Chhu and Kuri Chhu valleys, principally below 1,500 m. Several tens can be encountered in a day, particularly in April–May. However, in higher parts of the species's range it is less common than Oriental Turtle Dove with which it frequently associates. Males call in early April–September, but the breeding season is unclear: an egg-laying bird was collected at 1,400 m on 2 May[1], and a nest with eggs was found at 1,300 m on 7 August[52]. The latter was probably a second or third brood.

Spotted Dove
*John Cox*

# Red Collared Dove
## *Streptopelia tranquebarica*

N=9(5)

The Red Collared Dove occurs in open country and cultivation across the Indian subcontinent, except the wetter south and east, and the Himalayas. Further east its range stretches from northern China to the Philippines and northern and central parts of mainland south-east Asia.

In Bhutan the species is an uncommon resident found only in the central and eastern foothills, around the border towns of Gelephu and Samdrup Jongkha, and at Manas[22], below 400 m. It is not recorded annually and numbers are always low, not exceeding four per day.

# Eurasian Collared Dove
*Streptopelia decaocto*

N=17(5). R 200-400

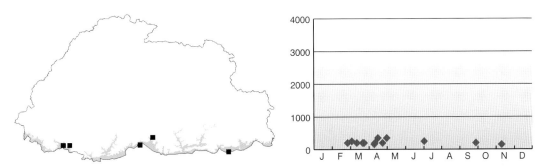

The Eurasian Collared Dove occurs in a vast zone from Western Europe to Japan, including most of the Indian subcontinent, and has recently started to colonise the Americas. Habitat consists of settlements and cultivation, particularly in drier zones.

In Bhutan the Eurasian Collared Dove is a rare resident, being restricted to the lowest foothills, mostly in the border town areas, and reaching up to 350 m. It is commonest in Phuntsholing where up to 20 have been reported. Further east it becomes even scarcer, with only one record from Samdrup Jongkha[19]. There are no confirmed breeding records.

# Barred Cuckoo Dove
*Macropygia unchall*

N=219(44). R 600-2400

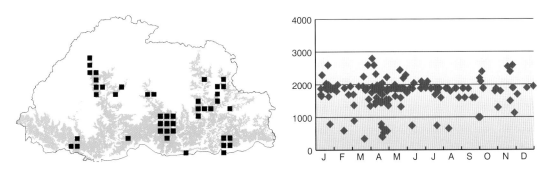

The Barred Cuckoo Dove is found in the Himalayas from central Nepal to Arunachal Pradesh and in north-east India, and is widespread in south-east Asia. It is a forest species, feeding on fruits and on the ground in clearings. Habitat consists of dense broadleaf forest in the subtropical and temperate zones.

In Bhutan this cuckoo dove is a common resident throughout the temperate zone and in the foothills. It is commonest in the centre of the country, in the Sunkosh Chhu and Mangde Chhu valleys, and the central foothills, at 600–2,600 m, occasionally reaching 400 m[44] and 2,800 m[44]. It is usually found singly, in pairs or in small flocks. In some winters, such as 1997/1998 and 1999/2000, it gathers in larger flocks of up to 20, which may be remarkably confiding, feeding on *Erythrina* seeds near houses[52]. In suitable habitat it may reach considerable densities, e.g. a mean 4.0 territories per km at 1,900 m near Zhemgang[52], but with considerable annual fluctuations, the number of pairs in this area varying from 5–9 over three years. Birds mostly call from late April, occasionally at other seasons. Territorial activity peaks in May, but is high throughout summer and into August.

# Emerald Dove
*Chalcophaps indica*                                        N=72(20). R 400-1600

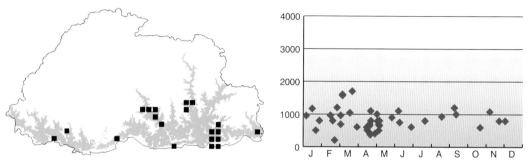

The Emerald Dove is widespread in south-east Asia and Australia, and extends over most of the Indian subcontinent. It is a bird of the forest floor in moist tropical and subtropical forests.

In Bhutan the Emerald Dove is a frequent resident in the western, central and eastern valleys, and eastern foothills, with isolated records from the western and central foothills. It occurs at 400–1,200 m, occasionally to 200 m and 1,800 m[36]. Higher records are all from March, suggesting limited dispersal prior to breeding. At one regularly visited site, in a humid valley at 800 m near Zhemgang, the species is present year-round, with no seasonal pattern[52]. It is often encountered in pairs, which are rather thinly distributed, with a maximum of four birds encountered in a day[14].

# Orange-breasted Green Pigeon
*Treron bicincta*                                                          N=3(2)

Like all *Treron* pigeons, the Orange-breasted Green Pigeon is arboreal and feeds largely on fruits. It is patchily distributed along the Himalayan foothills from Himachal Pradesh east, and in north-east India, Bangladesh, and southern and eastern India. Its range continues south and east to Vietnam and Bali. Habitat is broadleaf forest in the subtropical zone.

In Bhutan the Orange-breasted Green Pigeon is rare and has been recorded only at Samdrup Jongkha (February 1995)[29] and Manas (April 1993)[22] at *c*.200 m. Further surveys of forested areas along the Indian border may reveal a wider presence.

# Pompadour Green Pigeon
*Treron pompadora*                                                         N=4(3)

The Pompadour Green Pigeon occurs in hill areas of south-west and north-east India, and the Himalayan foothills west to central Nepal. Further east its range includes much of mainland south-east Asia and the Philippines. It is found in forested and well-wooded areas in the tropical and subtropical zones, where it is mostly noted around dawn and in the evening, when the birds fly to and from their roost.

This is another rare pigeon, which in Bhutan is restricted to the extreme south. It has been found near Samdrup Jongkha[19,27] and at Manas[22], below 400 m. All records are in mid-April.

# Thick-billed Green Pigeon
*Treron curvirostra*                                          N=21(4). R 200-600

The range of the Thick-billed Green Pigeon comprises south-east Asia, south to Sumatra and Borneo, and west to north-east India and the Himalayan foothills as far as central Nepal, where it is generally scarce. It occurs in forest areas of the tropical and subtropical zones.

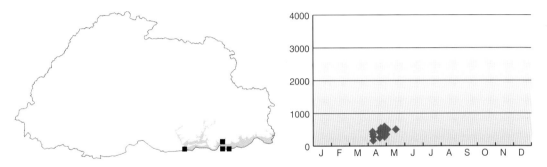

Thick-billed Pigeon in Bhutan is confined to the eastern foothills, where it has been found in the forests above Samdrup Jongkha, at 200–600 m. Records are limited to April–May, when bird tour groups visit the area, and it is observed in small flocks of 1–6, often at fruiting trees. Fifteen is the maximum count[28].

# Yellow-footed Green Pigeon
## *Treron phoenicoptera*

N=1(1)

The Yellow-footed Pigeon is the most widespread of the *Treron* pigeons in the Indian subcontinent, being absent only from the north-west and east, and parts of the Himalayas. Further east its range reaches central Vietnam. It occupies a variety of habitats where fruiting trees are available.

In Bhutan the Yellow-footed Pigeon has been recorded just once. On 24 April 2000, a flock of *c*.15 was observed in the town of Samdrup Jongkha at *c*.200 m[27].

# Pin-tailed Green Pigeon
## *Treron apicauda*

N=52(8). R 200-1000

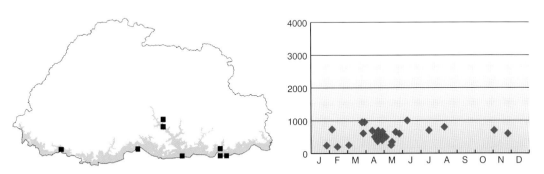

The Pin-tailed Green Pigeon occurs patchily in the Himalayan foothills, from Uttar Pradesh to Arunachal Pradesh and the hills of north-east India, and east to central Vietnam. It inhabits tall forest in the tropical and subtropical zones.

In Bhutan the Pin-tailed Green Pigeon is a frequent resident in the subtropical zone and central valleys, becoming gradually more common further east. Its altitudinal range spans 200–1,000 m, i.e. slightly lower than its commoner relative, Wedge-tailed Green Pigeon. Most frequently encountered in pairs, and several pairs may be present at the same site. Larger numbers, involving several tens, have been reported in late April to early May 2001, in the forests above Samdrup Jongkha[5,28]. On 3 May 2001 a flock of *c*.50 was present there, at 500 m, feeding in a fruiting *Ficus* tree[5]. The breeding season has already commenced by this period, as evidenced by the observation of a pair carrying nest material near Tingtibi, Zhemgang district, at 700 m, on 28 April[52].

# Wedge-tailed Green Pigeon
*Treron sphenura*

N=317(54). R 1000-2200

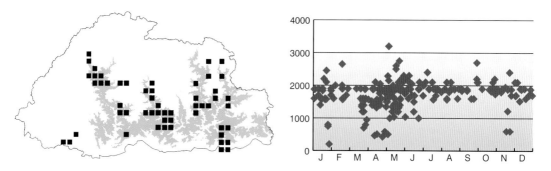

The Wedge-tailed Green Pigeon reaches higher elevations than other *Treron* pigeons. In the Indian subcontinent, it is a common resident of the Himalayas, from Pakistan to Arunachal Pradesh and north-east India, and it reaches further east to mainland south-east Asia and south to Indonesia.

In Bhutan the Wedge-tailed Green Pigeon is the commonest *Treron* and is found throughout the temperate zone and foothills, but its stronghold is the central valleys. The species is resident at 1,000–2,200 m, occupying higher elevations than other *Treron*, but occasionally occurs to 200 m and 2,800 m. The species is usually found in pairs or small flocks. In winter 1999/2000, from December to January, a remarkable concentration occurred near Zhemgang, with a max. flock of 60[52]. Vocalisations can be heard year-round, but peak territorial activity appears to be in May–July[52]. The breeding season is relatively late, as evidenced by the observation of a pair with a recently fledged young at 2,100 m on 15 August[52]. A pair was observed nest building at 1,900 m on 11 May[52]. A mean 4.0 breeding pairs per km was found near Zhemgang, at 1,600–1,900 m, with densities gradually decreasing at lower altitudes[52].

Wedge-tailed Green Pigeon
*John Cox*

# Green Imperial Pigeon
*Ducula aenea*

N=1(1)

The Green Imperial Pigeon occurs in hill areas of south-west, eastern and north-east India, as well as further east to mainland south-east Asia, the Philippines and parts of Indonesia. Habitat consists of tropical broadleaf forest, where it frequents fruiting trees.

In Bhutan this pigeon has been recorded just once, in the subtropical forest above Samdrup Jongkha, below 500 m in April 1998[5].

# Mountain Imperial Pigeon
*Ducula badia*

N=122(30). R 400-2000 (broadleaf forest)

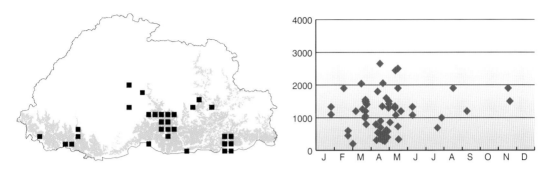

The Mountain Imperial Pigeon is discontinuously distributed in the Indian subcontinent, occurring in the Himalayas from central Nepal to Arunachal Pradesh and north-east India, and again 1,800 km further south in the hills of south-west India. Further east its range continues through mainland south-east Asia to the Greater Sundas. It is a bird of tall broadleaf forest, and a strict frugivore.

In Bhutan the Mountain Imperial Pigeon is a frequent resident throughout the foothills and in the western, central and eastern valleys. There is only one record from the Sunkosh Valley[22] and its occurrence at individual localities is erratic, in response to the presence of fruiting trees. Its main range spans 400–2,000 m, with occasional records to 200 m and 2,500 m. However, observations of displaying and calling birds are all from below 1,600 m, suggesting that higher-altitude records are reflective of dispersal and movements in search of food, and have been observed in just two months, March and July. Outside these, it is usually found in flocks of up to five and sometimes ten, but in April an exceptional concentration of 65 was observed near Samdrup Jongkha[19].

# Demoiselle Crane
*Grus virgo*

N=1(1)

The Demoiselle Crane breeds from North Africa, Turkey and the Ukraine, through the steppes of central Asia east to Mongolia. It winters in north-east Africa and in the Indian subcontinent, where it occurs mostly in Pakistan and north-west India.

In Bhutan the Demoiselle Crane is a vagrant, which is reported occasionally amongst the wintering Black-necked Cranes (Inskipp 1995).

# Common Crane
*Grus grus*

N=4(2)

The Common Crane breeds across a broad swathe of Eurasia, from Eastern Europe to eastern Siberia, and winters in southern Europe and North Africa, the Middle East, the Indian subcontinent and eastern China. In the Indian subcontinent it occurs mostly in the north-west.

The Common Crane is a rare and irregular winter visitor to Bhutan. Occasionally a single bird associates with the Black-necked Crane flocks at Bumdeling (1996/97[49], 2001/2002[47]) and Phobjikha (autumn 1999 and 2000[47]). At the latter Common Crane has been noted only in November, staying for a couple of days. In Bumdeling, on the other hand, it has been recorded throughout the winter. Bumdeling is relatively close to its regular wintering areas in south-east Tibet (Meine and Archibald 1996).

# Black-necked Crane
## *Grus nigricollis*

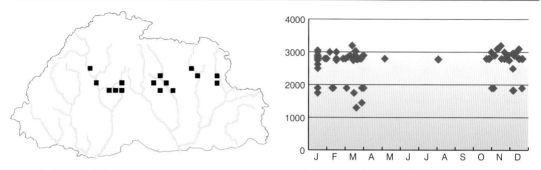

The Black-necked Crane breeds in high-altitude marshes on the Qinghai–Tibetan Plateau, by lakes, rivers and in alpine bog meadows. It winters at a few sites in southern and eastern Tibet, Yunnan and in Bhutan. It is globally threatened, classified by BirdLife International as Vulnerable, with the global population estimated at 6,000 birds (Meine and Archibald 1996), and declining due to loss and degradation of wetlands in its winter and summer ranges, changes in agricultural practices and increasing human disturbance of habitats.

In Bhutan the Black-necked Crane is a frequent winter visitor, found annually at four main traditional sites. It has important cultural significance, being referred to in various myths and traditions. Since the late 1980s, it has also become one of the flagships for bird conservation in Bhutan. The largest flock winters in Phobjikha Valley, with 130–260 counted in the last ten years[47], i.e. up to 4% of the world population (Wetlands International 2002). Here, the birds occupy a vast open marshland at 2,800 m, attending a traditional roosting site in the wet centre of the valley. They forage on dwarf bamboo in the marsh and on crop residues in the surrounding potato fields. Numbers have steadily increased in the past ten years, from 100–120 in the late 1980s to a max. 260 in 2000/2001[47]. Adjacent to the Phobjikha Valley is the Kotokha Valley with a winter population of up to 20[47]. Birds have been observed roosting here, and there appears to be regular movement to and from the Phobjikha Valley. Bumdeling, at *c.*1,900 m, harbours smaller numbers than the latter, with 130–180 birds in the last ten years[47]; birds roost on a shingle bank in the river, making daily foraging flights over 20 km to the paddyfields near Chorten Kora town. Numbers have fluctuated at this site in recent years, with some evidence of decline, apparently because the habitat is less suitable than that in Phobjikha, and their dependency on a relatively small agricultural area makes them vulnerable to changes in cropping patterns. Also, the roost site has been partly washed away. Finally, there is a small population dispersed over the Bumthang Valley, at *c.*2,900 m, which is in long-term decline, now with only a few wintering birds. In March 1985 26 cranes were reported from Gyetsa[16], whereas in recent years only one pair returns, sometimes with one or two young[52]. Loss of wetland habitat to agricultural development of the area appears to be the main reason for the decline.

The overall population of wintering Black-necked Cranes in Bhutan was in long-term decline until the late 1980s. In the 1990s numbers recovered to the level of the mid-1980s due to the increase in numbers in the Phobjikha Valley[47]. The latter appears to be *the* favoured winter site, possibly attracting birds from other areas in Bhutan or even further afield where the habitat has deteriorated. It is probable that the decline in Bumthang and the increase in Phobjikha are indicative of the birds belonging to the same population. They indeed appear to follow a similar autumn migration route, entering Bhutan through the Kuri Chhu valley, thence moving east over the Chamkhar Chhu and Mangde Chhu valleys to reach Phobjikha. Observations of small flocks staging for short periods along this route in November and early December support this (P. v. d. Poel pers. comm.), with a regular presence particularly in the upper Kuri Chhu valley[6,7]. Although it has been suggested that the Bumdeling population enters through the Kuri Chhu valley as well[5,7], there are no records to support this supposition and they may follow a different route. Spring records in the higher Sunkosh Chhu valley[19,40,43] suggest that the Phobjikha cranes may follow a different spring migration route, returning via the Sunkosh Chhu. However, records of migrating cranes both in spring and autumn are few, making it possible that the pattern described above is too simplistic. The first cranes in Phobjikha arrive in mid-October and *c.*2 weeks later in Bumdeling[47], with numbers peaking by mid-December. Departure commences in late February, and the last birds depart in late March. In the summers of 2000 and 2001 a single bird remained in the Phobjikha Valley[47,52].

# Slaty-breasted Rail
## *Gallirallus striatus*

The Slaty-breasted Rail is widely but thinly distributed over much of the Indian subcontinent. Further east it occupies a vast range in eastern and south-east Asia, from central China to Indonesia. It inhabits marshes, which makes the species easily overlooked. In consequence, its status is often difficult to assess.

In Bhutan the Slaty-breasted Rail has been found three times in the western, central and eastern valleys. The first record for the country involved one found dead on 8 May 2000, at 2,200 m, at Trongsa[6]. The following year one was observed in the same period between Trashigang and Wamrong[6]. Finally, one was found in the Thimphu Valley in June 2002[49].

# White-breasted Waterhen
## *Amaurornis phoenicurus*

The White-breasted Waterhen is a common resident over most of the Indian subcontinent, including the Himalayan foothills. Further east, it occupies a broad range in southern and south-east Asia, from central China to Indonesia. Habitat consists of small waterbodies with well-vegetated banks, often near settlements.

In Bhutan the waterhen is a rare resident. One regular site is the Punakha area and the Mo Chhu valley upstream to Tashithang at *c*.1,400 m. It has been recorded there in four different years[14,28,39,48], mostly in April. Another site is Bumdeling, Trashi Yangtse district, where it has been noted at 1,900 m in May[49].

# Black-tailed Crake
## *Porzana bicolor*

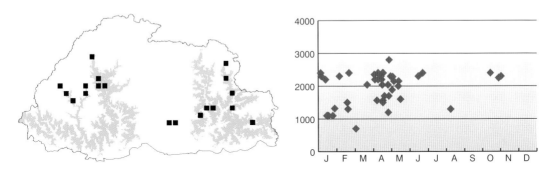

The Black-tailed Crake is an uncommon resident of the Himalayas, from Sikkim to Arunachal Pradesh and in north-east India, and further east to northern Vietnam. It is a relatively little-known bird of marshy habitats.

In Bhutan the Black-tailed Crake is an uncommon resident throughout the temperate zone, at 1,200–2,400 m, and occasionally to 700 m[5] and 2,800 m[22]. It occurs in small marshes, often at the edge of paddyfields, with *Typha* vegetation as a typical component. Such wetlands may be as small as 0.2 ha and directly adjacent to habitation. At these, birds may be observed feeding in ditches in the marsh or even between the houses. Whilst previously considered rare, the species is now known from at least 20 sites. Although generally secretive the birds can usually be located by their call or observed as they feed at the edge of the marsh early morning. Once confirmed at a certain site the species can often be found there regularly. Most sites are in valleys with extensive areas of irrigation, e.g. the Paro, Thimphu, Punakha/Wangdue Phodrang and Trashigang/Trashi Yangtse valleys. In Thimphu several sites are known, even within towns, due to intensive ornithological activity. In the Mangde Chhu and Kuri Chhu valleys relatively few sites are known and its occurrence is possibly more localised due to the restricted availability of habitat. At favoured sites up to seven birds have been seen[5,52]. Calls are heard from mid-March to October, and local residents have reported nests with eggs.

# Ruddy-breasted Crake
*Porzana fusca*                                                                     N=6(3)

The Ruddy-breasted Crake has a scattered distribution in the Indian subcontinent, with its main strongholds in the hills of south-west India and the Himalayan foothills from central Nepal to Arunachal Pradesh and north-east India. Further east it is widespread from Ussuriland south to Indonesia. Habitat consists of reedy marshes and the edges of paddyfields.

In Bhutan the Ruddy-breasted Crake is a rare resident of the western and eastern valleys, known mostly from two sites in the Thimphu Valley, at 2,300–2,400 m. Elsewhere, it has been found at Paro at 2,100 m[31] and at Lingmethang, Mongar at 800 m[13]. It breeds in Thimphu Valley, as evidenced by the observation of a pair with young in ditches near Tashichho Dzong[49]. On 26 September a juvenile was found dead at Babesa, Thimphu[52].

# Purple Swamphen
*Porphyrio porphyrio*                                                               N=1(1)

The Purple Swamphen has a vast world distribution stretching from the Mediterranean and Africa through South Asia to the Pacific. It occurs throughout the Indian subcontinent except parts of the north-west, north-east and the Himalayas. Habitat consists of large marshes in the tropical zone.

In Bhutan the Purple Swamphen is a vagrant which has been recorded once, at Lhuntse (1,400 m), where a bird was captured sometime immediately prior to 2 December 1989[38] by local villagers.

# Common Coot
*Fulica atra*                                                       N=22(3). W 1400-2400

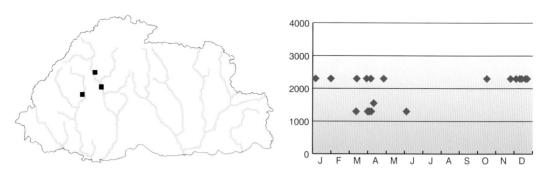

The Common Coot is found throughout Eurasia and the Oriental region. In the Indian subcontinent it is a widespread resident, with numbers augmented in winter by trans-Himalayan migrants. It is a bird of lakes and ponds with emergent aquatic vegetation.

The species is an uncommon and irregular winter visitor and passage migrant to Bhutan. At the sewage ponds at Babesa, Thimphu district, it has been found wintering in three out of five winters in the period 1997/98 to 2001/2002, with a maximum of four birds. It also occurs here on spring and autumn passage in similar numbers. The other site where it has been found is along the Puna Sang Chhu and Mo Chhu, between Wangdue Phodrang and Tashithang, Punakha district, where it is only a passage migrant. The earliest autumn record is 14 October[52]. On spring passage it is noted from mid-March to April, with late records on 20 May[55] and 3 June[52] from the Puna Sang Chhu. Wintering birds are present in December–February.

# Eurasian Woodcock
## *Scolopax rusticola*

N=60(32). S 2600-3600 (Apr-Oct); W 1200-2600

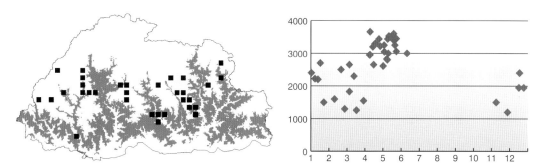

The Eurasian Woodcock is found in temperate and boreal zones of Eurasia, from Europe to Japan, with a disjunct population breeding in the Himalayas, from Pakistan to Arunachal Pradesh, wintering at lower altitudes in the hills of south-west and north-east India. Habitat consists of damp forest with dense undergrowth. During the breeding season, males perform their characteristic roding flight over the breeding territories.

Eurasian Woodcock
*Chris Orgill*

In Bhutan the woodcock is a frequent altitudinal migrant found throughout the temperate zone and in the high west. Its summer range spans 2,600–3,600 m, and in winter it descends to 1,200–1,600 m. Breeding areas are occupied by early April, and roding males have been noted in the first half of April to May, throughout its summer range. A maximum of four roding birds were noted at 3,400 m near Thrumshing La on 9 May[5] and a nest with eggs was found at 3,050 m on 23 May[31]. From early November the species is present in the wintering areas, occupying a variety of habitats, from open tall grassland with bushes, to scrub and moist forest. In the latter habitat they are often noted when flushed from roadside ditches at dusk.

113

# Solitary Snipe
## *Gallinago solitaria*
N=29(15). W 2200-3000

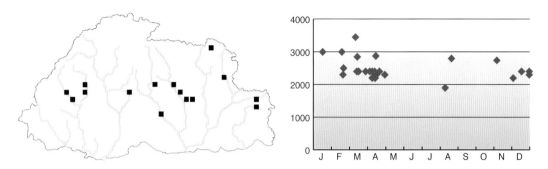

The Solitary Snipe is found in montane central and east Asia, from the Central Asian republics to Kamchatka and south to the Himalayas, where it occurs patchily from Pakistan to Arunachal Pradesh and in the hills of north-east India. It breeds in high-altitude bogs, descending in winter. Numbers in the subcontinent in winter are probably augmented by migrants from the Tibetan Plateau.

The Solitary Snipe is primarily an uncommon winter visitor in Bhutan. It is found throughout the temperate zone, with most records from the western valleys, where suitable habitats have been more intensively surveyed. There is one record from the high east, at 3,650 m, in summer, which might indicate that the species breeds in Bhutan[49]. This record is not included on the graph due to an imprecise date being reported. One collected by Ludlow, at 3,450 m on 11 March[31], perhaps suggests that birds arrive in their breeding areas relatively early, when ice in the mountain streams is still thawing. The first birds descend rather early, with one noted at 1,900 m on 8 August[52]. Its regular winter range appears to be 2,200–3,000 m, with the Paro Valley and around Thimphu being regular sites. It is noted there December–April, with the latest record on 29 April[14]. Between August and October the species is probably dispersed in wet paddyfields, retreating to remaining marshy patches along the rivers by December. Generally, it tolerates drier conditions than other snipes, and is often flushed from drier parts of wetlands. Despite its name, it is regularly found in small groups of 2–3, with a max. 5 near Paro on 7 April[14]. At least ten were found on 8 April 2002 at various sites in the Paro and Thimphu valleys[14]. Thus, spring numbers appear to be considerably higher than those during midwinter counts, with a maximum of just three in February 2000 despite extensive coverage of potential sites[49,52].

# Wood Snipe
## *Gallinago nemoricola*
N=23(8). S 3600-4000 (May-Oct); W 1800-2400

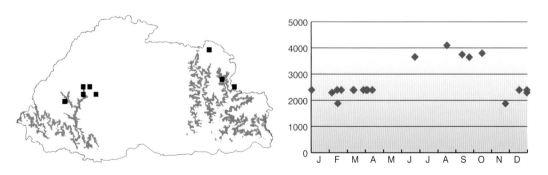

The Wood Snipe occurs in the Himalayas from Himachal Pradesh to Arunachal Pradesh and north-east India, and further east through Myanmar and north in montane China. It is considered globally threatened, being classified by BirdLife International as Vulnerable due to its small population., which is declining as a result of habitat loss and local hunting, both particularly in its winter range. There is relatively little available information on its breeding and migration habits. Breeding habitat consists of alpine meadows with scattered bushes and streams. In winter it descends to lower altitudes and disperses south into the Indian subcontinent, when it occurs in tall grass and overgrown swampy areas, usually close to or within forest.

The Wood Snipe is principally known in Bhutan from its winter range in the western and eastern valleys, at 1,800–2,400 m. In summer it has been found at 3,600–4,200 m both in the high west and east. The record of a 'drumming' bird in August at 4,100 m indicates possible breeding[44]. Drumming snipes reported as 'plentiful' from the Black Mountain in May 1937 were probably also this species[31]. Wintering sites are streams in forest as well as more open habitat of tall grass with scattered bushes. Birds are noted here from mid-November to mid-April and regular sites are around Thimphu town[52], Dochu La[10] and Bumdeling[49]. The single-day maximum is three at Bumdeling[49] and at various wetlands around Thimphu[52,49] which are increasingly threatened by urban development. Its summer sites are probably

Wood Snipe
*Craig Robson*

unchanged since Ludlow first reported the species in Bhutan. Although recent records are available from the same sites as he noted the species (above the Paro Valley[31] and the ridge between the Kulong Chhu and Kuri Chhu valley[49]), his accounts give the impression that the species was more formerly common. The reasons for possible decline are probably habitat loss in the wintering areas, outside as well as within Bhutan (due to urban and agricultural development in the upland valleys). Although probably largely overlooked, particularly in its summer range, the species is considered to be an uncommon altitudinal migrant.

# Pintail Snipe
## *Gallinago stenura*

N=16(4). W 1400-2400

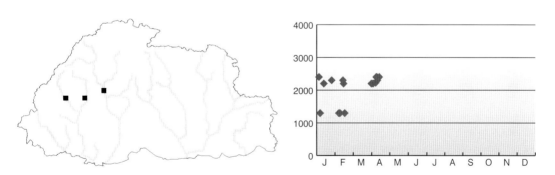

The Pintail Snipe breeds in the arctic and boreal zones of east Asia, roughly from the Pechora River eastwards. It winters in the Indian subcontinent and south-east Asia, including much of Indonesia. In the subcontinent it largely outnumbers the Common Snipe in the east and south. Winter habitat comprises damp paddyfields and the edges of marshes.

This snipe is a rare but regular winter visitor to Bhutan, having been noted in the western and Sunkosh valleys, albeit at only a few sites. Known sites are in the Paro Valley (2,200 m), around Thimphu town (2,300–2,400 m) and near Chime Lakhang and Bajo, Wangdue Phodrang district (1,300 m), where it occurs in marshy patches near rivers. Largest numbers, of up to ten at a single site, have been during midwinter waterbird counts, when suitable habitats are more intensively surveyed[52]. It has been observed in January to early April, with the latest spring record dated 13 April[5].

# Common Snipe
## Gallinago gallinago

N=21(8). W 1200-2800

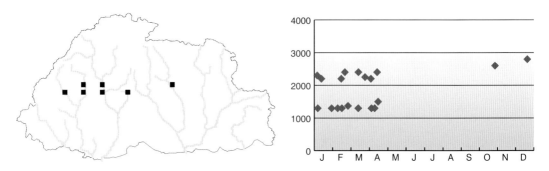

The Common Snipe breeds in a vast zone across Eurasia and North America, in the temperate as well as the boreal and arctic zones. Separate populations occur in Africa and South America, and there are isolated breeding populations in the Western Himalayas. Elsewhere in the Indian subcontinent it is a winter visitor, being commonest in the north and west. It occupies similar habitats to Pintail Snipe, but prefers wetter sites.

In Bhutan the Common Snipe is an uncommon winter visitor to a few sites with suitable habitat in the western, Sunkosh and central valleys, at 1,200–2,800 m. In general, it occurs in smaller numbers than Pintail Snipe, but is more widespread. Habitat includes patches of open marshland and occasionally riverbanks. Whereas the species may appear in small numbers at any small marsh, larger numbers are found only during the midwinter waterbird counts, as suitable habitats are then covered more systematically. The maximum in January/February at a single site is ten[52]. The species is present from late October to mid-April, with the earliest on 26 October[1] and the latest 15 April[14]. On 9 April a displaying bird was seen at Bajo, Wangdue Phodrang district, at 1,300 m. However, as there are no subsequent records and as the nearest breeding sites are in the Western Himalayas, this was most likely only a passage bird.

# Jack Snipe
## Lymnocryptes minimus

N=2(2)

The Jack Snipe breeds in the boreal zone of Eurasia, from Scandinavia east to the Kolyma Delta. It is a winter visitor to the Indian subcontinent, being less common than Pintail and Common Snipes. Winter habitat consists of marshes and wet paddy stubble.

In Bhutan the Jack Snipe is a rare passage migrant, albeit probably overlooked. It has been found on 2 April 2000 at Thimphu, at 2,400 m, in a small wetland[14]. Around mid-April a single was noted in a marshy area at the pass between Kikhar and Tali, Zhemgang district, at c.2,200 m[44].

# Whimbrel
## Numenius phaeopus

N=4(2)

The Whimbrel breeds in the boreal and arctic zones of Eurasia and North America. It is a widespread winter visitor to coasts of the southern Atlantic, the Indian and southern Pacific Oceans. In the Indian subcontinent it is a winter visitor to coastal areas and is occasionally found inland on passage.

In Bhutan this species is a rare passage migrant. Most records concern flyovers, located by their call, by day as well as at night. Passage periods appear to be April/May and August. The earliest spring record is dated 1 April[5] and the earliest in autumn from 30 July[52]. With the exception of one from Trongsa[5], all records are from the Phobjikha Valley, which appears to form a passage route.

# Eurasian Curlew
## *Numenius arquata*
N=1(1)

The Eurasian Curlew breeds from Western Europe through the boreal and temperate zones of Eurasia, to the upper Amur River. In winter it moves south to Mediterranean coasts, East Africa, southern and south-east Asia. In the Indian subcontinent it is a widespread winter visitor, mostly to coastal areas.

Eurasian Curlew has been recorded once in Bhutan. On 8 April birds were heard flying overhead at night at Punakha during a thunderstorm. The following morning a group of five was present along the river at Bajo, Wangdue Phodrang (1,300 m), which were presumably the same birds[19]. This record shows that birds may well cross Bhutan on migration occasionally, but go unnoticed unless forced down by bad weather.

# Common Redshank
## *Tringa totanus*
N=4(4)

The Common Redshank breeds in the boreal and temperate zones of Eurasia, from Western Europe to eastern China, and ranging south to the Tibetan Plateau and the adjacent Himalayas, in Kashmir, Ladakh and Sikkim. Over the rest of the Indian subcontinent it is a winter visitor, although it is largely absent from the Himalayas and the north-east at this season. Its habitat is the edges of marshes and muddy banks of rivers and lakes.

In Bhutan the Common Redshank is a rare spring passage migrant. It has been recorded four times, at Taba, Thimphu district (2,400 m)[52], at Bajo, Wangdue Phodrang (1,300 m)[19,52] and near Pele La (3,200 m)[5]. All concern singles from mid-April to mid-May. That observed at Pele La on 19 April 2001 showed alarm behaviour as if nesting[5]. The absence of autumn records suggests that breeders from the Tibetan Plateau do not cross the Himalayas on a broad front at this season, but follow the Brahmaputra River valley. The scarcity of spring records might signify direct passage over the Himalayas, with birds only rarely pausing midway.

# Common Greenshank
## *Tringa nebularia*
N=36(10). W 200-2800

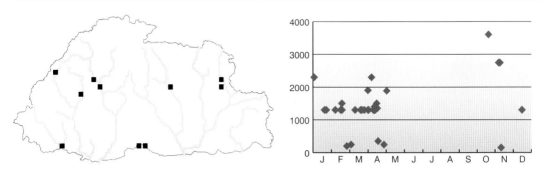

The Common Greenshank breeds in the boreal forests of Eurasia from Scotland and Scandinavia to Kamchatka. In winter it occurs from southern Europe and Africa to south-east Asia, including almost the entire Indian subcontinent. It occurs in a variety of freshwater habitats, often feeding in somewhat deeper water.

In Bhutan it is an occasional winter visitor and passage migrant throughout the temperate zone, in the high west and in the western and central foothills. In winter it is regular along the Puna Sang Chhu, between Wangdue Phodrang and Punakha (1,300–1,400 m). Here 1–4 are present from mid-December to mid-April. It has also been recorded in winter at Babesa, Thimphu district[22,49] (2,300 m), Bumdeling, Trashi Yangtse district (1,900 m)[49] and near Phuntsholing and Gelephu (200 m)[1,19,22]. In March–April birds in these areas may be passage migrants, although in general passage appears rather weak, with no real influx of birds. There are just isolated records in late October and early November, notably at higher altitudes such as the Bumthang Valley (2,800 m)[1] and at Soe, Paro district (3,600 m)[51]. The earliest autumn record is 20 October[51], the latest in spring on 26 April[1]. Thus the major routes into and from the Indian subcontinent appear to bypass Bhutan.

# Green Sandpiper
## Tringa ochropus

N=122(18). W 400-2400

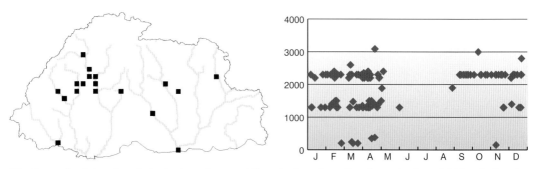

The Green Sandpiper breeds in the boreal zone of Eurasia from Scandinavia to the Sea of Okhotsk. In winter it occurs across a vast area south of the breeding range, from Western Europe and sub-Saharan Africa to Japan and Australia. It is a common winter visitor throughout the Indian subcontinent, being found regularly on small wetlands with abundant bankside vegetation.

In Bhutan this species is a frequent winter visitor and passage migrant. Broad river valleys in the western and Sunkosh valleys are regular wintering areas. Further east, in the central and eastern valleys and in the eastern foothills, records are limited to migration periods and involve only isolated records. The species's main wintering areas are the Paro Valley (2,200 m), Babesa, Thimphu district (2,300 m) and the Puna Sang Chhu between Wangdue Phodrang and Punakha (1,300 m). At each of these a max. 10 has been counted in winter, with a mean 0.4 birds per km of river in February 2000[49,52]. The Torsa Chhu near Phuntsholing (200 m) probably holds similar numbers, but no winter counts have been made there as yet. Birds arrive at their winter sites by early September, with the earliest a bird heard over Zhemgang at night on 27 August[52]. Numbers peak in October, indicating ongoing passage, which is also confirmed by an October record at Jakar at 2,800 m[1]. Thereafter numbers remain stable throughout winter, with birds departing by mid-April. Spring passage is noted from mid-April to late May, and is marked by a few observations east of its winter range and the observation of a flock of 17 at Bajo on 24 April[52]. The latest spring record is dated 31 May from Wangdue Phodrang[15].

# Wood Sandpiper
## Tringa glareola

N=2(2)

The Wood Sandpiper breeds across the boreal and arctic zones throughout Eurasia, wintering in a vast zone from sub-Saharan Africa to Japan and Australia. It winters throughout the Indian subcontinent, in a variety of freshwater habitats.

In Bhutan the Wood Sandpiper is a rare spring passage migrant recorded twice. Two were present near Punakha at c.1,400 m on 26 April 1994[1] and several were near Paro on 15 April 1997[5].

# Common Sandpiper
## Actitis hypoleucos

N=204(23). W 600-2800

The Common Sandpiper breeds beside mountain streams and rivers throughout Eurasia, extending into the Himalayas from Pakistan to Uttar Pradesh. Further east in the Himalayas breeding is suspected, but there is only one confirmed record, from eastern Bhutan. Elsewhere in the Indian subcontinent it is a common winter visitor, primarily occurring inland and usually at small waterbodies.

In Bhutan the Common Sandpiper is a common winter visitor and passage migrant throughout the temperate zone and the foothills, but concentrated at favourable sites in the western and Sunkosh valleys. Favoured sites are particularly the broad and slow-flowing stretches of rivers in broad glacial valleys, where it feeds along riverbanks, often concealed amongst the coarse gravel. The first birds arrive in early September,

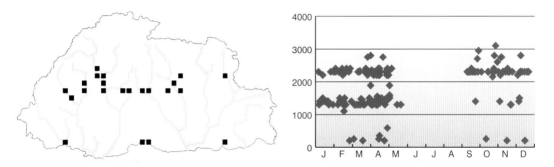

and the last depart by mid-May, with the latest spring record being 20 May[55]. Within this period it is found at its regular wintering sites, namely the Torsa Chhu at Phuntsholing (200 m), Paro Valley (2,200 m), the sewage ponds and adjacent stretches of the Thim Chhu at Thimphu (2,300 m), and the Mo Chhu and Puna Sang Chhu at Wangdue Phodrang/Punakha (1,300–1,600 m). During the midwinter count of 2000 a mean 0.6 birds per km of river was found in the western and Sunkosh valleys, with highest numbers at the sewage ponds at Babesa, Thimphu district, where up to 15 have been counted in winter. In the mild winter of 2000/2001 one was found in Phobjikha Valley at 2,800 m in December[53]. Autumn passage spans September to early November, as demonstrated by high numbers at Babesa and records from the Bumthang Valley (2,800 m). A broad-front crossing of the Himalayas seems likely, as migrants have be found up to 5,400 m in Nepal (Inskipp and Inskipp 1985). Also, the winter range in India extends well east into Assam. However, the limited number of records from high altitudes and from the centre and east of the country suggests that most cross Bhutan in non-stop flights, due to the lack of suitable staging sites. April appears to be the main month of spring passage, which is apparently channeled mostly through the Sunkosh Chhu valley, with only one record from the Bumthang Valley. Breeding was proven in spring 2000, when a pair was sighted with young at Bumdeling Wildlife Sanctuary at 1,900 m on 2 May[49]. The habitat consisted of a broad stretch of the Kulong Chhu with adjacent marsh. This was the first confirmed breeding for the Eastern Himalayas, at considerable distance from known populations in the Western Himalayas and north of the Tibetan plateau.

# Temminck's Stint
## Calidris temminckii                                    N = 12(3). W 200-2400

Temminck's Stint breeds in the arctic zone from Norway in the west to the Bering Strait in the east. It migrates inland over a broad front to its winter quarters from North Africa to Indonesia and Japan. It is a common winter visitor over much of the Indian subcontinent, where it occupies freshwater habitats.

In Bhutan this species is a rare passage migrant and winter visitor. Passage birds have been noted in September and November at the sewage ponds near Thimphu (2,300 m). The earliest autumn record is 22 September[52]. Although it probably crosses the Himalayas on a broad front and in considerable numbers, the species is rarely recorded in Bhutan due to the lack of suitable staging sites. In spring it has been observed along the Puna Sang Chhu between Punakha and Wangdue Phodrang, with 29 April the latest date[39]. In winter it is not recorded annually. At this season sites include the Torsa River near Phuntsholing (200 m) and Bajo, Wangdue Phodrang district (1,300 m). A maximum two was present at the latter site in winters 1997/1998 and 1998/1999[43,52].

# Curlew Sandpiper
## Calidris ferruginea                                                N = 1(1)

The Curlew Sandpiper breeds near the Arctic Sea in a relatively small area from the Yenisey Delta to the Taimyr Peninsula. It is a widespread winter visitor to coasts of Africa, southern and south-east Asia. In the Indian subcontinent it is mostly coastal, but may occur inland on passage.

In Bhutan the Curlew Sandpiper is a vagrant, recorded once, at Bajo, Wangdue Phodrang (1,300 m) on 29 January 2000[49,22].

# Ruff
## *Philomachus pugnax*

N=1(1)

The Ruff breeds in Eurasia from Scandinavia to the Bering Strait, mostly in boreal and arctic zones. In winter it migrates to Africa, southern and south-east Asia. As a winter visitor to the Indian subcontinent it is largely confined to the western half, entering the subcontinent via the Indus Valley. Habitat consists of a range of freshwater wetlands.

In Bhutan the Ruff is a vagrant recorded just once. On 10 April 2000 a single was present amongst waders delayed on passage by bad weather, at 1,300 m at Bajo, Wangdue Phodrang district[49,57].

# Bronze-winged Jacana
## *Metopidius indicus*

N=5(1)

The Bronze-winged Jacana is widespread in the Indian subcontinent, although it does not penetrate the Himalayas. Further east its range extends through mainland south-east Asia to Sumatra and Java. It is a bird of ponds and lakes with floating vegetation.

In Bhutan the Bronze-winged Jacana is a vagrant. From 13 May to at least 10 June 2001 an adult male, presumably the same bird, was observed on several occasions near the sewage ponds at Babesa, Thimphu district[15,52].

# Eurasian Thick-knee
## *Burhinus oedicnemus*

N=1(1)

The Eurasian Thick-knee occurs from Europe and North Africa to south-east Asia. It occurs over much of the Indian subcontinent, affecting dry, stony habitats, including dry riverbeds.

In Bhutan the Eurasian Thick-knee has been found just once, in a dry riverbed at Manas at 250 m, on 18 April 1993[22], suggesting that it might breed there.

# Great Thick-knee
## *Esacus recurvirostris*

N=1(1)

The Great Thick-knee is distributed from Pakistan to Vietnam. In the Indian subcontinent it has a localised distribution, occurring amongst others along the Brahmaputra river system. Its habitat consists of stony river beds.

The Great Thick-knee was first found in Bhutan in 2004. A breeding population was discovered near Gelephu at an approximate altitude of 200 m. Nest and fledglings were observed here in early spring[49].

# Ibisbill
## *Ibidorhyncha struthersii*

N=305(34). S 1400-2800 (Mar-Nov); W 200-2400

The Ibisbill occurs along the Himalayas from Kashmir to Arunachal Pradesh, and elsewhere is found on the high plateaus from Turkestan, through Tibet to northern China. It is a bird of fast-flowing mountain streams, where it uses its curved bill to feed between boulders.

In Bhutan the Ibisbill is a common altitudinal migrant throughout the temperate zone, with occasional records from the high west and high east and in the western and eastern foothills. It becomes gradually scarcer in the east. The species's localised occurrence can be explained by its preference for the broader and slower flowing parts of rivers. Thus, it is apparently absent along the Mangde Chhu and is scarce on the Kuri Chhu (one record[22,49]) and Drangme Chhu. The broad riverbed of the Kulong Chhu at Bumdeling, Trashi Yangtse

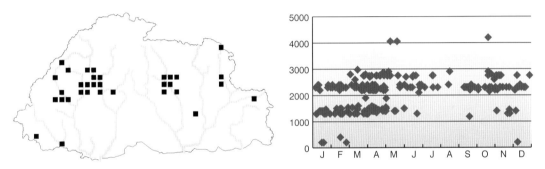

district, is one of the few sites in the east where it is regular, although other occupied sites may have been overlooked. It is an early breeder and pairs with chicks are observed from late March to mid-May, when the species is mostly found at traditional sites in the Punakha/Wangdue Phodrang area (1,300–1,600 m), the Bumthang Valley (2,800 m), and the Thimphu and Paro valleys (2,200–2,400 m). Post-breeding, some move up the valleys, vacating the Punakha/Wangdue Phodrang area, and reaching 4,000 m, but at Paro, Thimphu and in Bumthang the species appears to be at least partly resident. From November it moves downslope again, with some descending as low as 200 m. By March all have returned to their breeding sites. At traditional sites, highest numbers are present in November–February. During midwinter counts of these areas a maximum of c.80 was counted in February 2000[49,52] and January 2002[42,52]. Numbers in 2000 corresponded to a mean density of 1.2 birds per km of river. It is unclear whether such peaks reflect the presence of wintering birds from higher-altitude breeding areas. Certainly, a lack of records in March–April from higher altitudes makes it unlikely that the species breeds in such areas. An alternative explanation could be that birds from large areas concentrate, forming small flocks that are relatively easy to locate. Relatively large groups are encountered in January, particularly along the Puna Sang Chhu, where the largest flock totalled 27[52]. Breeders may occur at considerable densities, locally up to one pair per km of river, with for example four pairs around Punakha[39]. At the sewage ponds at Babesa, Thimphu district (2,300 m), the number of breeding pairs fluctuates annually, with 1,1,3 and 2 pairs in 1998 and 2000–2002 respectively[43,52].

Ibisbill
*Jan Wilczur*

# Pied Avocet
## *Recurvirostra avosetta*

N=4(1)

The Pied Avocet breeds on European coasts, in Africa and the Central Asian steppes, where it reaches east to northern China and Pakistan to the south. It winters in Africa, India and southern China. It is mainly a winter visitor to the Indian subcontinent, being concentrated in the north-west. It favours shallow alkaline or brackish pools, suited to its foraging habit of sweeping its upcurved bill to collect small aquatic life.

In Bhutan the avocet is a rare spring passage migrant, with four records, all from the Puna Sang Chhu, between Punakha and Wangdue Phodrang at c.1,300 m[5,52,19,42]. Almost all were in the last week of March and first week of April, suggesting that passage through Bhutan is concentrated. The maximum number observed is ten[5]. Outside this period it has been observed once, a single on 21 June[42].

# Long-billed Plover
## *Charadrius placidus*

N=27(4). W 1400-2400

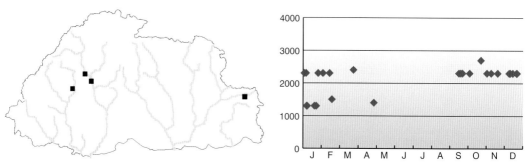

The Long-billed Plover breeds from western China to Ussuriland, North Korea and Japan. It winters south to China, Myanmar and the northern Indian subcontinent, on rivers with shingle banks. On the whole, it is rather sparsely distributed.

In Bhutan the Long-billed Plover is an uncommon but regular winter visitor, recorded mostly at the sewage ponds near Thimphu, where it arrives in mid-September and departs by mid-February. In midwinter up to 12 have been observed here[52]. Elsewhere this plover has been found on the Puna Sang Chhu near Punakha and Bajo, Wangdue Phodrang district, from where only occasional records exist, but as the species is easily overlooked due to its unobtrusive behaviour, a few perhaps winter here annually. A max. 7 was counted in this area during the midwinter count of January 2002[42,52]. Spring records are scarce after February, the latest being on 26 April near Punakha[10]. It has been found once at Sakten, at 2,700 m, in October, which probably involved passage migrants[31].

Little Ringed Plover
*Mike Langman*

# Little Ringed Plover
## *Charadrius dubius*

N=33(3). W 1400-1400

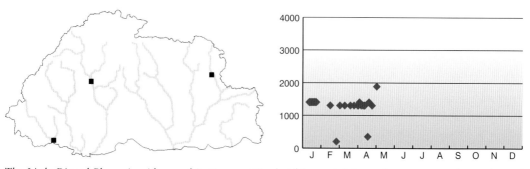

The Little Ringed Plover is widespread in Europe, North Africa and Asia, and occurs over almost the entire Indian peninsula, where numbers in winter are augmented by migrants from north of the Himalayas.

In Bhutan this plover is mainly an uncommon winter visitor, found along the Puna Sang Chhu between

Punakha and Wangdue Phodrang and along the Torsa Chhu near Phuntsholing, where it has been observed from early January to mid-April, the latest being on 24 April[52]. Numbers appear to increase slightly in March–April, to a max. 6 on 10 March[49,57], indicating passage from wintering areas in India. The species has bred at Bumdeling, Trashi Yangtse district: on 2 May 2000, three breeding pairs with young were observed, at 1,900 m, on a broad stretch of the Kulong Chhu[49].

# Kentish Plover
## Charadrius alexandrinus
N=3(3)

The Kentish Plover breeds in North America and from Europe and North Africa, through much of Central Asia to Korea. It breeds locally in the Indian subcontinent, but is primarily a wintering bird. Habitat consists of coasts, inland lakes and rivers in steppe and desert areas.

In Bhutan the Kentish Plover is a rare passage migrant and winter visitor, recorded three times, on autumn migration in September at the sewage ponds near Thimphu[52], on spring migration in April at Punakha[19] and as a winter visitor in February at Phuntsholing[19]. The largest flock was of ten on 9 April[19].

# Lesser Sand Plover
## Charadrius mongolus
N=3(2)

The Lesser Sand Plover breeds across the Central Asian steppes, the Tibetan Plateau and eastern Siberia, and winters along the northern coast of the Indian Ocean, from East Africa to Indonesia. There are few inland records of birds on passage, indicating direct flight from the high-altitude breeding areas to the coast.

In Bhutan the Lesser Sand Plover is a rare passage migrant , recorded on just three occasions. The first record involved a single at Bajo, Wangdue Phodrang, on 9 April 1999[19], and there were further records in spring 2000[2] and 2001. The latter is from 13 June, on the Mo Chhu above Punakha[15]. This is a rather late record, as most have left their winter quarters on Indian coasts by late May.

# Northern Lapwing
## Vanellus vanellus
N=21(4). W 1400-2800

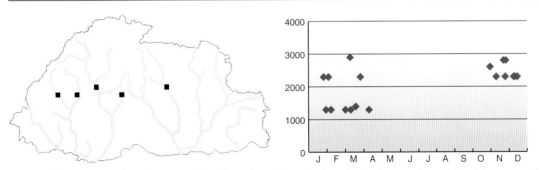

The Northern Lapwing breeds across a broad swathe of Eurasia, from Iceland to northern China. The centre of its distribution lies in the west and it is scarcer in the east of its range. In the Indian subcontinent it is a winter visitor to the northern plains, particularly the north-west, and it is a bird of wet, open habitats.

In Bhutan the Northern Lapwing is mainly an uncommon passage migrant which occurs in the western and Sunkosh valleys at a few regular sites: Babesa, Thimphu district (2,300 m), the Puna Sang Chhu between Punakha and Wangdue Phodrang (1,300 m), and Phobjikha Valley, Wangdue Phodrang district (2,800 m). Elsewhere, it has been found just once, on 29 October when two were at Jakar, Bumthang district, at 2,800 m[22]. The main autumn passage is in November, the 29 October record being the earliest at this season. In spring passage is noted from February to mid-April, whilst in 1997/98 and 1999/2000 a single wintered at Babesa, Thimphu[52]. The mean flock size of passage birds is six, with a max. 17 recorded on 1 March 1995[19].

# Yellow-wattled Lapwing
## *Vanellus malarbaricus*

The Yellow-wattled Lapwing is endemic to the Indian subcontinent. It is found in most of the subcontinent but is largely absent from the north-east. It is a bird of open dry country.

The Yellow-wattled Lapwing was confirmed for Bhutan in early spring 2004, when it was found in Gelephu, at around 200 m altitude[49].

# River Lapwing
## *Vanellus duvaucelii*

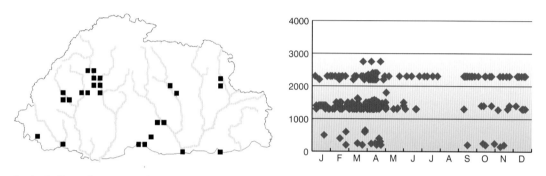

In the Indian subcontinent the range of the River Lapwing comprises the Ganges and Brahmaputra drainages, including montane rivers in the Himalayan foothills. Its range extends further east to Vietnam, and the species's habitat consists of sand and shingle banks in rivers.

The River Lapwing and Ibisbill dominate the avian scene of larger rivers in Bhutan. The former is typically encountered in pairs and is difficult to locate among the boulders until it flies. It is a common resident of the temperate zone and the foothills, primarily in broad valleys of the west, notably the Torsa Chhu near Phuntsholing (200 m), Paro and Thimphu valleys (2,200–2,400 m) and the Puna Sang Chhu in the Punakha/ Wangdue Phodrang area (1,300 m). Presence in the foothills is probably largely under-recorded. During the waterbird count of February 1999 more than 96 were counted in the Paro and Thimphu valleys and the Punakha/Wangdue Phodrang area[49,52]. Highest densities occurred in the latter with a mean two per km of river, whilst the Paro and Thimphu valleys held densities of 0.4 and 1.1 birds per km respectively. A max. 17 was at Bajo, Wangdue Phodrang, in January 2002[42]. The birds favour broader stretches of river, which are particularly well represented in the middle Sunkosh Valley. Outside these areas, the species has been observed particularly in February–March, for example at 2,800 m in the Bumthang Valley and at 600 m in the Mangde Chhu valley[14,52]. These were possibly birds dispersing from the plains seeking suitable nesting sites. Breeding has, however, been confirmed only from Babesa and along the Puna Sang Chhu, where pairs with chicks have been observed in April and June, with the first as early as 8 April[52].

River Lapwing
*Peter Hayman*

# Red-wattled Lapwing
## *Vanellus indicus*

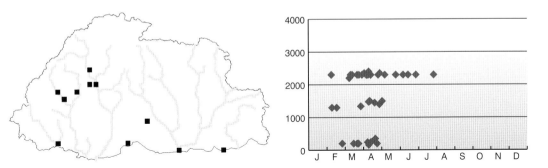

The Red-wattled Lapwing occurs from Asia Minor through south Asia to mainland south-east Asia. It is found throughout the Indian subcontinent, inhabiting flat, open areas near water.

In Bhutan this lapwing is an uncommon summer visitor to the western and Sunkosh valleys and throughout the foothills. In the latter it is mostly recorded in the west, in the Phuntsholing area, with only isolated records further east[10,19]. Higher up, it is regularly encountered in the Paro Valley (2,100 m), at Babesa, Thimphu district (2,300 m) and in the Punakha/Wangdue Phodrang area (1,300 m), where it occurs in marshy patches in paddyfields near rivers. Birds arrive from the second week of February and are present until July, with the latest record on 26 July[43,52]. The maximum observed is seven near Chime Lakhang, Punakha, on 16 February[49]. One to two pairs are present annually at Babesa. An individual giving alarm calls observed here on 26 June[43,52] establishes the species as probably breeding in Bhutan.

# Small Pratincole
## *Glareola lactea*

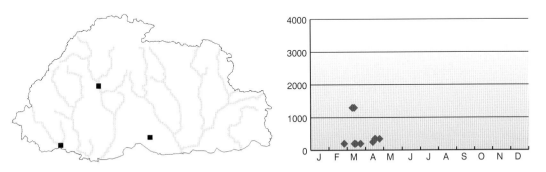

The Small Pratincole occurs over much of the Indian subcontinent, including the foot of the Himalayas. Further east it reaches Laos. Habitat consists of sandbanks in large rivers.

In Bhutan the Small Pratincole is an uncommon summer visitor, known primarily from the Torsa Chhu at Phuntsholing. There is one record from Gelephu plain[1], and it has been found once at 1,300 m on the Sunkosh Chhu, near Bajo, in March[14,49,57]. On 10 and 13 March 2000, two were present here. All records are from the period late February to April, suggesting that its presence in Bhutan is seasonal, vacating the riverbeds when water levels start to rise in the monsoon. A breeding colony of *c.*50 pairs was found *c.*5 km north of Phuntsholing on 23 March 2002[52]. The young were just hatching on this date, with at least ten chicks present. The easy accessibility of the site was remarkable, suggesting a low level of disturbance even relatively close to the town.

# Pallas's Gull (Great Black-headed Gull)
## *Larus ichthyaetus*

N=26(4). W 1200-1600

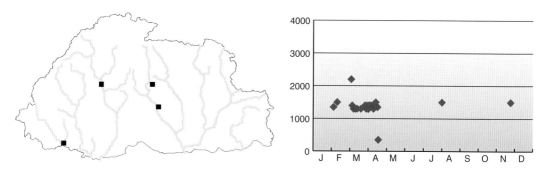

Pallas's Gull breeds in Central Asia, from the Crimea Peninsula to north-west Mongolia. It reaches the Indian subcontinent as a winter visitor, primarily on coasts, but also on large rivers in the north.

Pallas's Gull
*Phil Jones*

In Bhutan Pallas's Gull is an uncommon passage migrant, recorded regularly from the Puna Sang Chhu in the Wangdue Phodrang/Punakha area (1,300–1,400 m), on spring migration, between early February and mid-April. The earliest spring record is 3 February[29], the last 16 April[14]. Occurrence, however, is unpredictable as its stopover depends largely on weather conditions. For example, on 9 April 1999, 25 birds, which otherwise might have taken a direct flight across the Himalayas, arrived during a heavy rainstorm[19]. Large flocks on spring migration totalled 76[5] and c.100[40], the latter during a prolonged spell of bad weather. Most are adults in breeding plumage, with a few first- or third-winters. There is just one autumn record from this site, of one on 25 November[34]. Apparently in autumn birds bypass Bhutan or are unaffected by bad weather as they have already crossed the main Himalayan range. Besides the Sunkosh Valley, the species also passes via the Torsa Chhu and Mangde Chhu valleys, as evidenced by records at Phuntsholing (200 m) on 17 April[22], at Trongsa (2,100 m) and the lower Mangde Chhu valley (1,500 m). Records from this valley involve migrants flying overhead, one going north on 3 March[5] and an immature south on 31 July[52].

# Brown-headed Gull
## *Larus brunnicephalus*

N=15(4). W 1400-2400

The Brown-headed Gull breeds on lakes of the Tibetan Plateau, wintering in the Indian subcontinent and mainland south-east Asia, where it occurs mostly on the coast but also at large inland rivers in the north.

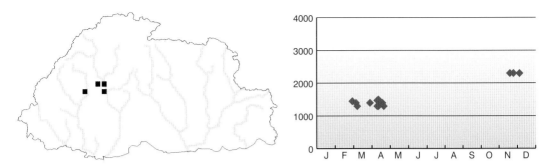

In Bhutan this gull is a rare passage migrant, with a similar pattern of occurrence as Pallas's Gull, and they are often found together. However, the present species's occurrence is more occasional and numbers are smaller, in only 10% of gull flocks on average, with a maximum of six[5,40]. The only regular site is the Puna Sang Chhu and Mo Chhu between Wangdue Phodrang and Tashithang, Punakha district. Spring passage is noted here from the first week of March to mid-April, with the latest spring record on 20 April[5]. Most are in breeding plumage, with a few first-years. There are virtually no autumn records. However, in November and early December 2000 there was a series of records from the sewage ponds at Babesa, Thimphu district (2,300 m), probably involving the same birds. Three were first noted on 18 November[15], followed by an immature on 24 November[43,52] and 5 December[53].

# Slender-billed Gull
## Larus genei
N=3(1)

The Slender-billed Gull has a scattered breeding distribution from the Mediterranean to the Persian Gulf and Central Asia. In the Indian subcontinent it breeds in coastal Pakistan and is an uncommon passage migrant and winter visitor elsewhere, mainly on the coast.

In Bhutan the Slender-billed Gull is a vagrant. On 15 February one was present near Punakha[15]. The same or possibly another was observed at the same locality twice until 21 April[15,28].

# River Tern
## Sterna aurantia
N=1(1)

The River Tern is widespread in the Indian subcontinent, and further east to the upper Mekong River. It is an inland bird affecting large rivers with sandbanks.

In Bhutan the River Tern is a very rare visitor to the foothills. On 19 April 1993 five were present at Manas at c.250 m[22].

# Common Tern
## Sterna hirundo
N=3(2)

The Common Tern has a vast distribution through Eurasia and North America, the nearest breeding area being the lakes of the Tibetan Plateau. It is a winter visitor to the Indian subcontinent, mainly to coastal areas.

In Bhutan the Common Tern is a rare passage migrant. It has been found at Bajo, Wangdue Phodrang, in spring (around 30 April 1989)[24] and autumn (22 September 1995)[29] At the latter season it has also been recorded once in the Bumthang Valley, around 25 October 1988[37].

# Osprey
## *Pandion haliaetus*

N=60(21). W 600-2400

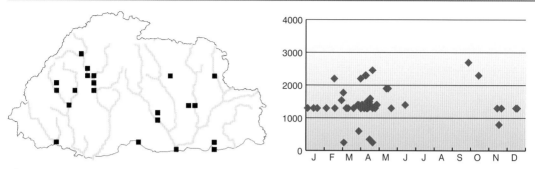

The Osprey is virtually cosmopolitan, with Eurasian breeders wintering in Africa and southern and south-east Asia. In the Indian subcontinent it breeds locally in the Western Himalayas and in Assam, but is mostly a winter visitor. It is a bird of large rivers and lakes, where it hunts large fish.

In Bhutan the Osprey is an uncommon passage migrant and winter visitor throughout the temperate zone and in the foothills, and passage is over a broad front. On passage it occurs over a broad altitudinal range, from 200 m to at least 2,800 m. Spring passage is from early March to mid-May, peaking in April, when up to two may be present at a site. There is a late record from 13 June at 1,400 m near Punakha[15]. In autumn passage has been noted from late September to mid-November, with the earliest record being 26 September[29]. The Sunkosh Chhu valley around Wangdue Phodrang and Punakha yields most records in these periods, indicating that this valley may be a favoured migration corridor. This site also occasionally harbours a wintering individual, e.g. in 1994/95, 1998/99 and 2001/2002, but almost certainly not in 1999/2000 and 2000/2001. Wintering probably also occurs along large rivers at 200 m, but there are too few records to ascertain this with confidence.

# Oriental Honey-buzzard
## *Pernis ptilorhyncus*

N=69(26). S 400-2800

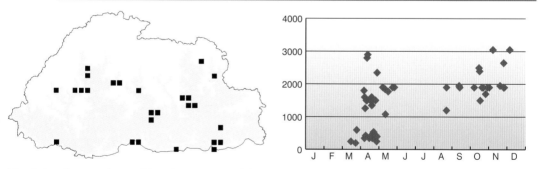

The Oriental Honey-buzzard breeds over most of the Indian subcontinent, as well as southern Siberia from the Altai region to Japan and almost throughout south-east Asia. Birds from the Eurasian population move south to winter in the Indian subcontinent and south-east Asia. It specialises in feeding on the nests of bees and wasps.

In Bhutan it is recorded in the temperate zone and foothills, and is primarily a frequent passage migrant, but may also breed. It has been found at 200–3,000 m. Spring passage is from late March to late May, peaking from mid-May, as evidenced by a total of 49 on 15 May in the eastern valleys[28]. Autumn passage is late September to late November, peaking in the second half of October. The latest autumn record was on 5 December over Dochu La[53]. Birds on autumn passage in November fed on old Rock Bee *Apis dorsata* nests, grabbing parts of the hive with the claws in flight[52]. Nine were observed once near such nests in this period[44]. It is unclear whether there is a significant breeding population in Bhutan. A pair was seen displaying on 19 April between Narphung and Wamrong in the eastern valleys[19]. Migration falls into two distinct periods: early March and in

May. May records stem from the central and eastern valleys, and probably represent passage to breeding areas north of Bhutan. In contrast, March records probably refer to local breeders and have also been noted in the west. Thus, April records at 400–2,000 m possibly concern breeders. If so, the Sunkosh and eastern valleys constitute the main breeding areas. The scarcity of summer records casts some doubt on the presence of a breeding population, although birds are likely to be overlooked in this period in their forest habitat.

# Black-shouldered Kite
## Elanus caeruleus

N=1(1)

The Black-shouldered Kite occurs in Africa, southern and south-east Asia to New Guinea. It is found over most of the Indian subcontinent, including the Himalayan foothills, and is a bird of open country with scattered trees.

It is a vagrant to Bhutan: one on electricity wires between Paro and Drugyel Dzong, on 26 May 2002[15].

# Black Kite
## Milvus migrans

N=133(34). R 200-3200

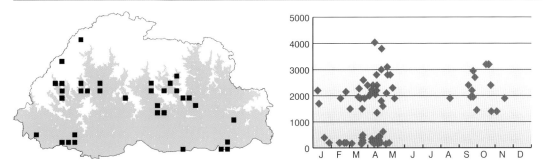

The Black Kite has a vast world distribution, comprising Eurasia, Africa, southern and south-east Asia, and Australia. It is common and widespread over most of the Indian subcontinent, where two subspecies are present, *govinda*, which is the resident subspecies in most areas, and *lineatus*, which breeds in the Himalayas. Numbers are augmented in winter by breeders from further north (east of western Siberia), which are of the subspecies *lineatus*. The race *govinda* commonly occurs in towns and villages, taking garbage and carrion, whereas *lineatus* tends to be more of a montane bird.

In Bhutan the Black Kite is a frequent resident and passage migrant, found throughout the foothills, the temperate zone and in the high west. It appears to be commonest in the western foothills and valleys. Most are the subspecies *lineatus*, which is a passage migrant with a few winter records. The subspecies *govinda* has been identified only at Phuntsholing and Samdrup Jongkha, where it is resident. On passage birds have been noted at 200–3,200 m, occasionally to 4,000 m[39]. Spring passage is from early March to mid-May, peaking in the second half of March and first half of April. Autumn migration is from mid-September to early November, peaking in September. In the second half of March large numbers have been observed at Phuntsholing, roosting and moving north along the Torsa Chhu[5], involving several tens and possibly hundreds. It is unclear whether all of these concerned migrant *lineatus*, or whether sedentary *govinda* were also involved. When identified to subspecies level, *govinda* outnumbers *lineatus* in the Phuntsholing area, with up to ten of the latter against 100 or more of the former. Large migratory flocks are known particularly from old records, with amongst others 180 seen migrating north over Zhemgang on 3 April 1967. Ludlow's record of hundreds following the Kuri Chhu valley on 5 September 1933[31] actually refers to the Kuri Chhu headwaters in Tibet, but nevertheless demonstrates that important numbers formerly passed Bhutan[1]. These numbers are generally unmatched by recent sightings, suggesting an overall decline in the east Asian population. With the exception of Phuntsholing, where resident *govinda* might be involved, the largest number reported on migration in recent years is 16 between Trongsa and Yotong La on 28 March[5], and typically only singles are seen. Winter records are mostly from Phuntsholing and Samdrup Jongkha and are of resident *govinda*, although *lineatus* is reported as well. At higher altitudes, there are winter records from Paro at 2,200 m in January[28] and February[29] and from the Kuri Chhu valley at 1,700 m in January[49,22].

# Brahminy Kite
## *Haliastur indus*
N=4(1)

The Brahminy Kite occurs over much of the Indian subcontinent, although it does not penetrate far into the Himalayan foothills. Further east its range reaches southern China and Australia. It is associated with wetlands, where it is an opportunistic feeder, taking fish amongst other prey.

In Bhutan the Brahminy Kite is a rare resident, confined to border areas. It has been found throughout the year in Samtse district[44]. On 25 March a single was noted between Pemagatshel and Samdrup Jongkha (altitude unknown)[46].

# Pallas's Fish Eagle
## *Haliaeetus leucoryphus*
N=117(24). W 200-1800

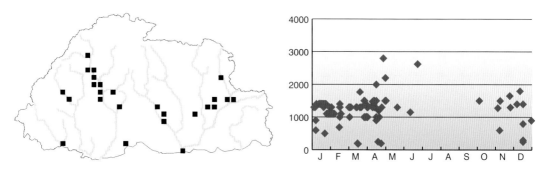

Pallas's Fish Eagle occurs in Central and East Asia south of Lake Baikal, reaching the Indian subcontinent and Myanmar in the south. It occurs along large rivers in the north of the subcontinent, including the Himalayan foothills. It is considered globally threatened by BirdLife International, and listed as Vulnerable, the once-large population having been decimated, mainly due to loss of wetlands and, possibly, excessive use of pesticides. Degradation of wetlands involves the disappearance of large trees suitable for nesting. Migratory movements are unclear, but may include summering on the Tibetan Plateau of breeders from the north of the subcontinent. It preys on fish and various waterbirds.

In Bhutan Pallas's Fish Eagle is found throughout the temperate and subtropical zones, primarily in winter, but it is only reported occasionally. Its main range spans 200–1,800 m, where it also breeds. Probable or confirmed breeding has been reported from four sites, the Sunkosh Chhu, Mangde Chhu, Kuri Chhu and Drangme Chhu valleys. Suitable sites have not been systematically surveyed and it is thus difficult to estimate the total breeding population. Breeding densities have apparently always been low in Bhutan, given the sparse records by Ludlow during a period when the species was still numerous in the northern Indian subcontinent. However, numbers do appear to have remained stable, as in Bhutan its breeding habitat is still relatively intact. Logging of mature riverine forest represents a potential threat, similar to that posed to White-bellied Heron. Pallas's Fish Eagle breeds in September–April, largely coinciding with low water levels in the major rivers and, in the case of the Sunkosh Chhu, the presence of wintering waterbirds. Near Zhemgang a breeding territory was occupied from November and young were observed on the nest in February–April[14,52]. They appeared fully grown by late March, but remained at the nest until at least 20 April. Immatures have been recorded in the Mo Chhu valley in late March[19]. The nest near Zhemgang was occupied in 1999/2000 and 2001/2002, with respectively two and one young fledged. In April birds disperse, as evidenced by one at Paro on 30 April[14,33]. They are present until at least June, but summer records are generally scarce, corresponding with the suggested summer migration to the Tibetan Plateau. Birds return in September, as shown by a pair seen near a nest in the Drangme Chhu valley[31]. From October, 1–2 birds are again regularly observed at the best-known site along the Sunkosh Chhu between Punakha and Wangdue Phodrang, where they have been observed hunting waterbirds, once taking a Common Teal[49]. A max. 5 has been found together here[42].

# White-tailed Eagle
## *Haliaeetus albicilla* N=4(1)

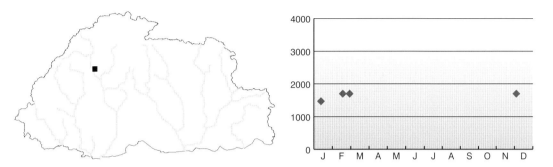

The White-tailed Eagle breeds across Eurasia from Europe to Kamchatka. Although largely resident in this range, it is a scarce winter visitor to the northern Indian subcontinent. Habitat consists of large lakes and rivers. The species is listed by BirdLife International as Near Threatened, as it is affected by the loss and disturbance of wetland habitats, pollution and poisoning.

White-tailed Eagle
*Jan Wilczur*

In Bhutan this species is a rare winter visitor. All records are from the Mo Chhu valley near Goenshari, Punakha, where 1–2 have been present in at least three different winters, 1994/95[19,28], 1999/2000[49,52,53] and 2000/2001[53]. Immatures as well as adults have been observed. The earliest record is 6 December[53], the latest 28 February[19].

# Lesser Fish Eagle
## *Ichthyophaga humilis* N=1(1)

The Lesser Fish Eagle is a rare resident of the Himalayan foothills and adjacent plains, from Kashmir to Arunachal Pradesh. Further east it occurs in Myanmar, through mainland south-east Asia to Indonesia. Habitat consists of forested streams and lakes. It is listed by BirdLife International as Near Threatened, mainly owing to habitat loss.

There is a single record in Bhutan, of one seen between Sarpang and Gelephu on 15 March 1986 at *c*.250 m[10]. As wetland sites in the foothills have been insufficiently surveyed, it is unclear whether Bhutan harbours a sizeable population of this species.

# Lammergeier
*Gypaetus barbatus*                                                          N=30(19). R 3000-4800

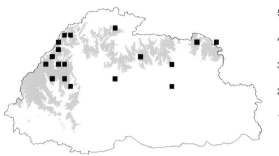

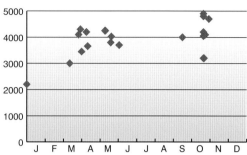

The Lammergeier occurs in high mountains of the Mediterranean region, the Middle East, East and South Africa, the Himalayas and Central Asia. In the Himalayas it is found from Pakistan east to Arunachal Pradesh. It is a bird of the alpine zone, feeding on carrion and bone fragments.

In Bhutan the Lammergeier is a frequent resident in the high west and east, and in adjacent areas of the western, Sunkosh and central valleys. It is one of the highest-ranging birds, found in Bhutan from at least 3,000–4,800 m. The regular range appears to lie above 3,600 m, with birds occasionally straying lower in October–March. There is one record from Paro, presumably below 2,500 m[20]. Most records are from the upper Wang and Sunkosh valleys, which have been more intensively explored than sites in the centre and east. However, the species's apparent scarcity east of the Sunkosh Valley might be genuine, as it approaches its easternmost limit in the Himalayas there. Most records involve individuals soaring high overhead, with occasionally two together. On the western part of the Snowman trek, between Jangothang and Laya, it has been seen on more than 50% of days, with a max. 5[51].

Lammergeier
*Jan Wilczur*

# Egyptian Vulture
*Neophron percnopterus*                                                                      N=1(1)

The Egyptian Vulture is distributed from southern Europe and sub-Saharan Africa through central Asia to the Indian subcontinent. It is a widespread resident of the subcontinent but absent from the north-east. It is frequently associated with towns and villages.

The Egyptian Vulture is a vagrant to Bhutan with a single record. On 22 April 2003 a single bird was seen soaring over the dzong at Wangdue Phodrang[14].

# White-rumped Vulture
*Gyps bengalensis*                                                           N=22(7). R 200-1400

The White-rumped Vulture ranges from south-east Iran to Myanmar, including most of the Indian subcontinent. It formerly occurred more widely in south-east Asia, but is now largely extinct there. BirdLife International has recently listed it as Critically Endangered, as the population has been decimated within a very short timescale in recent years. Recent evidence points to poisoning as a cause, by a veterinary drug ingested by the birds while

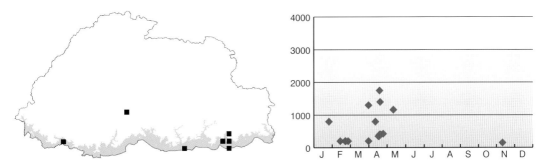

feeding on carcasses (Shulz *et al.* 2004, Oaks *et al.* 2004). It is closely associated with towns and villages, where it scavenges on garbage and carrion.

Prior to the population crash, the status of this vulture in Bhutan was that of an uncommon resident, found mostly in the foothills, at Phuntsholing, Gelephu, Manas and Samdrup Jongkha. More occasionally, birds were found higher in the Nyera Amo Chhu valley, to 1,800 m, particularly in April and probably involving post-breeding dispersal from the Assam plains. There is one record of ten from the Sunkosh Chhu valley at *c.*1,200 m on 11 May[22], which fits the same pattern. A serious decline is apparent in Bhutan, as elsewhere in its range. In March/April 1996 *c.*50 were found roosting in the plantations around Phuntsholing and Samdrup Jongkha towns[5], with around 100 reported in 1994[5]. This apparent abundance sharply contrasts with the complete absence of records since 1998. The most recent records in Bhutan involved individuals observed in the eastern valleys in April 1998[14,19] and a report from the Gelephu area in April/May 1998[4]. Since 1998, both the Samdrup Jongkha and Phuntsholing areas have been regularly visited by birders, suggesting that the absence is real. Bhutan being at the periphery of the bird's range, undoubtedly the local population has received a serious blow, possibly to the extent that it is now extirpated.

# Himalayan Griffon
## *Gyps himalayensis*   N=179(51). S 1000-4000 (mid-Dec-Mar); W 2800-4000

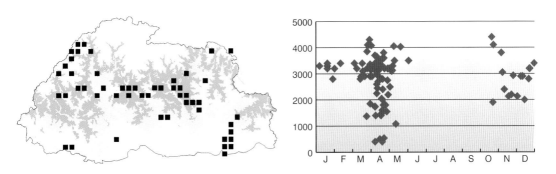

The Himalayan Griffon occurs in mountainous areas of the Central Asian republics, Afghanistan, Tibet and the Himalayas east to western and northern China. It is the largest of the region's vultures.

In Bhutan the Himalayan Griffon is common and widespread throughout the alpine and temperate zones, and in the western and eastern foothills. Its altitudinal range spans 1,400–4,000 m, with occasional records to 400 m and 4,800 m. However, its occurrence is determined by complex seasonal movements. Most records are in November–May, which largely coincides with the breeding season. From early June to mid-October there are no records. As the few visits to higher elevations in summer did not yield any Himalayan Griffons, it seems likely that the species departs Bhutan during this period, and summers on the Tibetan Plateau. By mid-October there is a return movement, with initial records above 4,000 m followed by records, in the first half of November, of birds moving south and west over the temperate zone, at elevations down to 2,000 m. The first migrant was seen on 21 October over Zhemgang at 1,900 m[52]. From mid-December to March birds occupy a relatively narrow altitudinal range, 2,800–4,000 m, where the species presumably breeds. In April–May there is an influx to lower elevations, down to

400 m, which may represent local dispersal at the end of the breeding season, although observations of birds flying east, e.g. at Yotong La[52], suggest that these birds are largely migrants, possibly from the large population further west in the Himalayas. The best-known site is the Pele La area, where in November–April a flock of *c*.20 is present, with a mean six birds observed per visit. Elsewhere numbers are smaller, with a mean three birds per sighting and max. 10. Observations of 20 at Phuntsholing and 25 in Paro in April 1970[20] suggest that it was formerly commoner in the west of the country. So far no evidence has been found that the Himalayan Griffons in Bhutan are affected by the same factor that decimated the White-rumped Vulture population. The risk of contamination is obvious, as the birds reach the foothills in spring. The flock around Pele La appears to be still healthy, numbering 30 and 26 respectively in January 2000[53] and 2001[52].

# Cinereous Vulture (Eurasian Black Vulture)
## *Aegypius monachus*

N=4(3)

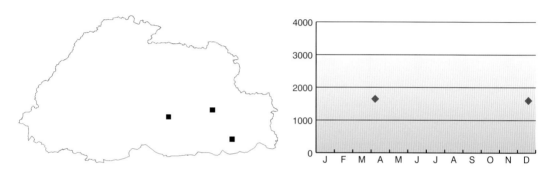

The Cinereous Vulture breeds from southern Europe and the Middle East, east across a relatively narrow swathe of south Asia to Mongolia and northern China. It breeds in the western Indian subcontinent and formerly also in Assam. Elsewhere it is a rare winter visitor, mainly to the west. It forages on carcasses in a wide range of habitats, but is listed by BirdLife International as Near Threatened, its small global population facing multiple threats such as loss of breeding habitat, poisoning and trade in its feathers.

In Bhutan the Cinereous Vulture is a rare passage migrant from across the Himalayas. It has been observed four times in December, January and April, mostly in the eastern valleys below 2,000 m[19,28], with one record from the central valleys of a bird at 1,600 m on 18 December[52].

# Red-headed Vulture
## *Sarcogyps calvus*

N=4(4)

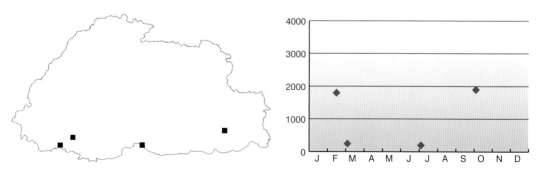

The Red-headed Vulture is distributed over much of the Indian subcontinent but is generally scarce. Its range extends further east to mainland south-east Asia. It feeds on carrion in open country near villages, and is listed by BirdLife International as Near Threatened, owing to a decline in numbers caused by largely obscure reasons.

The Red-headed Vulture was recorded in Bhutan in the 1960s, when it may have been quite regular. It was found in the western and central foothills at Phuntsholing and Gelephu, with two records at *c*.1,800 m in the eastern and western valleys[1]. Once, even a flock of 25 was reported[20]. There are no recent records, in line with the overall long-term decline noted elsewhere in the Indian subcontinent.

# Short-toed Snake Eagle
## *Circaetus gallicus*                                                    N=2(1)

The Short-toed Snake Eagle breeds from the Mediterranean east to northern China, wintering mostly in sub-Saharan Africa. In the south of its range, the species is resident over most of the Indian subcontinent, but not in the north-east or in most parts of the Himalayas. It is a bird of dry open country, where it mainly hunts snakes.

In Bhutan this eagle is a vagrant, recorded twice in the Kuri Chhu valley near Lhuntse[11,25]. Whilst one record is undated, the other is from 25 October 1988, the peak migration season for most raptors.

# Crested Serpent Eagle
## *Spilornis cheela*                      N=262(51). S 400-2200 (mid-Mar-Jul); W 1200-2000

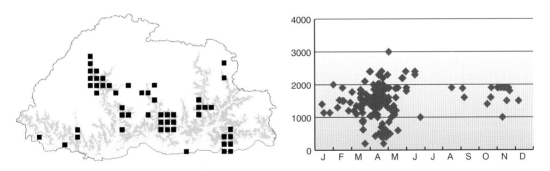

The Crested Serpent Eagle occurs over most of the Indian subcontinent including the Himalayas, as well as east through mainland south-east Asia to the Philippines and Greater Sundas. It is a bird of forests and well-wooded country, feeding mostly on snakes.

In Bhutan the Crested Serpent Eagle is a common altitudinal migrant throughout the temperate zone and foothills, with its stronghold in the Sunkosh Valley. The breeding season is unclear. Birds are noted throughout the winter at 1,200–2,000 m, where display is noted from March to late April[5,19,25]. Seventy percent of records concern singles, whereas the other 20% involve two together and in 10% three. The latter are all in November–May, providing further indication that breeding is early and yet prolonged. From April to June, towards the end of the supposed breeding season, birds disperse both lower and higher, reaching from 400 m to 2,200 m, occasionally to 2,400 m, with one exceptionally high record at 3,000 m in May[55]. There are few records in July–August, when birding activity is low and birds may be less conspicuous within forest.

# Eurasian Marsh Harrier
## *Circus aeruginosus*                                                  N=1(1)

The Eurasian Marsh Harrier has a wide distribution from Western Europe to Lake Baikal. In the Indian subcontinent it is a winter visitor, ranging throughout, but becoming more local in the north-east. Habitat consists of wetlands, where it hunts low over the vegetation in typical harrier fashion.

Eurasian Marsh Harrier is a vagrant to Bhutan, with one record from an unknown locality in 1989[25].

# Hen Harrier
## Circus cyaneus

N=72(23)

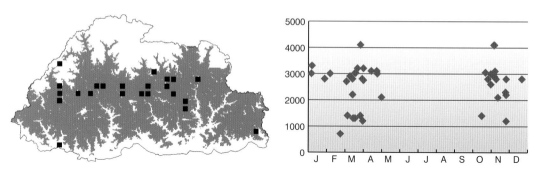

The Hen Harrier breeds in a broad zone across Eurasia east to Kamchatka and into North America. In the south it reaches Tibet, and is a partial migrant that moves south in winter to the Indian subcontinent, mainly to the Himalayas from Pakistan to Arunachal Pradesh and north-east India. It occurs in open country.

In Bhutan the Hen Harrier is a frequent winter visitor and passage migrant throughout the temperate zone, in the high west and in the western foothills. It has been recorded at 1,200–4,000 m, with the highest record 4,100 m and an exceptionally low record from 700 m[29]. Its actual winter range probably lies at 2,600–3,400 m and is restricted to several traditional sites. One of these is Phobjikha Valley, where up to three are present November–March. Records at lower and higher altitudes represent passage to wintering areas south of Bhutan. Birds appear to cross the Himalayas on a broad front, although passage is most frequently noted in the western and Sunkosh valleys. Autumn migration is evident mid-October to mid-November, with the earliest record on 20 October[22], on which date there was also a maximum day count of three on active migration, above the Paro Valley, at 4,100 m[22]. Spring passage commences in March, particularly in the second half of the month, with several records of 2–3 at a site. The final spring records are in April, with the latest on 30 April[5]. Adult males outnumber females and immatures, comprising 60% of sightings, particularly during spring migration. In Europe males winter further south than females but are outnumbered by females as a whole. Bhutan being towards the southern limits of the species's winter range explains the high proportion of males reported.

# Pied Harrier
## Circus melanoleucos

N=3(3)

The Pied Harrier breeds in East Asia, from Lake Baikal to Ussuriland and south to north-east China and North Korea. It occurs in the Indian subcontinent as a winter visitor, mainly to the north-east, with occasional breeding reported in the Assam plains. Habitat is open grassland and cultivation.

In Bhutan the Pied Harrier is a rare passage migrant, recorded just three times. On 11 April 1967 a male was in the central valleys at 1,100 m[1]. In autumn, a male was found at the sewage ponds at Babesa, Thimphu district, at 2,300 m in the western valleys[43,52] and a migrating female in the central valleys at 1,500 m[52]. The two latter records are both from the last week of September from different years, suggesting regular but rapid autumn passage through the country.

# Crested Goshawk
## Accipiter trivirgatus

N=75(25). R 400-2000

The Crested Goshawk is a bird of subtropical and warm broadleaf forest, mostly in south-east Asia but extending west along the Himalayan foothills to northern Uttar Pradesh. A separate population occurs in the hills of south-west India and Sri Lanka.

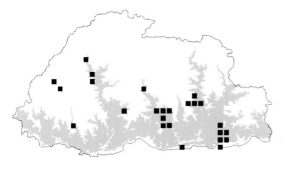

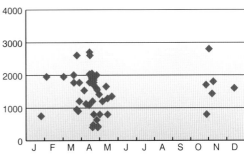

In Bhutan the Crested Goshawk is a frequent resident throughout the temperate zone and in the central and eastern foothills. Its distribution shows a clear west–east trend, becoming gradually commoner further east. Its main altitudinal range spans 400–2,000 m, with occasional records to 2,800 m. Records above 2,000 m are mostly from Paro Valley[5,14], and thus relatively isolated from the main range and in atypical habitat of Blue Pine forest. Elsewhere it occurs in broadleaf forest, where it hunts small birds and mammals, and is mostly seen when soaring above the canopy. Most records are in March–May when it frequently displays above its breeding territory, the white undertail-coverts conspicuously splayed. In the non-breeding season it is seen quite rarely, with no records from June to mid-October, and no confirmed breeding records.

Crested Goshawk
*Alan Harris*

# Shikra
## *Accipiter badius*

N=28(17). R 400-2000

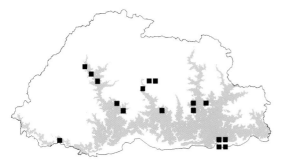

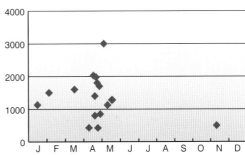

The Shikra has a vast range from sub-Saharan Africa to south-east Asia. In the Indian subcontinent it is widespread and common. Of the genus *Accipiter* it is most partial to open country. With its limited degree of food specialisation, taking small mammals, birds, lizards and insects, it adapts well to cultivated areas and habitation.

In Bhutan the Shikra is an uncommon resident, with a rather scattered distribution in the Sunkosh, central and eastern valleys, and the eastern foothills, with one record in the western foothills[22]. It prefers dry valleys with Chir Pine forest, hence its altitudinal range of 400–2,000 m. There are occasional records to 200 m and an exceptional record from 3,000 m[5]. Records are all in November–May, suggesting that it may be only a seasonal visitor, rather than a resident, dispersing from its main range in India during the dry season. However, a displaying and copulating pair was observed near Mongar, at 1,600 m on 26 April[5], establishing it as a probable breeder in Bhutan.

# Besra
## *Accipiter virgatus*

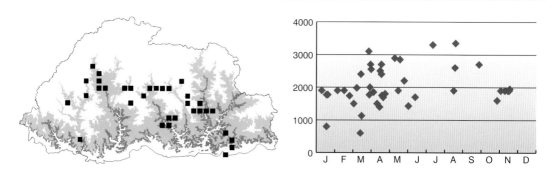

The Besra is one the smallest *Accipiter*s in the region, occurring in the Indian subcontinent mainly along the Himalayas, in south-west India and Sri Lanka. Further east it is present over much of south-east Asia, south to the Greater Sundas. Like Crested Goshawk it is a bird of dense forest, where it can be seen flying at dashing speed through the forest understorey. It specialises in preying on small forest birds.

In Bhutan the Besra is an uncommon altitudinal migrant throughout the temperate zone, with several records from the eastern foothills. In the breeding season it occurs at 1,400–3,200 m, in broadleaf and conifer forest, favouring hemlock and mixed forests. It occupies this range April–October. Breeding is probable as a displaying pair was observed in the Sunkosh Valley at 2,700 m in mid-April[52], and in the same period a displaying male was reported from the eastern valleys[5]. It vacates higher areas in winter, when it is present at 800–2,000 m, and occasionally to 600 m, in March[52], and 3,400 m, in August[52]. In March a male was caught inside a house at Lobeysa, Wangdue Phodrang district, which it probably entered in pursuit of sparrows[52], showing that it may also hunt in more open areas.

# Eurasian Sparrowhawk
## *Accipiter nisus*

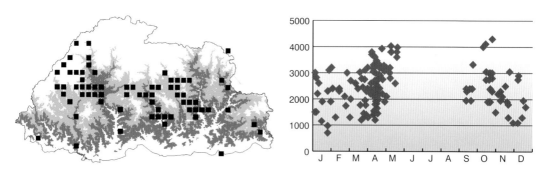

The Eurasian Sparrowhawk prefers open wooded country. Unlike most accipiters, it is frequently observed in open areas, where it hunts birds to the size of doves. Two subspecies probably occur in Bhutan. The resident subspecies *melaschistos* is distributed along the Himalayas from Pakistan to Arunachal Pradesh, whilst *nisosimilis* breeds in East Asia, north of the Tibetan Plateau, with some wintering south of the Himalayas. Other subspecies occur further west in the Palearctic.

In Bhutan the Eurasian Sparrowhawk is common and widespread throughout the alpine and temperate zones and the western and eastern foothills. Birds collected during the 1960s and 1970s were all *melaschistos*, proving the presence of a resident population. Displaying pairs have been noted several times, notably on 12 April at 3,600 m and on 24 April at 2,400 m, both in the central valleys[19], confirming the species as a probable breeder. If May records are indicative of the breeding range of residents, this is located at 2,200–4,000 m, which corresponds well with the records of displaying birds. However, records from summer are relatively few and its occurrence in winter appears much more marked, both in numbers and distribution. The winter range spans 1,200–3,600 m, with occasional records to 700 m[22] and 4,300 m[1]. Active migration has been noted in spring (mid-March–April) and autumn (mid-September–October). Most records above 3,600 m are from these periods, suggesting that they, at least partly, concern migrants moving across the main Himalayan range. The highest day count is of eight migrants on 21 October above the Paro Valley at 4,100 m[22].

Northern Goshawk
*Ren Hathway*

# Northern Goshawk
## *Accipiter gentilis*

N=78(34). R 1400-4200

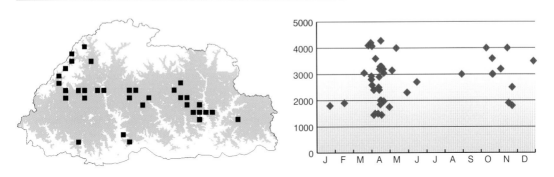

The Northern Goshawk is a bird of forested landscapes that is widespread in the Holarctic, from Europe to East Asia and North America. It occurs in the Indian subcontinent mainly as a scarce winter visitor. Breeding has been confirmed only in the high north-east Himalayas and presumed for high-altitude areas in Nepal. It is the largest *Accipiter* in the region, hunting birds the size of a pigeon or jay, but capable of attacking larger birds including herons and other raptors.

In Bhutan the Northern Goshawk is frequent throughout the temperate zone, but apparently commoner in the western valleys, where it also extends into the high west. On several occasions it has been observed in the Thimphu Valley hunting Rock Pigeons, one of its favoured prey species. Records are known from 1,400 m to 4,200 m. Most records are from spring and autumn passage periods, in April and October/November. As winter records are relatively few, it may be primarily a passage migrant, en route to and from areas further west in the Himalayas and adjacent parts of the subcontinent. Westbound migrants have been noted in October above the Paro Valley at 4,000 m[22]. The number of high-altitude records in these periods suggests regular passage over the main Himalayan range. Several summer records confirm the presence of a resident population and some spring records presumably concern breeders. On 15 April a pair was seen in display over the Ura Valley at 3,300 m[19], establishing it as probably breeding.

# Common Buzzard
*Buteo buteo*

N=220(60). W 1200-3600

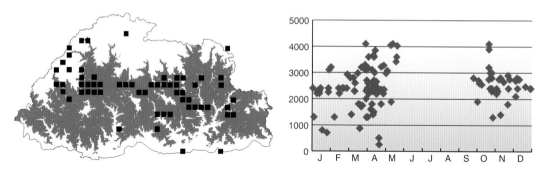

The Common Buzzard breeds in the temperate and boreal zones of Eurasia, from Western Europe to Japan, reaching south in the east to Tibet and the Baikal region. In the Indian subcontinent it breeds in small numbers in the Himalayas, in northern Pakistan, Kashmir and possibly Nepal. However, it is mostly a winter visitor to our region. It is a bird of open country, particularly in its winter quarters, specialised in hunting small rodents.

In Bhutan this buzzard is primarily a common winter visitor, found throughout the country, except the western foothills. Its overall altitudinal range spans 1,200–3,600 m, but wintering birds are primarily found at 2,000–3,000 m, reaching 700 m in January–March. During passage periods the species is more widespread, with occasional records to 200 m and 4,100 m. High-altitude records at both seasons suggest passage over the Himalayan main range. Arrival commences in the first week of October, the earliest record being 24 September[43]. Passage peaks in the second half of October, when a max. 10 was counted in a day[22]. Like the *Aquila* eagles, the main passage appears to be west, although some move south over the Thimphu and Bumthang valleys. In spring migrants have been noted in March–April. Whilst birds are mostly noted at traditional wintering sites until April, May records are largely from higher altitudes, 3,000–4,000 m. These might concern late migrants or, alternatively, indicate the presence of a resident population. Thus far no clear evidence of breeding has been found, although a displaying buzzard near Lingshi, Thimphu district at 4,100 m in May was most likely this species[38]. Only a few have been identified to subspecies, including a single report of the resident Himalayan race *refectus* in November[45]. Most wintering birds are of the migrant subspecies *japonicus*. In October, December and March *vulpinus* has been noted; these were probably passage birds. In the second half of March three *vulpinus* were noted, along with Steppe Eagles, moving north-east over the central valleys near Zhemgang[35,52], suggesting that passage of this subspecies through Bhutan could be a regular feature.

Common Buzzard
*Lawrence Chappell*

# Long-legged Buzzard
## *Buteo rufinus*

N=36(21). W 800-4200

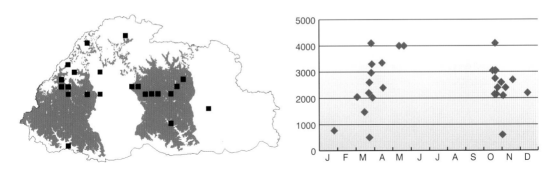

The Long-legged Buzzard breeds from southern Europe throughout the Central Asian steppe zone to western Mongolia, and south to the Western Himalayas. It is a winter visitor over the rest of the Indian subcontinent, but is found particularly in the north. It is a bird of dry open habitats.

In Bhutan the Long-legged Buzzard is an uncommon passage migrant throughout the temperate zone, in the western foothills and the high west. Records are concentrated in the western and central valleys, which are apparently preferred passage routes. The highest records at both seasons have been from 4,100 m, suggesting regular crossing of the Himalayan main range. The lowest record is of a migrant at 500 m[52,53]. In autumn the passage lasts from mid-October to mid-November, with the earliest record on 15 October[52]. The highest day count is of five moving west over Chimding, Paro, on 19 October[22]. A few records from late November to January demonstrate that some occasionally winter in Bhutan, probably mostly below 2,000 m. Spring migration is more leisurely, with records from early March to late May, at gradually higher altitudes.

# Upland Buzzard
## *Buteo hemilasius*

N=11(7). W 3000-4000

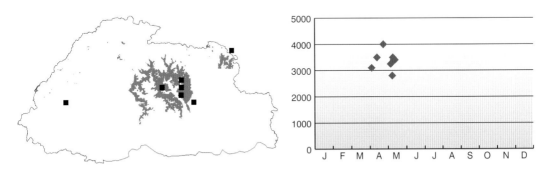

The Upland Buzzard occurs in eastern Asia, east of Lake Baikal to Amurland, and south to Tibet. Its status in the Indian subcontinent is probably that of a rare winter visitor, although it has bred in Nepal.

In Bhutan the Upland Buzzard is an uncommon visitor, with most records from the central valleys, and single records from the western valleys, the eastern valleys and the high east. Most are in April to mid-May, with additional records in November[16] and January[28], at 3,000-4,000 m, with the lowest from 2,800 m[52]. Status is unclear, as they could either be migrants or potential breeders. However, if they were migrants a broader distribution, in both altitude and area, might be expected. A possible breeding population may therefore exist, centred on pastures above the Bumthang Valley, although this requires further investigation. Other open pastures representing potentially suitable breeding habitat, where birds have been found in April–May, are Sengor, Mongar district[22], on the east side of Thrumshing La, and the Chilai La pass above Paro[15].

# Black Eagle
## *Ictinaetus malayensis*

N=400(90). S 600-2800 (Mar-Sep); W 1200-2400

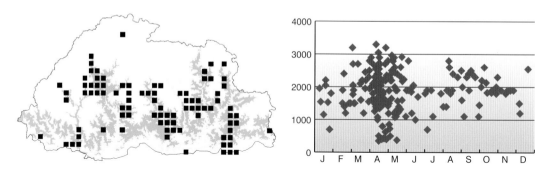

The Black Eagle occurs widely in south-east Asia, from Indonesia in the south to western Pakistan in the north-west. It is a bird of broadleaf forests, mostly in hills and mountains. Its specialised foraging technique involves soaring low above the forest canopy and robbing bird nests.

In Bhutan this eagle is regularly distributed throughout the temperate zone and foothills, with one record from the high west. Being a conspicuous and impressive bird of prey, it is frequently sighted and reported, and the species appears to be a reasonably common altitudinal migrant. The breeding season is unclear. Birds carrying nest material were observed at 2,100 m in the western valleys as early as 12 October[1], whilst one was observed at a nest in the eastern valleys on 17 April[19]. It thus appears to have prolonged breeding season, from early winter to late spring. An early season would have advantages, as the young would fledge during the peak breeding season of other birds, thus ensuring an ample supply of eggs and young. In October–February it occurs in a relatively narrow altitudinal range, 1,200–2,400 m, where it presumably breeds. By late March it becomes more widespread, at 600–2,800 m, with occasional records to 400 m and 3,300 m.

# Greater Spotted Eagle
## *Aquila clanga*

N=10(8)

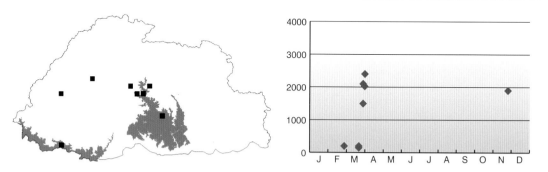

The Greater Spotted Eagle breeds across a vast area from Eastern Europe to northern China and Amurland, albeit at very low densities. It occurs in the Indian subcontinent mostly as a scarce winter visitor, with a few breeding in Pakistan. It is strongly reliant on wetland habitats, frequenting large lakes and rivers. It is globally threatened and classified as Vulnerable by BirdLife International, as the small world population is declining and now severely fragmented, due to wetland drainage and persistent persecution.

In Bhutan the Greater Spotted Eagle is a rare passage migrant, with records at 200–2,400 m in the western, Sunkosh and central valleys, and the western foothills. Spring migration is noted from the last week of February to late March. The most spectacular record concerns a flock of ten high over Trongsa on 28 February 1994[5,40]. There are two autumn records, both from the last week of November[34,52]. The Mangde Chhu valley appears to be a major migration corridor at both seasons. Migrants have also been observed over Phuntsholing and in the Sunkosh Valley. Passage through Bhutan appears rapid and to be confined temporally. There are no reports of staging birds, undoubtedly due to the lack of large wetlands.

# Steppe Eagle
## *Aquila nipalensis*

N=56(25). R 200-3800

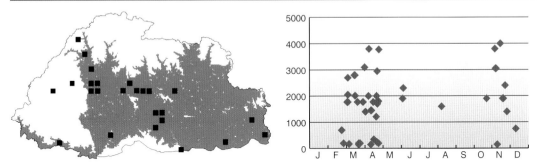

The Steppe Eagle breeds from the Caspian Sea to Mongolia and eastern Siberia, and is a winter visitor to the northern Indian subcontinent. In Nepal it winters commonly to 2,200 m. Massive autumn migration involving several hundreds per day has been observed in central Nepal (de Roder 1989, Bijlsma 1991) and one has been found at 7,900 m on Mount Everest, where it had perished on migration.

In Bhutan the Steppe Eagle is a frequent passage migrant throughout the temperate zone and in the western and eastern foothills, at 200–4,000 m. Migration periods are well defined, with peak numbers passing within a relatively short period. Early autumn records are available from 6 August and 21 October[52], but peak passage is in November, with the latest record on 23 December. The highest day count in this period was of 14 birds. As documented in Nepal, the main direction of movement is west, birds crossing the main Himalayan range on a broad front through the various river valleys before forming a growing stream of westbound birds over the mid-level mountains and foothills (Inskipp and Inskipp 1985). The lower numbers compared to Nepal may be explained by large numbers joining this movement west of Bhutan. Spring passage commences in late February and continues to late April, with isolated records in the central valleys on 2 and 3 June[52]. With a day maximum of 13 birds[52, 53], numbers match those in autumn and will probably prove to exceed them once systematic counts are undertaken. As spring movement has not been reported from Nepal, this may not be a long-distance west–east movement, but perhaps concerns birds en route from the Indian plains, acquiring optimal benefit from thermals in the foothills and lower mountains, before crossing the main Himalayan range. Spring migration appears very localised at favourable passage points. Two of these are Phuntsholing[5,52, 53] and a site at 1,800 m near Zhemgang[5,52], where migrants have been observed regularly. Near Zhemgang birds appear to follow a narrow corridor, large numbers passing at one particular site but none in adjacent areas. The near absence of records from the eastern valleys is remarkable. Apparently birds commence their Himalayan crossing following a north-east direction from the plains across low passes south of the Daga La, Black Mountain and Thrumshing La ranges, then heading north primarily through the Sunkosh, Mangde Chhu and Chamkhar Chhu valleys. Further observations are needed to confirm this. There are few records of staging birds. One observed at Phobjikha on 15 March 2000, hunting on the ground, is exceptional[14].

# Imperial Eagle
## *Aquila heliaca*

N=1(1)

The Imperial Eagle breeds from south-east Europe through Central Asia to eastern Russia. It occurs in the Indian subcontinent as an uncommon winter visitor, mostly in the north-west. It is globally threatened and listed by BirdLife International as Vulnerable due to loss of its breeding habitat (mature lowland forest) and persecution. Its world population may number just a few thousand pairs.

There is one record of this vagrant to Bhutan. On 6 April 1998 one was observed between Trongsa and Jakar[28].

# Golden Eagle
## *Aquila chrysaetos*

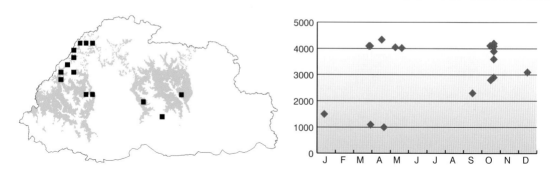

The Golden Eagle is widespread across the Holarctic, inhabiting harsh, rugged country above the treeline in mountainous areas. It breeds in the Himalayas from Pakistan east to Arunachal Pradesh. A powerful bird of prey, it hunts mostly birds from crow or pheasant size, but also mammals up to the size of a young Musk Deer.

In Bhutan the Golden Eagle is an uncommon resident of the high west, and is occasionally noted in the adjacent western, Sunkosh and central valleys. It is absent from the high east, thus its westernmost limit in Bhutan is the Kuri Chhu valley. It occurs at 1,000–4,400 m, but records from low altitudes are over-represented, as the species is more readily noticed there than in their insufficiently surveyed main range, which appears to lie above 3,400 m. Elsewhere in the Himalayas it breeds in January–March. Two adults and an immature between Shamuthang and Robluthang, Gasa district, on 30 March, were therefore possibly local breeders[2]. Although it is mostly resident, in the non-breeding season it also disperses lower and stragglers have been noted in the western, Sunkosh and central zones down to 2,300 m, particularly in October–December, prior to the breeding season. There is a January record of three at 1,500 m in the Sunkosh Valley[13,28]. The lowest record is, however, an adult at 1,000 m, noted at the same site in the Mangde Chhu valley in consecutive years on 20 April[5] and on 29 March[53]. Whilst this was probably the same bird, its provenance is unclear, particularly as the site is far from the main Himalayan range. Breeding perhaps occurs in the alpine zone in the Black Mountain and Dib La areas, south of the main range, but this requires confirmation.

Golden Eagle
*Tim Worfolk*

# Bonelli's Eagle
## *Hieraaetus fasciatus*

N=13(8). R 1400-2400

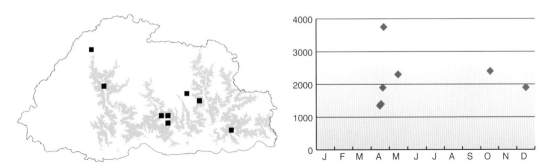

Bonelli's Eagle is widespread in the Mediterranean, the Middle East, sub-Saharan Africa and south Asia east to Myanmar. It occurs in the west, centre and northern Indian subcontinent, and along the Himalayas east to Bhutan, in well-wooded country.

In Bhutan Bonelli's Eagle is uncommon and extremely local. It has been found at around six sites in the Sunkosh, central and eastern valleys, and in the high west. For three of these there are records from several years: the Punakha area[5], Zhemgang-Tingtibi[22,48,52] and the Namling area, Mongar district[5,52]. October and January records at Zhemgang[52] and an October record at Namling[52] suggest residency at these sites. In addition, a juvenile was observed at Namling on 10 April[5], providing evidence of breeding. A small resident population of widely scattered pairs may exist in Bhutan. It is unclear whether passage migrants and winter visitors may also occur, although a wider distribution would be expected if so. Birds have been found at 1,400–2,400 m, with one record in the high west at 3,800 m on 22 April[22].

# Booted Eagle
## *Hieraaetus pennatus*

N=15(12). W 200-3800

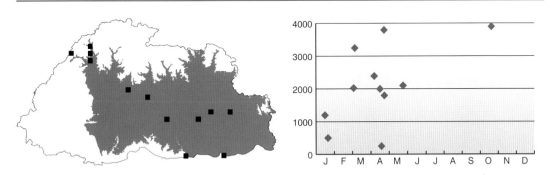

The Booted Eagle breeds in the Mediterranean, Eastern Europe, the Middle East, Central Asia and around Lake Baikal. In the Indian subcontinent it breeds in the Western Himalayas east to central Nepal, but is primarily a widespread winter visitor. Habitat consists of well-wooded country and cultivated areas.

In Bhutan the Booted Eagle is an uncommon passage migrant and winter visitor, recorded in five of the eight years since 1995. It has occurred in the Sunkosh, central and eastern valleys, in the high west and in the eastern foothills. Records are concentrated in the Sunkosh and central valleys, which appear to be the main migration routes. It is mostly seen in spring, at 200–3,800 m, with just one autumn record, from *c.*3,800 m in October[51]. Spring migration is noted in March–April, with a late record on 24 May at 2,100 m[55]. There are two winter records from the eastern valleys and foothills, at *c.*500 m[44] and at 1,200 m[22] in January.

# Rufous-bellied Eagle
## Hieraaetus kienerii

N=86(29). R 600-2200

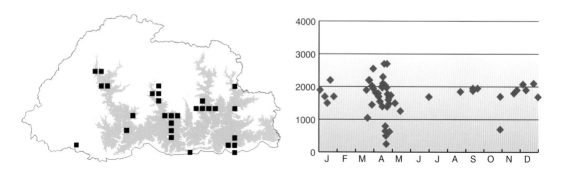

The Rufous-bellied Eagle is a rare forest eagle, which in the Indian subcontinent occurs in the hills of south-west India, Sri Lanka and along the Himalayas from Uttar Pradesh to Arunachal Pradesh and north-east India. Further east it occurs through mainland south-east Asia to Indonesia. Habitat is broadleaf forest where it primarily hunts birds, both in flight and from a concealed tree perch.

In Bhutan this eagle is a frequent resident throughout the temperate zone and in the central and eastern foothills, but is rare in the western valleys, only becoming gradually commoner further east. It is resident at 600–2,200 m, with occasional records to 400 m and 2,700 m. It probably withdraws from the upper valleys in winter, as suggested by the observation of one flying north below Dochu La on 17 April[43,52] and several moving south in the Mangde Chhu valley in September[52]. Observed in pairs year-round and particularly evident October–January, when they regularly soar above the forest on thermals. Summer records are very scarce, the birds apparently being more secretive at this season. The distinctive juveniles and immatures are infrequently reported, compared to adults, but juveniles have been noted in April[5,19], with records of immatures the following spring. Displaying birds have also been seen in April[5,19], leaving some doubt as to the timing of breeding, of which there are no confirmed records. The frequency of observations points to the existence of a significant population, and Bhutan probably constitutes the species's stronghold in the Indian subcontinent.

# Mountain Hawk Eagle
## Spizaetus nipalensis

N=349(70). R 1000-3000

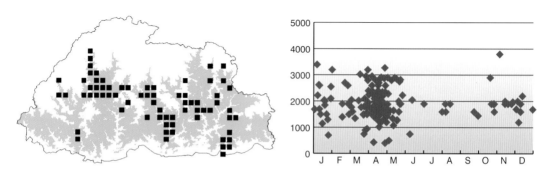

In the Indian subcontinent the Mountain Hawk Eagle is found in the hills of south-west India, Sri Lanka and rather patchily in the Himalayas from Pakistan to Arunachal Pradesh and north-east India. Further east it reaches mainland south-east Asia and north to north-east China. It is a bird of forested montane areas, where it hunts ground-dwelling prey surprised from a tree perch.

In Bhutan the Mountain Hawk Eagle is a common resident throughout the temperate zone and the central and eastern foothills, with one record from the high west. Its regular altitudinal range spans 1,000–3,000 m, with occasional records to 400 m and 3,400 m. It has been found once at 3,800 m in November[17,52]. Juveniles are reported from late March to mid-April, indicating an early breeding season. Data suggest that it occupies its entire altitudinal range by early January, probably at the onset of breeding. In the post-breeding period, from May, it largely disappears from above 2,000 m. Movement south-west was noted on 21 October near Zhemgang at 1,900 m, involving five birds[17,52], but it is unclear whether this was a long-distance migration. It is the commonest large raptor in forested areas, with up to five birds regularly seen at a given site. The species inhabits subtropical and temperate broadleaf forests, as well as fir forest at higher altitudes, but avoiding pine forest, such as in open parts of the Thimphu and Bumthang valleys.

# Collared Falconet
*Microhierax caerulescens* N=5(4)

The Collared Falconet is patchily distributed in the Himalayas, from Uttar Pradesh to Bhutan, and in eastern India. Its main ranges lies further east, from Myanmar to southern Vietnam. It inhabits edges and clearings of broadleaf tropical forest, where it hunts insects from a perch.

In Bhutan the Collared Falconet is a rare bird of the foothills, with the easternmost record being from Manas in the eastern foothills[22]. It is most regularly reported in the Phuntsholing area[19,20], with a maximum of two birds[53]. Records fall within the range 200–600 m, with the highest from 800 m[20]. It has been found in October–April, suggesting that the species is resident.

Collared Falconet
*Ren Hathway*

# Pied Falconet
*Microhierax melanoleucos* N=6(1)

The Pied Falconet occurs through the Himalayan foothills from eastern Bhutan to Arunachal Pradesh, and in the hills of north-east India. Further east its range reaches southern China and northern Vietnam. Its habitat and habits are similar to those of Collared Falconet, but it preys on birds more regularly.

In Bhutan this falconet is a rare resident, known from just one area, in the eastern foothills at *c*.400 m, where there are 1–2 records per annum of a single bird. The highest record is from the same area at 1,100 m[28]. It is mostly found in April, when bird tours visit the area, with one record from January[28].

# Common Kestrel
## *Falco tinnunculus*

N=454(77). S 1200-3200 (May-Sep); W 800-2800

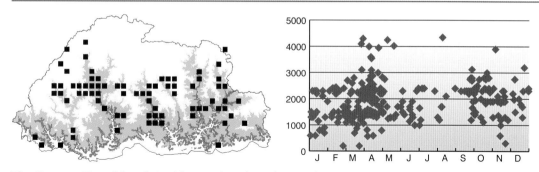

The Common Kestrel breeds in Africa and in the Palearctic from Western Europe to Japan. In the Indian subcontinent it is resident in the Himalayas from Pakistan to Bhutan. Elsewhere it is a widespread winter visitor in open country, hunting from exposed perches such as electricity pylons or whilst hovering in the open.

In Bhutan the Common Kestrel is abundant and among the most widespread of birds, occurring in all biogeographic units. Its regular year-round altitudinal range spans 1,000–2,800 m, with occasional records to 200 m and 4,400 m.. The winter range appears to lie largely at 1,000–2,400 m, reaching the foothills in November–April. A resident population occurs in the temperate zone, concentrated in a number of traditional breeding areas, namely Thimphu and Paro valleys, the Punakha/Wangdue Phodrang area, the Samchoeling area in Trongsa district, and the Trashigang area. In these areas, at 800–2,400 m, the presence of extensive paddyfields and ruined farmhouses provide suitable foraging and nesting opportunities. The breeding season appears to be similar across various altitudes. Displaying and copulating pairs have been observed in the second half of March and the first half of April, with nest material being carried on 5 April at 800 m[19]. Pairs with fledglings have been noted on 20 and 26 June at 1,300 and 2,300 m[52]. Second or late broods may be quite common, as evidenced by 2–3 pairs observed nest building in an old tower on 9 July[20] and a family group on 17 September[52]. On passage and in winter trans-Himalayan migrants augment the resident population. The main migration periods appear to be mid-March to mid-May and late September to late November, evidenced by an increase in numbers during these periods and more widespread occurrence, with birds appearing in the Bumthang region and in southern parts of the western, central (Zhemgang) and eastern valleys. Records at higher altitudes are mostly from these seasons, with records up to 4,400 m suggesting regular Himalayan passage. Spring passage peaks in mid-March to mid-April, following which records of individuals and pairs dominate and birds are noted in regular breeding areas. However, continued high-altitude records show that passage probably continues into May. There are few records of active migration, but observations of flocks of up to ten in the last week of October and first week of November[52] undoubtedly concern passage birds.

# Amur Falcon
## *Falco amurensis*

N=12(7). W 2000-3000

The Amur Falcon breeds in East Asia, between Lake Baikal, Amurland and northern China, and winters in East Africa. Along its long autumn migration route it passes through the Indian subcontinent, prior to crossing the Indian Ocean. In spring it appears to follow a different route, largely bypassing the subcontinent. It has bred in Assam and occasionally winters in the north of the subcontinent. It is a gregarious falcon that mainly feeds on large insects caught on the wing.

In Bhutan the Amur Falcon is mainly a rare autumn passage migrant, noted in the Sunkosh, central and eastern valleys. With the earliest record 14 October[22] and the latest 29 October[22], migration through the Himalayas appears to be very rapid. Most records concern flocks, with the largest involving 30 near Mongar[25]. In spring there is one record from the central valleys on 30 April[4] and several from the Paro Valley, where it probably bred at the ruined Drugyel Dzong in 2000 and 2001: a pair was observed in late April 2000[15] and a copulating pair on 26 May 2001[15].

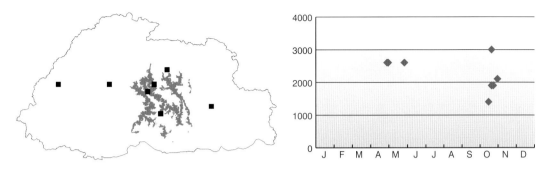

# Merlin
## *Falco columbarius*
N=3(3)

The Merlin breeds in the boreal zone of Eurasia and North America, as well as in steppe areas of Central Asia. It winters to the south of this range, reaching southern China and the northern Indian subcontinent, although it is rare in the latter. It inhabits open country and specialises in capturing small birds in flight.

The Merlin is a rare passage migrant and winter visitor to Bhutan, observed in early February at Tangsibji, Trongsa district, and at Chorten Kora, Trashi Yangtse district[29]. One seen at sunset on a cliff at 4,000 m, on 5 November, at the Sage La, Paro district, was probably a migrant roosting for the night[17,52].

# Eurasian Hobby
## *Falco subbuteo*
N=95(24). S 800-3000

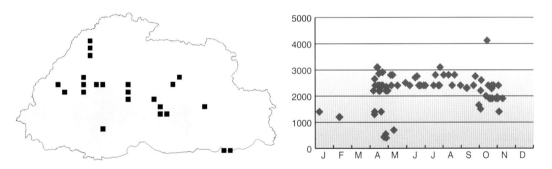

The Eurasian Hobby is distributed throughout the temperate zone of Eurasia, wintering in Africa, the Indian subcontinent and southern China. In the Indian subcontinent, it also breeds in the Himalayas from Pakistan to Bhutan. It prefers more wooded habitat than other Palearctic falcons, and preys on small birds and large insects captured in flight.

In Bhutan the Eurasian Hobby is a frequent passage migrant, summer visitor and winter visitor. In summer it is present in breeding areas in the western, Sunkosh and central valleys, notably the Paro and Thimphu valleys, around Gasa, and in the Phobjikha and Bumthang valleys. It arrives from the first week of April. Spring passage appears little pronounced, with scattered records at low elevations in the Sunkosh and central valleys in the first half of April, probably concerning birds en route to breeding areas higher in the valleys. However, regular passage is apparent in the eastern foothills by late April, with a max. 11 noted on 28 April[14]. The only spring record in the eastern valleys, on 10 May, probably relates to the same movement, to an unknown destination. Autumn is different, with a marked passage through the western valleys and, to a lesser extent, the Sunkosh and central valleys, evidenced by records outside the breeding areas and an observation of active migration. A maximum day total of six has been recorded, migrating over Thimphu Valley on 15 October[52]. Numbers appear to exceed those of the local breeding population and may therefore involve trans-Himalayan migrants. Autumn passage lasts from late September to the first week of November, with the final record on 8 November[52], and peaks in the second half of October. Occurrence as a winter visitor appears casual, with three records from the Sunkosh and eastern valleys at 1,200–1,500 m in January–February, all outside its normal summer range. Preferred breeding habitat appears to be open agricultural valleys surrounded by Blue Pine forest at 2,400–3,000 m. A displaying pair was seen on 9 April at 2,400 m[19], whilst birds were observed at the same site in a subsequent year, on 20 June, at an old crow's nest in a Blue Pine [52]. Fledged young have been noted from 8 September to the last week of that month[29,52]. As the species is quite conspicuous throughout the breeding season, there are probable breeding records for most breeding areas, with confirmed records for Thimphu Valley.

# Oriental Hobby
*Falco severus*                                                                       N=14(9). R 1000-2600

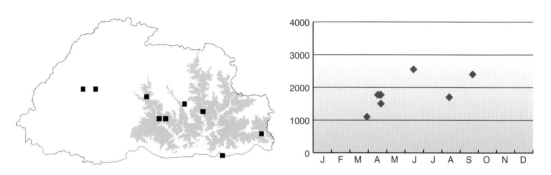

The Oriental Hobby is widespread in south-east Asia, from the Philippines south to New Guinea. Further west it reaches the north-east Indian subcontinent, occurring in the Himalayas from Uttar Pradesh to Arunachal Pradesh and the hills of north-east India, but is generally rare. It is a bird of open woodland, with similar habits to Eurasian Hobby, but is more specialised in hawking for insects.

There are few records of this species in Bhutan and it generally appears to be rare and erratic. During the breeding season, April–August, it has been found in warm and cool broadleaf forests at 1,000–2,600 m[52], in parts of the Sunkosh, central and eastern valleys. A regular site is the southern slope of the Dib La range in northern Zhemgang district. Outside the breeding season it has occurred low in the eastern foothills in February[48] and moving south over the Thimphu Valley on 20 September[52].

# Peregrine Falcon
*Falco peregrinus*                                         N=54(23). S 600-2400 (mid-May-Sep); W 200-2800

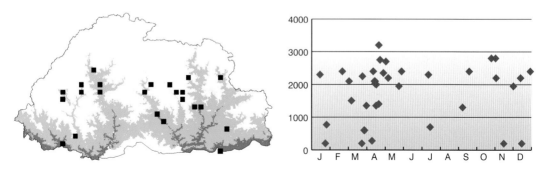

The Peregrine Falcon has a worldwide distribution, occurring on all continents except Antarctica. Two subspecies regularly occur in our region: *peregrinator* is a widespread but uncommon resident over most of the Indian subcontinent, whilst *calidus* is a winter visitor from north of the Himalayas. The species breeds mostly on steep cliffs, hunting over open habitats in winter, for birds the size of pigeons, crows and various water-birds.

In Bhutan this falcon is frequently recorded throughout the temperate zone and in the western and eastern foothills. Although widespread there are no regular sites. In winter it occupies an altitudinal range from 200 m to 2,800 m, the highest record being at 3,200 m[22]. The commonest subspecies at this season is *calidus*, which arrives in late October and remains until late May. It shows no preference for wetlands, but rather to areas well stocked with Rock Pigeons. *F. p. peregrinator* has been noted in March–September, and is restricted to a few localities. Observations over an area of at least 25 sq km and an altitudinal range of 600–1,900 m near Zhemgang apparently relate to a single probable breeding pair at a cliff site at 600 m[14,52]. Overall, it appears to be a scarce breeder within the altitudinal range 600–2,400 m.

# Little Grebe
## *Tachybaptus ruficollis*
N=3(2)

The Little Grebe has a vast world distribution including Europe, Africa, southern, south-east and eastern Asia north to Japan and south to New Guinea. It is a widespread resident in the Indian subcontinent. Habitat consists of lakes, pools, ditches and other shallow waters.

In Bhutan the Little Grebe is a rare visitor, recorded just three times: at Phuntsholing on 19 October 1991[22] and 25 February 1995[7], which were perhaps on dispersal from India, and one at Bajo[53], Wangdue Phodrang district, on 31 March 2002 at 1,300 m, which was a passage migrant. The latter was of the subspecies *poggei*, which breeds in Eurasia north of the Himalayas.

# Great Crested Grebe
## *Podiceps cristatus*
N=6(1)

The Great Crested Grebe range comprises Eurasia from Western Europe to Japan, as well as parts of Africa and Australia. In Eurasia it reaches south to the Tibetan Plateau and is a winter visitor to the northern Indian subcontinent, where it occurs on larger open inland waters and the coast.

Great Crested Grebe is a rare spring passage migrant, noted in four out of six years on the Puna Sang Chhu between Punakha and Wangdue Phodrang at *c*.1,300 m. Passage occurs from the second week of March to mid-April, and mean flock size is 3.5 birds, with a max. 10 on 26 March 1996[5]. Those in Bhutan are already in full breeding plumage and are probably en route to the Tibetan Plateau. It is possible that most cross Bhutan in a direct flight, thus occurrence on the Puna Sang Chhu is perhaps related to adverse weather conditions.

# Little Cormorant
## *Phalacrocorax niger*
N=9(1)

The Little Cormorant is distributed throughout the Indian subcontinent, except parts of the north-west, the north-east and the Himalayas. Further east it is patchily distributed across mainland south-east Asia and Java. It uses a variety of mostly freshwater habitats, breeding in colonies in trees, often with heron species.

In Bhutan this species is uncommon and has been found at just a single locality, the Torsa Chhu at Phuntsholing, where it has been noted in March–April and November. However, due to limited coverage of the area, its precise seasonality there is unclear. It is also uncertain whether birds are linked to any nearby breeding colony. The species is commonly observed at the site, with up to 30 reported.

Little Egrets
*Norman Arlott*

# Indian Cormorant
*Phalacrocorax fuscicollis*

N=3(2)

The Indian Cormorant is of similar widespread occurrence in the Indian subcontinent as Little Cormorant, but absent from larger areas of the north-west, north-east and the entire Himalayas. Its range extends east to southern Vietnam, and it inhabits a variety of freshwater and coastal habitats.

In Bhutan the Indian Cormorant was recorded during the surveys of the 1960s and 1970s, when around 12 were observed near Chazam, Trashigang, in January 1966 and again in 1973[1]. The origin of these birds is unclear, particularly in view of the absence of any breeding population in adjacent north-east India.

# Great Cormorant
*Phalacrocorax carbo*

N=305(44). W 600-2800

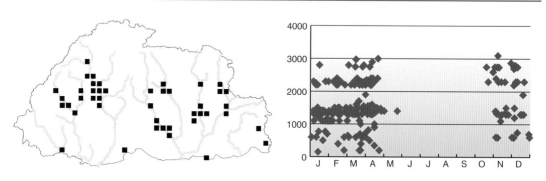

The Great Cormorant has a vast world distribution, including parts of North America, Europe, North Africa, Asia and Australia. It breeds throughout the Indian subcontinent, except parts of the north-west, the north-east and the Himalayas. Habitat is similar to other cormorants in the region, generally keeping to larger waterbodies.

In Bhutan the Great Cormorant is a common winter visitor throughout the temperate zone and in the foothills, at 600–2,800 m, and occasionally down to 200 m. It is particularly common in the west but less so further east. During midwinter counts a max. 99 has been counted in the Punakha/Wangdue Phodrang area. Max. numbers in other areas are much lower: Paro 7, Thimphu 3, Mangde Chhu 20, Jakar 15, Trashigang 15[16,28,49,52]. They gather at roost sites, the Punakha/Wangdue Phrodrang birds roosting on the Po Chhu near Punakha and an (unknown) site south of Wangdue Phodrang bridge. Thimphu and Paro birds roost at an unknown site south of Chuzom bridge and only depart there 1–2 hours after sunrise[52]. Birds arrive from mid-

October, with the earliest record being 18 October[52]. By November the full complement is present. Departure is marked by decreasing numbers after mid-April, with the latest record 10 May[28]. The origin of Bhutanese wintering birds is unclear.

# Little Egret
## *Egretta garzetta*

N=23(5). R 200-400

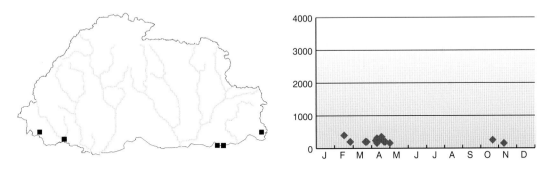

The Little Egret breeds from Europe and the Middle East to south-east Asia, reaching Japan and Australia. In the Indian subcontinent it is a widespread and common resident, occurring to 1,400 m in the Himalayas in Nepal.

In Bhutan the Little Egret is uncommon in the western and eastern foothills, and confined to 200–400 m. Records throughout the year in Samtse district[44] prove that it is resident in Bhutan. It is regular along the Torsa Chhu at Phuntsholing, with a max. 40 in February[19]. At Samdrup Jongkha its presence in spring is less regular, with a max. 2. Two at Samdrup Jongkha on 9 April 1996 were in breeding plumage[5], but it is unknown whether there are heronries in Bhutanese territory.

# Grey Heron
## *Ardea cinerea*

N=10(2). R 200-1400

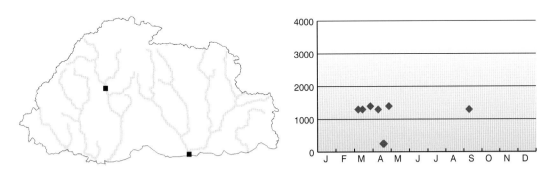

The Grey Heron is widespread in Europe, North Africa and Asia, being resident over most of India, with numbers augmented in winter by Palearctic migrants.

In Bhutan the Grey Heron is an uncommon passage migrant observed along the Puna Sang Chhu between Wangdue Phodrang and Punakha (1,300–1,400 m), where a max. 2 has been seen[39]. It passes in March–April, with one record from September[52]. Occurrence is irregular, the species being found in spring in four out of eight years since 1995. Aside from the timing of records, a bird heard at night flying north over Punakha offers further indication that those along the Puna Sang Chhu concern Palearctic migrants. The same might be true of birds seen in Manas in mid-April[22], although these could equally be part of a resident Indian population that plausibly extends into Bhutan.

# White-bellied Heron
*Ardea insignis* N=28(9). R 600-1400

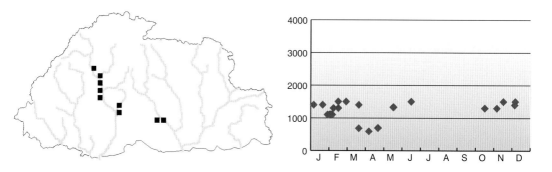

The White-bellied Heron is a rare bird restricted to the Eastern Himalayan foothills, north-east India, north-east Bangladesh and northern Myanmar. It is listed by BirdLife International as Endangered due to its tiny population and loss of its habitat. It is a bird of rivers, marshes and lakes in tropical and subtropical forests.

In Bhutan this heron is a rare resident, found mainly in the Sunkosh Chhu valley, from Adha Tsho, Wangdue Phodrang in the south, to Tashithang and along the Po Chhu in Punakha district in the north, at 1,300–1,500 m. More recently it has been found in the Mangde Chhu valley at *c*.600 m. Between October and February its regular haunts are the Mo Chhu near Goenshari, the Po Chhu near Samdekha and Adha Tsho, and it is occasionally recorded along the river near Punakha and Wangdue Phodrang. At these sites 1–2 are regularly observed. In January it has been observed in flight during the evening at Kamechu[44], presumably en route to Adha Tsho. It is unclear how many birds are present at these three sites, given some movement between them. From mid-March records are scarce, although the species is occasionally noted until June[42]. Records from small forest streams in the Mangde Chhu valley in March[12] and April[5,52] and at Adha Tsho in May[22] suggest that it withdraws from broader rivers in this period. Its habitat includes invariably well-forested riverbanks with mature trees, and despite its large size it may have been overlooked in such areas. It probably breeds in Bhutan, as there is a record of two adults and a well-grown immature in February[44]. The population is tentatively estimated at fewer than 20 (BirdLife International 2001), which nevertheless represents a significant percentage of its small world population. The main sites are within the Jigme Dorji and Jigme Singye Wangchuck National Parks; nevertheless logging of mature riverine forest may represent a potential threat.

# Great Egret
*Casmerodius albus* N=3(1)

The Great Egret has a vast world distribution that includes large parts of Eurasia and parts of south-east Asia. In the Indian subcontinent it is a locally common resident with an influx of Palearctic migrants noted in winter.

In Bhutan the Great Egret is a rare visitor to the western foothills. Singles have been observed on three occasions along the Torsa Chhu at Phuntsholing, in November[22], February[19] and April[22]. These were probably on dispersal from the nearby resident population in Darjeeling.

# Intermediate Egret
*Mesophoyx intermedia* N=4(1)

The Intermediate Egret occurs in Africa and southern and south-east Asia, including most of the Indian subcontinent, reaching 900 m in the Himalayas in Nepal.

In Bhutan the Intermediate Egret is a rare visitor to the western and central foothills, with four records in total. It has been found in March–May[4,22,52,53] and autumn[44]. Further surveys of low-elevation wetlands will probably reveal it to be more regular than currently known.

# Cattle Egret
## *Bubulcus ibis*

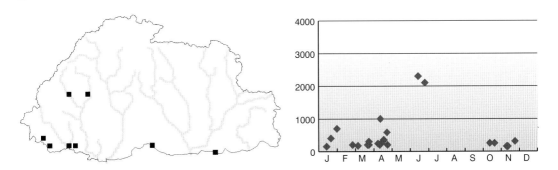

The Cattle Egret is virtually cosmopolitan, even reaching Antarctica moderately regularly. It occurs throughout most of the Indian subcontinent and to 1,500 m in the Himalayas in Nepal and India. It is bird of grassland, associating with grazing animals and feeding on insects disturbed by them.

In Bhutan the Cattle Egret is an uncommon resident in the foothills, up to 600 m and more occasionally 1,000 m[5]. Most records are from the western foothills, in the Phuntsholing area, where several tens are regularly present and up to 100 reported[22]. Further east it is scarcer, with single records from the eastern foothills at Nanglam, Samdrup Jongkha district, in January[44], and 5–10 observed departing their roost at Gelephu in October[52]. At Phuntsholing a breeding colony was discovered in April 2002[19]. In June of that year there were two records higher in the Wang Chhu valley, at 2,200 m near Paro and 2,300 m at Babesa, Thimphu district[42]. These were probably on dispersal from the Phuntsholing area or colonies in nearby Darjeeling.

# Indian Pond Heron
## *Ardeola grayii*

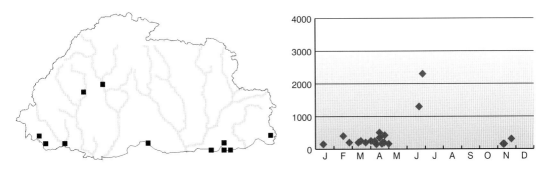

The Indian Pond Heron occurs from the Persian Gulf to Myanmar, including most of the Indian subcontinent up to 1,500 m in the Himalayas in Nepal and India. It is a bird of marshes and paddyfields, usually feeding alone.

In Bhutan the Indian Pond Heron is a common resident throughout the foothills. Most records are from the Torsa Chhu near Phuntsholing, with up to 15 in November[22]. At Samdrup Jongkha a max. 7 was found in April[19]. Records from Samtse prove that it is present year-round[44], including summer, which is the breeding season over most of the subcontinent. There is, however, no evidence of breeding in Bhutan. In June 1999, singles were found at Bajo, Wangdue Phodrang district (1,300 m), and at Babesa, Thimphu district (2,300 m)[52]. As these were in non-breeding plumage, they were probably young that had straggled from their normal range.

# Little Heron
*Butorides striata*

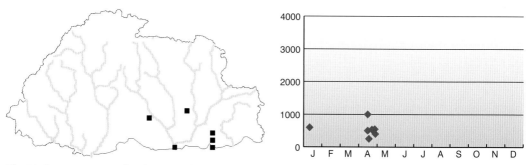

The Little Heron is another heron with a near-cosmopolitan distribution. It occurs over much of the Indian subcontinent, reaching 900 m in the Himalayas in Nepal.

In Bhutan this heron is an uncommon visitor. Records are confined to January[52] and April, suggesting that its presence relates to dry-season dispersal from breeding areas in India. It is mostly recorded in the eastern foothills, where it has occurred at Manas and, regularly, in the Samdrup Jongkha area, with a maximum of two present[14]. Occasionally it straggles higher into the eastern and central valleys, with records above Deothang[14], near Lingmethang, Mongar district (*c*.700 m)[44] and at Birti, Zhemgang district (600 m)[52].

# Black-crowned Night Heron
*Nycticorax nycticorax*

The Black-crowned Night Heron occurs in the Americas, Africa, southern Europe and southern and south-east Asia, including most of the Indian subcontinent and reaching 1,400 m in the Himalayas in Nepal. It is mostly nocturnal, and roosts by day in shrubs and trees.

In Bhutan the Black-crowned Night Heron is a rare resident in the western and eastern foothills at *c*.200 m. Approximately 20 were present near Phuntsholing on 25 February 1995[19], and it was observed there again on 23 April 2002, when two adults were present in a breeding colony of Cattle Egrets, providing evidence of possible breeding in Bhutan. There is also a record from Samdrup Jongkha, where a bird was noted in April 1996[19].

# Cinnamon Bittern
*Ixobrychus cinnamomeus*

The Cinnamon Bittern occurs in south Asia east of the Indus Valley to west China and Taiwan, and over mainland south-east Asia and Indonesia. In the Indian subcontinent it has a scattered distribution.

In Bhutan the Cinnamon Bittern is a vagrant that has been recorded three times since 1999. In April 1999 one was near Samdrup Jongkha below 800 m[28]. The other records are from high elevations in summer. Singles were found near Lingshi at 4,000 m on 11 July 1999[49] and in the Phobjikha Valley at 2,800 on 8 June 2001[44]. As these records are far outside its normal altitudinal range, they probably concerned migrants overshooting their breeding areas on northbound migration. The main breeding season in India is June–September, during the monsoon rains.

# Black Stork
*Ciconia nigra*

The Black Stork breeds from central Europe to northern China and Korea, and in montane areas from Turkey to Central Asia, with an isolated breeding population in South Africa. It winters in Africa and the northern Indian subcontinent.

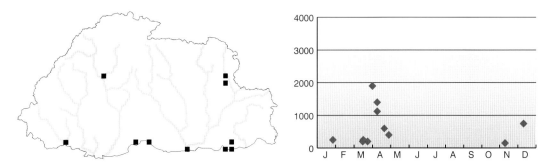

In Bhutan the Black Stork is an uncommon winter visitor and passage migrant. As a winter visitor it occurs throughout the foothills, mostly around 200 m, with one December record from 800 m[44]. Whilst records are usually of singles, a max. 9 has been reported[44]. Spring migration apparently commences in the first half of April, when birds have been recorded higher up the eastern[19,49] and Sunkosh valleys[19], to 1,900 m. However, the main routes into and away from northern India are probably outside of Bhutan. Records of migrants are confined to lower elevations, suggesting that there is no direct passage over the Himalayan range.

# Woolly-necked Stork
## Ciconia episcopus
N=1(1)

The Woolly-necked Stork is widespread in southern and south-east Asia and Africa. It is found over much of the Indian subcontinent, including the foothills of the Himalayas in Nepal. It inhabits open wetlands in the vicinity of forests.

In Bhutan the Woolly-necked Stork is a vagrant that has been recorded just once, on 30 October 1973, near Gelephu at c.250 m[1].

# Blue-naped Pitta
## Pitta nipalensis
N=15(6). S 1400-1800 (Apr-Sep); W 600-1200

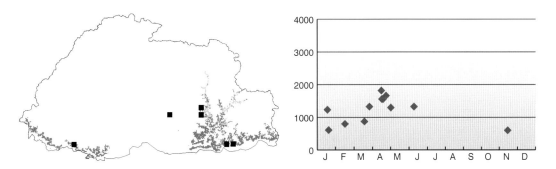

The Blue-naped Pitta is a localised resident of the Eastern Himalayas, from central Nepal to Arunachal Pradesh and north-east India, and thereafter further east to northern Vietnam. It inhabits a variety of habitats in the tropical and subtropical zones, always favouring dense undergrowth and deep shade.

In Bhutan the Blue-naped Pitta is a rare resident of the central and eastern valleys and the eastern foothills. There is one record from the western foothills, at 600 m near Phuntsholing[1]. It is an altitudinal migrant, occurring in winter at 600–1,200 m and in March–April moving to its presumed breeding range of 1,400–1,800 m. As the species is usually located by its fine flute-like call, records are concentrated in spring. It appears to be rather localised, with multiple records only from the Deothang area of Samdrup Jongkha district, the forests around Yonkhola and Lingmethang in Mongar district.

# Hooded Pitta
## *Pitta sordida*

N=11(3). R 200-600

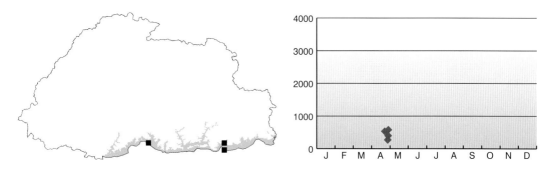

The Hooded Pitta occurs locally in the Himalayan foothills from Himachal Pradesh to Arunachal Pradesh and north-east India. Further east its range continues through mainland south-east Asia to New Guinea. Northern populations winter in Sumatra and Java. Habitat consists of subtropical broadleaf forest and dense second growth.

In Bhutan the Hooded Pitta is an uncommon summer visitor in the eastern foothills. Calling birds have been encountered regularly from the last week of April to mid-May between Samdrup Jongkha and Deothang, up to 600 m. A maximum of six was once located here in May[28]. Outside this stronghold, there are isolated records from Gelephu[1] and above Lingmethang, Mongar district[14], the latter the only record from the temperate zone. The record is not included on the graph and map as the exact altitude and locality are not known. The earliest spring date is 22 April[28]. The majority of records are from the last week of April, possibly signifying a synchronised arrival from its winter quarters, followed by a short period of peak territorial activity.

# Silver-breasted Broadbill
## *Serilophus lunatus*

N=3(3)

The Silver-breasted Broadbill has a south-east Asian distribution, reaching the Indian subcontinent in the hills of north-east India. In the Himalayan foothills it is rare, penetrating west to Sikkim. Habitat comprises tropical and subtropical broadleaf forest, second growth and bamboo.

In Bhutan the Silver-breasted Broadbill is recorded rarely in the central and eastern foothills[1,28], at *c*.200 m, with the largest flock, of 12, sighted on 12 January 1995 near Samdrup Jongkha[13,28]. The three records are all in winter, in November–January, perhaps indicating that occurrence in Bhutan relates to dispersal from its main range in north-east India along the base of the Himalayan foothills, rather than the presence of a resident population.

# Long-tailed Broadbill
## *Psarisomus dalhousiae*

N=119(26). R 400-2000

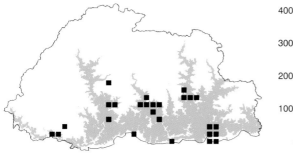
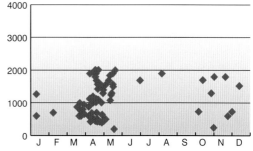

The Long-tailed Broadbill is widespread in south-east Asia, south to Sumatra and Borneo. In the west its range reaches north-east India and along the Himalayan foothills west to Uttar Pradesh, albeit rather patchily. It inhabits tropical and subtropical forests.

In Bhutan the Long-tailed Broadbill is an occasionally encountered resident, found throughout the temperate zone and in the foothills. It occupies altitudes of 400–2,000 m, and is occasional down to 200 m. The core range lies in the subtropical zone, however, particularly in the central and eastern valleys. Most records above 2,000 m are from the springs of 2001 and 2002, when it was notably more common and widespread than before, for example reaching Kori La[14] and occupying a breeding territory at 1,900 m near Zhemgang[52]. Its globular nest is rather conspicuous and in consequence there are several breeding records. Nests and birds carrying nest material have been observed in April–May, mostly at *c*.500 m. In the breeding season it is found in pairs and sometimes in small flocks. From November to March it sometimes forms larger flocks of *c*.10. Calling birds are heard from mid-March to August, with peak activity mid-April to mid-May.

Long-tailed Broadbill
*Dan Cole*

# Asian Fairy Bluebird
## *Irena puella*

N=53(9). R 200-1000

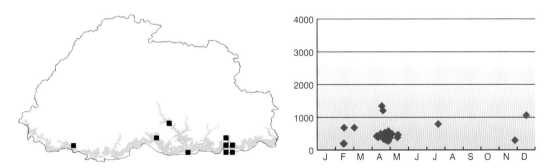

The Asian Fairy Bluebird occurs widely in southern Asia, reaching the Philippines and the Greater Sundas, and the western limit of its breeding range in the Indian subcontinent, where it occurs in the Himalayas from eastern Nepal to Arunachal Pradesh, as well as in the hills of north-east, eastern and south-west India and Sri Lanka. It is a bird of moist dense broadleaf forest.

In Bhutan the Asian Fairy Bluebird is a frequent resident in the foothills and the central and eastern valleys, at 200–800 m, and occasionally to 1,400 m. The eastern foothills are its stronghold, with regular records from the forests above Samdrup Jongkha. Birds have been noted here annually in April/May, with a max. 40 reported[14]. Occurrence higher in the central[52] and eastern valleys is less frequent. The single record from the western valleys[1] was made during surveys in the 1960s, and current presence there requires confirmation. The record in the western valleys has not been mapped due to an imprecise locality being reported.

# Golden-fronted Leafbird
*Chloropsis aurifrons*                                          N=42(14). R 200-800

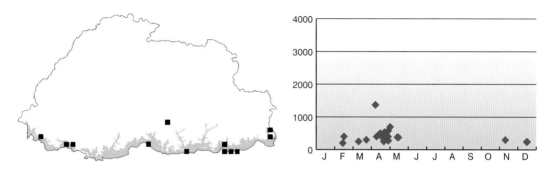

The Golden-fronted Leafbird is widespread in south-east Asia, reaching south to Sumatra. In the west of its range it spreads in two narrow bands across the Indian subcontinent, through eastern India to Sri Lanka and south-west India, the other along the Himalayan foothills, west to Uttar Pradesh. It is a bird of broadleaf forest, taking insects, fruits and particularly nectar, and is a frequent constituent of flocks feeding at flowering trees.

In Bhutan the Golden-fronted Leafbird is a common resident throughout the foothills, with isolated records from the western[19], central[48] and eastern valleys[29]. It occupies altitudes at 200–800 m, with one record from *c.*1,400 m near Kamji in Chhukha district[19]. It partially replaces the Orange-bellied Leafbird at lower elevations, although even where the latter is scarcer towards its lower altitudinal limit, Golden-fronted Leafbird hardly outnumbers it. A max. 10 was found in the forests above Samdrup Jongkha[28].

# Orange-bellied Leafbird
*Chloropsis hardwickii*                                         N=461(60). R 400-2000

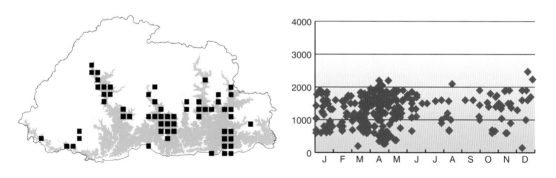

The Orange-bellied Leafbird occurs along the Himalayas from Himachal Pradesh to Arunachal Pradesh and north-east India. Outside the Indian subcontinent it reaches south China and mainland south-east Asia. It has similar habitat preferences and habits to Golden-fronted Leafbird, but occupies higher altitudes and more evergreen habitat, particularly *Loranthus*-infested trees.

In Bhutan the Orange-bellied Leafbird is an abundant resident throughout the temperate zone and the foothills, at 400–2,000 m. However, spring records as low as 200 m are not rare, indicating that it may breed at such altitudes. There are few records above 2,000 m, the highest being 2,500 m in December[1]. It is relatively scarce in the western valleys. Singing birds are heard almost year-round, but the peak season is early April to mid-June, when birds are on breeding territories. Near Zhemgang a mean density of 2.5 territories per km was found at 1,600–1,900 m[52], with numbers increasing to more than 4.0 territories/km in the lower part of this range. Apart from singing birds, there is no evidence of breeding. At this season it is mostly found singly or in pairs, but in October–January it also gathers in flocks of 5–20, and in January is a conspicuous member of mixed flocks feeding on flowering *Bombax* trees, together with Streaked Spiderhunter, Red-vented Bulbul and Spangled Drongo. The species is also occasionally found in mixed parties with babbler species.

# Brown Shrike
*Lanius cristatus*                                                                 N=39(22). R 200-3400

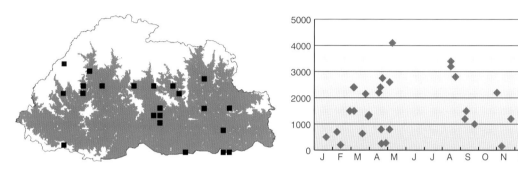

The Brown Shrike breeds in east Asia, south to eastern and central China, wintering in southern and south-east Asia. In the Indian subcontinent it is a winter visitor from north-east to southern India, including the Himalayan foothills from Uttar Pradesh east. It is a bird of forest edge, clearings and scrub.

In Bhutan the Brown Shrike is an uncommon passage migrant and winter visitor throughout the temperate zone and in the foothills, at 200–3,400 m. It has been found once at 4,100 m in the Wang Chhu valley, on spring migration[22]. Records in November–February involve winter residents and are concentrated in the eastern foothills and valleys below 1,000 m, including the middle Kuri Chhu valley. Spring passage is noted from early March to mid-May. In 2000 relatively large numbers were reported during the last week of March, with a max. 5 in the Wangdue Phodrang/Punakha area[14]. Autumn passage is from mid-August to late September, with a late record of two at 2,200 m at Paro on 31 October[14]. The main migration corridor for the species is the Brahmaputra

Brown Shrike
*Chris Orgill*

Valley, from where it spreads west. However, the limited data available do not reveal an east–west trend in the records, but rather suggest that some direct Himalayan passage may occur, with the latest spring records and earliest autumn arrivals being at higher altitudes.

# Bay-backed Shrike
*Lanius vittatus*                                                                           N=4(3)

The Bay-backed Shrike occurs over most of the Indian subcontinent except the north-east. Its range extends further west into Iran and the Central Asian republics, where it shows marked seasonal movements.

In Bhutan the Bay-backed Shrike is a vagrant that has been found twice, in the high west and the Sunkosh Valley. On 8 May 1996 one was seen between Soe Thangthangkha and Jangothang at c.3,700 m[22]. Between 26 and 28 April 2001 another was present near Nobding at c.2,900 m[33]. As these dates are at the beginning of the breeding season in northern India, they were probably birds that overshot their breeding areas on spring migration. The 2001 bird followed an early cyclone in the north-east of the subcontinent.

# Long-tailed Shrike
*Lanius schach*                    N=371(77). S 1000-2400 (Mar-Oct); W 800-2000

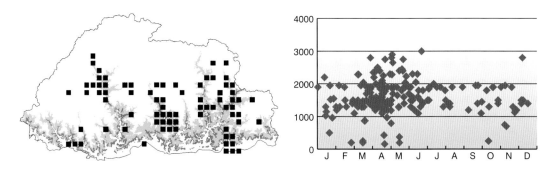

The Long-tailed Shrike is widespread in southern and south-east Asia, from Iran and the Central Asian republics to Vietnam and south to New Guinea. It occurs almost throughout the Indian subcontinent, including the Himalayas, in scrub in open country, often near settlements.

In Bhutan the Long-tailed Shrike is a common altitudinal migrant throughout the temperate zone and the foothills. Its summer range spans 1,000–2,400 m, with occasional records to 200 m and 3,000 m. In winter it withdraws below 2,000 m down to 800 m. The breeding range is occupied from mid-April, with the final birds at low elevations noted in mid-May. At 1,900 m, the first pair with fledglings was observed on 3 June, and they raised a second brood by 16 July[52]. In a subsequent year a pair with fledglings was seen on 22 July[22]. From August birds start descending to their winter quarters. Birds appear well dispersed, with in most cases no more than five encountered along the roadside in a day, although a max. 20 has been noted[5]. Birds with some intermediate characters between Grey-backed and Long-tailed Shrikes have been noted in the upper range[40,52], possibly the result of occasional hybridisation between these species.

# Grey-backed Shrike
*Lanius tephronotus*                    N=613(96). S 2200-3800 (mid-May-Sep); W 600-3200

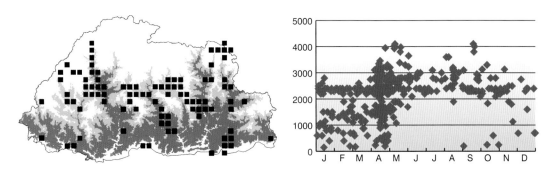

The Grey-backed Shrike breeds in the Himalayas from Ladakh to Arunachal Pradesh, some wintering in the adjacent plains of northern and north-east India and Bangladesh. Its range extends north to the Tibetan Plateau and montane northern and western China. Habitat is open scrub country, at higher elevation than other shrikes.

In Bhutan the Grey-backed Shrike is an abundant altitudinal migrant in all biogeographic units. Its summer range spans 2,200–3,600 m, only marginally overlapping that of Long-tailed Shrike. Both in winter and the breeding season it is more associated with open forested areas than Long-tailed Shrike, being found particularly in small clearings within Blue Pine forest. There are occasional records to 4,100 m[49], but it has perhaps been under-recorded at higher elevations. In winter it is found at 600–3,200 m, with occasional records to 200 m. The scarcity of winter records at 1,500–2,000 m is remarkable and might indicate that two (sub)populations are involved, migrants wintering largely below 1,500 m and residents at $c.$2,400 m, the latter much in evidence in the Thimphu Valley. Passage is noted at 1,500–2,000 m from mid-April to mid-May. At higher elevations this passage is also notable for the presence of peak numbers, several tens being counted along roadsides. It is unclear if all these breed at higher elevations in Bhutan or whether birds from the Tibetan Plateau are also involved. The number of territorial birds at 2,400 m reaches a maximum in June[52]. However, at least some start breeding in April, as evidenced by a pair nest-building on 21 April at 2,800 m[22]. The presence of singing birds in early March to early April also suggests this. The breeding season appears to be prolonged, with probably many pairs raising 2–3 broods. Pairs with juveniles are noted 18 July–3 October[52]. It can reach considerable densities, with e.g. three pairs noted in a patch of Blue Pine of $c.$10 ha at 2,400 m[52]. From October arrival in its winter range is evident.

# Eurasian Jay
## Garrulus glandarius

N=229(47). S 1400-3000 (Apr-Oct); W 1600-2600

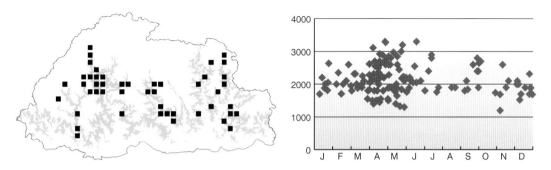

The Eurasian Jay occurs across Eurasia from Europe to Japan, with separate populations in the Himalayas from Pakistan to Arunachal Pradesh and the hills of north-east India, and in parts of mainland south-east Asia. Habitat consists of dense temperate broadleaf forest, with a preference for oak forest.

In Bhutan the Eurasian Jay is a common altitudinal migrant throughout the temperate zone. In the breeding season it occupies altitudes of 1,400–3,000 m, largely coinciding with limits of oak forest. From October it retreats below 2,600 m. In spring the species occasionally occurs to 3,300 m, whereas the lowest elevation is 1,200 m[31]. There are no confirmed breeding records, but juveniles have been collected on 1 July[31]. The jay is usually found singly or in pairs, and in September–March occasionally in small flocks of up to five. Densities are low, with 0.4 breeding pairs per km near Zhemgang at 600–1,900 m[52]. A max. 15 was noted in April on the east slope of Dochu La[5].

# Yellow-billed Blue Magpie
## Urocissa flavirostris

N=504(76)

The Yellow-billed Blue Magpie occurs in the Himalayas from Pakistan to Arunachal Pradesh, and further east through Myanmar and southern China. It is a bird of temperate broadleaf and conifer forests.

In Bhutan the Yellow-billed Blue Magpie is abundant and widespread, being found throughout the alpine and temperate zones. It is largely resident at 2,000–3,200 m, with occasional records to 1,400 m[27] and 3,800 m[52]. Records above 3,200 m are all in spring, when it appears to disperse more widely. In November–March it is mostly found in small flocks up to seven. From April observations of singles or pairs are the norm, indicating the onset of breeding. Birds have been observed at nests at 1,700 m on 7 May[49] and at 2,800 m on 28 May[49]. The species shows no clear preference for specific forest types, being found in cool broadleaf, Blue Pine, fir, spruce and hemlock forests.

# Common Green Magpie
## Cissa chinensis

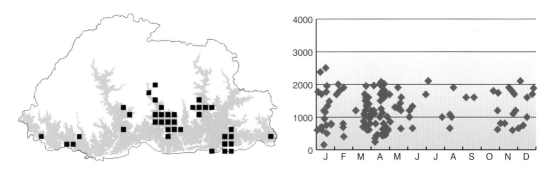

The Common Green Magpie is widespread in south-east Asia, reaching south to Sumatra and Borneo. In the west of its range it occurs in the Himalayas from Uttar Pradesh to Arunachal Pradesh and the hills of north-east India. It is a bird of tropical and subtropical forests, favouring dense thickets along streams and ravines.

In Bhutan this magpie is a common resident in the temperate zone and the foothills. Its range spans 400–2,000 m, with occasional presence to 200 m and 2,500 m. It appears relatively local, being associated with extensive stands of warm broadleaf forest. Most records are from the eastern foothills and adjacent lower eastern valleys, and the lower and middle Kuri Chhu and Mangde Chhu valleys. In western Bhutan, particularly the Sunkosh Valley, it seems quite scarce and only reaches 1,400 m[22]. Extensively cultivated areas around Punakha and Wangdue Phodrang, with no continuous forest cover below 2,000 m, possibly constitute a dispersal barrier. The same might account for apparent absence in the Kuri Chhu valley above Lhuntse and the lack of records from the Drangme Chhu valley. However, the species tolerates some habitat degradation, occurring in relatively dry and open forests provided there is abundant scrub. Numbers seen together rarely exceed three, although birds are easily overlooked and are more often heard than seen. Just one territory was found along 7.5 km of road surveyed near Zhemgang at 1,600–1,900 m[52], showing low densities in the upper part of its range.

# Rufous Treepie
## Dendrocitta vagabunda

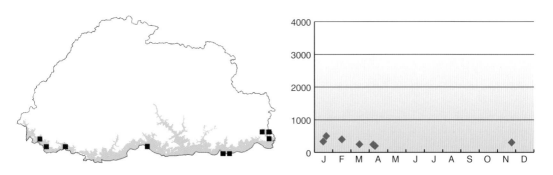

The Rufous Treepie is found in most of the Indian peninsula, including the Himalayan foothills, and in parts of mainland south-east Asia. It is a bird of open wooded country, often near habitation. It is an opportunistic feeder, joining feeding parties in fruiting trees and insect-hunting flocks, but it also takes carrion from predator kills.

In Bhutan the Rufous Treepie is an uncommon resident throughout the foothills to 400 m. Its limited altitudinal range and scarcity contrast with the situation in Nepal, where it is common to 1,000 m. All records are in November–April. The maximum number sighted is four at Gelephu in March 1986[10].

# Grey Treepie
*Dendrocitta formosae*

N=806(74). R 600-2000

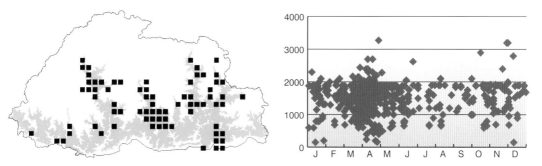

The Grey Treepie occurs in the Himalayas from Pakistan to Arunachal Pradesh and north-east India. Elsewhere in the subcontinent it is only found in the eastern hills, but its range extends east to Taiwan and northern Vietnam. Habitat is broadleaf forest and second growth, where it affects the upper storey.

In Bhutan the Grey Treepie is abundant and widespread throughout the temperate zone and the foothills. However, it is scarce in the western valleys, where its broadleaf habitat is largely absent at higher levels. It is resident in warm broadleaf forest at 600–2,000 m, with occasional records to 200 m and 3,200 m. Breeding is confirmed by the observation of two recently fledged juveniles on 9 August at 800 m[52]. Calling territorial birds are particularly active in March and early April[52]. Year-round it mostly occurs in pairs or small flocks, with up to 40 birds present at a site. Sometimes it gathers in loose flocks of up to 20. A density of 2.6 breeding pairs per km was found near Zhemgang at 1,600–1,900 m[52].

# Collared Treepie
*Dendrocitta frontalis*

N=12(8). R 600-2000

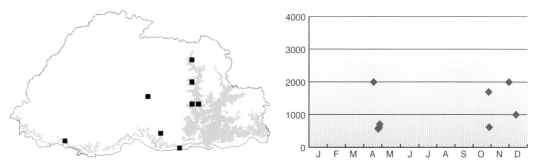

The Collared Treepie has a relatively restricted distribution in the Himalayas from eastern Bhutan to Arunachal Pradesh and the hills of north-east India, and in Sikkim, Darjeeling and West Bengal, where it is rare. Outside the subcontinent it occurs in northern Myanmar and northern Vietnam. It inhabits dense, moist evergreen forest with bamboo thickets and is less conspicuous than other treepies.

In Bhutan this treepie is a rare resident and probably overlooked. Spring records are concentrated in the central and eastern foothills in Royal Manas National Park, at 500–700 m[22]. There are two spring records from higher, in the Mangde Chhu and Kuri Chhu valleys, at 1,200[12] and 2,000 m[19]. The former record is not included on the graph due to an imprecise date being recorded. In autumn there is a series of records from the Kuri Chhu in October–November 1988 and 1991, with flocks of up to 20 reported at 600–2,000 m[7,22,25]. These records possibly reflected an irruptive movement similar to that witnessed in the Hill Myna, during which birds move locally upslope in search of fruiting trees. Whilst these records probably concern a single population in south-central Bhutan, the record from Phuntsholing at 600 m in December[53] almost certainly relates to the Sikkim/Darjeeling/West Bengal population penetrating south-west Bhutan.

# Black-billed Magpie
*Pica pica*

N=157(18). R 2600-3400

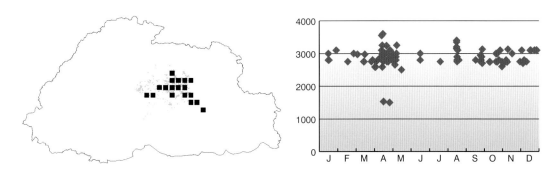

The Black-billed Magpie is widespread in North America, Europe and Asia, including the Tibetan Plateau. Its range just reaches the Indian subcontinent in the north-west and in Bhutan. It is a bird of cultivated upland valleys around villages.

In Bhutan an isolated population of this species exists in the Bumthang region, which apparently originated from stray birds from across the Himalayan range. The population has long been established, as evidenced by reports from the 19th century. On the whole, its status is that of a frequent resident, but it is particularly common in the Chamkhar Chhu valley, but does not breed in other valleys with equally suitable habitat. There are isolated records from the adjacent Mangde Chhu[5,55] and Kuri Chhu valleys[5,19]. The latter concerned a single at Yonkhola, Mongar district, in April 1997 and 1998. Its altitudinal range in the Chamkhar Chhu valley spans 2,600–3,400 m, occasionally reaching 3,600 m[19]. The lowest records involve stray birds to the Mangde Chhu (2,400 m)[55] and the Kuri Chhu valleys (1,500 m)[5,19]. Birders passing through Bumthang regularly report several tens, with a max. 50[14]. Although mostly occurring in pairs, flocks of up to eight are sometimes observed in the fields around Jakar. There are no direct observations of nesting, but particularly in winter the characteristic globular nest is easily located in willow trees around the fields.

# Spotted Nutcracker
*Nucifraga caryocatactes*

N=518(63). R 2200-3600

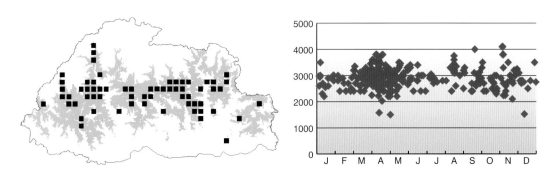

The Spotted Nutcracker occurs in the boreal and montane zones of Eurasia, extending through China to the Himalayas, where it is found from Afghanistan to Arunachal Pradesh. It is a bird of conifer forest, feeding particularly on seeds of Blue Pine and spruce.

In Bhutan the Spotted Nutcracker is abundant and widespread throughout the temperate zone and in the high west, with an isolated record from the eastern foothills. It becomes gradually scarcer further east and is resident at 2,200–3,600 m, although probably retreating lower in midwinter. Stray birds are occasionally found to 1,500 m. It mostly occurs singly or in pairs, dispersed in conifer forest. However, densities can be high, with up to 20 present at some sites. The breeding period appears to be well-synchronised, with fledglings food-begging in the first three weeks of May at 2,800–3,200 m[22,49]. In some years, there appear to be irruptive movements as in other parts of its range, when years of peak numbers are followed by a mediocre harvest of conifer seeds. These irruptions appear to occur in October/November, with records to 2,100 m, and birds turning up, for example, near Trongsa, as well as higher, in patches of fir forest at the treeline, to 4,100 m. This was the case particularly in 2001, when presence

Spotted Nutcracker
*Phil Jones*

at unusual localities in autumn coincided with the highest spring numbers reported. However, irruptive movements appear small, probably because local conifer forests offer sufficient alternative foods to outlast periods when one species experiences low seed production.

# Red-billed Chough
## *Pyrrhocorax pyrrhocorax*

N = 457(60). S 2200-3800 (Mar-Sep); W 2200-3400

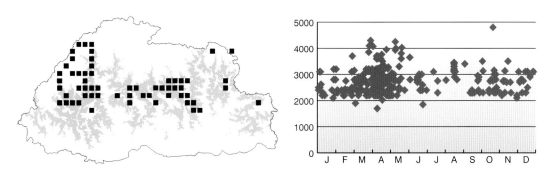

The Red-billed Chough occupies a wide range from the mountains of Western and southern Europe and North Africa through Central Asia, reaching eastern China. In the Indian subcontinent it occurs in the Himalayas from Pakistan to western Arunachal Pradesh. It inhabits open country at high altitudes, affecting pastures and cultivation.

In Bhutan the Red-billed Chough is an abundant altitudinal migrant throughout the alpine and temperate zones. It is markedly more common and widespread than the Yellow-billed Chough, and occupies a somewhat lower altitudinal range, in summer spanning 2,200–3,800 m, more occasionally to 4,300 m. There is one record from 4,800 m in October[51]. In winter it retreats to below 3,400 m and has reached 1,900 m in the Kuenga Rabten area, Trongsa district[14,29,52]. As the species approaches its easternmost limit in eastern Bhutan, it becomes scarcer and confined to higher altitudes. Thus, whilst in the western and Sunkosh valleys its lower limit is 2,200 m, and even 1,900 m in the central valleys, in the eastern valleys the species is not found below *c.*2,800 m in the Kuri Chhu valley, and in the Kulong Chhu valley it is rare and found only at *c.*3,900 m[49]. In October–April birds are concentrated at lower elevations and are regularly found in large flocks, sometimes up to 200 birds. The largest flock numbered 350 in February[52]. The breeding season appears well synchronised, with noisy young in the nest or recently fledged young in the second half of June, at 2,400 m and 2,800 m[52]. It nests under the roofs of houses and in dzongs. Breeding has been confirmed from the Thimphu and Bumthang valleys. A flock of 180 above the Thimphu Valley on 24 May[52] indicates the size of the breeding population in and around the capital.

# Yellow-billed Chough
## *Pyrrhocorax graculus*

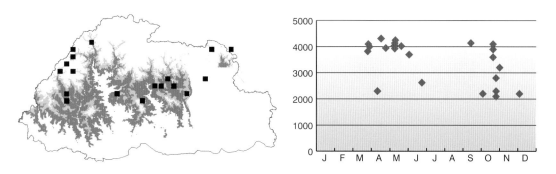

The Yellow-billed Chough is found in montane areas from south-west Europe to Central Asia and the Himalayas. In the Indian subcontinent it occurs east to western Arunachal Pradesh. It generally occupies higher areas than Red-billed Chough, frequenting alpine pasture and cultivation.

In Bhutan the Yellow-billed Chough is a common altitudinal migrant throughout the alpine and temperate zones. Its summer range spans 3,600 m to at least 4,400 m, probably being overlooked at high altitudes. In October and mid-April it occurs at 2,200–4,000 m, although the majority appear to remain at higher elevations. The lower limit overlaps with that of Red-billed Chough, with which it forms mixed flocks. Low-altitude records are concentrated in Paro Valley[25,51,53], with one record from Trongsa at 2,100 m in October[25]. A record of two pairs at the National Museum building in Paro (2,200 m) on 11 April[53] possibly concerned breeders. The largest concentration, of *c.*100 birds, was noted at 3,600–4,000 m, between Soe Thangthangkha and Jangothang, Paro district, in March[2].

# House Crow
## *Corvus splendens*

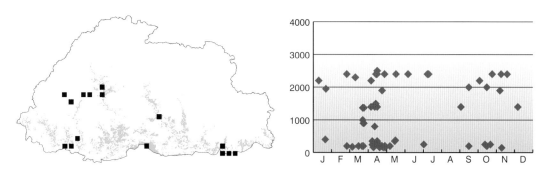

The House Crow occurs throughout densely populated areas of the Indian subcontinent, being closely associated with habitation and sometimes very numerous in towns and villages.

In Bhutan the House Crow is a common resident throughout the foothills as well as in the western, Sunkosh and central valleys. It is well established in the border towns. Up to 100 have been observed in and around Phuntsholing and Samdrup Jongkha, with similar numbers likely in Gelephu. Elsewhere in Bhutan its presence is more occasional, with not more than 1–3 birds at any site. Following the urbanisation process in Bhutan, it appears to be slowly colonising towns higher in the valleys, being reported from Gedu, Paro, Thimphu, Punakha, Wangdue Phodrang, Zhemgang and Deothang. Among these, small permanent populations seem to be established only in Thimphu and Punakha. Considering that strays were already reported here in the early

1990s, the colonisation process appears rather slow. However, the pattern appears to be similar to that of the Common Myna, with records concentrated in the western and Sunkosh valleys. Thus far it has not reached higher than Thimphu, at 2,500 m. In line with this, numbers in Phuntsholing appear to be increasing, with several tens reported in the mid-1990s against *c*.100 at present. It is also becoming more widespread in adjacent rural areas, with e.g. 24 noted at Kamji, Chhukha district, in March 2002[52].

Large-billed Crows
*Dan Cole*

# Large-billed Crow
## *Corvus macrorhynchos*

N=998(108). R 800-3200

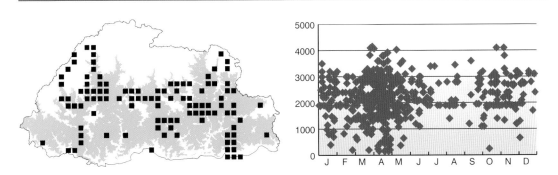

The Large-billed Crow occurs throughout the Indian subcontinent, except the dry north-west. Outside the subcontinent it occurs in northern Afghanistan and Tajikistan, through China and south-east Siberia, and widely in south-east Asia. Compared with House Crow it is much more a bird of rural areas, although still largely associated with habitation and herders' camps. Two races occur in Bhutan, *tibetosinensis* and *levaillantii*, the former occurring in higher areas and being distinguished by its heavier bill. However, separating the two subspecies in the field appears difficult.

In Bhutan the Large-billed Crow is undoubtedly the most widespread bird, recorded in all biogeographic units. It is resident at 800–3,200 m, with occasional records to 200 m and 4,200 m. In midwinter it is regularly found to at least 3,400 m, where it is one of the few birds that is conspicuous throughout winter. It is, however, likely to vacate highest altitudes at this season. Several tens are found together around dzongs or near villages, with for example maxima of 80, 80 and 100 near, respectively, the Trongsa[52], Zhemgang[52] and Gangtey dzongs[19]. A max. 300 was reported between Trongsa and Jakar in April[28]. In forest areas normally only small numbers are encountered, although up to 100 were noted in fir forest around Thrumshing La pass[5]. Along high-altitude treks its omnipresence is shown by the rapid appearance of a few at a new campsite. Despite its abundance, there is relatively little information on breeding. Nest-building has been observed at 1,800 m on 28 March and at 2,400 m in mid-April[52], whilst recently fledged young were observed on 21 June at 2,400 m[52].

# Common Raven
## *Corvus corax*

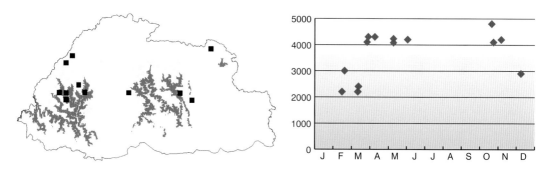

The Common Raven is widespread in Eurasia, with the subspecies *tibetanus* inhabiting dry country on the Tibetan plateau. It extends to the southern slopes of the Himalayas from Pakistan to Bhutan, but remains restricted to high elevations.

This is the national bird of Bhutan and figures in various tales and legends. It is a regular inhabitant of the old dzongs guarding the passes into Tibet. As a bird of extremely high elevations, there are relatively few records and it is generally uncommon, but has been found in the high west and the western, Sunkosh and central valleys. There are single records from the eastern valleys and the high east, where it reaches its easternmost limit, respectively from Sengor, Mongar district in January[29] and Singye dzong, Lhuntse district in summer[49]. It appears to be resident at 4,000–4,400 m, with the highest record from 4,800 m[51]. In winter, between December and mid-March, it occasionally wanders lower, reaching 2,200 m[52,57]. Presence at such elevations appears to be related to heavy snowfall, with most such records in March 2000. It is invariably found singly or in pairs, with no confirmed breeding records.

# Ashy Woodswallow
## *Artamus fuscus*

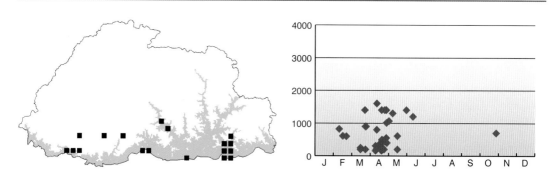

The Ashy Woodswallow is widespread in the southern and eastern Indian subcontinent, and across mainland south-east Asia. In the Himalayan foothills it occurs from central Nepal to Arunachal Pradesh, in open wooded country.

In Bhutan the Ashy Woodswallow is common, primarily in the foothills, with several records in the adjacent part of the temperate zone. It has been found at 200–1,400 m, mostly from February to mid-June. There is an October record at 700 m[52]. The paucity of records outside the breeding season suggests that it is largely a summer visitor. Being a conspicuous bird, despite the limited availability of records, there are several of breeding. Nesting pairs were found around 20 April and on 1 May between Deothang and Samdrup Jongkha[5,19] at 300–800 m. One was seen entering a nest cavity at 1,300 m on 7 May[55]. In the forests above Samdrup Jongkha up to ten have been reported.

# Eurasian Golden Oriole
## *Oriolus oriolus*

N=8(6)

The Eurasian Golden Oriole breeds from Western Europe to western Siberia and the Central Asian republics, and south to the northern and central Indian subcontinent including the Himalayan foothills. The Indian population is partially resident, but northern and western populations migrate south-west to winter in southern India and sub-Saharan Africa. It is a bird of open woodland and edges of cultivation.

In Bhutan the Eurasian Golden Oriole is a rare passage migrant and summer visitor at 200–1,900 m[52], with scattered records in the Sunkosh, central and eastern valleys, and the western and eastern foothills. Records are concentrated between mid-April and the first week of May, suggesting that most refer to spring-passage birds from populations breeding north of the Himalayas, as further suggested by the lack of reports of singing birds. However, records from low elevations, at Manas[22] and in Samtse district, could involve breeders. In Samtse the species has been found in spring and early summer[44]. Summer visitors to the foothills are probably overlooked due to a lack of surveys in this period.

# Slender-billed Oriole
## *Oriolus tenuirostris*

N=42(9). S 1200-1600

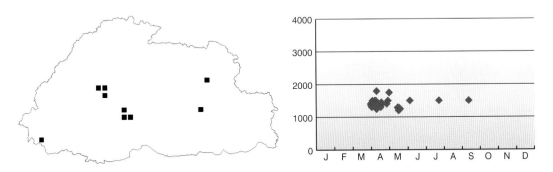

The Slender-billed Oriole breeds in a relatively small area of the Eastern Himalayas from Bhutan east, and in north-east India and Myanmar. In winter it reaches west to Nepal. Further east its range reaches northern Vietnam. It is a bird of open wooded country and large trees in the open.

In Bhutan this oriole is an uncommon summer visitor restricted to a narrow altitudinal range between 1,200 m and 1,600 m in the Sunkosh and eastern valleys, being confined in the latter to the Kuri Chhu. There is one record from the western foothills[44]. In the Kuri Chhu valley it was noted as relatively common by Ludlow in July[31] and there are three recent records from the area[5,38]. In the Sunkosh Valley it is scarce but regular, being recorded annually, and affects large trees in cultivated areas and at the edge of Chir Pine forests, being one of the few birds to be strongly associated with this habitat. There are no winter records and it appears to be a summer visitor only. A max. 5 was encountered in the Punakha/Wangdue Phodrang area on 12 April[14]. The earliest spring record is 30 March[19], the latest autumn record 10 September[52]. Singing males are noted in the first half of April, which is the only indication of breeding.

# Black-hooded Oriole
## Oriolus xanthornus

N=9(6). R 200-400

The Black-hooded Oriole is widespread in southern and south-east Asia, occurring through mainland south-east Asia south to Indonesia. It is resident in the south, centre and north of the Indian subcontinent, including the Himalayan foothills. It inhabits open forest.

In Bhutan the Black-hooded Oriole is an uncommon bird of the foothills, found from west to east at 200–400 m. There is an isolated record from higher in the Sunkosh Valley at 1,200 m[12]. Records span October–April, suggesting that its presence relates to dry-season dispersal from breeding areas in northern India. On the whole it is scarce, with never more than two birds recorded at the same site.

# Maroon Oriole
## Oriolus traillii

N=444(66). S 800-2400 (mid-Mar-Sep); W 400-1000

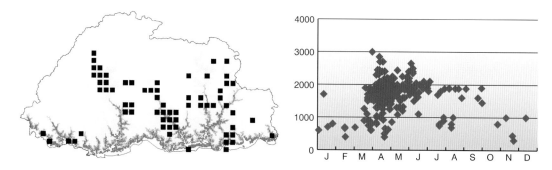

The Maroon Oriole is distributed along the Himalayas from Himachal Pradesh to Arunachal Pradesh and in the hills of north-east India. Its range extends further east to Taiwan and Vietnam. Habitat is dense, moist broadleaf forest, where it inhabits the canopy.

In Bhutan the Maroon Oriole is a common altitudinal migrant throughout the temperate zone and the foothills. It appears to be relatively scarce in the western valleys, where moist broadleaf forests are largely absent at higher elevations. The main summer range spans 800–2,400 m, with occasional records to 400 m and 3,000 m. In winter it occurs at 400–1,000 m with one January record from 1,700 m, in the relatively mild winter of 1999/2000[22,49], and the lowest record 300 m in November[1]. Winter records are rather few, as the species is secretive and silent in this period. In January/February singles are readily noticed when they join feeding flocks of drongos and leafbirds at flowering *Bombax* trees. Birds arrive on their breeding areas by mid-March and remain there until September. Singing birds occupy territories from mid-March to August, with peak song activity from mid-April to May. At *c.*1,900 m a short peak in numbers of singing birds in early April[52] indicates passage to higher elevations. Breeding evidence includes a bird carrying nest material at 1,500 m on 1 May [22] and a recently fledged young at 2,100 m on 24 June[52]. A mean 3.3 territories per km was found near Zhemgang at 1,600–1,900 m, with density declining rapidly in the lower part of this range[52]. Number of territories was remarkably constant between years. The species is a regular member of the bird community in mid-level broadleaf forest, with over ten regularly present at a given site.

# Large Cuckooshrike
## Coracina macei

N=6(4)

The Large Cuckooshrike is widespread in the Indian subcontinent over most of the north and east, including the Himalayan foothills from Pakistan to Arunachal Pradesh and the hills of north-east India. Further east its range reaches Taiwan and Vietnam.

In Bhutan the Large Cuckooshrike is uncommon, unlike Nepal, where it is common to 2,400 m. It occurs in summer in the foothills, with most records from central and eastern parts, and particularly the Manas area. Its altitudinal range spans 200–400 m, with one record at 1,900 m in the central valleys, near Zhemgang in June[52]. Like Common Iora it can be considered a potential indicator species for monitoring deforestation levels.

# Black-winged Cuckooshrike
## *Coracina melaschistos*

N=475(63). S 800-2600 (mid-Mar-Sep); W 600-2000

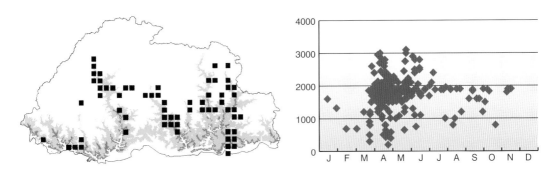

The Black-winged Cuckooshrike breeds in the Himalayas from Pakistan to Arunachal Pradesh, the hills of north-east India, and east to northern Vietnam. It is an altitudinal migrant, wintering mostly in the foothills and adjacent plains, but some straggle south as far as southern India. It is a bird of relatively open forest and forest edges in the broadleaf zone, principally inhabiting the canopy.

In Bhutan the Black-winged Cuckooshrike is an abundant altitudinal migrant throughout the temperate zone and in the western and eastern foothills. Its regular summer altitudinal range spans 800–2,600 m, with occasional records to 200 m and 3,100 m[52]. The upper limit thus coincides with that of temperate broadleaf forest. The species is found almost exclusively in broadleaf forest, with very few records from pine areas. Consequently it is scarce in the western valleys, where pines dominate higher levels. It arrives in the breeding areas in the last week of March, and immediately spreads over the entire summer range. Territorial birds are evident early April–August, with occasional song heard as late as October–November at 1,900 m[52]. Departure from the breeding areas is rather unclear as records are fewer in autumn due to the relative lack of observers and because the species is less vocal. Data suggest that it vacates areas above 2,000 m from July, but is regular below 2,000 m into October. Between November and late March there are few records, all below 2,000 m, suggesting that most winter in the plains or further south. In the breeding season it is widespread and common, with up to ten present at a site. A mean density of 2.3 territories per km was found near Zhemgang at 1,600–1,900 m[52]. There are no confirmed breeding records.

# Rosy Minivet
## *Pericrocotus roseus*

N=2(1)

The Rosy Minivet has a scattered distribution in the Himalayan foothills from Pakistan to Arunachal Pradesh and the hills of north-east India. Further east its range reaches Vietnam. It is migratory, wintering mostly in the north-east subcontinent. It occurs in forest, both broadleaf and coniferous, at low elevations.

In Bhutan the Rosy Minivet has been recorded once in the eastern foothills: on 22 and 24 April 1994 1–3 birds were found in the foothills at Manas at 400–500 m[22].

# Grey-chinned Minivet
## *Pericrocotus solaris*

N=258(46). R 600-2400

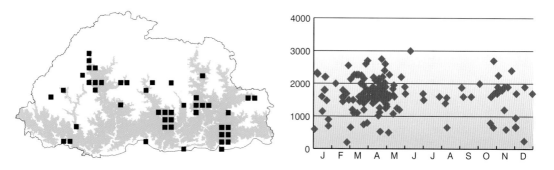

The Grey-chinned Minivet is widespread in south-east Asia, from southern China and Taiwan south to Sumatra and Borneo. In the west its range penetrates the Indian subcontinent, where it occurs in north-east India and the Himalayas west to central Nepal. It inhabits middle and top storeys of moist broadleaf forest, particularly in the subtropical zone.

In Bhutan the Grey-chinned Minivet is a common resident throughout the temperate zone and the foothills. The core distribution is in the temperate zone, and it is relatively uncommon in the western valleys, where it approaches the westernmost limits of its range. It is found at 600–2,400 m, roughly between the lower-altitude Scarlet Minivet and the higher-altitude Short-billed Minivet. However, the ranges of all common minivets overlap, particularly in winter, when up to three species occur in the same flock. Occurrence is occasional to 200 m and 2,800 m, the highest record being from 3,000 m in June[31]. In winter it forms flocks of up to 20, sometimes 30, which regularly associate with mixed flocks of smaller babblers and other minivets. By mid-March flocks disband and pairs form. Near Zhemgang a mean density of 0.3 breeding pairs per km was found at 1,600–1,900 m[52]. A female was observed on a nest at 1,800 m on 3 April[5] and by mid-April small family parties are noted. In the second half of April displaying males are again visible and a further wave of pairs commence breeding, these possibly giving rise to second broods. On 21 April two nests were observed at 1,700–2,000 m[14]. Pairs and family groups are noted until August, after which larger flocks start to gather.

# Long-tailed Minivet
## *Pericrocotus ethologus*

N=347(78). S 1400-3400 (mid-Mar-Oct); W 600-2800

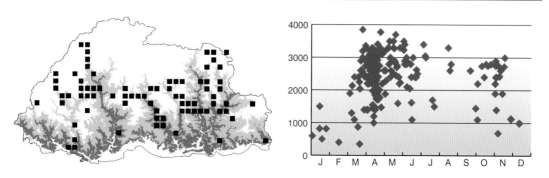

The Long-tailed Minivet occupies the highest range of minivets in the Himalayas and shows marked altitudinal movements. It breeds throughout the Himalayas and north-east India, moving in winter to the adjacent plains and further south in the subcontinent. It has a more northerly range in south-east and eastern Asia than other minivets, occurring through Myanmar to northern Vietnam and even northern China. Habitat consists of open broadleaf and conifer forests with a preference for the latter.

In Bhutan this minivet is a common altitudinal migrant, found in all biogeographic units except the insufficiently explored central foothills. Its core range is the western valleys, where it is the commonest minivet, summering at 1,400–3,400 m and wintering at 600–2,800 m. The majority withdraw well below 1,500 m in midwinter, with a few records to 300 m[44] and up to 3,800 m[22]. Altitudinal movements are also evidenced by the regular presence of flocks moving through the centre of Thimphu in the second half of March and the first half of April, en route to their breeding areas. Autumn migration is less noticeable, with apparently gradual descent in September–November. From August to April birds frequently associate in larger flocks of 10–20, with 30 the maximum. In May–July most records concern pairs and singles. There are no confirmed breeding records.

Long-tailed Minivet
*Dan Cole*

# Short-billed Minivet
## *Pericrocotus brevirostris*

N=357(63). S 800-2800 (mid-Apr-Oct); W 600-2000

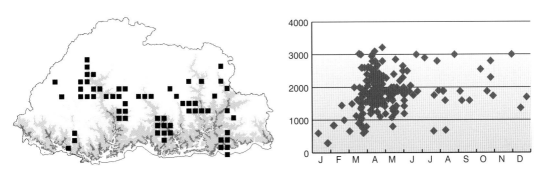

The range of the Short-billed Minivet includes the Himalayas from eastern Nepal to Arunachal Pradesh and the hills of north-east India. Further east it reaches northern Vietnam. It is a bird of broadleaf forest, preferring more open areas than Grey-chinned Minivet with which it overlaps in altitudinal range, and they are often found together in mixed flocks in winter.

In Bhutan the Short-billed Minivet is a common altitudinal migrant in the temperate zone and the foothills, but is relatively less common in the western valleys, where it approaches its westernmost limits. Its summer range spans 800–2,800 m, occasionally 3,200 m[5]. In winter it descends and is mostly found at 400–2,400 m, occasionally down to 300 m[28]. Birds move to the breeding areas between mid-March and mid-April. Autumn movements are not clearly marked and birds probably disperse gradually. In its movements and altitudinal range the species is intermediate between the resident Grey-chinned Minivet and migratory Long-billed Minivet. In July–March birds gather in flocks of 5–20, sometimes 30, which disband in April when pairs form. Near Zhemgang a density of 1.1 breeding pairs per km was found at 1,600–1,900 m[52]. A pair was observed carrying nest material on 14 April[19]. Family groups with recently fledged juveniles were noted on 15 May at 1,900 m[52].

# Scarlet Minivet
## *Pericrocotus flammeus*

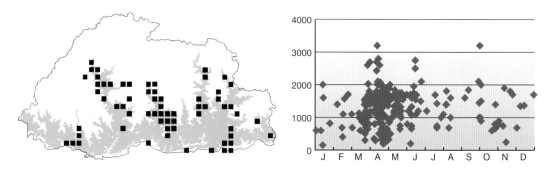

The range of the Scarlet Minivet includes the Himalayas from Kashmir to Arunachal Pradesh, north-east, east and south-west India and Sri Lanka. Further east it extends through mainland south-east Asia to the Philippines and the Greater Sundas. Habitat consists of open broadleaf and conifer forests, mainly in the subtropical zone.

The Scarlet Minivet is the common minivet at lower elevations in Bhutan, found throughout the temperate zone and foothills, more especially the latter. It is resident at 400–2,000 m with occasional records to 200 m, where it is probably under-recorded, and to 3,200 m[19]. Higher-altitude records are mostly from the first half of April, when some join the Long-billed Minivets migrating upslope. It rarely forms larger flocks like other minivets, but individuals, pairs and family parties readily join mixed-species flocks of small babblers and other minivets, particularly in August–April. In April–June singing males are noted, which aside from juveniles is the only evidence of breeding in Bhutan. Near Zhemgang a mean density of 0.3 breeding pairs per km was found at 1,600–1,900 m[52]. Family groups with juveniles are especially obvious in July, indicating a relatively late breeding season.

# Bar-winged Flycatcher-shrike
## *Hemipus picatus*

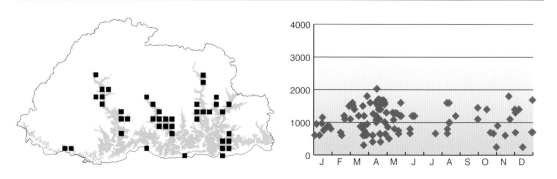

The Bar-winged Flycatcher-shrike is patchily distributed in the Indian subcontinent, in parts of the Himalayas, the hills of north-east, east and south-west India, Bangladesh and Sri Lanka. Elsewhere in south-east Asia it is widespread south to Sumatra and Borneo. It inhabits open forest in the tropical and subtropical zones.

In Bhutan the Bar-winged Flycatcher-shrike is frequently recorded in the temperate zone, from the Sunkosh valley eastwards and in the foothills. It is resident at 600–1,600 m, occasionally to 200 m and 1,800 m. The highest record is from *c.*2,000 m in April[14]. In January/February it appears to withdraw below 1,000 m. In July–March birds gather in flocks of up to 20, with a mean flock size of approximately ten[52]. By late March they disband and pairs and individuals are seen. On 19 April one was observed on a nest at 650 m[5,52], which is the only confirmed breeding record.

Bar-winged Flycatcher-shrike
*Ren Hathway*

# Yellow-bellied Fantail
## *Rhipidura hypoxantha*

N=558(99). S 2000-3400 (May-mid-Sep); W 600-2800

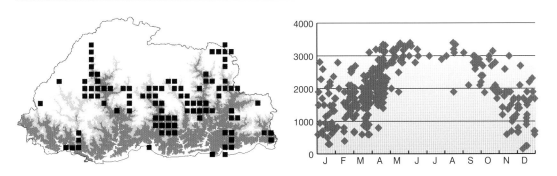

The Yellow-bellied Fantail breeds in the Himalayas from Pakistan to Arunachal Pradesh and in north-east India, its range extending further east to northern Vietnam. It is an altitudinal migrant, summering in high-altitude forest and descending to subtropical forest in the foothills in winter. It is one of the most regular members of insect-hunting mixed-species flocks.

In Bhutan the Yellow-bellied Fantail is an abundant altitudinal migrant in all biogeographic units. Summer range spans 2,000–3,200 m, occasionally to 3,400 m, although records below 2,800 m probably concern passage birds. As higher elevations have been little explored in summer its regular breeding range may extend higher. It winters widely at 600–2,800 m, reaching 200 m in midwinter. Movement to the breeding areas occurs in late March–April and it is present there over a relatively short period, from May to mid-September. In autumn a gradual downslope movement is evident from late September to November. Breeding commences immediately following arrival in the high-altitude forests, as revealed by a bird carrying nest material on 4 May at 2,900 m[22]. A recently fledged bird, being fed by an adult, was observed at 2,900 m on 26 July[52], suggesting double-brooding. In winter one or a few are commonly observed in mixed-species flocks of warblers and small babblers. Occasionally single-species flocks involving up to ten individuals are observed, with an exceptionally large flock of more than 50 at 1,700 m on 30 December[52].

# White-throated Fantail
*Rhipidura albicollis*                    N=476(63). S 1200-2400 (May-Oct); W 600-2000

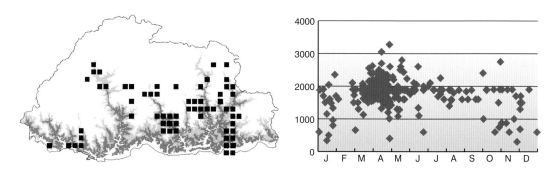

The White-throated Fantail is a resident of the Himalayas from Pakistan to Arunachal Pradesh, in north-east India, Bangladesh and most of the Indian peninsula. Further east its range continues through mainland south-east Asia to Sumatra and Borneo. It is a bird of shady ravines in broadleaf forest, occupying a lower altitudinal range than Yellow-bellied Fantail.

In Bhutan the White-throated Fantail is abundant and widespread in the temperate and subtropical zones, being particularly abundant in the central and eastern valleys. Altitudinal movements are less pronounced than those of Yellow-bellied Fantail. Summer range spans 1,200–2,400 m, with occasional records to 2,800 m and from c.3,200 m in April[14]. In winter it occurs lower, at 600–2,000 m, occasionally to 300 m[31]. Birds move upslope in March and descend again in October. Singing birds are heard occasionally throughout the year, but mostly in March–August when they occupy breeding territories. Near Zhemgang a mean density of 3.3 territories per km was found at 1,600–1,900 m, with the highest density in the upper part of this range. Despite its abundance, there are no confirmed breeding records. Outside the breeding season 1–3 commonly associate with mixed-species flocks of warblers and smaller babblers.

# Black Drongo
*Dicrurus macrocercus*                    N=60(18). S 200-2600 (Mar-Sep); W 200-400

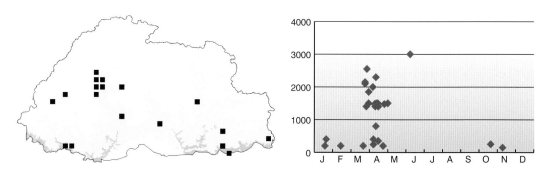

The Black Drongo occurs over much of the Indian subcontinent, including the Himalayan foothills, and further west to south-east Iran and east through much of south-east Asia. It inhabits open country, where it hunts insects and other small prey from perches such as telephone wires.

In Bhutan the Black Drongo is a common altitudinal migrant throughout the foothills, and the temperate belt. It is resident below 400 m, reaching 2,600 m from late March–April and possibly later. During this period it is found regularly in the Sunkosh Valley, in cultivated areas near Punakha and Wangdue Phodrang. In the western and eastern valleys presence at higher altitudes appears more occasional. The highest record concerns a specimen collected at Damthang, Ha district, at 3,000 m in June[31]. No confirmed breeding records, but reports of up to 20–30 birds[28] demonstrate it to be common and regular in the Punakha/Wangdue Phodrang area and breeding appears likely there.

# Ashy Drongo
## *Dicrurus leucophaeus*

N=851(96). S 1000-2800 (Apr-Oct); W 600-2000

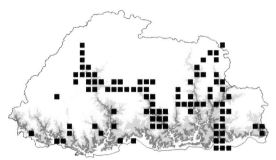

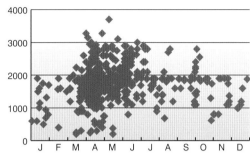

The Ashy Drongo breeds in the Himalayas from eastern Afghanistan to Arunachal Pradesh and the hills of north-east India. Further east it occurs throughout mainland south-east Asia, the Greater Sundas and the Philippines. In winter some northern populations migrate south reaching the Malay Peninsula and the entire Indian peninsula. A bird of open forests, it hunts insects from bare branches in the treetops and takes nectar at flowering trees. In denser forest below 2,000 m it is replaced by Bronzed and Lesser Racket-tailed Drongos.

In Bhutan the Ashy Drongo is an abundant altitudinal migrant and the commonest drongo, being found throughout the temperate zone and the foothills, with single records from the high west and high east. The upper western valleys represent a major gap in its distribution, due to the scarcity of broadleaf forest in this area. Its summer range spans 1,000–2,800 m, with occasional records to 200 m and 3,200 m, and one from 3,700 m[49]. The summer range is occupied during March, withdrawing to its winter range below 2,000 m in October. It is relatively scarce in winter, suggesting at least some migrate to India. There are many confirmed breeding records at 1,500–2,900 m. Singing birds are on territory from early April to the first half of July, and the species is perhaps double-brooded. Nesting appears to start

Ashy Drongo
*Dan Cole*

earlier at lower elevations. On 8 April one was seen on a nest at *c*.1,500 m[19], whilst nest building was observed at 2,300 m on 3 May[49], corresponding well with the observation of fledglings at 1,900 m on 9 June[52], given a total period between nest-building and fledging of five weeks, as was observed in one case[52]. Higher, pairs with fledglings were observed at 2,100 m on 24 June[40,52] and at 2,900 m on 5 July[40,52], suggesting that breeding could commence *c*.2 months later in its upper range, although there is probably considerable variation and second broods may have been involved. However, a pair constructed nests at the same site in two consecutive years with remarkably constant timing, the young fledging on the same date[52]. While young are in the nest the adults are very aggressive to potential predators. Pairs will attack Large-billed Crows undertaking roosting movements and Rufous-necked Hornbills in this period[52]. Near Zhemgang a density of 2.4 breeding territories per km was found at 1,600–1,900 m[52]. Being widespread and conspicuous, numbers encountered in the course of a day commonly run into several tens, with up to 20 at a single site.

# Crow-billed Drongo
## *Dicrurus annectans*                                      N=21(12). R 200-1400

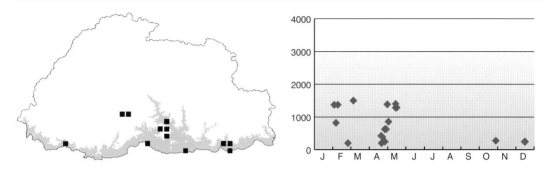

The Crow-billed Drongo occurs in the Himalayas from central Nepal to Arunachal Pradesh and the hills of north-east India. Further east it reaches northern Vietnam. A summer migrant, it winters in north-east India and south to the Greater Sundas. However, the species's distribution is somewhat unclear, as it is regularly confused with Black Drongo. Habitat is the lower strata of dense broadleaf forest.

In Bhutan the Crow-billed Drongo is uncommon but apparently resident in the foothills, particularly central and eastern parts, at Gelephu[1] and Manas[22]. In spring it reaches higher into the Sunkosh, central and eastern valleys, with scattered records throughout. Records in the eastern valleys have not been mapped due to imprecise localities being reported. Summer range spans 200–1,400 m, where it occurs from early February to May. The highest record is from 1,500 m in March[1]. A max. 7 was found in April at Manas[22] and the species is perhaps locally common there. The number of records during surveys in the 1960s suggests its presence has largely been overlooked since, possibly because the species occurs in the undergrowth of dense forest or because of its localised distribution.

# Bronzed Drongo
## *Dicrurus aeneus*                                         N=265(38). R 400-1800

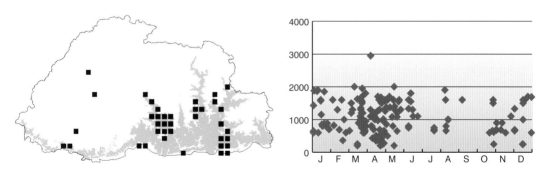

The Bronzed Drongo is widespread in south-east Asia, south to Sumatra and Borneo. In the Indian subcontinent it occurs along the Himalayas from Uttar Pradesh to Arunachal Pradesh and in the hills of north-east India, as well as the hills of east and south-west India. It inhabits moist broadleaf forest, in the midcanopy.

In Bhutan the Bronzed Drongo is a common resident throughout the temperate zone and the foothills, at 400–1,800 m, and occasionally to 200 m and 2,000 m. However, its breeding range is below 1,600 m, higher records mostly reflecting post-breeding dispersal. It has been found once at *c.*3,000 m on Dochu La[19], considerably above its usual range. Rather localised in its distribution, the species keeps to stretches of mature broadleaf forest. It is scarce in the western and Sunkosh valleys, and absent from apparently suitable habitat around Tashithang, Punakha district, probably because of the lack of continuous forest cover below 2,000 m there, connecting the area with the main range further south. Unlike Ashy Drongo, nesting appears to be well synchronised throughout its altitudinal range, with birds observed nest-building at 1,200–1,800 m on 21 April[27], at 600 m on 28 April[52] and at 1,600 m 30 April[52]. A density of 1.1 territories per km was found near Zhemgang at *c*.1,600 m[52]. Outside the breeding season it gathers in groups of up to 20, but rarely joins mixed feeding flocks.

# Lesser Racket-tailed Drongo
## *Dicrurus remifer*

N = 191(30). R 600-2000

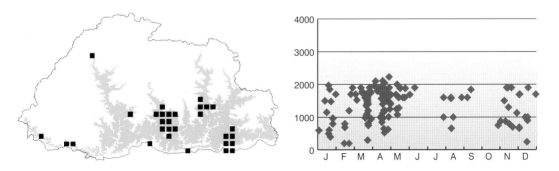

The Lesser Racket-tailed Drongo is widespread in south-east Asia, reaching Sumatra and Java in the south. In the Indian subcontinent it occurs in the Himalayas from Uttar Pradesh to Arunachal Pradesh, in north-east India and Bangladesh. Habitat is dense broadleaf forest, the species occupying the top canopy. Whereas Crow-billed, Bronzed and Lesser Racket-tailed Drongos occupy the same altitudinal range in dense broadleaf forest, they appear to be segregated to some extent by the strata they occupy, respectively undergrowth, mid-layer and top canopy.

In Bhutan the Lesser Racket-tailed Drongo is a common resident throughout the temperate zone and the foothills. It has a similar distribution to Bronzed Drongo, being scarce in the Sunkosh and absent from the western valleys. Like the latter, it appears mostly absent from the relatively isolated stretches of broadleaf forest in the upper Sunkosh and eastern valleys, suggesting that it is sensitive to habitat fragmentation. It is resident at 600–2,000 m with occasional records to 200 m and 2,200 m[22]. Singing birds have been observed from March to early June, with peak activity in May, indicating a relatively late breeding season compared to other drongos. There are relatively few records in June–July, when birds may be more secretive at their nests. Near Zhemgang a density of 0.5 breeding pairs per km was found at 1,600–1,900 m[52]. There are no confirmed breeding records. With the exception of May and June, it is found year-round in mixed feeding flocks of warblers, fulvettas and other small babblers. Most such flocks have one or two Lesser Racket-tailed Drongos among them, presumably benefiting from the insects displaced by the flock and serving a role by alarming at the approach of predators (cf. King and Rappole 2001). Below 600 m it is partially replaced by Greater Racket-tailed Drongo, which similarly associates with mixed flocks. Neither species gathers into larger flocks like Bronzed Drongo.

Greater Racket-tailed Drongo
*Jan Wilczur*

# Greater Racket-tailed Drongo
*Dicrurus paradiseus*                                                N=35(11). R 200-800

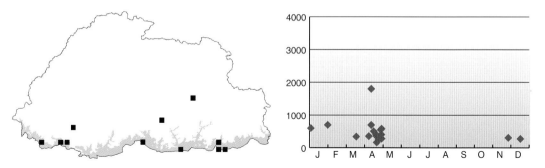

The Greater Racket-tailed Drongo is widespread in south-east Asia, south to the Greater Sundas. In the Indian subcontinent it occurs in most of the south, centre and north-east, and the Himalayas from Himachal Pradesh to Arunachal Pradesh. It inhabits tropical and subtropical broadleaf forests.

In Bhutan this drongo is an uncommon resident, largely confined to foothills below 800 m, with isolated records from the western[19], central[52] and eastern valleys[46], to c.1,800 m, in January–March and perhaps involving dispersal from lower elevations prior to breeding. In the forests above Samdrup Jongkha it is regular and is reported annually, with a day maximum of six. It is usually seen singly or in small flocks. The largest flock numbered ten and was part of a mixed-species flock, with amongst others White-browed Shrike Babblers, on 2 January, near Tingtibi, Zhemgang, at 600 m[52].

# Spangled Drongo
*Dicrurus hottentottus*                                              N=175(39). R 200-1800

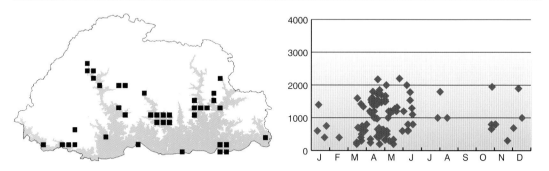

The Spangled Drongo occurs widely in south-east Asia, including most of Indonesia. In the Indian subcontinent it has a similar range to Bronzed Drongo, including the Himalayas and the hills of north-east, eastern and south-west India. It inhabits broadleaf forest, feeding on nectar at flowering trees.

In Bhutan the Spangled Drongo is a common resident throughout the temperate zone and the foothills, albeit somewhat scattered, with few records from the western valleys and the upper eastern valleys. The core range lies in the foothills, with the Sunkosh and central valleys as additional strongholds. In the foothills up to 20 are found at a site. Also, in the upper Sunkosh Valley up to 15 have been reported[14,28], proving that it is unaffected by fragmentation of forest cover like the more sedentary Bronzed and Lesser Racket-tailed Drongos. Its altitudinal range spans 200–1,800 m, with occasional records to 2,200 m. However, occurrence at particular localities is rather erratic, depending on presence of flowering trees. Concentrations of up to ten occur in January–February, when the species gathers at flowering *Bombax*. One was nest-building on 28 April at 600 m[52] and the surveys of the 1960s collected a female with brood-patch on 15 May at 300 m[1]. These records suggest that it breeds particularly in the lower parts of its range, and has a more nomadic presence at higher levels.

# Black-naped Monarch
## *Hypothymis azurea*

N=39(11). R 200-600

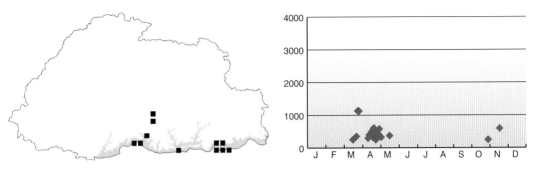

The Black-naped Monarch occurs in the southern and north-east Indian subcontinent, including the Himalayan foothills from western Nepal eastwards. This is the westernmost part of its range in the Oriental Region, which otherwise reaches to the Philippines and Indonesia. It inhabits tropical broadleaf forest and second growth.

In Bhutan the Black-naped Monarch is a common resident in the central and eastern foothills, becoming more regular further east. Its regular altitudinal range spans 200–600 m, with two records in the central valleys, at 1,100 m in March[1,12], probably relating to pre-breeding dispersal. This record has not been mapped due to an imprecise locality being reported. It has been recorded annually in April–May in some numbers in the forests above Samdrup Jongkha, with a max. 14 in a day[28].

Black-naped Monarch
*Jan Wilczur*

# Asian Paradise-flycatcher
## *Terpsiphone paradisi*

N=15(4). R 200-600

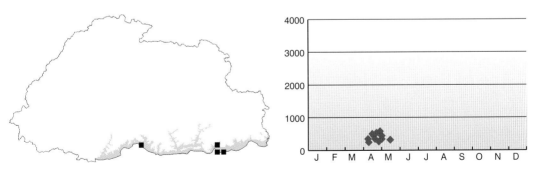

The Asian Paradise-flycatcher has a vast range in southern, eastern and south-east Asia, from Turkestan and Afghanistan through the Indian subcontinent, north to Ussuriland and south to the Lesser Sundas. In the Indian subcontinent it is a summer visitor to the north, including the Himalayan foothills, and wintering further south in the subcontinent, the migrants augmenting the resident population. Habitat consists of shady forest, where it particularly affects the top canopy.

In Bhutan the Asian Paradise-flycatcher is an uncommon summer visitor to the eastern foothills, reaching *c.*600 m, with one record from the central foothills near Gelephu in April[1]. In the east it is found almost annually in the forests above Samdrup Jongkha in early April to mid-May. A max. 4 has been noted here[28].

# Common Iora
*Aegithina tiphia*

N=46(11). R 200-800

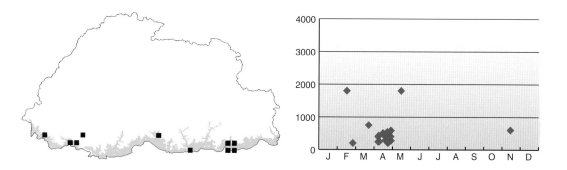

The Common Iora occurs throughout most of the Indian subcontinent, including the Himalayan foothills, and further east through mainland south-east Asia, the Philippines and Indonesia. It inhabits open forest, forest edge and second-growth forest. In Nepal and India it is regular to 2,000 m.

Common Iora has been found throughout the foothills, with occasional records in adjacent parts of the central[4], western[19,36,44] and eastern valleys[28]. Its regular altitudinal range spans 200–800 m. In the western valleys it has been recorded several times around Gedu at 1,800 m[19,36,44], where a max. 8 has been recorded. Its virtual absence above 800 m is probably indicative of the higher forest quality in Bhutan compared more degraded stretches in Nepal and India.

# Large Woodshrike
*Tephrodornis gularis*

N=42(13). R 200-1200

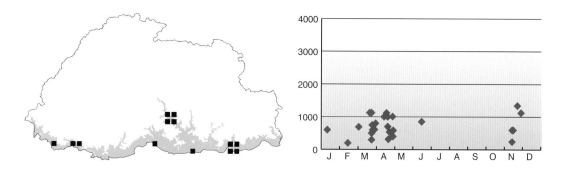

The Large Woodshrike has a scattered distribution in the Indian subcontinent, being found in the hills of the south-west, eastern and north-east India, and in the Himalayan foothills from Uttar Pradesh to Arunachal Pradesh. Further east it is widespread in south-east Asia south to the Greater Sundas. It inhabits broadleaf forest in the tropical and subtropical zones, where it affects the top canopy.

In Bhutan the Large Woodshrike is an uncommon resident in the foothills and central valleys, at 200–1,200 m, with the highest record from 1,400 m[1]. It is mostly observed in pairs throughout the year, which only occasionally assemble in larger flocks of 5–10 birds. A pair was observed attending a nest at 1,000 m on 19 April[5].

# White-throated Dipper
## *Cinclus cinclus*

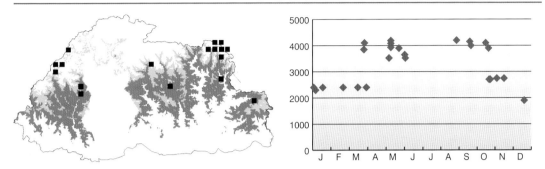

The White-throated Dipper occurs in montane areas from Europe and North Africa, through Central Asia and the Urals to western China. It is common on the north side of the Himalayas, but rather rare on southern slopes, where it is largely replaced by Brown Dipper. It keeps to higher altitudes and smaller streams than the latter.

In Bhutan the White-throated Dipper is a common altitudinal migrant found mostly in the alpine zone, with scattered records from the temperate zone. Its summer range spans 3,400–4,200 m (possibly higher), where it is present from at least March–November. In winter it occasionally descends lower, reaching 2,200 m, the lowest record being at 1,900 m[49]. However, such records invariably concern lone individuals and probably represent only a small fraction of the population. One was present at Taba, Thimphu district, at 2,400 m, during January to March in three successive winters[49,52]. A juvenile observed at 3,650 m on 1 June, near Singye Dzong, Lhuntse district, is the only evidence of breeding[49].

# Brown Dipper
## *Cinclus pallasii*

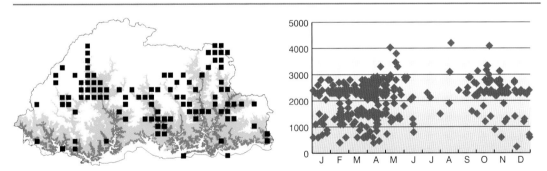

The Brown Dipper occurs in East Asia, from Sakhalin south to south-west China and northern Vietnam. From here, it extends in a narrow band over the Himalayas to Pakistan, and reaching Turkestan. It is a bird of fast-flowing mountain streams and rivers.

In Bhutan the Brown Dipper is an abundant altitudinal migrant, widespread and recorded in all biogeographic units. It is most frequently observed in winter at 600–2,800 m, with occasional records to 200 and 3,300 m. It breeds in December–April, with birds seen carrying nest material at 1,300 m on 20 December[52]. A pair with recently fledged young was observed at 2,400 m on 16 February[52]. Apparently it is double-brooded, as there are also nest records in March[5] and of adults feeding young on 19 April[22]. The species may reach considerable densities, as evidenced by the presence of six territorial pairs at Taba, Thimphu district, along *c*.1.5 km of river, in January 1998[52]. Post-breeding it disperses higher and onto smaller streams, largely vacating swollen rivers at lower altitudes, and reaching the range of White-throated Dipper. Between May and October it is found at 1,200–3,400 m, occasionally reaching 4,200 m[49]. At 2,400 m near Thimphu occasional birds are noted throughout the monsoon but most leave the area. In September–October it retreats downslope again and is widespread below 2,000 m.

# Blue-capped Rock Thrush
## Monticola cinclorhynchus

N=421(57). S 600-2200

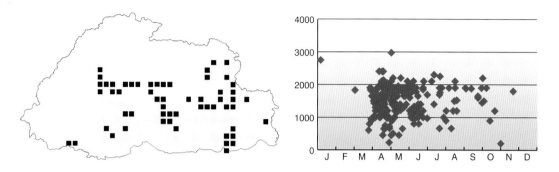

The Blue-capped Rock Thrush is a summer visitor to the Himalayas, from Afghanistan to Arunachal Pradesh and the hills of north-east India. It winters mostly in south-west India and, more occasionally, in Assam. Habitat consists of open dry forest on hill slopes.

In Bhutan the Blue-capped Rock Thrush is a common summer visitor to the Sunkosh, central and eastern valleys, and the western and eastern foothills. Whilst the lack of records from the central foothills perhaps reflects limited survey work, its absence from the western valleys appears real, the species apparently being relatively scattered. Its strongholds are the central and eastern valleys, and its regular altitudinal range spans 600–2,200 m, with occasional records to 200 m and 2,400 m, and one from 3,000 m[10]. Birds arrive in the breeding areas from the last week of March, reaching peak numbers by the second half of April. Given the highly synchronised arrival, one on 2 March at 1,800 m was an exceptionally early record[1]. Departure is in September–October, with a late record on 21 November[15]. As records below 600 m are scarce, birds apparently arrive and depart the breeding areas directly. Singing males occupy territories early April to early June. Breeders are rather conspicuous, partly because of the species's preference for rather open habitat, but also its frequent occurrence along roadsides. There is some variation in the timing of breeding. A female was observed on a nest with eggs at 700 m on 21 and 28 April[5,52], while another pair at 1,300 m was still nest-building on 16 May[5]. Adults carrying food have been observed mid-May to the third week of June[52], and pairs with fledged juveniles are evident from the third week of July to mid-August[52], after which departure to the winter areas probably commences. Near Zhemgang a mean density of 1.3 territories per km was found at 1,600–1,900 m, with considerable variation between years[52]. Up to ten have been found at certain sites, underlining the species's abundance in Bhutan.

# Chestnut-bellied Rock Thrush
## Monticola rufiventris

N=382(59). S 1600-3400 (Apr-Sep); W 600-2200

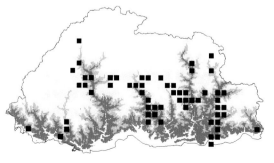
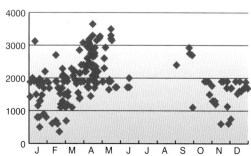

The Chestnut-bellied Rock Thrush occurs along the Himalayas from Pakistan to Arunachal Pradesh and the hills of north-east India, and further east to central China and northern Vietnam. Habitat consists of open forest on rocky slopes.

In Bhutan the Chestnut-bellied Rock Thrush is a common resident throughout the temperate zone and the foothills, with one record in the high west[22]. Winter records are common at 600–2,200 m, with the lowest from 400 m in February[31]. In May records become scarcer and there few records in June, after which it is only noted again in September. The April–June and September records are largely from 1,600 to 3,400 m, which is presumably its breeding range. The highest record is from 3,600 m[19]. However, the paucity of summer records contrasts with its common and widespread winter presence, suggesting that a large percentage of the wintering population breeds elsewhere. Furthermore, its presence in the breeding season appears rather localised, with a concentration of records in late May–June in the Kuri Chhu valley at 1,500–2,000 m, but at other well-surveyed sites in its expected summer range the species has not been noted beyond mid-May. Indications of breeding are limited to occasional sightings of pairs and the observation of a singing male at 1,900 m on 29 March[52]. It is usually solitary or in pairs, but groups of up to five are occasionally found at the same cliff, particularly in December–January.

# Blue Rock Thrush
## *Monticola solitarius*

N=219(46). W 400-2400

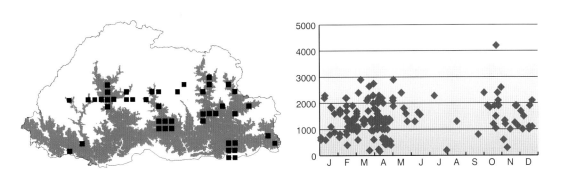

The Blue Rock Thrush breeds in a rather narrow band from the Mediterranean, through southern Asia, to Japan and Taiwan. In the Indian subcontinent it breeds in the north-west, reaching central Nepal. Elsewhere in the subcontinent it is a winter visitor, occurring in dry rocky areas.

In Bhutan the Blue Rock Thrush is a common winter visitor throughout the temperate zone and in the western and eastern foothills. It occupies a similar altitudinal range to other rock thrushes, at 400–2,400 m. However, it is more restricted to lower altitudes, being most regular below 1,500 m, with occasional records to 200 m and 3,000 m, principally in spring. Most have departed their winter quarters by mid-May, but scattered records are available from June to August, probably involving stray birds from breeding areas further west in the Himalayas. Both July records were made during the surveys of the 1960s, when the species was perhaps commoner at this season. The first autumn migrants are noted from early October, initially at higher altitudes, but rapidly occupying lower areas. A record of one on 20 September[52] at 600 m was relatively early. Autumn migration is marked by the observation of one on active southbound migration at 1,900 m on 24 October[52] and a specimen from 4,200 m, which coincided with a large fall of migrants pre-empted by bad weather conditions[1]. Wintering birds show strong site faithfulness, with birds found in the same locality annually in mid-November–March. It is rather solitary, although up to five may be dispersed over some distance at suitable sites.

# Blue Whistling Thrush
*Myophonus caeruleus*

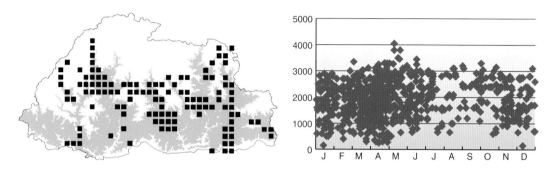

The Blue Whistling Thrush occurs in the Himalayas from Pakistan to Arunachal Pradesh and the hills of north-east India. Outside the Indian subcontinent its range extends north-west to Turkestan, north-east into China, and south to Sumatra and Java. It inhabits forested areas, usually close to water such as small fast-flowing streams.

In Bhutan the Blue Whistling Thrush is abundant throughout the temperate zone and foothills, and more occasional in the alpine zone. Its summer range spans 600–3,200 m, but in winter it withdraws below 2,800 m. More occasionally it occurs to 200 m and 4,100 m[22]. It is a partial altitudinal migrant, with some remaining present at higher elevations in winter, whilst others occupy a non-breeding range in winter and early spring. Birds are present in the upper part of the range in April–October, and song is heard from late February to June. Breeding records are surprisingly scarce and birds may be rather secretive around their nests. Road culverts appear to be a regular nest site[5]. One was seen carrying nest material at 600 m on 28 April[52], whilst a pair giving alarm calls was present at 1,700 m on 1 June[52]. Near Zhemgang a mean density of 0.8 breeding pairs per km was found at 1,600–1,900 m, with all pairs in the lower part of this range[52]. It is the commonest bird species along roadsides, with several tens of birds or even over 100 encountered during journeys, with one every km. Largest numbers are present in such areas in late winter. Aside from its occurrence in forest areas, it is also a common bird of towns and villages.

# Orange-headed Thrush
*Zoothera citrina*

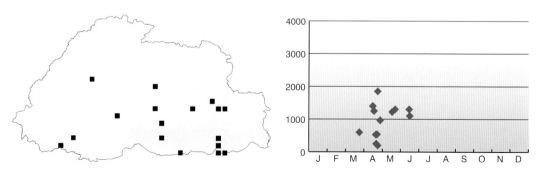

The Orange-headed Thrush is mainly a summer visitor to the Himalayas from Pakistan to Arunachal Pradesh. Elsewhere in the subcontinent it occurs in north-east India and Bangladesh and parts of the peninsula, where it is a resident and winter visitor. Further east the species reaches southern China and the Greater Sundas. It inhabits the forest floor, affecting damp, shady places in broadleaf forest and dense second growth.

In Bhutan this thrush is an uncommon summer visitor. Although recorded throughout the temperate zone and foothills, occurrence is erratic and no sites appear to be occupied annually. Records are known from 200–1,800 m, between mid-April and June, with the earliest on 24 March[40,52]. Although the limited numbers of records do not permit firm conclusions, it appears that in the second half of April passage migrants occur, presumably en route to breeding areas in the Western Himalayas. May and June birds might be local breeders and are noted in a narrow altitudinal range between 1,100 m and 1,300 m. Whilst the maximum number observed at one site is three[14,28], a staggering total of 53 was banded at Gedu in the 1970s[36]. The circumstances behind this are unknown and, therefore, it is difficult to know if relying on sight records leads to the species going seriously under-recorded and/or if the above represents further evidence for heavy passage through Bhutan.

# Plain-backed Thrush
## *Zoothera mollissima*

N = 151(49). S 2200-3800 (mid-Apr-Sep); W 1400-2800

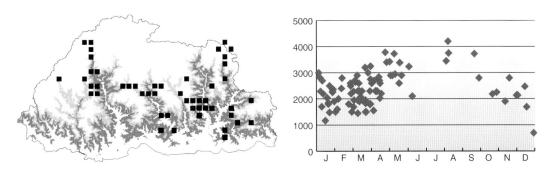

The Plain-backed Thrush breeds on open grassy slopes with dense bushes near the treeline and winters in broadleaf forest. In the Indian subcontinent it occurs in the Himalayas from Pakistan to Arunachal Pradesh, its range extending east and north to Yunnan, northern Vietnam and Sichuan.

In Bhutan the Plain-backed Thrush is an occasionally recorded resident and the commonest *Zoothera*, being found throughout the temperate and alpine zones, and is known in the central foothills from a single record. It is an altitudinal migrant, summering at 2,200–3,800 m, probably mostly in higher parts of this range, where probably largely under-recorded. The highest record is from 4,200 m in August[31]. In winter it occurs at 1,400–2,800 m, with the lowest record *c*.700 m[50]. Occurrence at this season is erratic, with few records in some years and influxes in others. In autumn birds gradually descend from the breeding areas in October–December and influxes may occur from early January. From mid-March to mid-April birds return to the breeding areas. In spring 1995 there was an influx, particularly to the Sunkosh Valley. A large influx occurred in late March 1998, in the Thimphu and Paro valleys, with several tens reported[5,28]. Further east, in the Punakha/Wangdue Phodrang area and in the forest above Yonkhola, Mongar district, a higher than usual presence was noted as well, although no large numbers were encountered. Spring 2000 witnessed another influx with widespread presence in the central and eastern valleys, which unlike in spring 1998 reached south to Zhemgang[52]. Although normally birds are encountered singly, quietly feeding at the forest edge, during influxes the species occurs in loose flocks of up to six. Influxes coincide with irruptions of Dark-throated and other thrushes, indicating that the Plain-backed Thrushes may originate outside Bhutan, possibly from montane western China. However, the local nature of these influxes points to heavy snowfall at higher elevations as a potential factor, in which case presumably local birds are primarily involved.

# Long-tailed Thrush
## *Zoothera dixoni*

N=46(23). S 3000-4000 (mid-Apr-Oct); W 1200-2800

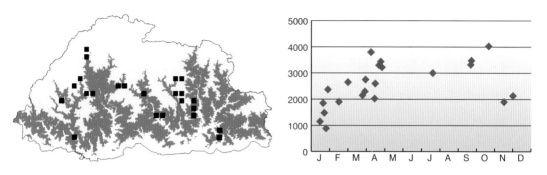

The Long-tailed Thrush has a scattered distribution in the Himalayas, from Himachal Pradesh to Arunachal Pradesh and in north-east India. Further east and north its range reaches Yunnan and Sichuan. Habitat consists of undergrowth in dense high-elevation forest. In winter it moves downslope but still prefers denser forest than Plain-backed Thrush.

In Bhutan the Long-tailed Thrush is an uncommon altitudinal migrant throughout the temperate zone and in the high west. Its summer range spans 3,000–4,000 m, while in winter it descends to 1,200–2,800 m, with the lowest record *c*.1,000 m[22]. During influxes of Plain-backed Thrush, this species appears somewhat more widespread, but numbers are lower than of its lookalike relative. No more than two have been found at any one site. Singing birds have been found in fir forest at *c*.3,400 m in late April[5].

# Scaly Thrush
## *Zoothera dauma*

N=59(28). S 1800-3200 (May-Oct); W 200-2400

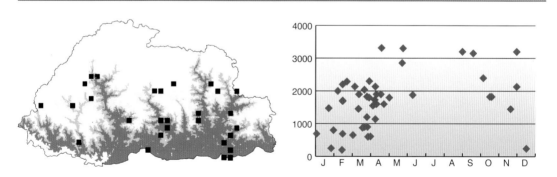

The distribution of the Scaly Thrush is extremely scattered, with separate populations in the Urals, east Asia, the Himalayas, southern India and various parts of south-east Asia. In winter some Himalayan birds migrate to the southern Indian peninsula. It inhabits dense undergrowth in shady forests.

In Bhutan the Scaly Thrush is an uncommon altitudinal migrant throughout the temperate zone and in the central and eastern foothills. Due to its secretive behaviour, its summer range is unclear but appears to be 1,800–3,200 m, possibly more frequent at higher altitudes. It occupies the lowest winter range of the *Zoothera*, occurring at 200–2,400 m. Winter presence appears unrelated to influxes of other thrushes and birds are found at the same site annually. Numbers are generally low, with 1.3 birds per sighting on average. In April there is a larger presence related to passage through mid-elevations to the breeding areas. Some passage birds perhaps originate from elsewhere, but numbers remain small. Ten observed on 4 April at 1,500 m was exceptional[5]. Breeding starts in early May as evidenced by a pair carrying food at 2,900 m on 23 May[22]. From mid-October birds are again noted in the wintering areas.

# Long-billed Thrush
## *Zoothera monticola*

N=55(30). S 2000-2800 (mid-Apr-Sep); W 1400-2600

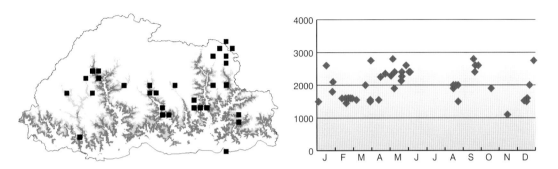

The Long-billed Thrush is patchily distributed in the Himalayas from Himachal Pradesh to Arunachal Pradesh and in north-east India. Further east it occurs in Myanmar and northern Vietnam. Habitat consists of dense undergrowth and swampy patches in deep forest in the temperate zone.

In Bhutan the Long-billed Thrush is an uncommon altitudinal migrant that appears to be quite widespread. It has been found throughout the temperate zone and the high east, and is known in the eastern foothills from a single record[28]. In summer it occupies the cool broadleaf forest zone at 2,000–2,800 m, reaching 3,000 m[14]. The latter record is not included on the graph due to an imprecise date being recorded. In winter it remains present to 2,600 m but descends to 1,400 m, more occasionally to 1,100 m[52], where it regularly accompanies forktails feeding in road drainage ditches or along small streams in forest. By mid-March most have left the wintering areas, although it is still occasionally noted at lower altitudes until mid-April. Singing has been heard in the second half of April at *c*.2,400 and 3,000 m[14]. Breeding commences in this period, as evidenced by a pair with a recently fledged young at 2,000 m on 20 May[49]. From August birds disperse, and are again found outside the breeding areas. On average 1.3 birds are noted per sighting, with a max. 3.

# Tickell's Thrush
## *Turdus unicolor*

N=13(7). S 1400-2000

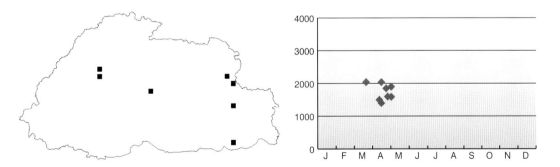

Tickell's Thrush is a summer visitor to the Himalayas from Pakistan east to Bhutan, being commonest in the west. Its main winter area is the east and north-east of the subcontinent. Habitat consists of open forest and well-wooded areas.

In Bhutan Tickell's Thrush is apparently a rare passage migrant, found in the Sunkosh, central and eastern valleys in warm broadleaf forest at 1,400–2,000 m, from late March to early May. This temporal pattern suggests the arrival of breeders further west, as records cease after early May. On 12 April 1996 one was singing in the Mo Chhu valley, Punakha district, at *c*.1,500 m[19], which is the only indication of breeding. Numbers are low with never more than two noted together. There are no records in autumn.

# White-collared Blackbird
## Turdus albocinctus

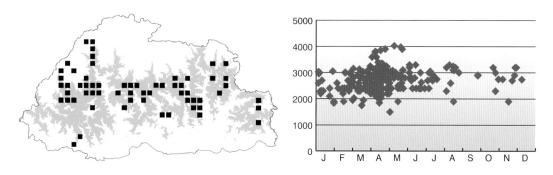

The White-collared Blackbird ranges along the Himalayas, from Himachal Pradesh to Arunachal Pradesh, as well as the hills of north-east India. Its range continues north-east to south-east Tibet and Sichuan. It occurs in various forest types in the temperate zone, often near cultivation.

In Bhutan the White-collared Blackbird is an abundant resident throughout the temperate zone and in the high west. It is particularly common in the Thimphu and Paro valleys, where it finds favoured habitat in abundance: Blue Pine forest near cultivation. The species is common in open areas of Thimphu town. The species's regular altitudinal range spans 2,000–3,400 m, with occasional records to 1,500 m[5] and 4,000 m[22]. Years of thrush irruptions that particularly involve Dark-throated Thrush clearly involve White-collared Blackbird as well. In the winters of 1994/1995, 1997/1998 and 1999/2000 there were large influxes, with two to four times (for 1997/98 and 1999/2000 respectively) more records than in other years, during December to April. Moreover, larger numbers were observed, with c.8 birds per sighting in irruption years and 3.5 in other winters. Largest numbers were, e.g., 27 at Nobding, Wangdue Phodrang district, on 1 March 1995[19] and more than 100 at Babesa, Thimphu district, on 26 March 2000[24]. Peak numbers occur in late March and early April, with wider presence already noted from January, particularly below 2,000 m, where records are entirely limited to irruption years. Singing males are heard April–June and nesting occurs late April–June, with some variation. A female was seen carrying nest material at 3,300 m on 26 April[22], birds carrying food were noted at 2,900 m on 22 May[22] and at 2,400 m on 18 June[52], whilst a pair with recently fledged young was seen at 2,400 m on 14 June[52].

# Grey-winged Blackbird
## Turdus boulboul

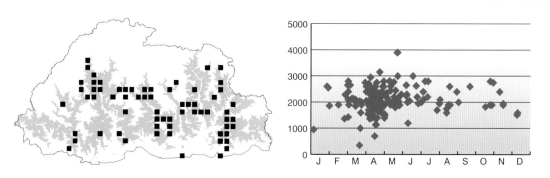

The Grey-winged Blackbird generally occupies lower altitudes than White-collared Blackbird. It is similarly distributed in the Indian subcontinent, along the Himalayas from Pakistan to Arunachal Pradesh and in north-east India, and extending east to northern Vietnam. It prefers denser forest habitat, broadleaved and mixed, being associated particularly with oak forest.

In Bhutan the Grey-winged Blackbird is a common resident throughout the temperate zone, with a few records from the eastern subtropical zone. Its regular altitudinal range spans 1,400–2,800 m, coinciding with the distribution of oak forest. More occasionally it is recorded to 400 m and 4,000 m[44]. It is normally found singly or in pairs, with day totals sometimes approaching 20, but rarely forms flocks. A concentration of 10–15 with many other thrushes at Nobding, Wangdue Phodrang district, on 1 April 1995[19] was rather exceptional. It does not appear to be a constituent of thrush irruptions, which is unsurprising given its range south of the Himalayan main range. Singing birds are noted in April–May, but the two confirmed breeding records probably represent extremes or multiple broods. On 8 April a male was seen carrying food at 1,900 m[52] and on 29 August a nest with eggs was found at 2,400 m[31].

# Eurasian Blackbird
## *Turdus merula*

N = 14(7). W 2400-3200

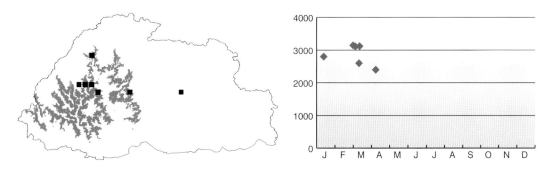

The Eurasian Blackbird is an adaptable thrush with a wide range in Eurasia, from Western Europe to south-east China. In the Indian subcontinent it breeds in the Western Himalayas east to Uttar Pradesh, in Arunachal Pradesh and south-west and eastern India. The nearest breeding areas to Bhutan are on the Tibetan Plateau.

In Bhutan the Eurasian Blackbird is an uncommon winter visitor with occurrence linked to large-scale irruptions of thrushes, particularly Dark-throated Thrush. The species was first recorded in Bhutan on 12 January 1992[39] at 2,800 m in the Phobjikha Valley, a record that points to a thrush irruption, although no such influx was documented that year due to the limited number of observers. Most records were in March to mid-April 2000 during a massive thrush influx, with the first birds noted around 1 March, near Gasa, Wangdue Phodrang district[57], and flocks of up to nine, with a mean 4.5 birds per sighting, subsequently noted in the Thimphu Valley, at Dochu La, the Phobjikha Valley and Ura, Bumthang district, at 2,400–3,200 m. Birds remained until mid-April, the latest records being on 16 April[28]. The species occurred at the same localities as Kessler's Thrush and the two often formed mixed flocks.

# Chestnut Thrush
## *Turdus rubrocanus*

N = 14(8). W 2000-3000

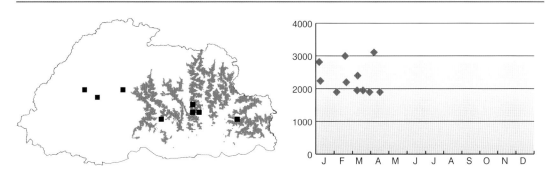

The Chestnut Thrush has two distinct subspecies. One, *rubrocanus*, breeds in the Western Himalayas, from Pakistan to Uttar Pradesh, and winters in the Eastern Himalayas and north-east India. Subspecies *gouldii* breeds in montane western China and eastern Tibet, and mainly winters in Myanmar, occasionally reaching the north-east subcontinent. Winter habitat consists of open woodland with fruit trees.

In Bhutan the Chestnut Thrush is a rare and erratic winter visitor, recorded throughout the temperate zone, mostly in the central and eastern valleys, at 2,000–3,000 m. It appears primarily during influxes of other thrushes, particularly Dark-throated Thrush. Timing is similar to that of other thrushes during these irruptions, with arrival in January and departure by mid-April. The winters of 1994/95, 1997/98 and 1999/2000 yielded respectively three, one and six records. There was one record in April 1999, when few Dark-throated Thrushes were present[19]. Most records concern singles, feeding close to cover secretively, and the majority concern *gouldii*, which suggests a north-eastern origin for these irruptions. Subspecies *rubrocanus* has been recorded twice, in February 1995[28] and January 2000[22,49], during periods when *atrogularis* Dark-throated Thrush was prevalent, and suggesting a western component origin.

# Kessler's Thrush
*Turdus kessleri*                                                      N=16(6). W 2400-3200

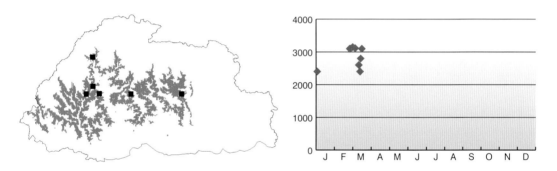

Kessler's Thrush breeds above the treeline in eastern Tibet and western China, and is a rare winter visitor to the Eastern Himalayas from central Nepal to Bhutan.

Kessler's Thrush is an uncommon winter visitor that reached Bhutan only during the large-scale thrush irruption of 1999/2000. The first birds were noted on 2 January above the Thimphu Valley[56], followed by presence at various sites of small flocks of up to 14. Mean flock size was 5.4. Birds were particularly evident in the Thimphu Valley, at Dochu La, near Gasa, in the Phobjikha Valley and at Ura, Bumthang district, often with Eurasian Blackbirds. The species remained present at 2,400–3,200 m until departure in mid-April, with the last record on 16 April[28].

# Eyebrowed Thrush
*Turdus obscurus*                                                      N=8(8)

The Eye-browed Thrush breeds in Siberia from the Yenisey River to Kamchatka, and south to Japan. It winters in mainland south-east Asia, its main range just reaching the north-east subcontinent, where it is common in north-east India. Elsewhere, it is a rare winter visitor, west to central Nepal. Winter habitat consists of open forest.

In Bhutan the Eye-browed Thrush is a rare passage migrant. Autumn passage is noted late November to early January, spring passage in May–early June. The eight records are scattered throughout the temperate zone, at 1,100–3,200 m. Birds are invariably encountered singly, underlining an erratic presence in Bhutan. Fifty percent of records concern specimens collected in the 1960s and 1970s, suggesting that it was more common formerly.

Eyebrowed Thrush
*Jan Wilczur*

# Dark-throated Thrush
*Turdus ruficollis*

N=163(50). W 1200-3200

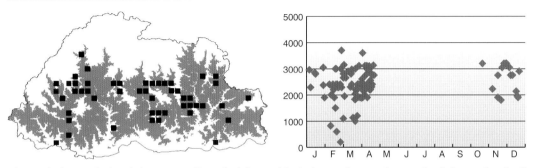

The Dark-throated Thrush has two well-marked forms, black-throated *atrogularis* and red-throated *ruficollis*. The former breeds in Siberia from the Urals to the Yenisey River, the latter from the Yenisey to Kamchatka. In winter both reach the northern Indian subcontinent. Numbers vary considerably from year to year. Winter habitat consists of forest edge and adjacent open areas.

In Bhutan the Dark-throated Thrush is a frequent winter visitor throughout the temperate zone, with isolated records in the western and eastern foothills. Presence varies between years, with very few records in one year and large influxes in another. During 1995 to 2002, the winters of 1994/95, 1997/98 and 1999/2000 produced irruptions. Largest numbers appeared in 1999/2000, when an influx of various thrushes was noted over large parts of south-east Asia. In the winters 1995/96 and 2000/01 Dark-throated Thrushes were almost absent, with respectively one and two records. In non-irruption years birds are typically seen from mid-March to mid-April; numbers are low, with a mean 2.7 birds per sighting and ten the maximum. Irruption years produce, on average, four times as many records and larger flocks, with a mean 7.4 birds per sighting. Influxes commence with the observation of large flocks, of up to 80, from late November, with the earliest date being 21 November[52]. These are first noted in the upland valleys of Bumthang and Phobjikha, and at their passes. Soon they disperse and smaller flocks of up to 20 appear at many sites at lower altitudes. As in non-influx years, the birds depart by mid-April. The usual altitudinal range of the species in Bhutan spans 1,200–3,200 m, with the highest record from 3,800 m[57]. However, lower areas, below 2,000 m, are only occupied during irruptions, when birds occasionally reach 200 m[19]. Of the two subspecies, *atrogularis* is commonest and occurs annually. The occurrence of *ruficollis* is almost entirely related to irruption years. However, *atrogularis* remains commoner during influxes, with slightly more records and somewhat larger numbers (8.0 *atrogularis*/sighting vs. 5.3 *ruficollis*/sighting). The only exception to this was the 1995 irruption when *ruficollis* was commoner. The regular presence of Dark-throated Thrushes in spring may represent a direct northerly movement of a (small) part of the *atrogularis* population en route to their central Siberian breeding areas from the Indian winter quarters. In irruption years the presence of *ruficollis* points to a more easterly origin to the thrush influxes, a notion supported by the presence of other thrushes from western China and eastern Siberia in these years.

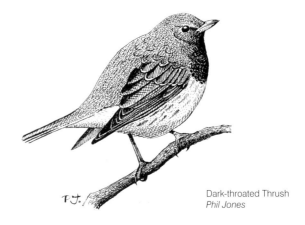

Dark-throated Thrush
*Phil Jones*

# Dusky Thrush
*Turdus naumanni*

N=13(4). W 2600-3200

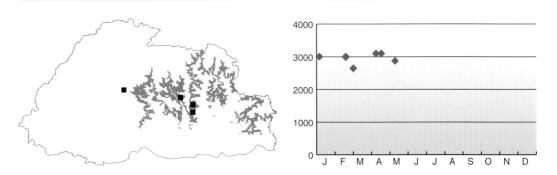

The Dusky Thrush breeds in Siberia from the Yenisey River to Kamchatka, wintering in east Asia from Japan to northern Myanmar and Taiwan. It is a rare winter visitor to the Himalayas, from central Nepal to Arunachal Pradesh and north-east India. In winter it affects open habitats with thinly scattered trees.

In Bhutan this thrush is a rare winter visitor, recorded in the Sunkosh, central and eastern valleys. Occurrence is related to irruptions of Dark-throated Thrushes. During the influxes of 1994/1995, 1997/1998 and 1999/2000 it was recorded respectively on two, two and six occasions. Most records were, therefore, during the large thrush influx of 1999/2000, which also produced slightly higher numbers, with a max. 3 reported[22,49]. In other years there is just a single record from 5 May 1996[19]. Except for an observation at Nobding, Wangdue Phodrang district, all records are from the Bumthang region. Birds have been noted in January to mid-May, joining flocks of Dark-throated Thrushes, but staying longer. Two subspecies are involved, *eunomus* and *naumanni*, each represented equally. Some are intermediates between the two, suggesting that birds probably originate from the area of intergradation.

# Gould's Shortwing
*Brachypteryx stellata*

N=9(7). S 2800-4200

Gould's Shortwing is patchily distributed in the Himalayas from Uttar Pradesh to Arunachal Pradesh. Further east its range reaches western China and northern Vietnam. It summers at high altitude, in rhododendron and bamboo scrub, dense undergrowth in fir and rhododendron forests, sometimes even among boulders far from scrub. It is a generally rare and little-known bird.

In Bhutan Gould's Shortwing is an uncommon and localised altitudinal migrant, mainly known from specimens collected by Ludlow in 1933–34. He collected a total of ten from the Dib La and Pang La ridge between Trashi Yangtse and Lhuntse[31] in August–September. The bird was apparently quite common there, but Ludlow did not record it elsewhere. In recent years, the species was reconfirmed in this area, on the Trashi Yangtse side of the ridge, with three records in early spring and May[49] at 2,800–4,200 m. Those collected in September by Ludlow were probably still on the breeding grounds, as revealed by the presence of juveniles. His record of one at 2,700 m on 23 September possibly indicates altitudinal movements to lower areas[31]. Whilst all these records are from a relatively small area, within the boundaries of Bumdeling Wildlife Sanctuary, there is a record from further west, where on 1 November 1999 one was observed below Sengor, Mongar district[45], suggesting that other populations may exist at high elevations. The juveniles collected by Ludlow are the only breeding evidence obtained anywhere, as the nest remains undescribed.

# Rusty-bellied Shortwing
## *Brachypteryx hyperythra*

N=1(1)

The Rusty-bellied Shortwing is a poorly known species with a restricted range along the Himalayan foothills from West Bengal to Arunachal Pradesh, and into northern Myanmar. Records are centred on Sikkim/Darjeeling and in eastern Arunachal Pradesh. It is globally threatened, classified by BirdLife International as Vulnerable, as the small population is probably under pressure through deforestation. Habitat and possible altitudinal movements are poorly understood.

In Bhutan the Rusty-bellied Shortwing has been found once. In April 2002 three singing males were located in the western valleys at *c*.2,000 m[19], in an area characterised by steep slopes and scrubby vegetation. Significant numbers of singing males have recently been found at similar altitude and habitat in Darjeeling: steep, damp vegetated gullies with secondary growth (Mauro and Vercruysse 2000). The Bhutan record represents an extension of the range of the Darjeeling population.

# Lesser Shortwing
## *Brachypteryx leucophrys*

N=137(29). R 1400-2800

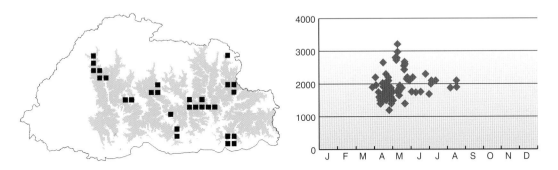

The Lesser Shortwing is widespread in eastern and south-east Asia, from Sichuan in the north to Indonesia in the south. In the Indian subcontinent it occurs rather sparingly in the Himalayas, from eastern Nepal to Arunachal Pradesh and in north-east India. Habitat is dense undergrowth in moist broadleaf forest.

In Bhutan the Lesser Shortwing has only been recorded in spring and summer, when its song reveals its presence. Outside the breeding season the species is very difficult to find due to its skulking behaviour. Thus, status is unclear, it possibly being an altitudinal migrant like White-browed Shortwing. It is occasionally recorded in the Sunkosh, central and eastern valleys, and the central and eastern foothills. Its range spans 1,400–2,800 m, with occasional records to 3,200 m[22], but mainly below 2,000 m. Song is heard from the first week of April, with the earliest record 28 March[52]. Birds are heard throughout summer, the latest records in mid-August[52]. Near Zhemgang a mean density of 0.4 territories per km was found at 1,600–1,900 m[52]. Near Yonkhola, Mongar district (1,500–2,000 m), the greatest number of singing males per km in April is in the same order of magnitude, with an average in 1996–2002 of 0.4, varying between 0.1 and 0.6[14,28], thus revealing large annual fluctuations.

197

# White-browed Shortwing
*Brachypteryx montana*                    N=114(41), S 2200-3400 (May-Sep); W 1200-3200

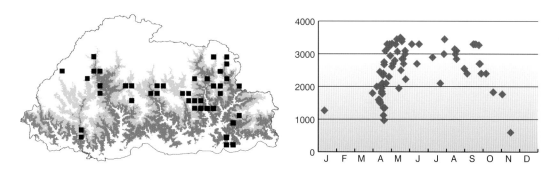

The main range of the White-browed Shortwing is in south-east Asia, from Taiwan south to the Philippines and Indonesia. In the Indian subcontinent it reaches along the Himalayan range, from central Nepal to Arunachal Pradesh and north-east India. Habitat is moist forest at higher altitudes—fir, oak and rhododendron—often near streams and gullies.

In Bhutan the White-browed Shortwing is a common altitudinal migrant throughout the temperate zone, with occasional records from the high west and the eastern foothills. In summer it occurs at 2,200–3,400 m. As it is mostly located by voice, winter records are relatively few. However, in spring there appears to be a gradual movement to higher altitudes, and the winter range appears to be roughly below 2,000 m. There is one record at 600 m from November[31]. In summer it appears to be most common above 3,000 m and is therefore largely segregated from Lesser Shortwing, which is commonest below 2,000 m. Breeding areas are occupied mid-April to mid-October. A max. 15 singing was counted along the road from Sengor to Yonkhola, Mongar district, in mid-April to mid-May[28]. The annual mean number of singing birds in this area (1,500–3,000 m) was 0.3 per km in 1996–2002, varying between 0.1 and 0.4[14,28]. There are no definite breeding records for Bhutan, but Ludlow collected a juvenile at Tobrang, Trashi Yangtse district, at 2,400 m on 3 September[31].

# Dark-sided Flycatcher
*Muscicapa sibirica*                    N=318(68). S 800-3400

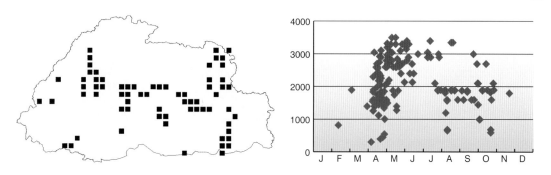

The Dark-sided Flycatcher breeds in the Himalayas from Pakistan to Arunachal Pradesh and the hills of north-east India. Its winter quarters are imperfectly known. A separate population exists in northern China, the Altai, Kamchatka and Japan, which winters from southern China south to the Greater Sundas. It inhabits open patches in temperate forest, broadleaf as well as conifer, where it hunts insects, returning to the same perch repeatedly.

In Bhutan the Dark-sided Flycatcher is a common summer visitor throughout the temperate zone, with occasional records in the alpine zone and the foothills. It is mostly found at 800–3,400 m, with occasional records to 300 m and 3,500 m. Arrival is generally in the first two weeks of April, but one was collected at 800 m on 10 February[20]. It is initially noted at lower elevations, reaching higher altitudes by early May. From May to August almost all records are above 2,000 m, indicating this as its breeding range. A nest was found at 2,100 m on 30 May[20] and juveniles have been noted by mid-July at 2,100 m[20] and mid-August at 3,200 m[52]. From mid-July birds disperse to lower altitudes, gradually retreating from higher areas. By the last week of October all have returned to their winter quarters outside Bhutan. The species occurs in a variety of habitats from cool broadleaf forest to fir, hemlock and Blue Pine forests. It is common, being frequently noted along roadsides, perched on electricity wires. A max. 40 was noted between Sengor and Yonkhola, Mongar district (1,500–3,000 m)[28], equivalent to c.1 per km.

# Asian Brown Flycatcher
## Muscicapa dauurica

N=18(12). S 200-2400

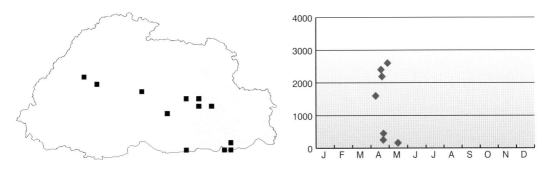

The Asian Brown Flycatcher is a summer visitor to the Himalayas from Pakistan to Bhutan, wintering in southern India and Sri Lanka. It also breeds in south-west India, and a further population, which breeds in eastern Siberia to Japan, winters in south-east Asia. Habitat in the subcontinent consists of open subtropical broadleaf forest.

In Bhutan the Asian Brown Flycatcher is uncommon, with scattered records throughout the temperate zone and the eastern foothills, at 200–2,400 m, with the highest from 2,600 m[5]. In spring it is noted only during a short period, from mid-April to the first half of May, with the earliest on 8 April[28]. It is unclear whether these records represent arriving local breeders or whether passage also occurs, but suggestive of the latter is the concentration of records in the central and eastern valleys. As a breeder it becomes more common further west in the Himalayas, whilst in the east passage of the east Asian population might be expected. Up to five have been noted in a day[28]. There is one autumn record from 31 October[22]. The latter record is not included on the graph due to an imprecise altitude being reported.

# Brown-breasted Flycatcher
## Muscicapa muttui

N=1(1)

The Brown-breasted Flycatcher breeds in north-east India and winters mainly in south-west India and Sri Lanka. Its range extends further east into Yunnan and Sichuan. Habitat consists of dense thickets in evergreen broadleaf forest.

In Bhutan the Brown-breasted Flycatcher is a vagrant noted only once. On 25 April 2001 a single was observed near Samdrup Jongkha at 400 m[32].

# Ferruginous Flycatcher
*Muscicapa ferruginea*                                                    N=57(29). S 1400-2800

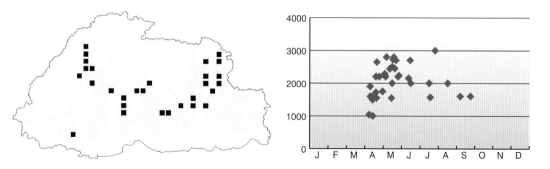

The Ferruginous Flycatcher is a summer visitor to the Himalayas from central Nepal to Arunachal Pradesh and the hills of north-east India, its range extending further east through southern China to Taiwan. It winters in mainland south-east Asia, the Philippines and the Greater Sundas. Habitat is humid broadleaf forest, particularly of oak and fir.

In Bhutan the Ferruginous Flycatcher is an uncommon summer visitor throughout the temperate zone, with an isolated record from the high west. Its altitudinal range spans 1,400–2,800 m, coinciding with the distribution of oak forest. The species arrives in the second week of April, initially at lower elevations, reaching higher altitudes by early May. Summer presence is short-lived, the birds having departed by late September. The earliest record is 7 April[12], the latest 23 September[52]. Breeding is confirmed by the observation of adults with juveniles on 21 July[20], and a juvenile collected at 3,000 m on 25 July[31], which is also the highest record. Birds are seen singly or in pairs and are probably easily overlooked in the lower storey of the forest.

# Slaty-backed Flycatcher
*Ficedula hodgsonii*                                                      N=34(15). W 200-2200

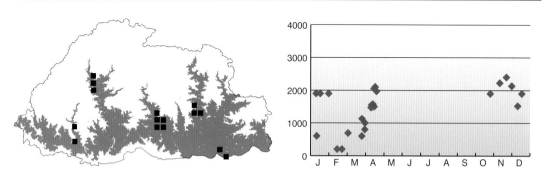

The Slaty-backed Flycatcher occurs sparsely in the Himalayas from central Nepal to Arunachal Pradesh and in the hills of north-east India. Further east it reaches Myanmar and western and south-west China. It is an altitudinal migrant that breeds in broadleaf and conifer forests at higher altitudes and winters in warm broadleaf forest.

In Bhutan the Slaty-backed Flycatcher is an uncommon altitudinal migrant, with scattered records throughout the temperate zone and in the eastern foothills. As noted by Ludlow, its behaviour in the breeding season is very unobtrusive and it 'disappears' completely between mid-April and late October, during which period it presumably breeds at higher altitudes. In general, the migration pattern appears rather similar to that of Rufous-gorgeted Flycatcher, with a gradual descent in November and ascent from mid-March to April. In November–April it occurs at 200–2,200 m, which is presumably the winter range. The highest record is from 2,400 m in April[52]. Whereas normally singles are reported, on 9 January a flock of *c*.10 was seen at 1,900 m near Zhemgang[52].

Rufous-gorgeted Flycatcher
*Dan Cole*

# Rufous-gorgeted Flycatcher
## *Ficedula strophiata*

N=514(90). S 2600-3400 (May-mid-Oct). W 1000-3200

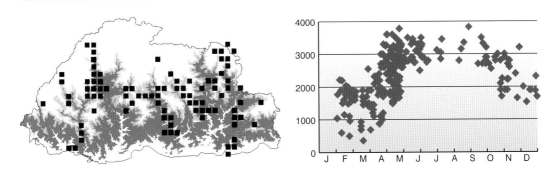

The Rufous-gorgeted Flycatcher occurs in the Himalayas from Himachal Pradesh to Arunachal Pradesh and in north-east India. Further east its range extends to southern China and northern Vietnam. It is an altitudinal migrant that occurs in a variety of forest habitats.

In Bhutan this flycatcher is an abundant altitudinal migrant throughout the alpine and temperate zones, and in the central and eastern foothills. In the breeding season it occurs at 2,600–3,400 m, and occasionally to 3,800 m, especially in April. At other seasons it is found at 1,000–3,200 m, with its winter range largely below 2,000 m, and occasional records to 400 m. From March there is a gradual movement to the breeding areas, the first arrivals reaching 3,400 m in early April. By early May all have vacated altitudes below 2,600 m. Descent to the winter quarters is more rapid, commencing in the second half of October, and almost all records are from below 2,000 m after mid-November. Initially the birds remain in the upper part of the winter range, above 1,500 m, but spread lower by January. There are no confirmed breeding records, but juveniles appear by mid-August[31,52]. During the breeding season it is widespread in cool broadleaf, fir and hemlock forests, with up to ten at a site. In the first half of April, when the bulk of the population moves through mid-elevations, it can be abundant, with several tens encountered in a morning. For example, a concentration of eight males was found at 2,100 m on 12 April[52]. In winter it is found singly or in small flocks of up to five, sometimes with mixed feeding flocks of minlas, tits and warblers.

# Red-throated Flycatcher
## *Ficedula parva*

N=83(18). W 200-2000

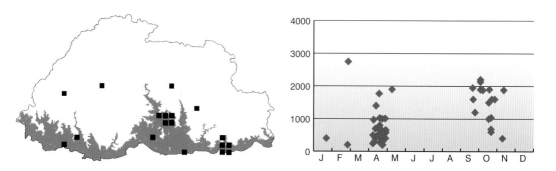

The Red-throated Flycatcher is a winter visitor over most of the Indian subcontinent, including the Himalayan foothills. Its breeding range covers the temperate zone of Eurasia from Eastern Europe to Sakhalin, as well as the Caucasus. Winter habitats comprise bushes, open forest and forest edge.

The Red-throated Flycatcher is a frequently recorded passage migrant and winter visitor to Bhutan, found throughout the temperate zone and the foothills. The subspecies involved is *albicilla*, which breeds east of the Urals and is now frequently considered to represent a separate species from *parva* (Taiga Flycatcher). Records of wintering are scarce and confined to foothills below 500 m. On spring and autumn passage it occurs principally at 200–2,200 m, with records concentrated in the central and eastern valleys, and just isolated occurrences in the western and Sunkosh valleys. Spring passage is noted from the second week of April, with the latest on 8 May[52]. There is an early spring record at 2,800 m on 26 February[43]. The first autumn migrants appear around 20 September and passage continues to mid-November. Movement through Bhutan probably concerns birds passing along the base of the Himalayas, crossing the main range further east, presumably in the Brahmaputra Valley. That records are confined to low elevations and are scarce in the west suggest this. In spring it appears to become gradually more numerous further east, with up to ten noted in forests above Samdrup Jongkha. Insufficient coverage in autumn does not permit conclusions concerning an east–west trend. In the lower central valleys it is widespread in this period, with a peak in late September and early October, when birds are present along the road every 5–10 km.

# Kashmir Flycatcher
## *Ficedula subrubra*

N=1(1)

The Kashmir Flycatcher is endemic to the Indian subcontinent, breeding in the Western Himalayas in Pakistan and India, and wintering in the south-west hills and Sri Lanka. It is a scarce passage migrant or vagrant to the Eastern Himalayas. Because of its very restricted summer and winter ranges, and forest destruction in these areas, it is considered globally threatened, classified by BirdLife International as Vulnerable.

Kashmir Flycatcher is a vagrant to Bhutan. On 15 October 1973 a male was collected at Bumthang[1].

# White-gorgeted Flycatcher
## *Ficedula monileger*

N=128(20). S 1600-2000 (mid-Mar-Oct); W 600-2000

The White-gorgeted Flycatcher is a scarce resident of the Himalayas from central Nepal to Arunachal Pradesh and the hills of north-east India, as well as further east to northern Vietnam. It is an elusive bird of dense undergrowth in moist broadleaf forest, affecting ravines and bamboo thickets.

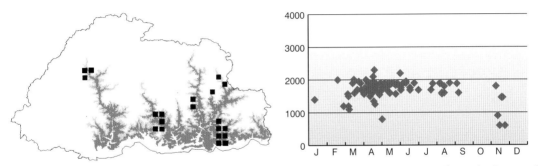

In Bhutan the White-gorgeted Flycatcher is a generally common altitudinal migrant in the Sunkosh, central and eastern valleys, and the central and eastern foothills, although it is scarce in the Sunkosh Valley, and the absence of records in the western valleys appears to be a genuine gap in its range. The species is mostly noted in the breeding season, when it is located by voice. Due to its skulking habits it is likely to be overlooked and most winter records are of specimens. In the breeding season it appears to occupy a narrow altitudinal range at 1,600–2,000 m, occasionally to 2,300 m. In winter it probably remains present in the same range, whilst also reaching to 600 m[31]. Singing birds are noted from early March at c.1,600 m and towards the end of the month at 2,000 m. Singing continues as late as early September. Peak song activity is in March at 1,600 m and around mid-May at 1,900 m, in both cases followed by a second peak in August. This perhaps indicates that timing of breeding is related to altitude and that two broods are probably produced. In its limited altitudinal range it can reach considerable densities, as shown by 2.1 territories per km near Zhemgang at 1,600–1,900 m[52]. There are no confirmed breeding records.

# Snowy-browed Flycatcher
## *Ficedula hyperythra*

N=58(27). S 1800-2800 (Apr-Oct); W 200-2200

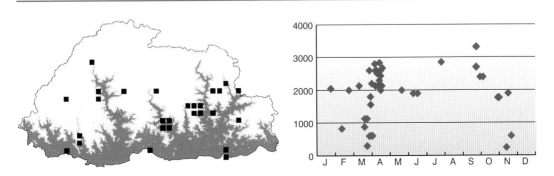

The Snowy-browed Flycatcher ranges widely in south-east Asia, reaching Indonesia and the Philippines. In the west its range extends to the north-east Indian subcontinent, where it occurs patchily in the Himalayas from Uttar Pradesh to Arunachal Pradesh and the hills of north-east India. Habitat is moist broadleaf forest with dense undergrowth.

In Bhutan the Snowy-browed Flycatcher is an uncommon altitudinal migrant throughout the temperate zone and the foothills. Its summer range spans 1,800–2,800 m, while in winter it descends to 200–2,200 m. However, as it tends to be overlooked due to its unobtrusive behaviour, this picture may be incomplete, as suggested by a number of records outside these ranges. For example, the highest records are from autumn, when it has been found at 3,300 m in September[1]. The only confirmed breeding record is from 600 m, where a nest was found on 1 April[1]. Most records are from mid-March to mid-April, when it presumably establishes territories. A max. 4 was found in a day in this period[28], suggesting that it may not be scarce. On the whole, it appears to be largely overlooked and is probably more common and widespread than appears from the available records.

# Little Pied Flycatcher
## *Ficedula westermanni*

N=205(42). S 1000-2400 (mid-Mar-Oct); W 200-1400

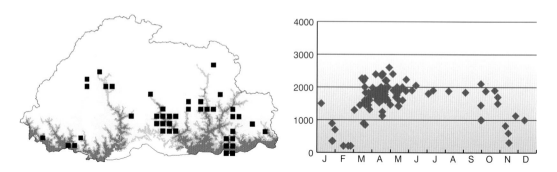

The Little Pied Flycatcher is widespread in mainland south-east Asia, Indonesia and the Philippines, and reaching the north-east Indian subcontinent in the west. Here it occurs in the Himalayas from Himachal Pradesh to Arunachal Pradesh and in north-east India. Habitat is broadleaf forest, particularly the midcanopy.

In Bhutan the Little Pied Flycatcher is a common altitudinal migrant throughout the temperate zone and the foothills. It is, however, scarce in the western and Sunkosh valleys, and probably occurs here only on passage. In the breeding season it is found at 1,000–2,400 m, while in November to mid-March it winters at 200–1,400 m. The breeding range is occupied in the second half of March, but migration continues until early May, with for example a flock of five observed in the western valleys at 2,400 m on 4 May[52]. Territories are established from early April, as shown by the presence of pairs and singing males in breeding habitat. Nest-building was observed on 11 May at 1,900 m[52]. A density of 1.0 breeding pairs per km was found near Zhemgang at 1,600–1,900 m[52]. In September–October it occasionally joins mixed-species flocks, with minlas, tits and warblers.

# Ultramarine Flycatcher
## *Ficedula superciliaris*

N=231(52). S 1400-2800

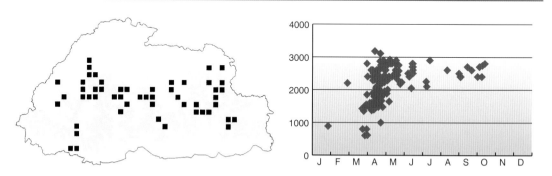

The Ultramarine Flycatcher is a summer visitor to the Himalayas, from Pakistan to Arunachal Pradesh and the hills of north-east India, descending in winter to the plains. Further east its range reaches south-east Tibet, Sichuan and Yunnan. Habitat comprises cool broadleaf and pine forests, where it affects the mid- and upper storeys.

The Ultramarine Flycatcher is a common summer visitor to Bhutan, found throughout the temperate zone, with one record from the western foothills. Its range spans 1,400–2,800 m. It arrives in the breeding areas from late March and is also noted at lower elevations, below 2,000 m, in April to early May, which perhaps denotes onward migration to breeding areas above 2,000 m. Although records are fewer beyond May, primarily due to a decrease in birding activity, the species is probably present in its breeding range until mid-October. The latest autumn record is 25 October[25]. In winter it mostly vacates the country, but there are records at 800 m in the Kuri Chhu valley on 26 January[22,49] and at Kori La on 27 February[43], both in the eastern valleys. It is a regular inhabitant of Blue Pine forest around Thimphu, and breeding has been confirmed in the western and Sunkosh valleys. Females carrying nest material were observed on 28 April at 2,200 m and on 22 May at 2,600 m[22], suggesting later breeding at higher altitudes. A nest with eggs was found on 13 June at 2,700 m[31] and adults with juveniles at 2,900 m on 12 July and at 2,600 m on 10 August[52]. Generally, the species appears widespread but rather thinly distributed, with up to six encountered in a day during spring migration, when its presence is widest. The largest number found at a site was ten, on the east slope of Dochu La in mid-April[5].

Ultramarine Flycatcher
*Dan Cole*

# Slaty-blue Flycatcher
## *Ficedula tricolor*

N=172(60). S 2600-3600 (mid-May-Sep); W 1200-3200

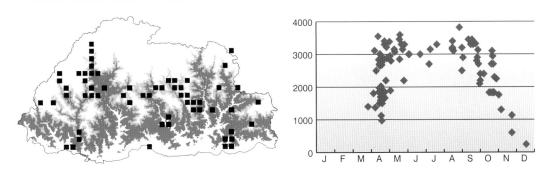

The Slaty-blue Flycatcher occurs in the Himalayas from Pakistan to Arunachal Pradesh and in the hills of north-east India, extending north-east to south-east Tibet, western and south-west China, and northern Vietnam. It is an altitudinal migrant that summers in scrub in the subalpine zone and dense undergrowth in high-altitude forest, and winters in the foothills and plains.

The Slaty-blue Flycatcher is a common altitudinal migrant, found in all biogeographic units. Pronounced altitudinal migration occurs, with the summer range lying at 2,600–3,600 m, and probably wintering largely outside Bhutan, although there are winter records from the foothills, in December[1] and February[19], and it may be regular but under-recorded here. The first spring migrants are noted by late March, passing through at 1,200–3,200 m, and passage continuing until early May. A total of 20, reported along 10 km of road around 2,400 m in April, shows that large numbers occur[14]. Due to its skulking habits it is easily overlooked. Autumn migration is noticeable from late September to late November. There are no confirmed breeding records, but Ludlow collected juveniles from 19 July[31]. The highest record is from 3,800 m in August[31].

# Sapphire Flycatcher
## *Ficedula sapphira*

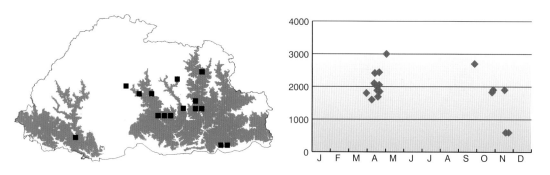

The Sapphire Flycatcher is a rare resident of the Himalayas, from central Nepal to Arunachal Pradesh and the hills of north-east India. Further east its range reaches northern Vietnam. Habitat is moist broadleaf forest, where it affects the mid- and lower storeys.

In Bhutan the Sapphire Flycatcher is an uncommon altitudinal migrant, with scattered records in the western, central and eastern valleys, and the eastern foothills. Records are concentrated in the central and eastern valleys. Generally, its occurrence is unpredictable and the majority, if not all, of the records are of migrants moving between their summer and winter ranges, which are as unclear and mysterious as those of Slaty-backed Flycatcher. It appears to follow a similar pattern of altitudinal migration as Rufous-gorgeted Flycatcher, with a gradual movement to higher altitudes from late March to late April, descending again in October–November. During these periods it has been noted at 600–2,800 m, with the highest at 3,000 m on 2 May[5]. Peak spring passage is in the second half of April, with a maximum of three noted near Chendebji, at 2,400 m, in the central valleys[19].

# Verditer Flycatcher
## *Eumyias thalassina*

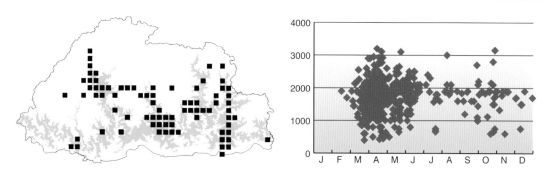

The Verditer Flycatcher breeds at mid-elevations of the Himalayas, from Pakistan to Arunachal Pradesh and in north-east India, and winters mostly in the foothills. Further east it ranges widely in south-east Asia south to Sumatra and Borneo. It inhabits open forest and forest edge, often perching on electricity wires beside roads.

In Bhutan this flycatcher is an abundant altitudinal migrant throughout the temperate zone and the foothills, with one record from the high west. Being closely associated with broadleaf forest, it is scarce in the western valleys, with only few records from Paro and Thimphu. Its regular summer range spans 600–2,600 m, with occasional records to 400 m and 3,200 m. It reaches the breeding areas from early March and remains present over its entire altitudinal range until October, thereafter apparently moving below 2,200 m in November–

December. There are very few records in January–February, most below 500 m. The paucity of winter records suggests that most of the population winters outside Bhutan. Singing birds occupy territories from early March until the first half of July. Nest-building has been noted at 1,700–1,900 m around mid-April[19,22,52] and food-carrying was noted at these altitudes around mid-May, when other pairs were nest-building[52], presumably starting a second brood. Timing coincides with peaks in territorial activity, with most singing birds noted in the second half of April and late May–early June. It is a numerous breeder and several tens can be found in a morning. Near Zhemgang a density of 3.4 breeding pairs per km was found at 1,600–1,900 m[52]. Singles sometimes associate with mixed-species flocks of minlas, tits and warblers.

# Large Niltava
## *Niltava grandis*

N=290(46). S 1600-2200 (May-Nov); W 800-2200

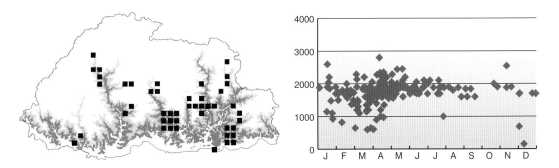

The Large Niltava occurs along the Himalayas from central Nepal to Arunachal Pradesh and in the hills of north-east India, as well as through mainland south-east Asia to Sumatra. It inhabits dense moist broadleaf forest, particularly near streams.

In Bhutan the Large Niltava is a common and widespread altitudinal migrant throughout the temperate zone and in the central and eastern foothills, but is relatively scarce in the Sunkosh and western valleys, where it approaches its westernmost limits. Its summer range spans 1,600–2,200 m. In winter it remains present in this zone but some disperse lower, down to 800 m. More occasionally it occurs to 200 m and 2,800 m, the former particularly in winter. It appears to occupy the breeding areas fully rather late, largely by May and June, when records from lower altitudes peter out and a peak in vocal activity is noted. Singing birds can, however, be heard from mid-February to December, also at lower elevations. A female carrying nest material was observed on 14 April at 1,900 m[19]. Near Zhemgang a mean density of 2.5 territories per km was found at 1,600–1,900 m, with considerable annual variation[52].

Sapphire Flycatcher
*Dan Cole*

# Small Niltava
## *Niltava macgrigoriae*

N=415(59). S 800-2000 (mid-Mar-Oct); W 400-1400

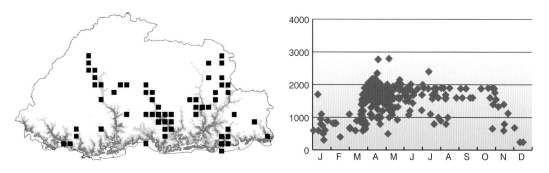

The Small Niltava breeds in the Himalayas from Uttar Pradesh to Arunachal Pradesh and in north-east India. Further east its range reaches northern Vietnam. It winters in the foothills. Habitat consists of scrub along streams and at the edge of broadleaf forest.

In Bhutan the Small Niltava is a common altitudinal migrant throughout the temperate zone and foothills, but is relatively scarce in the western valleys. Its summer range spans 800–2,000 m, occasionally to 2,800 m. In winter it moves somewhat lower, being recorded at 400–1,400 m and occasionally to 200 m. The summer range is occupied from late March, reaching the upper part by mid-April. Descent to the winter areas is mainly in November. Song is heard from mid-March and continues until mid-October, with peak activity in mid-April to mid-May, suggesting that the breeding season is relatively late. The first adults carrying food were noted on 22 May at 1,900 m[52], with similar records from the same altitude on 10 July[52], and at 1,200 m on 30 June[20]. Near Zhemgang a mean density of 4.1 territories per km was found at 1,600–1,900 m[52]. Up to 20 have been reported at a site, demonstrating it to be one of the more abundant birds of warm broadleaf forest.

# Rufous-bellied Niltava
## *Niltava sundara*

N=218(64). S 1600-3000 (Mar-Oct); W 200-2400

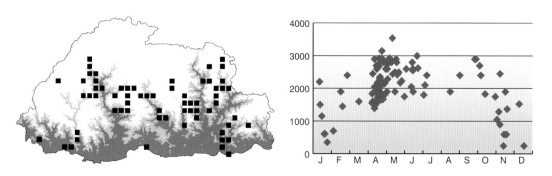

The Rufous-bellied Niltava is found in the Himalayas from Pakistan east to Arunachal Pradesh and north-east India, its range extending further east to Myanmar and to western and central China. In winter it descends to lower elevations, reaching the foothills. It has the highest range of the niltavas, summering in bushes and undergrowth of temperate broadleaf and mixed coniferous–broadleaf forests.

In Bhutan this niltava is frequent throughout the temperate zone and the foothills, and shows the most pronounced altitudinal movements of the genus. Its summer range spans 1,600–3,000 m, largely coinciding with the temperate broadleaf forest zone. In winter it descends to 200–2,400 m. The highest altitude recorded is 3,600 m in May[22]. Birds move to their breeding areas in April. A female at a possible nest was seen on 13 June at 2,800 m[52] and a pair with fledged young on 4 July at 2,100 m[52]. As the song is easily overlooked, most records concern sightings and it is not found in high densities, unlike most other niltavas, with usually fewer than five birds at a site. In winter it is invariably found singly, in undergrowth. Summer habitat consists of broadleaf forest, often mixed with hemlock.

# Vivid Niltava
## *Niltava vivida*
N=3(3)

The Vivid Niltava is a rare resident of the north-east Indian subcontinent, with records in the Himalayan foothills west to Sikkim and the hills of north-east India. Its range reaches south-east Tibet and northern mainland south-east Asia to Taiwan, though it is perhaps only a winter visitor to some areas. Habitat is broadleaved and mixed forest, where it affects the top canopy.

In Bhutan the Vivid Niltava is a rare summer visitor, recorded three times between mid-April and May. On 18 April 1997 a male was near Lumitsana, Wangdue Phodrang district[5]. A pair found near Zhemgang on 20 May 2001 were eventually identified as probable Vivid Niltavas[52]. Finally, a female was discovered at Nobding, Wangdue Phodrang, on 16 April 2002[5]. All sightings were in mature stands of broadleaf forest, in a narrow altitude zone around 2,000 m.

# Pale-chinned Flycatcher
## *Cyornis poliogenys*
N=12(9). R 200-1400

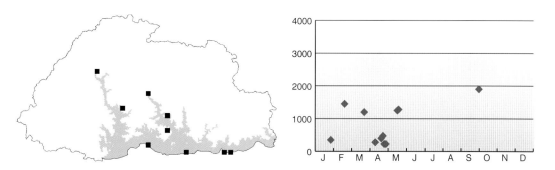

The global distribution of the Pale-chinned Flycatcher is largely restricted to the Indian subcontinent, where it occurs in the Himalayas from central Nepal to Arunachal Pradesh and north-east India, and scattered through eastern India. Elsewhere, it is found in adjacent Myanmar and south-west China. It inhabits undergrowth in open broadleaf forest.

In Bhutan the Pale-chinned Flycatcher is uncommon and appears rather local, having been found in the Sunkosh and central valleys and the central and eastern foothills. The only site with records from more than one year is the forest above Samdrup Jongkha[19,28], although the species is probably overlooked. Most records are from 200–600 m, with another cluster at 1,200–1,400 m. The highest record is from 1,900 m in September[29]. A January record at 400 m in the eastern foothills suggests that the species is probably resident[28]. Otherwise, most records are from mid-March to May, coinciding with the period of greatest birding activity.

# Pale Blue Flycatcher
## Cyornis unicolor

N=166(37). S 1200-2200 (Apr-Oct); W 200-1800

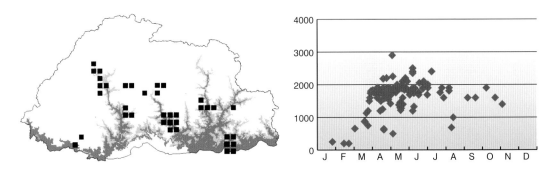

The Pale Blue Flycatcher occurs in the Himalayas from central Nepal to Arunachal Pradesh and in north-east India, but is generally rare and local in the west of this range. Further east, its distribution extends to Vietnam and south through the Malay Peninsula to the Greater Sundas. Habitat consists of dense broadleaf forest and second growth, where it affects particularly the mid- and top storeys.

In Bhutan this flycatcher is reported occasionally from the Sunkosh, central and eastern valleys, in areas with well-developed broadleaf stands. There are single records from the western valleys[36] and western foothills[52], the Dochu La ridge constituting the western limit of its range in Bhutan. Its regular altitudinal range appears to span 1,200–2,200 m, where it is present from late March to at least early August. In the breeding season it is occasional up to 2,400 m, with the highest record from 2,900 m[55]. The only record of birds carrying nest material is from 600 m on 9 April[5,52]. There are few January/February records, all from c.200 m in the eastern foothills[28,29], suggesting that the species largely winters south and east of Bhutan. From March passage birds occur at 200–1,800 m, whilst singing birds occupy territories from early April, and are vocal until late July. From August autumn migration is evident, but some are noted in the breeding range until early November. Near Zhemgang a density of c.4.0 territories per km was found at 1,600–1,900 m[52]. This contrasts with the relatively limited number of overall records, suggesting that the species is overlooked to some extent.

# Blue-throated Flycatcher
## Cyornis rubeculoides

N=124(40). S 200-1800

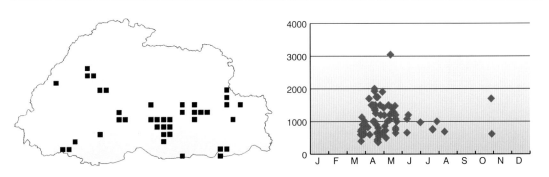

The Blue-throated Flycatcher occurs patchily in the Himalayas from Pakistan to Arunachal Pradesh and in north-east India, and extends to parts of mainland south-east Asia and north to central China. It is a partial migrant that winters in the Himalayan foothills and scattered localities elsewhere in India. Habitat consists of undergrowth in open forest at low elevations.

In Bhutan the Blue-throated Flycatcher is a common summer visitor throughout the temperate zone and the foothills. Its altitudinal range spans 200–1,800 m, with occasional records to 2,000 m. However, it is most numerous below 1,000 m, where more than ten can be present at a site. There is one record from 3,050 m on 12 May[22]. It is noted mostly in mid-March to late May, when singing birds are on territory. There are few records until mid-August and only two autumn records, from late October[22], suggesting that most, if not all, of the population winters outside Bhutan. Arrival in the breeding quarters is marked by a sudden influx in the last week of March, first noted at low elevations, involving loose flocks of several birds, followed by observations in the upper part of the range during April.

# Pygmy Blue Flycatcher
## *Muscicapella hodgsoni*

N=114(32). S 1400-2600 (Mar-Oct); W 200-600

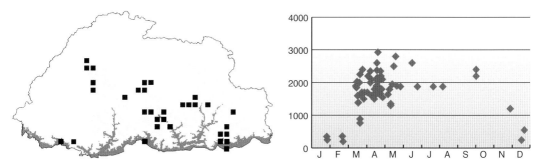

The Pygmy Blue Flycatcher occurs in the Himalayas from central Nepal to Arunachal Pradesh and the hills of north-east India, its range extending further east to Vietnam and south through the Malay Peninsula to Borneo and Sumatra. It is a bird of dense, damp, broadleaf forest.

In Bhutan the Pygmy Blue Flycatcher is a common altitudinal migrant throughout the temperate zone and the foothills, with isolated records in the western valleys and foothills, where it approaches its westernmost limits. The record in the western valleys has not been mapped due to an imprecise locality being reported. The summer range spans 1,400–2,600 m, the highest records being from c.2,800 m[14,55]. In winter it descends to the foothills, below 600 m. It occupies the breeding areas by mid-March. Once the song is known, it appears to be quite frequent, e.g. more than five heard in a small valley near Zhemgang at c.2,000 m on 19 March[52]. Song is mostly heard in March and again in May to early August, the birds apparently being rather silent in April, although the species is often noted amongst birds attracted to playback of the Collared Owlet's call. Mostly found singly or in pairs, with small flocks of up to five sometimes noted in the early breeding season. From October it probably makes a gradual descent to its winter quarters.

# Grey-headed Canary Flycatcher
## *Culicicapa ceylonensis*

N=748(89). S 1000-2800 (Mar-mid-Oct); W 600-2000

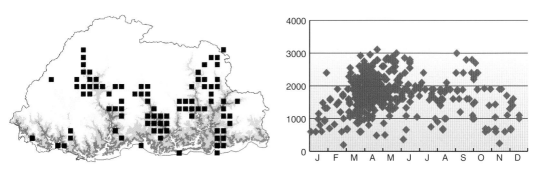

The Grey-headed Canary Flycatcher inhabits hills and mountains and is widespread in eastern and south-east Asia, from central China to Indonesia. It occurs in the Indian subcontinent in the Himalayas from Pakistan to

Arunachal Pradesh and the hills of north-east India, but is more scattered elsewhere. It occupies a wide range of forest habitats, and is an altitudinal migrant that winters mostly in the foothills.

In Bhutan the Grey-headed Canary Flycatcher is an abundant altitudinal migrant throughout the temperate zone and foothills, with single records from the high west and east. Its summer range spans 1,000–2,800 m, occasionally 3,000 m. It is present here until early November, when it retreats to 600–2,000 m. Occurrence to 200 m is more occasional. By mid-March it is numerous on passage in the lower valleys, with passage noted at 2,400 m until about mid-April[52], beyond which the lower winter range is largely vacated. From April to mid-July birds occupy breeding territories, with peak song activity in late May and early June. Found carrying nest material at 1,600 m on 1 April[52] and at 1,100 m on 8 June[52], with adults feeding fledglings on 14 June at 2,800 m[52], suggesting a slightly later breeding season at higher altitudes, as well as multiple broods. A density of 5.5 territories per km was found near Zhemgang at 1,600–1,900 m[52]. From mid-July birds start to form flocks again. It is one of the most frequent members of mixed flocks hunting insects, with *Phylloscopus* and *Seicercus* warblers, Nepal Fulvetta and *Stachyris* babblers as regular company. Usually fewer than five are found following a flock, waiting for insects to be flushed by other birds, but in August–October up to ten are sometimes noted within such flocks. In March–April it can be sufficiently numerous on passage to form the core of such mixed flocks.

# Siberian Rubythroat
## *Luscinia calliope*
N=8(6)

The Siberian Rubythroat breeds in east Asia from the Urals to Sakhalin, wintering from the eastern Indian subcontinent to the Philippines and Taiwan. Winter habitat consists of bushes and dense undergrowth, often near water.

In Bhutan the Siberian Rubythroat is an uncommon passage migrant and winter visitor, found mostly in the western, central and eastern foothills below 400 m. While most are in spring, records from December and February reveal the presence of a wintering population. The maximum count was three in riverine scrub near Phuntsholing in April[19]. Spring passage occurs in the first half of April and is marked by more frequent sightings at low elevations, as well as from up to 1,900 m, the latter all in the central valleys[48,52], where also seen in autumn, at 1,900 m on 9 October[52]. Whilst the central valleys may constitute a migration corridor, the lack of records at higher elevations points to the presence of an west–east movement along the base of the Himalayas, as suggested by Inskipp and Inskipp (1995), the birds skirting the main range east of Bhutan. The latest spring record is from 18 April at 400 m[19].

Siberian Rubythroat
Jan Wilczur

# White-tailed Rubythroat
*Luscinia pectoralis*

The White-tailed Rubythroat breeds in the Himalayas from Pakistan to Arunachal Pradesh, and further west to Turkestan and east to Myanmar, western and northern China. It breeds above the treeline in dwarf scrub, wintering in the foothills and into north-east India. In winter it occurs in similar habitats as Siberian Rubythroat.

In Bhutan the White-tailed Rubythroat is rare with only two records, both in the eastern foothills below 600 m. The records are dated 16 November 1936[31] and 19 April 1999[19], and presumably involved birds in their winter quarters. There is no evidence to suggest the species might breed at higher elevations in Bhutan.

# Bluethroat
*Luscinia svecica*

The Bluethroat breeds in the arctic and boreal zones of Eurasia, from Europe to Kamchatka, and into Alaska. It winters further south, from North Africa through the Middle East, southern and south-east Asia, including most of the Indian subcontinent, where it also breeds in the north-west. Winter habitat consists of bushes, reedbeds and tall grass, often close to water.

In Bhutan the Bluethroat is a vagrant, having been found at the end of April 1998 in the central valleys between Trongsa and Yoormu[4].

# Indian Blue Robin
*Luscinia brunnea*

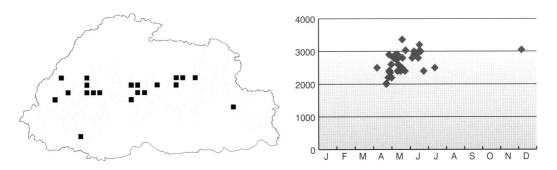

The Indian Blue Robin breeds in the Himalayas from Pakistan to Arunachal Pradesh and in north-east India. It winters in Sri Lanka, the hills of south-west and north-east India, and occasionally in the Himalayan foothills. Its range extends further east through Myanmar to western and northern China. Breeding habitat consists of dense undergrowth in temperate forest, broadleaf as well as conifer.

In Bhutan this species is a common summer visitor throughout the temperate zone at 2,400–3,200 m, occasionally to 2,200 m[19] and 3,400 m[22]. It prefers conifers, particularly Blue Pine, hemlock and mixed conifer forests. Being rather secretive, it is mostly noted when singing males are present. Birds arrive in the breeding areas from *c*.20 April, with an early record on 8 April[52], followed by a peak in song activity in the first half of May. Birds are vocal until the second half of June, with the latest record 11 July[52]. A nest with eggs was found on 3 June at 3,000 m[31]. The species can reach considerable densities, with up to five singing at a single locality. There is one winter record from a densely vegetated gully below Dochu La at *c*.3,000 m on 5 December[53].

# Orange-flanked Bush Robin (Red-flanked Bluetail)
## *Tarsiger cyanurus*

N=280(77). S 2400-4000 (Apr-Sep); W 1000-3200

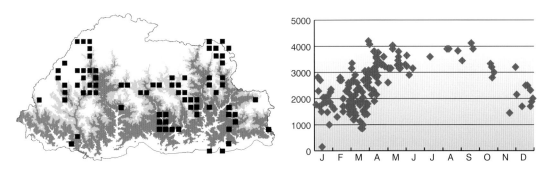

The range of the Orange-flanked Bush Robin comprises the boreal zone of Eurasia from Finland to Kamchatka, and montane western China and the Himalayas, where it occurs from Pakistan east. It is an altitudinal migrant, summering in temperate and alpine zones and wintering in the subtropical zone. It inhabits forest understorey.

In Bhutan the Orange-flanked Bush Robin is a common altitudinal migrant, found in all biogeographic units except the western foothills. It summers at 2,400–4,000 m, although territorial males have been noted in fir forest from 3,200 m to the treeline, suggesting that records below 3,200 m concern migrants still en route to the breeding areas. The highest record is from 4,200 m[2]. The species winters at 1,000–3,200 m, occasionally to 800 m, with one record from 200 m[44]. Movement to the breeding areas commences mid-March and continues to late April, by which time lower altitudes are entirely vacated. Singing males occupy territories from the first week of April. It is common in suitable habitat, with up to 25 in fir forests around Sheltang La between Jakar and Ura, Bumthang district[28], and up to 15 at Thrumshing La[14,28]. In October birds descend gradually, with the lower winter range reached only late in the season. Winter presence at lower elevations is partly related to snowfall higher up. In January to early April 2000 there was a large influx at lower elevations, the result of heavy snowfall above 3,000 m, which lasted into March, following an otherwise relatively mild winter. Large numbers were also reported in January 1995[28]. Aside from weather conditions, the thrush irruptions of 1995 and 2000 might constitute another factor in the influx. It is usually seen singly or a few birds together, frequently in scrub near roads. During influxes several tens may be seen in a day. There are no confirmed breeding records, but Ludlow collected a juvenile on 1 September[31].

# Golden Bush Robin
## *Tarsiger chrysaeus*

N=162(58). S 3000-4200 (May-Sep); W 1200-3400

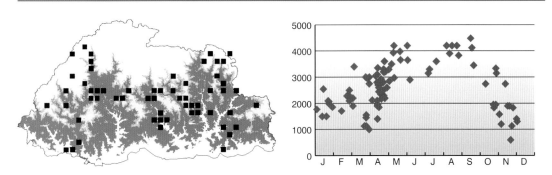

The Golden Bush Robin occurs in the Himalayas from Pakistan to Arunachal Pradesh and in north-east India, and thence east to Myanmar, Yunnan and north through western China. It is an altitudinal migrant that breeds in scrub near the treeline and winters in the foothills, where it affects dense forest undergrowth.

In Bhutan the Golden Bush Robin is a common altitudinal migrant throughout the alpine and temperate zones, with an isolated record in the eastern foothills. Its summer range spans 3,000–4,200 m, with occasional records to 4,500 m. In winter it is found in a broad zone from 1,200–3,400 m, occasionally to 1,000 m. The lowest record is from 600 m[31]. Unlike Orange-flanked Bush Robin, it tends to appear at the same winter sites annually, irrespective of weather conditions. It also shows a more clearly marked migration between breeding and winter areas, ascending between mid-March and late April and descending in October–November. Birds are mostly noted singly and are generally skulking. Singing males are noted in mid-April to mid-May, and breeding confirmed by the observation of a nesting pair on 10 May in the Thrumshing La area[5]. Ludlow collected several juveniles in summer, the first dated 6 July[31].

# White-browed Bush Robin
## *Tarsiger indicus*

N=66(26). S 2800-3600 (May-Nov); W 2400-3200

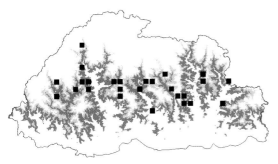

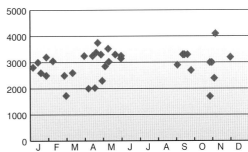

The White-browed Bush Robin occurs along the Himalayas from central Nepal to Arunachal Pradesh, with a more scattered distribution west to Uttar Pradesh and in north-east India. The range extends north and east to Sichuan, Taiwan and northern Vietnam. It inhabits the forest floor, summering in subalpine forest, particularly with abundant bamboo, and winters in damp places within dense forest.

In Bhutan the White-browed Bush Robin is the commonest of the *Tarsiger* bush robins and is frequently recorded. It is thinly distributed throughout the temperate zone, with one record in the western alpine zone. Summer range spans 2,800–3,600 m, with occasional records to 4,100 m. In winter it descends slightly, to 2,400–3,200 m, and occasionally as low as 1,700 m. However, it appears essentially resident, descending only during adverse weather at higher elevations. The period March to mid-April 2000 brought such an influx, due to late snowfall. While most records concern singles, in this period up to four were seen at a site. Possibly a similar influx occurred in January 1995, which might suggest a link with Dark-throated Thrush irruptions from areas north-east of Bhutan. Evidence of breeding comes from the observation of a female carrying food at *c.*3,200 m on 31 May[40,52], in mixed hemlock–broadleaf forest with a well-developed bamboo understorey.

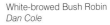

White-browed Bush Robin
*Dan Cole*

# Rufous-breasted Bush Robin
## *Tarsiger hyperythrus*

N=83(39). S 3200-4000 (Apr-Oct); W 1000-3000

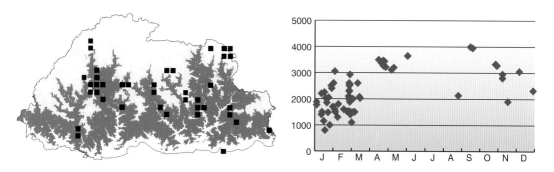

The Rufous-breasted Bush Robin is a scarce resident in the Himalayas from central Nepal to Arunachal Pradesh and in north-east India. Further east its range reaches Yunnan. It summers in the undergrowth of subalpine forest and winters in moist oak–rhodendron forest, particularly near streams.

In Bhutan the Rufous-breasted Bush Robin is a frequently recorded altitudinal migrant throughout the alpine and temperate zones. Its summer range spans 3,200–4,000 m, and it descends in winter to 1,000–3,000 m. The lowest record is from 800 m in January[28]. Birds reach the breeding areas in April, descending from October. Occurrence between years is variable, with large numbers reported particularly in 1995 and, to a lesser extent, in 2000. In January 1995 more than 40 were counted at various localities between Thimphu and Trashigang districts[28]. The influx was presumably related to adverse weather conditions at higher altitudes, but it is also possible that some birds originated from outside Bhutan, being part of the irruptions of Dark-throated and other thrushes from the north-east. Evidence of breeding comes from a nest with eggs in fir forest at 3,200 m on 10 May[49]. A female giving alarm calls was seen at a similar altitude on 26 April[22].

# Oriental Magpie Robin
## *Copsychus saularis*

N=392(61). S 200-2000 (Mar-Nov); W 200-1400

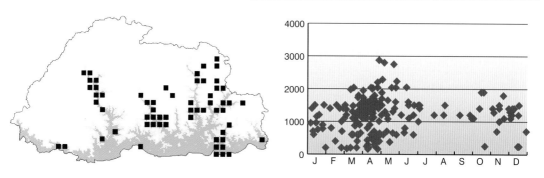

The Oriental Magpie Robin is widespread in southern and south-east Asia, north to central China. It occurs over much of the Indian subcontinent, including the Himalayas. Habitat consists of gardens, cultivation and open forest near habitation.

In Bhutan the Oriental Magpie Robin is an abundant altitudinal migrant in the foothills and in the Sunkosh, central and eastern valleys. The reasons for its apparent absence from the western valleys are unclear. Summer range spans 200–2,000 m, but it is commonest below 1,600 m. It is present March–June and appears to breed relatively early, with territorial birds noted in March and, to a lesser extent, in April. Ludlow collected a juvenile on 23 June at 600 m[31]. In May there are higher records, occasionally up to 2,800 m[49], probably reflecting post-breeding dispersal. From July to mid-March it retreats lower, below 1,400 m. Breeding has not been confirmed, despite the records cited above and the fact that it inhabits areas around settlements.

# White-rumped Shama
## Copsychus malabaricus

N=49(10). R 200-600

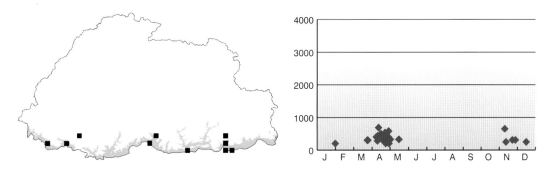

The White-rumped Shama is irregularly distributed in the Indian subcontinent, including in the Himalayan foothills from Uttar Pradesh to Arunachal Pradesh. Further east it ranges through mainland south-east Asia to the Greater Sundas. Habitat is undergrowth in broadleaf forest, where it particularly favours bamboo.

In Bhutan the White-rumped Shama is a common resident of the foothills, with one record from the western valleys[36]. It ranges between 200 m and 600 m. Most records are in spring, from late March to mid-May, when the foothills are most frequently visited by birders. However, several autumn and winter records confirm that it is resident in Bhutan. Largest numbers are noted in the forests above Samdrup Jongkha, with a maximum of eight[28], although it is still outnumbered there by a factor of three by Oriental Magpie Robin. There are no confirmed breeding records.

# Indian Robin
## Saxicoloides fulicata

N=1(1)

The Indian Robin is a widespread resident in the Indian subcontinent, but absent from the north-east. It inhabits dry open, rocky habitats, often in the vicinity of villages.

In Bhutan the Indian Robin is a vagrant that has been recorded just once: on 11 March 1986 a single was observed near Phuntsholing[10].

# Blue-capped Redstart
## Phoenicurus caeruleocephalus

N=3(3)

The Blue-capped Redstart breeds in the Western Himalayas, with sparse records east to Bhutan. In the west its range reaches Afghanistan and Turkestan. Summer habitat consists of rocky slopes in juniper and open forest, wintering lower in open forest.

In Bhutan the Blue-capped Redstart is a rare visitor or resident. One was collected in the 19th century (Inskipp 2001) and in recent years there are three records, in the period late March to late April, scattered in the Sunkosh, central and eastern valleys. On 22 March 1997 a male was present in forest above Yonkhola, Mongar district, at 2,250 m[46]. Subsequently a female was observed on 2 April 1998 near Dochu La at 2,900 m[5], with a pair on 28 April 2002 at 3,500 m near Yotong La[5].

# Black Redstart
## *Phoenicurus ochruros*

N=46(21). W 200-3200

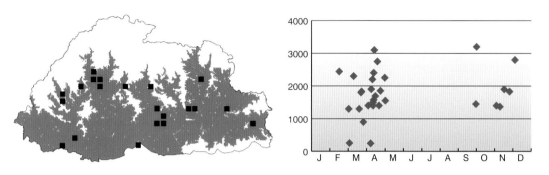

The Black Redstart's breeding range extends from Europe to western and northern China, extending south to the Himalayas from Pakistan to Sikkim. Elsewhere in the Indian subcontinent it is a winter visitor. It breeds in the Himalayas in scrub above the treeline and winters in open cultivated areas.

In Bhutan the Black Redstart is an uncommon passage migrant throughout the temperate zone, with a greater presence in the west. There are single records from the western and central foothills. It occurs on passage at 200–3,200 m, in spring from early March to late April, with two records in February[1,48] and the latest on 1 May[5], and in autumn from late September to early November, with the earliest on 29 September[29] and the last on 4 December[53]. Peak passage periods appear to be mid-April and late September. During the latter period a day maximum of more than five was reported[29]. In spring almost all records concern lone males, the females possibly being overlooked amongst other redstarts.

# Hodgson's Redstart
## *Phoenicurus hodgsoni*

N=455(78). W 800-2800

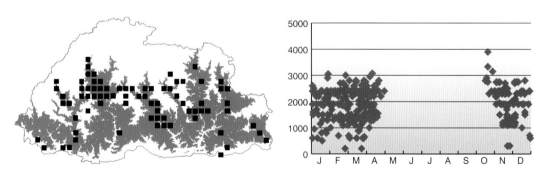

Hodgson's Redstart breeds in barren uplands of eastern Tibet and western and northern China, and is a winter visitor to the Himalayas, scattered from Uttar Pradesh to Arunachal Pradesh and in north-east India. In winter its preferred habitat is scrub along boulder-strewn riverbeds, but the species also occurs in various open habitats including cultivation.

In Bhutan Hodgson's Redstart is an abundant winter visitor recorded throughout the temperate zone and in the western foothills. It appears commonest in the western valleys, reflecting the availability of suitable habitat. Its regular winter range spans 800–2,800 m, with occasional occurrence to 200 m and 3,000 m. In autumn birds have occasionally been noted above 3,000 m, with the highest at 3,900 m[51]. In view of the scarcity of passage records, particularly in spring, birds apparently cross the Himalayas in a non-stop flight between breeding and winter areas. Alternatively, west–east movement along the base of the Himalayan range could be involved. Arrivals are noted from mid-October, with 15 October the earliest date[51,52]. Large numbers are already present in the upper part of the winter range by the second half of October, with lower areas gradually occupied during November and December, with 2,000 m typically reached in early November, 1,000 m by mid-November and 500 m by late December. Departure occurs in the first half of April, with numbers declining rapidly throughout the range. The latest spring record is from 24 April[39]. The species is generally abundant in winter, with tens of birds, sometimes up to 50, encountered along roadsides during the course of a day. Concentrations of 20–30 are not uncommon at suitable sites such as riverine scrub adjacent to farmland.

# White-throated Redstart
*Phoenicurus schisticeps*

N=50(25). W 2000-4200

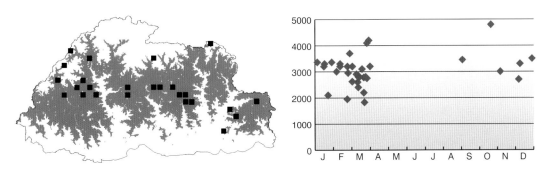

The White-throated Redstart occurs in the Himalayas from western Nepal to Bhutan, and north to eastern Tibet and western and northern China. Summer habitat consists of open scrub on rocky slopes and forest edge. In winter it affects cultivated areas and rocky bush-covered slopes.

In Bhutan the White-throated Redstart is a frequent winter visitor, recorded in the alpine and temperate zones. It occupies higher altitudes than other wintering redstarts, occurring at 2,000–4,200 m, with the lowest record from 1,800 m[1] and the highest 4,800 m[51]. Records fall largely in November–March, with the latest on 12 April[28]. A specimen taken on 1 September at 3,500 m[31] and a pair seen around 20 October at 4,800 m[51] perhaps involved birds still in their summer range. However, there are no other indications of presence in summer, although the species might very well have been overlooked. Numbers are highly variable between years. In most winters very few are noted and the species is perhaps even absent, e.g. 1993/94 and 2001/02. Large numbers were observed in 1994/95 and 1999/2000, coinciding with Dark-throated Thrush irruptions from areas north-east of Bhutan. Winter 2000/01 witnessed an intermediate influx, like that of Dark-throated Thrush. During these thrush influxes the first birds arrive in November–December, while peak numbers occur from late February to mid-March. Up to five have been found at a site, the largest concentration being a total of 30 along 15 km of road north of Thimphu[57].

# Daurian Redstart
*Phoenicurus auroreus*

N=5(4)

The Daurian Redstart breeds in western and northern China, north to Lake Baikal and Ussuriland. In the south its breeding range reaches south-east Tibet and Arunachal Pradesh. Elsewhere in the Himalayas, from Sikkim eastwards and in north-east India, it is mainly a winter visitor, occurring in cultivated areas and secondary forest.

In Bhutan the Daurian Redstart is a rare winter visitor, which has been recorded in the central and eastern valleys. The earliest record is from 31 October at 2,400 m[31]. The only spring record is from late April[37]. It has been found at 1,200[52] to 2,800 m[51], which presumably corresponds to its winter range.

# White-winged Redstart (Güldenstädt's Redstart)
## *Phoenicurus erythrogaster*                                            N=3(3)

The White-winged Redstart breeds in the dry alpine zone of the Caucasus, the Tibetan Plateau and western China, reaching north to Lake Baikal. It extends locally to the southern slopes of the Himalayas, from Pakistan to Arunachal Pradesh, and in winter may reach lower elevations in this region.

In Bhutan the White-winged Redstart is a rare winter visitor noted three times in March, at 1,400 m[5], 2,850 m[31] and unknown altitude. Records are scattered in the Sunkosh, central and eastern valleys.

# Blue-fronted Redstart
## *Phoenicurus frontalis*                     N=619(99). S 3400-4200 (May-Sep); W 1200-3200

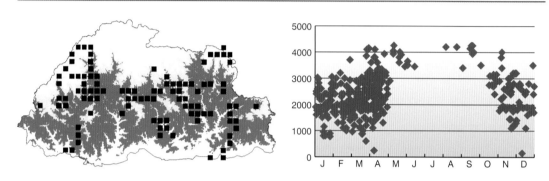

The Blue-fronted Redstart occurs throughout the Himalayas from Pakistan to Arunachal Pradesh and in north-east India. Its range continues north through eastern Tibet and western and northern China. In summer it breeds in subalpine scrub and winters at lower elevations in cultivated areas and open forest.

In Bhutan the Blue-fronted Redstart is an abundant altitudinal migrant throughout the country. In winter it often occurs in the same habitat as Hodgson's Redstart and like that species is commonest in open valleys in the west, although it is not particularly attached to streams. Its winter range spans 1,200–3,200 m, occasionally down to 200 m, and in summer 3,400–4,200 m and possibly higher. In the second half of March birds start to move to the breeding areas and a rapid decline in numbers is noticeable at lower elevations. In the middle and upper parts of its winter range numbers first increase due to passage, then decrease markedly in the first half of April, with the last departing by the end of the month. Descent in autumn starts in mid-October, with birds gradually spreading to 2,000 m in the first week of November and lower in the last week of the month. In winter up to 20 are regularly found at a site and over 200 in the course of a day[28]. There are relatively few records from breeding areas and no confirmed breeding records. A singing male was observed at 3,800 m on 8 April[52,53] and Ludlow collected juveniles in August[31].

# White-capped Water Redstart (River Chat)
## *Chaimarrornis leucocephalus*               N=744(110). S 1800-3600 (May-Oct); W 600-2800

The White-capped Water Redstart is distributed along the Himalayas from Pakistan to Arunachal Pradesh and in north-east India, thence west into northern Afghanistan and Tajikistan, and east over most of China and northern mainland south-east Asia. It is a bird of fast-flowing mountain streams and is an altitudinal migrant.

In Bhutan the White-capped Water Redstart is abundant throughout the country, albeit with marked altitudinal movements, its summer range spanning 1,800–3,600 m, descending in winter to 600–2,800 m, with occasional records in the latter season to 200 m and summer records from 4,250 m[49]. The summer range

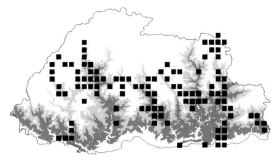

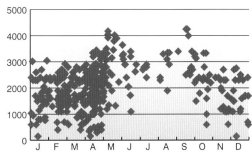

White-capped Water Redstart
*Ren Hathway*

is occupied from late April/early May, by which time its lower-elevation winter areas are vacated. Breeding commences quickly, as evidenced by a bird carrying nest material at 3,500 m on 6 May[22]. Descent from the breeding areas appears to be spread over a longer period, with a gradual movement in October–November. In winter several tens can be observed in a day from the national highways, where it occurs along small streams and near landslides, and is then also common along larger mountain rivers, feeding between the boulders.

# Plumbeous Water Redstart
## *Rhyacornis fuliginosus*

N=781(119). S 1000-3200 (Apr-Oct); W 600-2800

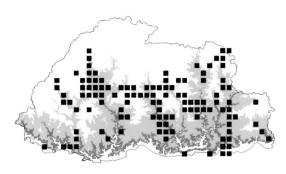

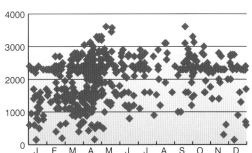

The Plumbeous Water Redstart inhabits fast-flowing mountain streams and rivers, where its high-pitched song is one of the few sounds audible above the noise of the water. It occurs in the Himalayas from Pakistan to Arunachal Pradesh and in the hills of north-east India. Further east its range reaches northern Vietnam and includes most of China and Taiwan.

In Bhutan this redstart is abundant, being found at every small stream or large river and recorded in all biogeographic units, although it rarely reaches the alpine zone. It shows some, albeit slight, altitudinal migration. Its regular summer range spans 1,000–3,200 m, while in winter it occurs at 600–2,800 m. There are occasional records to 200 m in winter and 3,600 m[49] in summer. Birds move to the highest part of the range in April to early May and descend between mid-October and mid-November. Song is commonly heard in March–September. The breeding season is prolonged, as evidenced by a nest with young on 29 March at 2,400 m[52] and pairs with recently fledged young on 28 July at 2,800 m[52]. Throughout the year, birds occur singly or in pairs, dispersed along the streams and rivers, with 1–5 birds per km.

# White-bellied Redstart
*Hodgsonius phaenicuroides*     N=11(7). S 3200-4200 (May-Oct); W 200-600

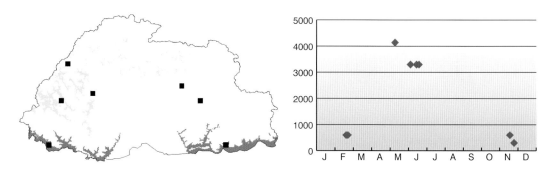

The White-bellied Redstart occurs in the Himalayas from Pakistan to Arunachal Pradesh, its range continuing north-east through central and northern China and northern Vietnam. It is an altitudinal migrant, summering in alpine scrub and wintering in dense undergrowth and at forest edge in the subtropical zone.

In Bhutan the White-bellied Redstart is an uncommon altitudinal migrant, with scattered records from the high west, the western, central and eastern valleys, and the western and eastern foothills. In May–June it has been noted at 3,200–4,200 m and in winter in the foothills at 200–600 m (November and February). Records from late April/early May at intermediate elevations (1,500–3,000 m) in the western and eastern valleys[5] reflect passage to the breeding quarters. These records have not been included on the graph due to imprecise altitudes being reported. The majority of records are of specimens collected during the 1930s and 1960s/1970s, as it as a secretive bird that is difficult to observe.

# White-tailed Robin
*Myiomela leucura*     N=278(42). S 1200-2200 (Mar-Aug); W 400-1800

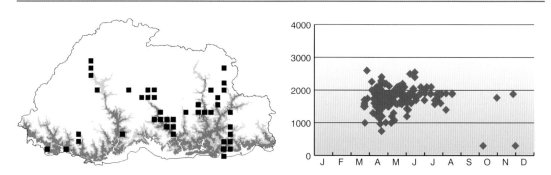

The White-tailed Robin occurs in the Himalayas from central Nepal to Arunachal Pradesh and in north-east India. Further east it reaches much of south-east Asia, from Taiwan south to the Malay Peninsula. Habitat is undergrowth in dense broadleaf forest, usually near ravines.

In Bhutan the White-tailed Robin is a common altitudinal migrant throughout the temperate zone and in the western and eastern foothills. It is scarce in the western valleys, becoming more common in the Sunkosh Valley, whilst the central and eastern valleys constitute its stronghold. The summer range lies at 1,200–2,200 m, with occasional records to 800 m and 2,600 m, and is occupied from around 20 March. Song is heard until late August, with the peak rather late in the season, from mid-May to July[52]. In suitable habitat it reaches considerable densities, as shown by a max. 20 noted in the Deothang area, Samdrup Jongkha district[28]. Near Zhemgang a density of 3.6 territories per km was found at 1,600–1,900 m, with the highest density around 1,700 m[52]. Once birds stop singing they are difficult to find and there are few autumn and winter records. It has been found in October and December at *c*.200 m[1], proving that it moves to lower elevations, but there are also records as high as 1,700 m[1] and 1,900 m[52] in November and December, demonstrating that at least some remain in the breeding areas in winter.

# Blue-fronted Robin
## *Cinclidium frontale*

N=49(11). S 1800-2600

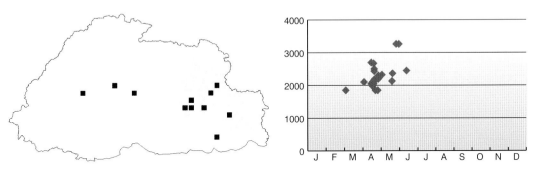

The Blue-fronted Robin is a rare and little-known species found at a few localities in the Himalayas, in Darjeeling, Sikkim, Bhutan and eastern Arunachal Pradesh. Further east it reaches south-west China, northern Thailand, northern Laos and northern Vietnam. It inhabits dark, densely vegetated gullies in humid broadleaf forest and is very difficult to observe.

In Bhutan the Blue-fronted Robin is an uncommon bird found at only *c*.10 localities, the majority in the eastern valleys, including the forests between Namling and Yonkhola, Mongar district, where it is recorded annually. It occurs at 1,800–2,600 m, in areas with mature broadleaf forest, where a max. 6 has been noted[28]. In the western, Sunkosh and central valleys there are only scattered records, with birds rarely found at the same site in consecutive years. Near Thimphu it was found at the same site in two different years, at the relatively high altitude of 3,200 m, in apparently unusual habitat, a small garden adjacent to a thickly vegetated gully in a conifer-dominated area[22,40]. However, as the species is easily overlooked, it may prove to occur more widely than presently known. All records are from March to early June, when chances of encountering the species are highest, as birds are singing, and birding activity is greatest. Its winter quarters and any altitudinal movements are unclear.

Grandalas
*Dan Cole*

223

# Grandala
*Grandala coelicolor*

N=20(10). R 3600-4600

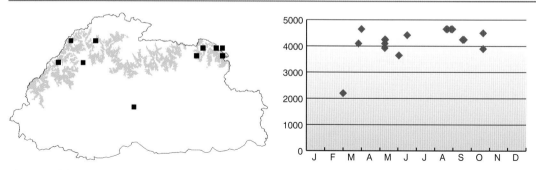

The Grandala is patchily distributed in the high Himalayas from Kashmir to Bhutan, as well as north-east to montane Yunnan, Sichuan and northern China. It inhabits rocky slopes and ridges in the alpine zone.

In Bhutan the Grandala is a common resident in the high west and east, with single records from the Sunkosh and central valleys. That from the central valleys is from the peak of Black Mountain, and is the only confirmed breeding record: a nest with a chick found on a cliff at 4,400 m in June[31]. Its regular altitudinal range spans 3,600–4,600 m and possibly higher. It only rarely descends lower in winter, with records from Pele La at 3,400 m[44] and one at the extremely low altitude of 2,200 m in the Sunkosh Valley in early March 2000[57]. The latter coincided with bad weather that forced the birds to wander below their normal ranges. Outside the breeding season it gathers in large flocks, with reported maxima of 200 at 4,500 m on 22 October[51] and 500 at 4,000 m on 26 March[2].

# Little Forktail
*Enicurus scouleri*

N=212(74). S 1200-3000 (Mar-Sep); W 600-2800

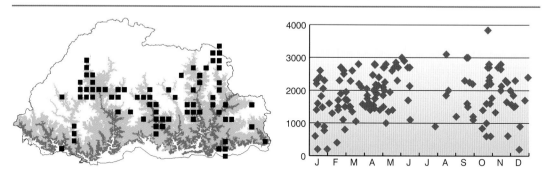

The Little Forktail occurs in the Himalayas from Pakistan to Arunachal Pradesh and in the hills of north-east India. Outside the Indian subcontinent it occurs west to Afghanistan and east through China, Taiwan and northern mainland south-east Asia. Habitat is fast-flowing mountain streams, including open stretches without forest cover.

In Bhutan this is among the most widespread forktails, found throughout the temperate zone, with occasional records from the foothills and the high east. It is a frequently recorded altitudinal migrant, summering at 1,200–3,000 m. In October–February it is present at 600–2,800 m, occasionally reaching 200 m. The highest record is from 3,800 m in October[1]. It appears to be among the most adaptable of the forktails, being found along open stretches of river, as well as fast-flowing streams in forest, and at small streams along the national highway. It is a regular winter visitor to the Thim Chhu at Thimphu. There are no confirmed breeding records and the season is unclear. Between the last week of March and late April, typically two occur together, presumably pairs, probably marking the start of the nesting season. Outside this period mostly singles are noted, with a max. 3 found at a site.

# Black-backed Forktail
## *Enicurus immaculatus*

N=49(20). R 200-2000

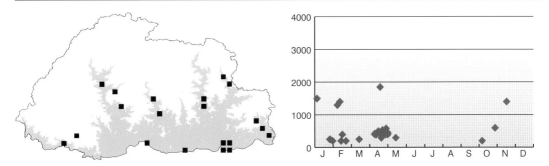

The Black-backed Forktail is distributed along the Himalayas from Uttar Pradesh to Arunachal Pradesh and in north-east India, being rare in the west of this range. Further east it reaches Myanmar and northern Thailand. It is a bird of fast-flowing streams in subtropical and tropical broadleaf forests.

In Bhutan the Black-backed Forktail is a common resident. Records are concentrated in the eastern foothills at 200–600 m. Further west it is scarcer, with only single records in the western and central valleys. In the temperate zone there are scattered records throughout, at altitudes up to 1,900 m. Records at higher elevations are from October to April and probably reflect dispersal outside the breeding season, although April records potentially concern isolated breeding pairs. At the regular site in the forests above Samdrup Jongkha several are present in April–May, with a max. 3 pairs on 14 May[5]. One of these was feeding a recently fledged young, confirming breeding.

# Slaty-backed Forktail
## *Enicurus schistaceus*

N=253(52). S 800-2200 (May-mid-Oct); W 400-1800

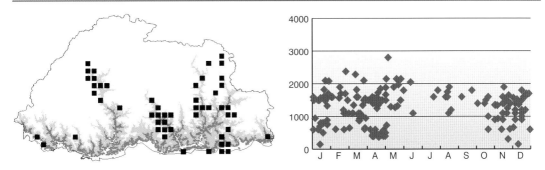

In the Indian subcontinent the Slaty-backed Forktail occurs in the Himalayas from Sikkim to Arunachal Pradesh and in north-east India, and more patchily west to Uttar Pradesh. Further east its range reaches Vietnam. Habitat comprises larger streams and rivers in tropical and subtropical forests.

In Bhutan the Slaty-backed Forktail is a common altitudinal migrant throughout the temperate zone and foothills. In the western valleys it is relatively scarce as it approaches its westernmost limits. The summer range spans 800–2,200 m, largely coinciding with the warm broadleaf forest zone. Of the forktails, its altitudinal movements are somewhat pronounced, retreating to 400–1,800 m in winter and occasionally 200 m. It has been found once at 2,800 m[49]. The upper part of its range is reached from February and nest-building has been observed on 26 March at 1,600 m[5]. An observation of a pair feeding fledglings at 1,800 m on 12 August[52] suggests a prolonged breeding season, probably with two or more broods. From late July they appear to maintain winter territories, with birds present at the same sites by the national highway for long periods. At the same sites, Spotted Forktails are often also present, and sometimes Little Forktails, with interspecific territories apparently maintained in such cases. A well-known site for the present species is the forest between Rimchu and Tashithang, Punakha district, where up to 15 have been noted in January[28].

# White-crowned Forktail
## *Enicurus leschenaulti*

The White-crowned Forktail is widespread in south-east Asia, south to the Greater Sundas, reaching central China in the north. In the west of its range it extends to the north-east Indian subcontinent, where it occurs in the Himalayan foothills in Darjeeling and West Bengal, from eastern Bhutan to Arunachal Pradesh, and in the hills of north-east India. Habitat consists of fast-flowing streams in dense tropical broadleaf forest.

In Bhutan the White-crowned Forktail is rare, with a few records from the eastern foothills in the forests above Samdrup Jongkha[13,14,28]. It has been found there in January and April at *c.*200 m, with a max. 4. Apparently those breeding in Assam reach Bhutan on winter dispersal.

# Spotted Forktail
## *Enicurus maculatus*

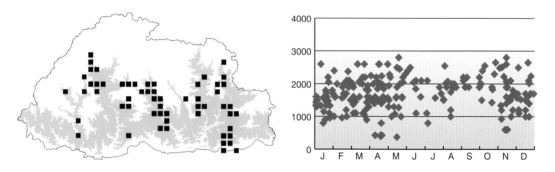

The Spotted Forktail occurs in the Himalayas from Afghanistan to Arunachal Pradesh and in the hills of north-east India. Further east its range extends to western China and northern Vietnam. It affects the smallest forest streams and generally occurs at higher altitudes than Slaty-backed Forktail.

In Bhutan the Spotted Forktail is a common resident throughout the temperate zone and the central and eastern foothills, at 800–2,600 m, occasionally down to 400 m and up to 2,900 m[43]. Its altitudinal range overlaps considerably with Slaty-backed Forktail. In the breeding season the species are largely segregated by habitat, Spotted Forktail occurring deeper in forest on very small streams. However, in winter they overlap, for example both being observed regularly in ditches and streams along the national highway. A well-known site for Spotted Forktail is the forest south of Trongsa along the Zhemgang road, where up to ten have been seen in December, along 20 km of road[52]. It is a probable breeder. A singing bird was observed in April–May at 1,600 m[52] and a displaying pair noted at 2,600 m on 30 April[5]. Juveniles emerge from early July[52].

Spotted Forktail
*Dan Cole*

# Purple Cochoa
*Cochoa purpurea*  N=22(7). R 1800-2800

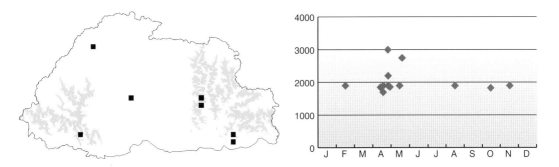

The Purple Cochoa is a rare and little-known bird, recorded locally in the Himalayas from Himachal Pradesh to Arunachal Pradesh and in north-east India, and reaching east to northern Vietnam. It is a secretive bird of the undergrowth of dense, moist broadleaf forest.

In Bhutan this cochoa is an uncommon resident in the western, Sunkosh and eastern valleys, and in the high west. It is very local, having been found in only 5 areas throughout the country. Regular localities are the forests around Gedu, Chhukha district[1,44], Gasa, Punakha district[22,44] and between Namling and Yonkhola, Mongar district[5,14,19,22,27]. It occurs at 1,800–2,800 m, with most records from 1,800–2,200 m in mature broadleaf forest. The highest record is from 3,000 m in the Sunkosh Valley[22], where it occurs particularly towards the upper limit of the cool broadleaf forest zone. Records concern singles, mostly calling males, with one record of a pair on 26 April[5].

# Green Cochoa
*Cochoa viridis*  N=3(3)

The Green Cochoa is as rare and little known as Purple Cochoa, with similarly unobtrusive habits. It is found in the Himalayas, from Sikkim to Arunachal Pradesh and in north-east India. Further west there are few records and it is probably extinct in Nepal. In the east its range extends to northern Vietnam. It is a bird of dense moist broadleaf forest on steep slopes.

In Bhutan the Green Cochoa is rare, with only three spring records all in the eastern[5,14] and central valleys[5,40,44]. It appears to occupy lower altitudes than Purple Cochoa, with all records at 1,000–1,800 m. A pair was found at 1,400 m on 1 May[5].

# Hodgson's Bushchat
*Saxicola insignis*  N=1(1)

Hodgson's Bushchat breeds at high elevations in Kazakhstan and Mongolia and is a winter visitor to the Indian subcontinent, in grasslands at the base of the Himalayas from Haryana to Assam. Winter habitat comprises tall grass, reeds and tamarisks along rivers. It is globally threatened, listed by BirdLife International as Vulnerable due its small and declining population. The principal threats lie in its winter range, where it is affected by the decline and deterioration of tall-grassland habitats.

In Bhutan Hodgson's Bushchat is a vagrant, recorded just once. A male was present at Bajo, Wangdue Phodrang district, at 1,300 m on 9 April 1999[19]. Potential winter habitat may exist in Royal Manas National Park, as it has been recorded in adjacent Manas Tiger Reserve in India.

Hodgson's Bushchat
*Ren Hathway*

# Common Stonechat
*Saxicola torquatus*

N=229(56). W 400-2800

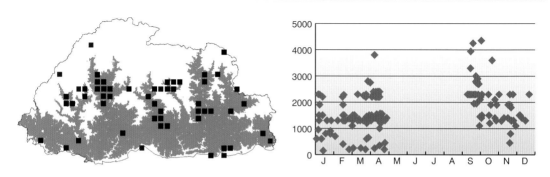

The Common Stonechat is widespread in Eurasia and Africa. The nearest breeding areas are the Tibetan Plateau and the Western Himalayas east to Nepal. It is a common winter visitor over most of the Indian subcontinent, inhabiting open country and often perching conspicuously atop bushes.

In Bhutan the Common Stonechat is a common winter visitor throughout the temperate zone and foothills, with a few records in the high west and east. Its range spans 400–2,800 m occasionally down to 200 m. Above 2,800 m it has been found in spring and, particularly, autumn, when it appears to stopover regularly at altitudes up to 4,400 m[31]. Arrival is from mid-September, with the earliest record 7 September[52]. In this period falls of up to ten have been noted at Babesa, Thimphu district, at 2,300 m[52]. The birds rapidly spread lower, to 1,000 m, with passage at higher elevations continuing until the second half of October. The lowest part of the winter range is reached mainly in January, by which time the species is widespread, but with never more than a few birds at any site. Spring passage at higher elevations is noted from the first week of April, continuing until the last week of April, with the latest on 29 April[33]. Particularly around mid-April, concentrations of up to ten are again noted at *c*.2,300 m, suggesting strong passage from lower altitudes and possibly further afield. The taxa involved appear to be mainly *przewalskii* and *stejnegeri*, winter visitors and passage migrants from across the Himalayas. The resident Indian subspecies *indicus* has been reported from the plains between Gelephu and Sarpang. This complex of taxa is increasingly treated as a species separate from Common Stonechat *torquatus*, and often known as the Siberian Stonechat *S. maurus*.

# Pied Bushchat
*Saxicola caprata*

N=7(4)

The Pied Bushchat's range extends from the Central Asian republics through southern and south-east Asia south to New Guinea. It occurs throughout the Indian subcontinent, but is absent in parts of the north-east. It occupies typical bushchat habitats, cultivation and open land with scattered bushes.

In Bhutan the Pied Bushchat is a rare resident known from the Sunkosh and eastern valleys, and the western foothills, at 800–1,600 m. It has been found in three years at the same site near Mongar, in agricultural fields in a dry valley[5]. Although such habitat is well represented in the above-mentioned zones the species appears to be very thinly distributed.

# Grey Bushchat
## *Saxicola ferreus*

N=602(97). S 1200-3200 (Apr-Nov); W 800-2200

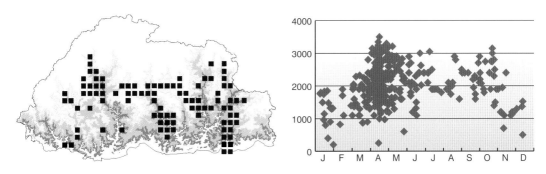

The Grey Bushchat is resident in the Himalayas from Pakistan to Arunachal Pradesh and in the hills of north-east India. Its range extends further east through northern mainland south-east Asia to Taiwan. Habitat consists of scrub-covered hillsides and cultivated areas with scattered bushes; it tolerates denser vegetation than other bushchats.

In Bhutan the Grey Bushchat is an abundant altitudinal migrant throughout the temperate zone and foothills, and is regularly found at 800–3,200 m, with occasional records to 200 m and 3,500 m[19]. There is marked altitudinal movement, with birds wintering largely at 800–2,200 m and summering at 1,200–3,200 m. From mid-March to mid-May it occurs over the entire altitudinal range, as birds move to the breeding areas, whilst others are already nesting. In October–November birds move downslope again. Song is heard from early March to mid-June and nesting appears to commence earlier at lower elevations, with nest-building observed at 1,900 m on 25 April[52] and 26 April[5], and a nest with eggs at 2,900 m on 14 May[49]. At least those birds at lower altitudes appear to be double-brooded, with e.g. a pair carrying food at 1,900 m on 13 July[52]. Throughout the year mostly singles and pairs are encountered, with regularly more than ten at a site.

# Pied Wheatear
## *Oenanthe pleschanka*

N=1(1)

The Pied Wheatear breeds in Central Asia, from the Black Sea to Lake Baikal and northern China, and reaching the Indian subcontinent in Pakistan. Its main winter quarters are in Africa, Arabia and Iran, occurring mostly as a vagrant in the subcontinent.

In Bhutan this wheatear is a vagrant, found only once. On 25 April 2001 a single was at Paro[32].

# Isabelline Wheatear
## *Oenanthe isabellina*

N=4(3)

The Isabelline Wheatear has a similar breeding range to Pied Wheatear, from the Black Sea to Lake Baikal, northern China and into Pakistan. However, its winter range extends further east, including a large part of the north-west Indian subcontinent. Elsewhere in the subcontinent it is a rare passage migrant.

In Bhutan the Isabelline Wheatear has been recorded on passage on four occasions, in the western[14,52,53], Sunkosh[39] and central valleys[4]. All records are from April, when individuals sometimes pause in the upper and middle parts of these valleys, at 2,400–3,200 m.

# Spot-winged Starling
## Saroglossa spiloptera

N=8(4)

The Spot-winged Starling is a specialised feeder on flower nectar. It occurs along the Himalayas from Himachal Pradesh to Arunachal Pradesh and in north-east India and Bangladesh, performing east–west migrations. It breeds in the Western Himalayas and winters commonly in north-east India, occasionally further east to Myanmar and north-west Thailand. Habitat comprises open broadleaf forest with flowering trees.

In Bhutan this starling is a rare summer visitor, recorded from the central and eastern valleys and the eastern foothills. Most records are from the Khosela area, in the central valleys between Trongsa and Zhemgang, at 1,200–1,600 m[5,14,52]. Here, a small flock is present annually in April–June, with a max. 14 noted in April 2002[14]. The observation of juveniles suggests that it breeds here[14]. The species migrates along the Himalayas in an east–west direction, with a westbound movement noted in Nepal in March–April, returning in June–July. Arrival and departure at Khosela corresponds well with this pattern. However, direct east–west passage is barely noticed in Bhutan and birds most probably pass at low elevations or south of the country. Only records from the eastern valleys and foothills, at 200 and 1,100 m, might involve passage birds, considering their timing in late March[1] to mid-April[19].

# Chestnut-tailed Starling
## Sturnus malabaricus

N=94(26). S 200-2200 (Mar-Jun); W 200-400

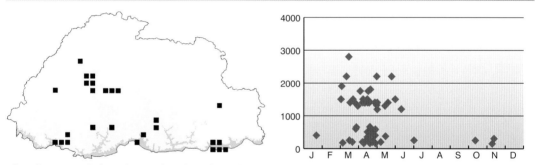

The Chestnut-tailed Starling is found in the Indian subcontinent in the north-east and south-west hills, its range continuing east to Vietnam. It is a winter visitor to central and western India, and inhabits open country, feeding mostly in flowering trees.

In Bhutan the Chestnut-tailed Starling is a frequently recorded altitudinal migrant. Its core range lies in the foothills and in the Sunkosh Valley, with scattered records elsewhere in the temperate zone. Its summer range spans 200–2,200 m. Higher-elevation records are particularly from the Wangdue Phodrang/Punakha area in the Sunkosh Valley, where it arrives from March, in which period there is also a record of one at the exceptionally high altitude of 2,800 m in the Phobjikha Valley[14]. In winter it retreats below 400 m and most of the population probably moves further south into India, judging by the paucity of winter records. The majority of birds appear to vacate higher elevations in July following the breeding season. However, it is unclear whether it breeds in Bhutan, with no evidence whatsoever. It is gregarious and flocks of up to ten are regular in the foothills and during the arrival period in the Punakha/Wangdue Phodrang areas. Maxima of 40 and 30 have been reported from Phuntsholing[5] and Samdrup Jongkha[19] respectively.

# Common Starling
## Sturnus vulgaris

N=1(1)

The Common Starling breeds in Eurasia, east to Lake Baikal and south to Pakistan. It migrates through the Indus Valley and winters commonly in northern India.

The Common Starling is a vagrant in Bhutan, where a specimen was collected at Rongthung, Trashi Yangtse district, on 20 March 1967[1].

# Asian Pied Starling
*Sturnus contra*

N=45(10). R 200-600

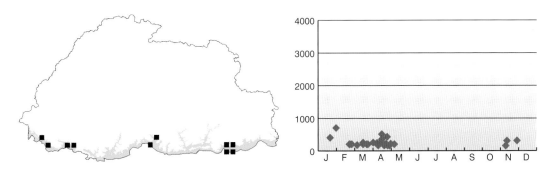

The Asian Pied Starling occurs in the north-east half of the Indian subcontinent, extending further east into mainland south-east Asia, south to Sumatra and Java. Like most starlings and mynas it frequently occurs around settlements. It mostly feeds on the ground.

In Bhutan the Asian Pied Starling is a common resident throughout the foothills, at altitudes of 200–400 m. There are no confirmed breeding records, but it has been found in flocks up to ten, with a max. 20 at Samdrup Jongkha[19,27].

# Common Myna
*Acridotheres tristis*

N=445(49). R 200-2400 (agricultural areas)

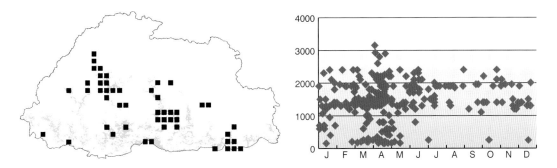

The Common Myna is distributed throughout southern and south-east Asia, from Kazakhstan to mainland south-east Asia, with introduced populations in various other parts of the world. It is common in villages and towns, adapting well to such environments.

In Bhutan this myna is an abundant resident, albeit with a rather scattered distribution. It occurs throughout the foothills and immediately adjacent parts of the temperate zone below 1,000 m. Higher in the temperate zone it is largely confined to the Sunkosh and central valleys, where it is abundant in towns and villages below 2,000 m, reaching 2,400 m in the Sunkosh and 2,100 m in the central valleys. Highest records are from Chumey, Bumthang district, at 2,800 m[19] in the central valleys, and from Gasa at 3,200 m² in the Sunkosh Valley. In the western valleys it is occasionally found in Paro and Thimphu between 2,200 m and 2,400 m. Its virtual absence from the eastern valleys is remarkable, as suitable habitat appears abundant and as the Common Myna is a strong coloniser, reaching the remotest villages. Colonisation of Bhutan appears to have occurred relatively recently. There is no mention of the species by Ludlow (Ludlow and Kinnear 1937, 1944), and for the 1960s and 1970s Ali *et al.* (1996) mention it as 'seen in small numbers only at a few localities from the foothills up to about 1550 m around villages', although it was 'common in and around Gaylegphug town'. At Phuntsholing it was seen occasionally in small flocks. In contrast, present-day numbers appear considerably higher and the distribution wider. In recent years a max. 50 has been reported from the Phuntsholing and Samdrup Jongkha areas and concentrations of up to 100 in the Wangdue Phodrang/Punakha area. When the survey teams visited Zhemgang (1,900 m) in the 1960s the species was apparently absent, but now there is a thriving population in the town of more than 50 birds[51]. Also, in the Sunkosh Valley it has expanded above 1,500 m, and is in the process of colonising Thimphu, at 2,400 m, with a max. 10 reported there[52]. Given such an increase, it seems likely that Common Myna started spreading from the foothills higher into Bhutan only in the 20th century, and that further expansion above 2,000 m and into the eastern valleys can be expected. The breeding season is extended: at Zhemgang nest-building has been noted in late February, while most young fledge in June–July[52]. At Phuntsholing a nest with young was observed on 23 March[52,53h]. From November to January the species may form flocks of several tens, with a max. 100 near Wangdue Phodrang[52].

# Bank Myna
## *Acridotheres ginginianus*                                                           N=2(1)

The Bank Myna is a native endemic to the Indian subcontinent, being patchily distributed in its northern half. A bird of grassland, villages and towns, the species breeds in holes excavated in earth banks.

In Bhutan the Bank Myna is a rare resident of the western and eastern foothills at *c*.200 m. It has been found at Phuntsholing in February 1995[19] and at Samdrup Jongkha in April 2000[27]. At the latter locality *c*.30 were present and were apparently breeding. As Bank Mynas appear to be increasing in India, this record could mark a recent colonisation of the area.

# Jungle Myna
## *Acridotheres fuscus*                                                      N=19(4). R 200-400

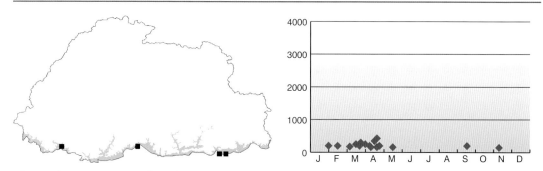

The Jungle Myna occurs in the Indian subcontinent along the Himalayan foothills from Pakistan to north-east India and in the extreme south-west. Further east its range reaches the Malay Peninsula. In India and Nepal it occurs in the Himalayas up to altitudes of 1,500 m and 2,100 m respectively. It is a bird of open wooded country, less associated with villages and towns than Common Myna.

In Bhutan the Jungle Myna is an uncommon resident of the foothills, at 200–400 m. Up to 15 have been reported from the Samdrup Jongkha area[14] and four at Phuntsholing[19]. On 23 March a pair was observed at 300 m near Phuntsholing, apparently competing for a nest hole with a pair of Alexandrine Parakeets[52,53]. Breeding, however, was not confirmed.

# White-vented Myna
## *Acridotheres grandis*                                                       N=7(2). R 200-200

The White-vented Myna occurs throughout most of mainland south-east Asia, its range extending west into the Indian subcontinent in north-east India.

In Bhutan the White-vented Myna is rare and was first found near the Samdrup Jongkha bazaar at 150 m in April 1999[19]. It was present here in subsequent years as well, with maxima of two, three and six noted in 1999–2001[19,14], suggesting the establishment and gradual growth of a small population.

# Hill Myna
## Gracula religiosa

N=50(15). R 200-800

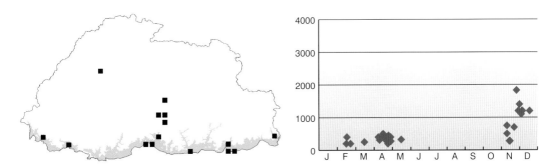

The Hill Myna occurs along the Himalayas from Nepal west. Further east it is widespread over mainland south-east Asia, the Philippines and most of Indonesia. It inhabits tropical broadleaf forest, feeding in trees on fruits and berries.

In Bhutan the Hill Myna is a common resident of the foothills, where it occurs at 200–800 m. Above Samdrup Jongkha it has been found annually in spring, with a max. 9 present[27]. An observation of a bird entering a possible nest hole on 22 April at 400 m in the central foothills[52] establishes it as a probable breeder. In November–December it has been found in flocks of several tens in the Mangdechu Valley, well above its usual altitudinal range, at Rani Camp, Zhemgang district (1,800 m) in November 1967[1], in Nubji-Korphu Valley, Trongsa district (1,100–1,500 m) in November 1997[52] and at Dungdung, Trongsa district (1,200 m) in November/December 2001[52]. The largest flock involved 55 birds[52]. There are no records from other years or from other valleys. Probably such presence reflects local irruptive movements, relating to variability in tree fruiting.

# Chestnut-bellied Nuthatch
## Sitta castanea

N=219(42). R 400-1600

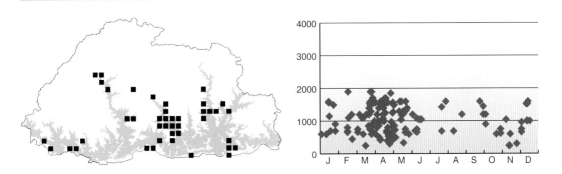

The Chestnut-bellied Nuthatch occurs in the Himalayas, mainly from Uttar Pradesh to Arunachal Pradesh, its range extending south to north-east, central, eastern and south-west India, and further east to Vietnam. Habitat is broadleaf forest, the species occupying lower altitudes than White-tailed Nuthatch.

In Bhutan the Chestnut-bellied Nuthatch is common throughout the temperate zone and foothills, being resident at 400–1,600 m, with occasional presence down to 200 m and up to 1,900 m. It is rare above 1,600 m, where it narrowly overlaps the range of White-tailed Nuthatch. Throughout the year it occurs in pairs or family groups. Territorial activity is noted from late March and breeding is confirmed by the observation of pairs feeding young in the nest, e.g. two different pairs at 1,600 m on 14 and 21 May[52].

# White-tailed Nuthatch
## *Sitta himalayensis*

N=452(67). R 1600-3000

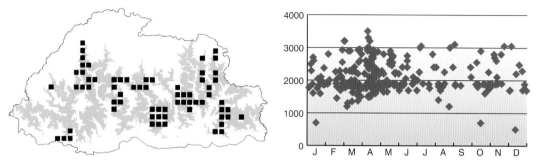

The White-tailed Nuthatch occurs along the Himalayas from Himachal Pradesh to Uttar Pradesh and in north-east India. Further east its range reaches northern Vietnam. Habitat is temperate broadleaf and mixed forests.

In Bhutan the White-tailed Nuthatch is a common resident throughout the temperate zone, with single records from the high west and the western foothills. It occupies altitudes above those of Chestnut-bellied Nuthatch, from 1,600 to 3,000 m, with a remarkably sharp divide between the two species, although there are occasional records of White-tailed Nuthatch down to 500 m[53] and up to 3,500 m[52,53]. Throughout the year it is noted singly, in pairs or a few together. Larger flocks of up to ten are seen in summer and early autumn, comprising family groups of pairs with young. Between August and mid-March it is a frequent member of mixed-species flocks, particularly with tit species. Territorial activity starts late February, when the first singing birds are noted, and continues until June, with a peak in March. On 27 March two different pairs, at 1,700 and 1,800 m, were observed collecting mud to plaster the entrance of their nesthole[52,53]. Birds carrying food were noted on 11 May at *c*.1,900 m[52], and family groups with recently fledged young have been seen from mid-May.

# Velvet-fronted Nuthatch
## *Sitta frontalis*

N=1(1)

The Velvet-fronted Nuthatch has a scattered distribution in the Indian subcontinent, mainly in the Himalayan foothills from Uttar Pradesh eastwards, as well as in north-east, eastern and south-west India. Its main range lies further east, in mainland south-east Asia, the Philippines and the Greater Sundas. It occurs in open broadleaf forest and well-wooded areas.

In Bhutan the Velvet-fronted Nuthatch is a rare resident recorded only once. On 26 April 1993 two were seen at Manas at *c*.350 m[22].

# Beautiful Nuthatch
## *Sitta formosa*

N=36(10). R 1200-2000 (broadleaf forest)

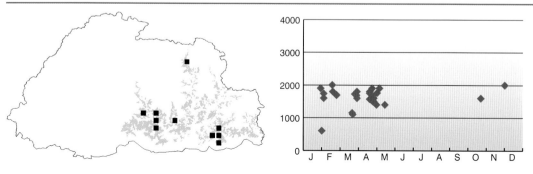

The Beautiful Nuthatch is a scarce resident of the Himalayan foothills from Sikkim to Arunachal Pradesh and the hills of north-east India. Further east its range reaches northern Vietnam. Important numbers occur in Bhutan and northern Myanmar (King *et al.* 2001). In contrast, there are no recent records from Sikkim or West Bengal, thus Bhutan may constitute the present westernmost limit of its range. The species occurs in subtropical broadleaf forest, being associated with tall trees with an abundant growth of epiphytes. It is globally threatened, being classified by BirdLife International as Vulnerable due to its small, severely fragmented population, which may be declining through habitat loss.

The Beautiful Nuthatch is one of the most sought-after specialities of the Bhutanese avifauna. It is an uncommon resident, found in the central and eastern valleys, where it occupies a narrow altitude zone between those of the commoner White-tailed and Chestnut-bellied Nuthatches, from 1,200–2,000 m. It may wander lower in winter, as revealed by a record at 600 m in January[38]. Thus far, six sites are known: the Zhemgang area[5,14,52,53], the Narphung area in Samdrup

Beautiful Nuthatch
*Dan Cole*

Jongkha district[5,14], the Thekpaling and Khomsar area in northern Zhemgang district[44], Subrang in Zhemgang district[5,40,44,52], Dungkhar in Lhuntse district[7] and Nubji-Korphu in Trongsa district[12]. Its absence from apparently suitable habitat in the well-explored forests near Yonkhola is remarkable. At these sites it is rather capricious, one important factor being that pairs occupy a large territory in which they move rapidly between canopy trees. Most records are in February–March, when the species is most active and is relatively easily located by voice. From April they are generally more silent and elusive, and their occurrence more unpredictable. Repeated visits to suitable sites may, however, reveal a significant presence. In February/March 2002, pairs were located at five sites near Zhemgang along 20 km of road[52]. In fact, almost all stretches of forest with at least a residual stand of tall canopy trees and abundant epiphytes appeared to hold these nuthatches. Another indication of the numbers in suitable habitat comes from the observation of a flock of 21 at Thekpaling at 1,900 m on 29 January 1997[44]. Discounting this flock, a mean 2.5 birds is reported per sighting. Even in the breeding season it regularly occurs in small flocks, often associated with mixed flocks of larger babblers, including Cutia and White-browed Shrike Babbler. It is thus the most gregarious of the nuthatches in Bhutan. Like Rufous-necked Hornbill, it depends on tall, mature forest with abundant epiphytes, making it vulnerable to logging of old-growth warm broadleaf forest, particularly as dense epiphytes take a long time to develop. Only the eastern and northern peripheries of its range in Bhutan fall within protected areas (Thrumshingla, Jigme Singye Wangchuck and Royal Manas National Parks), where logging activities are excluded, underlining the importance of developing sustainable forest management elsewhere, thereby protecting corridors of mature trees and permitting natural regeneration of a diversity of tree species.

# Wallcreeper
## *Tichodroma muraria*

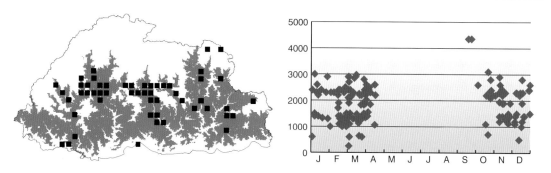

The Wallcreeper is a bird of Eurasian high mountain ranges from the Alps east to southern China, including the Tibetan Plateau. In the Himalayas it breeds east to eastern Nepal, occurring as a winter visitor further east. Winter habitat consists of cliffs and stony riverbeds.

In Bhutan the Wallcreeper is a frequently recorded winter visitor throughout the temperate zone, with a few records in the high west and east and the central foothills. Its regular winter range spans 1,000–3,000 m, more occasionally reaching the foothills. It has been found on passage at 4,400 m[49] in late September. Passage records at higher altitudes are otherwise rare, suggesting that they cross the Himalayas in direct flight. Arrivals in the winter range commence in the first week of October, with the bulk arriving in the latter half of the month. Throughout winter most records concern singles, although up to five may be present at a site, particularly in early winter and in late March, the latter near the upper limit of the winter range, prior to spring migration. Numbers decline rapidly during the first week of April, as spring migration commences. The last leave Bhutan by mid-April, with the latest record 16 April[52]. There is no indication of summer presence in Bhutan.

# Eurasian Treecreeper
## *Certhia familiaris*

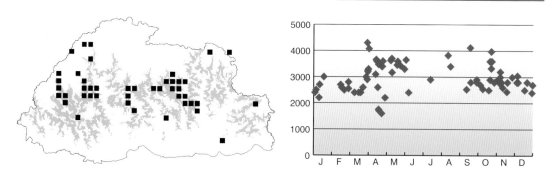

The Eurasian Treecreeper occupies a vast range from Western Europe to Japan. In the Indian subcontinent it occurs in the Himalayas from Pakistan to Arunachal Pradesh. It inhabits high-altitude conifer forest.

In Bhutan the Eurasian Treecreeper is a frequently recorded altitudinal migrant, occurring throughout the alpine and temperate zones. Summer range spans 1,800 m to the treeline at 4,000 m, with occasional presence to 1,600 m and 4,200 m. In November–March it retreats below 3,200 m. From July to March 1–3 are regularly found in mixed-species flocks of tits and leaf warblers. There are no confirmed breeding records. Although widespread it is mostly found in small numbers, with a max. 10 at Thrumshing La in May[5].

# Rusty-flanked Treecreeper
## *Certhia nipalensis*
N=166(57). S 2000-3400 (Mar-Oct); W 1600-3000

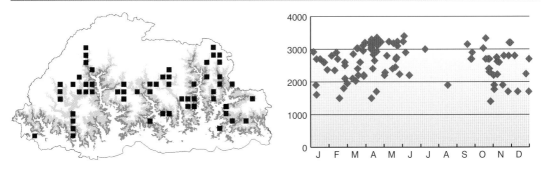

The Rusty-flanked Treecreeper is distributed along the Himalayas from Uttar Pradesh to Arunachal Pradesh, extending further east to south-east Tibet and northern Myanmar. It occurs at lower elevations than Eurasian Treecreeper and prefers broadleaf forest, particularly oak, occurring also in mixed and hemlock forests.

In Bhutan this treecreeper is a frequently recorded altitudinal migrant throughout the temperate zone, with isolated records in the alpine zone. In summer it occurs at 2,000–3,400 m in cool broadleaf and hemlock forests. In winter it descends slightly to 1,600–3,000 m, the lowest record being at 1,400 m[17,42]. It is present here from late November to February, and most winter observations concern singles within mixed-species flocks[52], although larger numbers may occur in the pre-breeding season (February–March), with a max. 8 in a flock[26]. During the breeding season typically singles are noted. Apart from territorial birds and a juvenile collected at 3,000 m on 8 July[31], there is no breeding evidence.

# Brown-throated Treecreeper
## *Certhia discolor*
N=260(50). S 1600-2600 (Apr-Oct); W 1000-2200

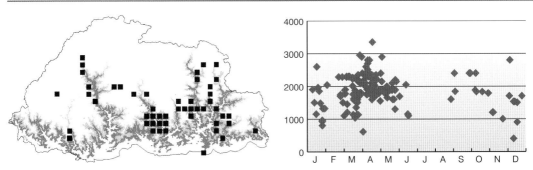

The Brown-throated Treecreeper occurs in the Himalayas from central Nepal to Arunachal Pradesh and in north-east India. Outside the Indian subcontinent its range reaches northern Vietnam. Among *Certhia* treecreepers in the region it has the lowest altitudinal range, preferring mossy oak forest.

In Bhutan the Brown-throated Treecreeper is a frequently recorded altitudinal migrant, being found throughout the temperate zone and in the central and eastern foothills, becoming gradually commoner further east. In summer it occurs at 1,600–2,600 m, occasionally to 2,900 m, with the highest record from c.3,300 m in April[5]. In November–February it retreats below 2,200 m, regularly spreading as low as 1,000 m and occasionally reaching c.400 m. It occupies breeding territories early in spring, with the first singing birds heard in February, but particularly from April to late May. Near Zhemgang a mean density of 1.1 territories per km was found at 1,600–1,900 m, with the highest density in the upper part of this range and considerable annual fluctuations[52]. There are no confirmed breeding records. Between August and December 1–5 individuals are regularly encountered in mixed-species flocks.

Brown-throated Treecreeper
*Dan Cole*

# Winter Wren
## *Troglodytes troglodytes*

N=149(59). S 2800-4600 (Apr-mid-Oct); W 2200-3200

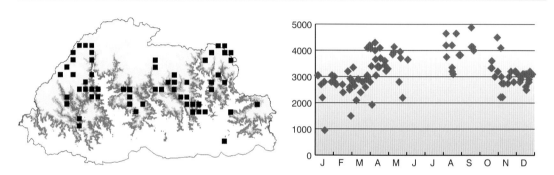

The Winter Wren has a vast distribution in the Holarctic, occurring from Western Europe to the Pacific Ocean and into North America. It occurs along the Himalayas from Pakistan to Arunachal Pradesh. Whereas elsewhere it prefers undergrowth in forest, in the Himalayas the species breeds primarily above the treeline in open areas at high altitude. It winters lower, amongst others in cultivated areas.

In Bhutan the wren is a common altitudinal migrant throughout the alpine and temperate zones. Its regular summer range spans 2,800–4,600 m, with the highest record from 4,900 m[1]. In winter it occupies a relatively narrow altitudinal range between 2,200 m and 3,200 m, occasionally lower, with the lowest record from 1,000 m[13,28]. It is present here until late April, after which the majority move higher, descending again from mid-October. Singing birds are noted in the breeding areas from early April. The core range appears to be above 3,800 m, records at lower altitudes possibly largely concerning passage birds, as indicated by the fact that juveniles taken by Ludlow in August were all from 3,800–4,700 m. One collecting nest material was observed at 4,100 m[49], thus probably breeding. Both in summer and winter, it appears to occupy a complementary altitudinal range and habitat to Scaly-breasted Wren Babbler, the latter occurring in lower zones and undergrowth in forest, i.e. traditional Winter Wren habitat throughout much of its range elsewhere.

# Fire-capped Tit
## *Cephalopyrus flammiceps*

N=55(19). S 1600-3000

The Fire-capped Tit is distributed along the Himalayas from Pakistan to Arunachal Pradesh, and further east to Sichuan and Yunnan. It is a summer visitor to the west of its range, but considered resident further east. It inhabits temperate deciduous broadleaf forest.

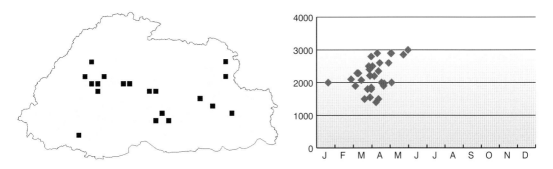

In Bhutan the Fire-capped Tit is an uncommon summer visitor throughout the temperate zone, with a concentration of records in the Sunkosh Valley. It is found at 1,600–3,000 m. There is little evidence that the species is resident in Bhutan, as winter records at 2,000 m in January[13,28] and 2,100 m in February[52] probably involved early migrants. An influx appears to occur in March, when birds are noted over the entire altitudinal range, often in mixed flocks with other tits. Observations of large flocks involving several tens in late March[5] suggest migration, as described by Ali and Ripley (1983) for the west of its range. May records are largely confined to 2,600–3,000 m, suggesting that it may breed in a relatively narrow altitudinal band, where one attending a nest was observed at 2,600 m on 13 April[5], and a nest with young was found on 23 May at 2,850 m[22]. Both records are from the same area near Dodena, Thimphu district. There are no records after May, the birds presumably departing to winter quarters outside Bhutan.

# Rufous-vented Tit
*Parus rubidiventris*    N=247(53). S 3000-3800 (mid-Mar-mid-Nov); W 2800-3200

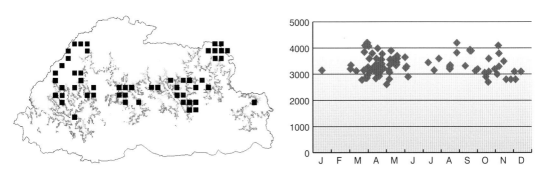

The Rufous-vented Tit occurs in the Himalayas from Himachal Pradesh to Bhutan, its range continuing into northern Myanmar and montane western China. It inhabits various forest types at high elevations, including juniper and rhododendron scrub.

The Rufous-vented Tit is the highest-ranging of the tits in Bhutan, reaching above the treeline. It is a common altitudinal migrant throughout the alpine and temperate zones, but less common in the eastern valleys where it approaches its easternmost limits in the Himalayas. In summer it is found at 3,000–3,800 m, occasionally to 2,600 m and in alpine scrub at 4,200 m. Altitudinal movements are not very marked, with records in mid-November to mid-March at 2,800–3,200 m. However, as higher elevations are hardly explored in winter it is possible that the species is present over most of its range at this season. In any case, there is no clear influx into lower areas in this period. Throughout the year it is mostly found in pairs or small flocks of up to six and it does not seem to gather in larger flocks like Coal Tit. It does not generally associate with other tits in mixed flocks. However, even though dispersed, important numbers may be present at a site, with a max. 60–70 in March/April[5,57]. Breeding is confirmed by the observation of a nest with young at 3,650 m on 1 June[49]. A juvenile was collected at 3,200 m on 19 July[31].

# Coal Tit
*Parus ater*

N=296(56). S 2400-3800 (Apr-mid-Nov); W 2400-3200

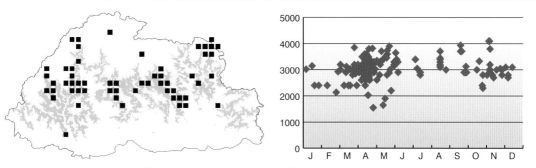

The Coal Tit is widespread from Europe east to Kamchatka and Taiwan. In the Himalayas it occurs from central Nepal to Arunachal Pradesh. It is a bird of conifer forest at higher elevations.

In Bhutan the Coal Tit is an abundant altitudinal migrant throughout the alpine and temperate zones, gradually becoming scarcer further east. It summers at 2,400–3,800 m, mostly in hemlock, fir and mixed forests. In December–March it withdraws from higher areas and appears in larger numbers at 2,400–3,200 m, when it also frequents Blue Pine forest. As early as July it occurs in flocks of up to 40, which often form the core of mixed-species flocks of tits and leaf warblers. By early April these flocks disband and singing birds occupy breeding territories. From mid-April to mid-May there are low-altitude records down to 1,600 m, possibly marking ongoing pre-breeding dispersal. Birds carrying food have been observed on 15 and 22 May at 3,500 m[52] and 2,900 m[22] respectively. The latest singing birds are heard early July.

# Grey-crested Tit
*Parus dichrous*

N=254(54). S 2600-4000 (Apr-Oct); W 2400-3200

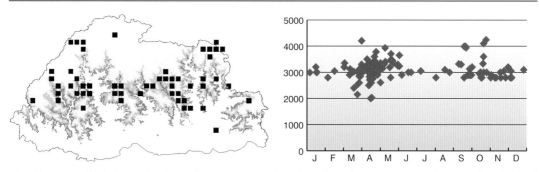

The Grey-crested Tit is another high-elevation tit species of the Himalayas, occupying broadleaf and mixed forests in the temperate zone, with a preference for oak. Its range stretches from Kashmir to Bhutan and thence to Yunnan and montane western China.

In Bhutan the Grey-crested Tit is a common altitudinal migrant throughout the temperate and alpine zones, becoming gradually scarcer further east where it approaches its easternmost limits in the Himalayas. It is found at 2,600–4,000 m with occasional records to 2,000 m and 4,200 m. It appears to retreat slightly in winter, as suggested by observations of larger numbers in the lower part of its range, particularly in November–December. In this period and into March it is found at 2,400–3,200 m. Habitat preference in Bhutan appears to be fir, hemlock and mixed forests, rather than broadleaf forest, reaching the highest patches of conifer forest at the treeline. It is normally found in small flocks of up to six, but it may associate in larger flocks of up to 20 in winter. It regularly joins mixed flocks with other tits. There are no confirmed breeding records and the species appears to be easily overlooked in the breeding season.

# Great Tit
## *Parus major*

N=15(5). R 400-2000

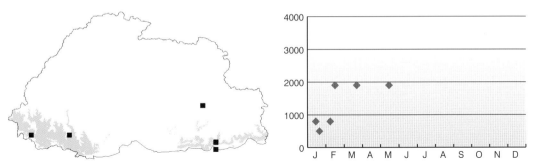

The Great Tit has the widest geographical range of the region's tits, occurring from Europe to the Pacific Ocean and south to Indonesia. In the Indian subcontinent it occurs in the Himalayan foothills from Pakistan to Arunachal Pradesh, and in parts of north-east India and the Indian peninsula. Habitat is open forest.

In Bhutan the Great Tit is uncommon, with scattered records in the western, Sunkosh and eastern valleys, and the western and eastern foothills. It appears to be resident in Samtse district[44], but elsewhere is found only in November–April[1,5,28,44], suggesting that occurrence in Bhutan reflects dry-season dispersal from the plains. In this period it has been found at 400–2,000 m, with a maximum of four at 800 m near Deothang, Samdrup Jongkha district, on 7 February[1].

# Green-backed Tit
## *Parus monticolus*

N=1204(114). S 1200-3000 (Apr-Oct); W 800-3000

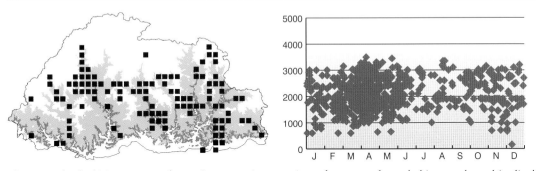

The Green-backed Tit is a versatile species occupying a variety of montane forest habitats and an altitudinal range complementary to the similar Great Tit. It ranges throughout the Himalayas from Pakistan to Arunachal Pradesh and north-east India. Further east it reaches southern China, Taiwan and northern Vietnam.

In Bhutan the Green-backed Tit is abundant and probably the most widespread forest bird, being found in all biogeographic units. Its main range spans 1,200–3,000 m, while in winter there is some altitudinal movement, birds dispersing to 800 m. More occasionally it is found at 400 m and 3,500 m. Its known seasonal altitudinal distribution is probably more a reflection of the intensity of birding activities at relevant altitudes. However, numbers at any given site are generally not very high, rarely exceeding 20 and more commonly fewer than ten. In winter it sometimes forms larger flocks of up to 20 and once 30, and is a regular member of mixed-species flocks, with one or a few present in most such aggregations. Singing birds occupy territories from mid-March and are heard until May. Near Zhemgang a density of 2.9 territories was found per km at 1,600–1,900 m[52]. There are numerous observations of nesting at 1,200–2,900 m[19,31,22,52]. The season appears well spaced, probably with multiple broods, with nest-building noted on 27–28 March[19,52], pairs carrying food on 5 May–6 July[31,52] and the first fledglings on 16 June[52]. By mid-July nesting activity has ceased and birds are regularly encountered again in mixed flocks. It occurs in a variety of habitats but prefers broadleaf forest.

# Yellow-cheeked Tit
## *Parus spilonotus*

N=243(44). R 1200-2400

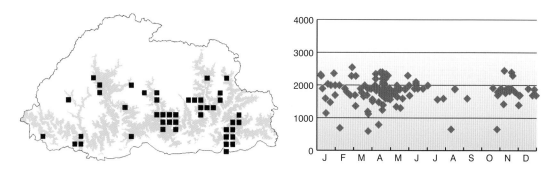

The Yellow-cheeked Tit occupies the lowest altitudinal range among *Parus* species in the Eastern Himalayas. It ranges from eastern Nepal to Arunachal Pradesh and north-east India, and further east to northern Vietnam and southern China. It inhabits open broadleaf forest.

In Bhutan the Yellow-cheeked Tit is a common resident throughout the temperate zone and in the western and eastern foothills. The core range lies in the central and eastern valleys, and it is scarcer further east where it approaches its westernmost limits. Its altitudinal range spans 1,200–2,400 m, with occasional records to 600 m and 2,600 m. Compared to other tits, it breeds relatively late, with singing birds noted mid-April to August. Near Zhemgang a density of 1.1 breeding pairs per km was found at 1,600–1,900 m[52]. On 23 June a pair was observed carrying food at 1,900 m[52]. From November to mid-April the species gathers in small flocks of up to 5–10, which regularly associate with other tits and medium-sized babblers in mixed-species flocks. In December 30 Yellow-cheeked Tits were once observed in such a flock[52].

# Yellow-browed Tit
## *Sylviparus modestus*

N=307(56). S 2200-3200 (mid-May-mid-Oct); W 1600-3200

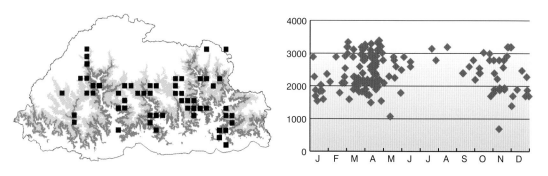

The Yellow-browed Tit is a *Phylloscopus*-like small tit species and a frequent member of mixed-species flocks. It is found in the Himalayas from Kashmir to Arunachal Pradesh and in north-east India. Further east its range reaches south-east China and northern Vietnam. It inhabits broadleaf forest, preferring oak.

In Bhutan the Yellow-browed Tit is a common altitudinal migrant throughout the alpine and temperate zones. Summer range spans 2,200–3,200 m, with occasional presence to 3,400 m. In winter it remains largely present in the same zone but also disperses to 1,600 m and occasionally lower. The lowest recorded elevation is 700 m[14]. Lower altitudes are vacated only by mid-May, and dispersal to this range occurs again in October–November. Birds are found in small flocks of up to 20 most of the year, frequently joining mixed-species flocks with other tits and leaf warblers. Only in mid-May to mid-July are birds mostly recorded singly. There is one record of a singing bird in this period, at 2,900 m on 2 June[52], which is the sole indication of breeding in Bhutan.

# Sultan Tit
*Melanochlora sultanea*

N=156(29). R 200-2000

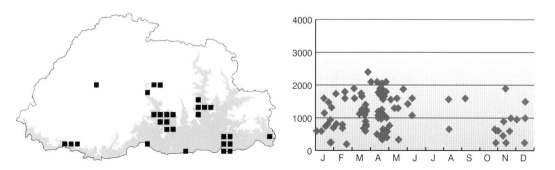

The Sultan Tit is distributed along the Himalayas from Ladakh to Arunachal Pradesh and in north-east India. Further east it extends over most of mainland south-east Asia. It is a bird of broadleaf forest, particularly inhabiting forest edges.

In Bhutan the Sultan Tit is a frequently recorded resident throughout the temperate zone and foothills. However, it is rare in the western and Sunkosh valleys, with just a few isolated records. Its regular altitudinal range spans 200–2,000 m, with occasional records to 2,100 m and the highest from the Sunkosh Valley at 2,400 m, underlining its status as a vagrant there. One was observed inspecting a nest hole at 1,100 m on 13 April[28,52], which in addition to the presence of territorial birds establishes it as a probable breeder in Bhutan. The breeding season appears to occupy April–September, when it is mostly found in pairs or singly. However, singing birds have also been noted in March and August[52]. From November to March it is mostly found in pairs or small flocks up to five, regularly associating with mixed feeding flocks, with Rufous Sibia and White-browed Shrike Babbler as typical components. The largest number involved 16 near Samdrup Jongkha at 200 m in January[13,28].

Black-throated Tit
*Ren Hathway*

# Black-throated Tit
## *Aegithalos concinnus*

N=387(79). R 1200-2600

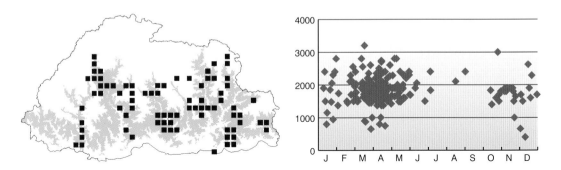

The Black-throated Tit occurs in the Himalayas from Pakistan to north-east India, as well as east to central China, Taiwan and northern Vietnam. It is one of two *Aegithalos* ('long-tailed') tits in Bhutan. Compared to Rufous-fronted Tit, it occupies moister habitats at lower elevations. Unlike most other tits, *Aegithalos* tits do not construct a tree-hole nest, but a ball of mosses and lichen placed on a branch in a tree or shrub.

In Bhutan the Black-throated Tit is a common resident throughout the temperate zone and foothills. Its regular altitudinal range spans 1,200–2,600 m, occasionally to 400 m and 3,200 m, with no obvious seasonal pattern. This range is complementary to that of Rufous-fronted Tit, with the divide between their regular ranges situated at 2,600 m in the Sunkosh, central and eastern valleys, and in the western valleys at 2,200 m, due to the predominance of dry habitats in the Thimphu and Paro valleys, which are unsuitable for Black-throated Tit. Outside the breeding season, in August–March, birds occur in flocks of up to 20, frequently with other tits and leaf warblers. During March these flocks disband into pairs. Nest-building has been observed at 1,600 m on 28 March[19] and the first fledglings as early as 11 April[19]. Family groups are therefore found throughout spring, while at the same time birds initiate broods, as shown by an active nest at 1,900 m on 20 May[52]. A mean density of 1.4 breeding pairs per km was found near Zhemgang at 1,600–1,900 m[52].

# Rufous-fronted Tit
## *Aegithalos iouschistos*

N=308(60). S 2200-3400 (mid-Mar-mid-Nov) W 2200-3000

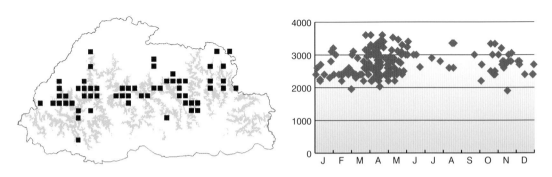

The Rufous-fronted Tit occurs in the Himalayas from central Nepal to Arunachal Pradesh. Compared with Black-throated Tit, it is a bird of drier habitat, both broadleaf and conifer forests at higher elevations.

In Bhutan the Rufous-fronted Tit is a common altitudinal migrant throughout the temperate zone and foothills. Its regular upper altitudinal limit is 3,400 m in summer, with birds retreating below 3,200 m in mid-November to mid-March. The lower altitudinal limit is 2,200 in the western valleys and 2,600 m further east, forming a relatively sharp divide with Black-throated Tit. In fact, the two species never occur syntopically. It is particularly common in the western valleys, where the dry Paro and Thimphu valleys offer favourable habitat, but becomes gradually scarcer further east. From July to early March it occurs in flocks of 10–30. Unlike Black-throated Tit it more frequently occurs in single-species flocks. March–June is the breeding season and birds normally occur in pairs or singly. Pairs have been noted carrying nest material at 3,000 m on 7 April[52,53] and at 2,900 m on 4 May[22].

# Sand Martin
## *Riparia riparia*

N = 16(9). W 1200-2400

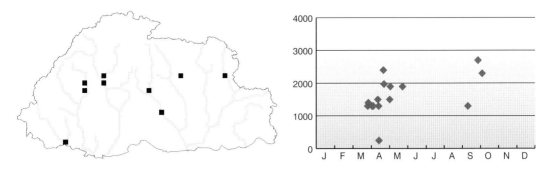

The Sand Martin has a vast world distribution, breeding across Eurasia from Europe to Japan, and wintering in Africa and south-east Asia. It also nests in North America, moving south as far as southern South America in winter. In the Indian subcontinent its status is unclear due to some confusion with Pale Martin. However, it breeds in Assam and possibly occurs widely as a winter visitor.

In Bhutan the Sand Martin is an uncommon passage migrant, seen mostly in the Sunkosh Valley, with irregular records from the western, central and eastern valleys, and the western foothills. Spring passage is from the last week of March to late May, while autumn passage is noted from the second week of September to early October. The species is mostly found singly or as two birds together, but larger flocks of up to 20 were noted in the Wangdue Phodrang/Punakha area in late March to early April 2002[52,53] and early May 1996[28]. Passage is noted from 1,200 m to 2400 m, with the lowest record at 200 m[15] and the highest 2,700 m[29]. The lack of records outside migration periods suggests that birds seen in Bhutan are trans-Himalayan migrants, rather than birds dispersing from breeding areas south of Bhutan. Autumn passage coincides with the breeding season in Assam, providing further evidence that different populations are involved. Possibly some records concern Pale Martins, as the two have recently been widely recognised as different species and separation in the field is difficult. However, of a flock of 20 birds at Bajo, Wangdue Phodrang, in late March[52,53], only one Pale Martin was found, perhaps suggesting that the vast majority of passage birds are Sand Martins.

# Pale Martin
## *Riparia diluta*

N=2(1)

The breeding range of the Pale Martin includes the Central Asian republics and parts of southern and south-east Asia. It breeds and winters in the western Indian subcontinent. In general the species's range is imperfectly known, as it has only recently been considered specifically distinct from Sand Martin. Like the latter, Plain Martin nests in holes excavated in riverbanks.

In Bhutan this species is a vagrant. One was collected during the 1960s, at Punakha at 1,400 m on 27 September 1968[1]. More recently one was identified in a flock of Sand Martins at Bajo, Wangdue Phodrang district, at 1,300 m on 25 March 2002[52,53]. The timing of this record coincides with the main passage of Sand Martin and it is possible that the species is overlooked among them, although numbers are probably still very small.

# Plain Martin
*Riparia paludicola*                                                    N=8(5)

The Plain Martin occurs in Africa, southern and south-east Asia. It is found in the northern and central Indian subcontinent, including the Himalayan foothills in Nepal and India.

In Bhutan the Plain Martin is a rare visitor to the temperate zone that has only been noted in spring, from late March to mid-May, at 1,000–2,400 m. Presence in Bhutan probably relates to dispersal of breeders in northern India, as its appearance coincides with the end of the breeding season in India. Given that the nearest breeding areas are to the south-west, this explanation tallies well with the predominance of records from the west of the country. The largest flock totalled 20 and was noted in the eastern valleys on 15 May[5].

# Eurasian Crag Martin
*Hirundo rupestris*                                         N=39(19). W 1000-2400

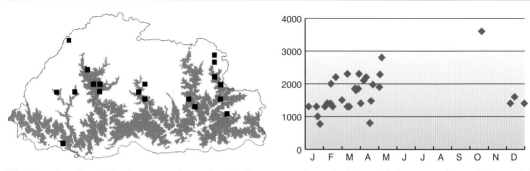

The Eurasian Crag Martin occurs from the Mediterranean through Central Asia to northern China and is largely resident. It breeds in the Himalayas from Pakistan west to Bhutan, occurring more widely in winter, reaching to the southern Indian peninsula. Habitat comprises steep cliffs where it nests.

In Bhutan this martin is an uncommon winter visitor to the temperate zone, with one record from the high west, and is present in December to early May at 1,000–2,400 m, with occasional records to 800 and 2,800 m. In midwinter, in December–January, it occurs in the lower part of this range, largely below 1,400 m, but from February it moves higher, to 1,200–2,400 m. After the first week of May the species is no longer noted in the winter range and it is unclear where the breeding areas are located, but they are possibly at elevations above 4,000 m. The observation of around three at 3,600 m in October might also suggest this[51]. Throughout winter and spring it is found in considerable numbers, with totals of 80 and 100 observed in December at Punakha and between Kamji and Rinchending, Chhukha district[53]. Most records are from Punakha/Wangdue Phodrang area, which is a regular winter site. At other sites presence appears more erratic.

# Barn Swallow
*Hirundo rustica*                        N=151(33). S 1800-2000 (mid-May-Aug); W 400-2400

The Barn Swallow breeds in North America and in Eurasia from Europe to Kamchatka. It winters in Africa, southern and south-east Asia. In the Indian subcontinent it breeds in the Himalayas from Pakistan to Arunachal Pradesh and in north-east India. Elsewhere in the subcontinent it is a common winter visitor to open country. The species breeds in sheds and houses.

In Bhutan the Barn Swallow is a local breeder as well as a common passage migrant. Records are well distributed throughout the temperate zone and foothills, indicating broad-front passage across Bhutan. It breeds in loose colonies in several towns at 1,000–1,800 m: Damphu in Tsirang district, Lingmethang area in Mongar district, Mongar itself and Trashigang. In Damphu more than 100 were nesting in April/May 2000 and 2001[15]. At other sites a max. 6 pairs has been reported from Trashigang[5]. Nesting has been noted between 8 April[5] and 1 July, with in the latter case almost full-grown young in the nest[52]. Spring migrants are noted

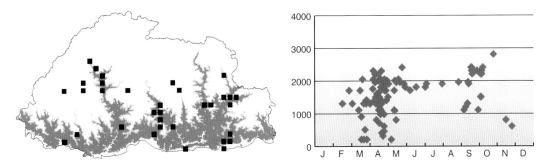

from late February, with the earliest record 15 February[49,52], and passage continues until late May, when it is still occasionally noted in non-breeding areas such as Thimphu and Zhemgang. Strays are noted outside the breeding areas in July, but autumn passage occurs from late August to late October, with the peak in the last week of September and first week of October, when up to 20 are present at a site. In Thimphu birds were found to appear regularly in the late afternoon[52], presumably after crossing the main Himalayan range earlier in the day. During passage periods, birds are noted mostly at 400–2,400 m, occasionally to 200 m and 2,800 m. Higher elevations are probably crossed in direct flight, as they present less favourable habitat. Records at c.600 m in the eastern foothills from November[31] possibly concern wintering birds. The subspecies breeding in Bhutan is *gutturalis*, which is also common on passage. East Asian *tytleri* has been found in the foothills in November[31] and March[20], but there are no recent records and annual occurrence is considered variable (Ali and Ripley 1983). Occurrence of western *rustica* is unsure, as it is difficult to differentiate from *gutturalis* in the field and there are no specimen records.

# Red-rumped Swallow
## *Hirundo daurica*

N=72(24). S 1600-2000 (May-Aug) W 200-2400

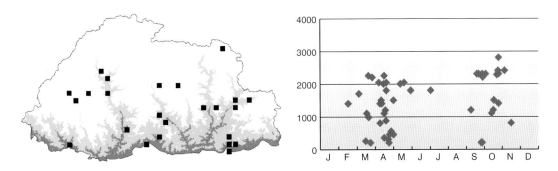

The Red-rumped Swallow breeds in sub-Saharan Africa, the Mediterranean and widely in south and east Asia. It is resident over much of the Indian subcontinent, except parts of the north-east and north-west, with numbers augmented in winter by migrants from east Asia. It occurs in similar habitat to Barn Swallow.

In Bhutan, the Red-rumped Swallow has a similar pattern of occurrence as Barn Swallow and they are often found together, although *daurica* is generally scarcer. Nevertheless, it is a frequently recorded passage migrant and summer visitor, found throughout the temperate zone and foothills on passage, at 240–2,400 m, occasionally to 2,800 m[25]. A breeding population is present at Damphu, Tsirang district, and in the Trashigang area. More than 60 were found nesting in Damphu in April/May 2000 and 2001[15]. Near Trashigang nesting pairs were found at Kanglung at 2,000 m on 14 April[5]. Passage occurs early March to mid-May, with the earliest on 15 February[29] and the peak in early April, when up to ten have been observed at a site. Autumn migration is noted early September to early November, with a marked peak in the last week of September. The highest day total in this period was 20, on 13 October[52]. November records at low elevations possibly concern winterers. Both the subspecies *daurica* and *nipalensis* have been collected in Bhutan, but their relative status and the possible occurrence of other subspecies are unclear, due to difficulties in field identification.

# Asian House Martin
## *Delichon dasypus*

N=148(62). S 2200-4400 (mid-May-Sep); W 400-3400

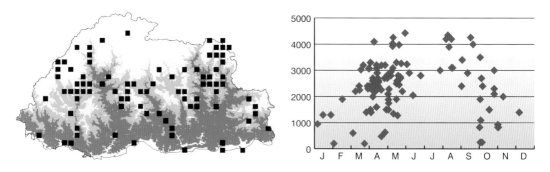

The Asian House Martin breeds in the Himalayas from Pakistan to Arunachal Pradesh, and further east through China to south-east Siberia, wintering south to the Greater Sundas. As many observers have considered Eurasian House Martin and Asian House Martin as one species, its distribution is unclear. It occupies higher elevations than Nepal House Martin and reaches alpine areas. It nests on cliffs and buildings, and winters in the foothills.

The Asian House Martin is a frequently recorded altitudinal migrant, found in all biogeographic units. Summer range spans 2,200–4,400 m, although its breeding range lies above 2,800 m, records at lower elevations probably being of late passage birds. In winter and on migration it has been found at 400–3,400 m, retreating in midwinter below 1,400 m. Birds ascend from the lowest areas in March, the last vacating lower elevations in mid-May. It is present at its cliff-nesting sites from early April, with nest-building observed at 3,000 m on 23 April[14] and occupied nests at similar altitudes by the month's end[40,43,52]. Breeding appears to start later at higher altitudes, with nest-building observed at 4,400 m on 30 May[49]. As late as 16 August birds were still nest-building at 3,100 m[52] and young were seen in a nest at 3,400 m on 1 September[43,52]. Late records probably relate to second or third broods. Nests have been observed on cliffs and on man-made structures such as chortens, where it forms small colonies of 5–10 pairs. In October birds migrate to their winter quarters in the foothills. It occurs in considerably smaller flocks than Nepal House Martin, the largest (up to 30) in March–April during spring migration. However, there are few midwinter records from the foothills, where it may occur in larger flocks.

# Nepal House Martin
## *Delichon nipalensis*

N=360(68). S 1200-2800 (Mar-Oct); W 600-2200

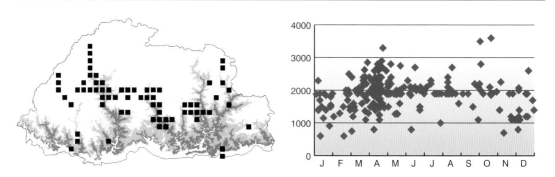

The Nepal House Martin breeds in the Himalayas from Uttar Pradesh to Arunachal Pradesh and in north-east India. Further east it extends to northern Vietnam. It nests exclusively on cliffs and occupies lower altitudes than Asian House Martin, though partially overlapping.

In Bhutan the Nepal House Martin is a common altitudinal migrant throughout the temperate zone, with scattered records in the western and eastern valleys and the high west. Summer range spans 1,200–2,800 m, where it is present in March–October. There are occasional records up to 3,600 m, particularly early and late in this period. In winter the species descends to 600–2,200 m. Compared to Asian House Martin its altitudinal movements are less pronounced, occupying mid-levels throughout the year, whereas *dasypus* 'leap-frogs' from the alpine zone to the foothills and plains. In contrast, Nepal House Martin is found in the vicinity of its breeding cliffs year-round, making it difficult to assess breeding season timing. Nest building has been observed at 2,700 m on 24 April [5] and at 2,100 m as late as 8 August[52]. However, the main season appears to start mid-March, when there is most activity at the nests. From mid-March to mid-August the birds feed over forest adjacent to the colony in a radius of *c*.1 km. Outside this season the birds roost in the colonies, departing in early morning[52]. During daytime they are mostly absent, as they presumably forage in higher air layers. Nesting colonies are generally large, numbering up to 50 nests, albeit well dispersed. Along 150 km of road in the Mangde Chhu valley, at suitable altitudes, 4–5 colonies have been located[52]. In winter flocks of up to 300 have been observed.

Nepal House Martin
*Chris Orgill*

# Goldcrest
## *Regulus regulus*

N=121(37). S 2600-3800 (May-Oct); W 2400-3600

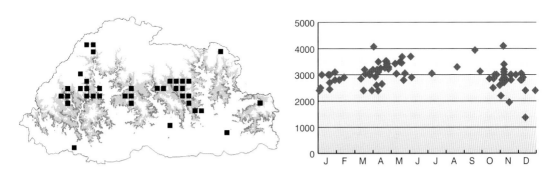

The Goldcrest occurs in various populations from Europe to Japan, and is associated with coniferous forest. Its range in the Himalayas stretches from Pakistan to Arunachal Pradesh, thence north into montane western China.

In Bhutan the Goldcrest is a common altitudinal migrant throughout the alpine and temperate zones. In summer it occupies altitudes at 2,600–3,800 m, with the highest record from 4,100 m[52,53]. In winter it descends to 2,400–3,600 m, occasionally reaching 1,400 m[53]. Birds move to the breeding areas in April and descend in October. During the breeding season it is found in fir and hemlock forests, but in winter the species occurs in a broader range of habitats, including Blue Pine and cool broadleaf forests. It moves around in small flocks, often joining mixed-species flocks with tit species. In December–March it occasionally gathers in larger flocks of up to 20. There is no breeding evidence from Bhutan.

# Striated Bulbul
*Pycnonotus striatus*

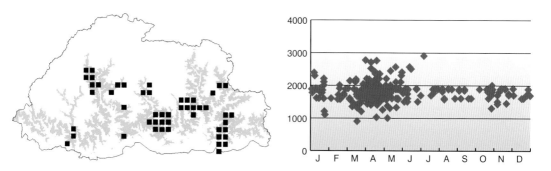

The Striated Bulbul occurs in the Himalayas from central Nepal to Arunachal Pradesh and in north-east India, and further east in other hill areas of northern mainland south-east Asia. It inhabits broadleaf forest.

In Bhutan the Striated Bulbul is a common and widespread resident throughout the temperate zone and foothills, but is scarcer in the west where it approaches its westernmost limits. The central and eastern valleys constitute its stronghold. It is resident at 1,400–2,400 m, with occasional records to 1,000 m and 2,600 m. The highest record is from 2,900 m in July[40,52]. The birds do not show clear territorial activity, loose flocks being seen throughout the breeding season. Based on numbers present near Zhemgang, density of breeding pairs was estimated at 3.6 per km at 1,600–1,900 m[52]. It has been seen carrying nest material on 17 April[51] and 20 April[22] at around 1,900 m, and on 13 May at 1,800 m[52]. In October–February it forms larger flocks of up to 20 and is one of the most abundant birds in warm broadleaf forest, with a max. 30 at one site.

# Black-crested Bulbul
*Pycnonotus melanicterus*

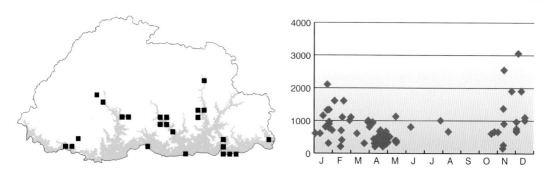

The Black-crested Bulbul is widespread in south-east Asia, ranging south to the Greater Sundas. In the Indian subcontinent it has a patchy distribution similar to that of Bar-winged Flycatcher-shrike, occurring in the hills of south-west, eastern and north-east India, and the Himalayas from Uttar Pradesh east. It inhabits moist broadleaf forest with dense undergrowth, as well as second growth.

In Bhutan this bulbul is a common resident throughout the temperate zone and foothills, with the central valleys and eastern foothills apparently its strongholds. The regular altitudinal range spans 200–1,200 m. In November–February it shows a marked dispersal to higher altitudes, particularly in relatively warm and dry winters, such as 2000/2001 and 2001/2002. The highest record in this period is from c.3,000 m[53]. In July–March it gathers in flocks of up to 20.There are no confirmed breeding records.

# Red-whiskered Bulbul
*Pycnonotus jocosus*                         N=59(10). R 200-600

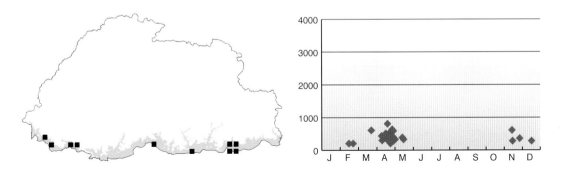

The Red-whiskered Bulbul is widespread in mainland south-east Asia. In the Indian subcontinent it occurs along the Himalayas from Himachal Pradesh east, and through north-east, central and western India and Bangladesh. Habitat consists of open forest and scrub, often around villages.

In Bhutan the Red-whiskered Bulbul is a common resident in the foothills, found at altitudes up to 600 m, with one record at 800 m[19]. Particularly in the forests above Samdrup Jongkha it has been found in considerable numbers, with a max. 40 reported on 15 May[28].

# Himalayan Bulbul
*Pycnonotus leucogenys*              N=127(26). S 400-1800 (Mar-Aug); W 600-1400

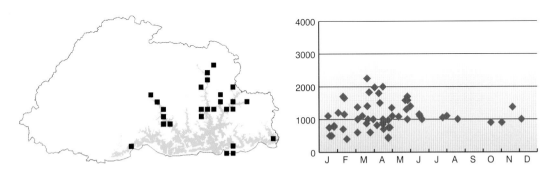

The Himalayan Bulbul has a mainly Western Himalayan distribution, being found from Pakistan to western Arunachal Pradesh. It is a bird of dry habitat, including scrub-covered hillsides.

In Bhutan the Himalayan Bulbul is frequently recorded in the central and eastern valleys, with a few records from the central and eastern foothills. It occurs on dry exposed slopes, in scrub vegetation. Its summer range spans 400–1,800 m. From October to February it is found at somewhat lower elevations, below 1,400 m. In suitable habitat it can occur in considerable numbers, with up to 20 reported from the dry valleys between Kori La and Trashigang.

# Red-vented Bulbul
## Pycnonotus cafer

N=703(82). R 400-2000

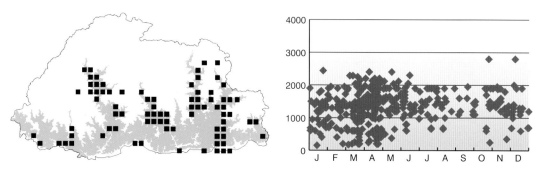

The Red-vented Bulbul occurs over most of the Indian subcontinent, including the Himalayas. Further east it reaches Myanmar and Yunnan. It inhabits open forest and scrub, generally close to settlements.

In Bhutan the Red-vented Bulbul is abundant and widespread throughout the temperate zone and foothills, being resident at 600–2,000 m, with occasional records to 200 m and 2,400 m. It has been found twice in the Phobjikha Valley at 2,800 m, in October[25] and December[53], probably as a result of dispersal like that noted for Black-crested Bulbul. In October–March it gathers in flocks that regularly number up to 40, sometimes even 100. In January–February it occasionally joins feeding flocks at flowering *Bombax* trees. Although common, there are relatively few breeding records: one was observed nest-building at 600 m on 20 April[52] and a pair with recently fledged young at 1,900 m on 23 June[52].

# White-throated Bulbul
## Alophoixus flaveolus

N=148(22). R 200-1000

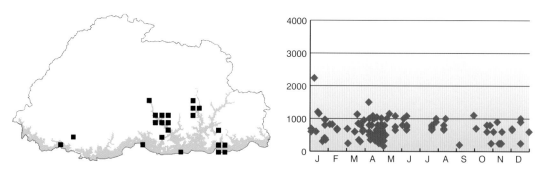

The White-throated Bulbul occurs in the north-east Indian subcontinent, extending further east to Myanmar and north-west Thailand. Along the Himalayas it is sparsely distributed from central Nepal east, becoming more common in Bhutan, Arunachal Pradesh, north-east India and Bangladesh. Habitat is evergreen forest at low elevations, where it particularly frequents forest understorey.

In Bhutan this bulbul is a common resident throughout the foothills and in the lower central valleys, where it is commonest. Up to 20 can been found here in a morning, especially by observers familiar with the call. Occurrence in the eastern valleys appears more occasional, and there is only a single record from the western valleys[36]. Its altitudinal range spans 200–1,000 m. In winter it appears occasionally to stray higher, with a record from the Kuri Chhu valley at 2,200 m in winter 1999/2000[22]. From October to March birds are regularly encountered in small flocks of *c.*5 birds, with occasionally up to ten together. The only evidence for breeding is of a bird carrying nest material at 800 m on 20 July[52].

# Ashy Bulbul
*Hemixos flavala*

N=181(24). R 400-1400

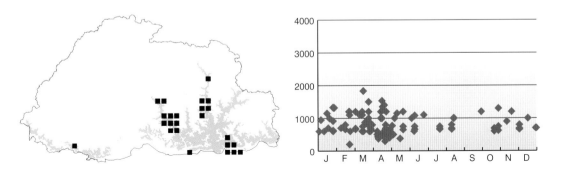

The Ashy Bulbul is distributed in the Himalayan foothills from Uttar Pradesh to Arunachal Pradesh and in north-east India and Bangladesh. Further east it is widespread in mainland south-east Asia, reaching Sumatra and Borneo in the south. It inhabits well-developed forest at lower elevations.

In Bhutan the Ashy Bulbul is a common resident in the western and eastern foothills, and the central and eastern valleys. It appears to be associated with well-developed forest in the more humid valleys, and is resident at 400–1,400 m, with occasional records to 200 m and 1,800 m. In January–March it forms flocks of up to ten, the birds being more dispersed the rest of the year. In its range the species is usually numerous, with up to 20–30 present at a site.

# Mountain Bulbul
*Hypsipetes mcclellandii*

N=238(51). R 800-2000

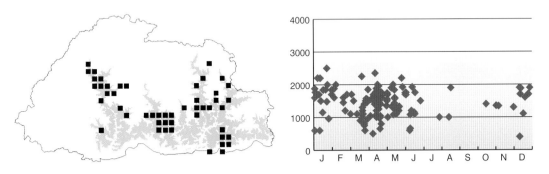

The Mountain Bulbul occurs in the Himalayas from Uttar Pradesh to Arunachal Pradesh, north-east India and Bangladesh. Further east it occurs in parts of mainland south-east Asia. It inhabits a variety of forest habitats at lower elevations.

In Bhutan the Mountain Bulbul is a common resident in the Sunkosh, central and eastern valleys, and the western and eastern foothills, with isolated records from the western foothills and valleys. It is resident at 800–2,000 m, and occasional down to c.400 m and up to 2,500 m. The breeding season appears relatively late, with birds in flocks of up to 20 from December well into April. The maximum flock is 56, in the eastern foothills at 1,400 m in April[19]. Concentrations appear at abundant supplies of fruit in the scrub layer. From late April to August mostly singles or pairs are encountered, which is the only evidence for breeding, there being no observations of nesting birds or fledglings. Based on presence in the breeding season, near Zhemgang the density of breeding pairs was estimated at 0.3 per km at 1,600–1,900 m[52]. The species is found almost exclusively in well-developed broadleaf forest, often on drier eastern and southern slopes.

# Black Bulbul
## *Hypsipetes leucocephalus*

N=882(107). S 600-2800 (mid-Mar-mid-Oct); W 600-2000

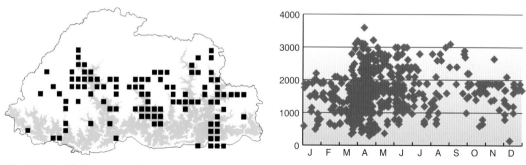

The Black Bulbul occurs in the Himalayas from Pakistan to Arunachal Pradesh and in north-east India, as well as the hills of south-west India and Sri Lanka. Further east it reaches central China and parts of mainland south-east Asia. It inhabits tall broadleaf forest, where it mostly keeps to the treetops.

In Bhutan the Black Bulbul is an abundant altitudinal migrant throughout the temperate zone and foothills. Among Bhutan's bulbuls it shows the most marked altitudinal movements, being a summer visitor to the Thimphu Valley for example. In summer it is found at 600–2,800 m, with occasional records to 300 m and 3,200 m. It has been found once at 3,600 m[19]. In winter it retreats below 2,000 m, but spreads upslope from mid-March, descending by mid-October. Birds carrying nest material were observed at 700 m on 8 June[52], and at the same altitude a bird carrying food was seen on 20 July[52], with flocks totalling *c*.80, comprising adults and recent fledglings, also present at the same site, but probably grouping from a wider area. Based on presence in the breeding season, near Zhemgang the density of breeding pairs was estimated at 0.5 per km at 1,600–1,900 m. Flocks of up of 40 are noted in winter, from September to March, with the highest day total being 300 in March[46]. From early April the flocks disband into smaller groups and pairs.

# Striated Prinia
## *Prinia criniger*

N=337(56). R 800-2200

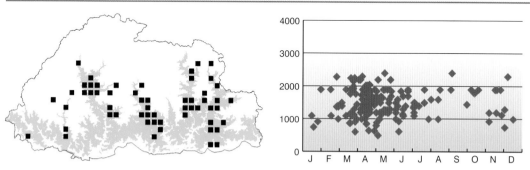

The Striated Prinia's range extends along the Himalayas from Afghanistan to Arunachal Pradesh, and the hills of north-east India. Further east it ranges through Myanmar and southern and central China east to Taiwan. Habitat consists of dry grass-covered slopes with scattered bushes or open pine forest, often near cultivation.

In Bhutan the Striated Prinia is a frequent resident throughout the temperate and subtropical zones. It occurs at 800–2,200 m, more occasionally to 500 m and 2,400 m, thus occupying the highest altitudinal range among *Prinia* species. However, it is rather localised, being associated with dry, rocky slopes, but can reach considerable densities in areas with extensive suitable habitat, e.g. parts of the Kuri Chhu valley, where up to 20 have been seen in a day. Song is heard from late March and birds are territorial until August, with some still singing in October. There are no confirmed breeding records.

# Hill Prinia
## *Prinia atrogularis*

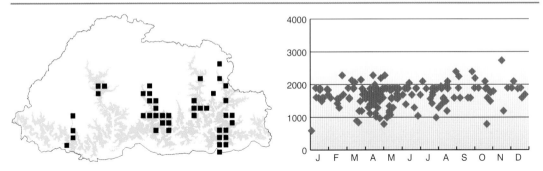

The range of the Hill Prinia spans southern China to Sumatra, and in the west reaches the Indian subcontinent, in north-east India and the Himalayas to eastern Nepal. It is a bird of scrub at forest edges, grassy hill slopes and open pine forest.

The Hill Prinia is a common resident throughout the temperate zone and in the western and central foothills, but in the western valleys it is distinctly less common, being close to its westernmost limits here. Its regular altitudinal range spans 1,000–2,000 m, with occasional records to 600 m and 2,400 m. The highest record is from 2,800 m in November[1]. Song is heard from late February to August, with occasional records in autumn. Peak territorial activity is in May, with perhaps a second peak in June/July, as some apparently attempt a second brood. The observation of an adult with two juveniles at 1,700 m on 30 June[52] would confirm this timing, although the age of the young was unclear. As this record is insufficient for a confirmed breeding record, status is that of a probable breeder, based on presence of pairs holding territories throughout spring. Territories are well spaced, particularly where birds occupy small openings in warm broadleaf forest. In dry valleys it is less common than Striated Prinia, with rarely more than ten reported in a day. After August it moves mainly in small family groups of up to five.

# Grey-crowned Prinia
## *Prinia cinereocapilla*

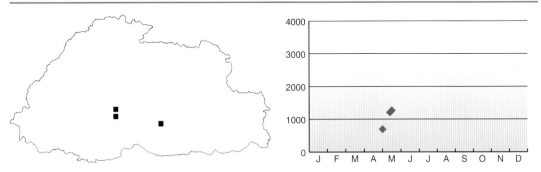

The Grey-crowned Prinia is endemic to the Indian subcontinent and very local in the Himalayan foothills from Pakistan to Bhutan and Assam, being associated with the natural terai landscape of Sal forest, tall grassland and scrub vegetation. It is one among a number of species suffering from the region-wide degradation of this landscape. Habitat consists of scrub at the ecotone between forest and grassland. It is globally threatened, classified by BirdLife International as Vulnerable, as its population appears to be rapidly declining through habitat loss.

In Bhutan the Grey-crowned Prinia is rare, with a breeding record from the early 20th century (BirdLife International 2001) and three recent records, all in May 1993[22]. At this time it was found in Chir Pine forest in the Sunkosh and central valleys at 700, 1,200 and 1,300 m. One to three birds were present at both sites. Despite searching, the species has not be found since at the more accessible site, in the Tingtibi area of Zhemgang district.

Grey-crowned Prinia
*Ren Hathway*

# Rufescent Prinia
*Prinia rufescens*                                    N=64(23). R 200-1400

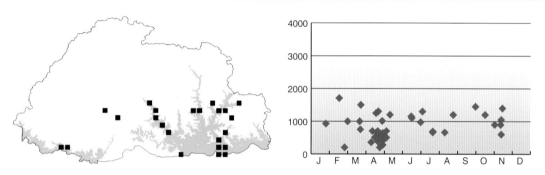

The Rufescent Prinia is resident in the Himalayan foothills from Sikkim to Arunachal Pradesh and in north-east and eastern India, its range extending east to Vietnam. It affects various edge habitats, in open forest, forest edge and in scrub around cultivation.

In Bhutan the Rufescent Prinia is frequently recorded, mainly in the central and eastern valleys and in the eastern foothills. Further west it is largely absent near its westernmost limits, although there are isolated records in the Sunkosh and western valleys. It is found at 200–1,400 m, with the highest record from 1,700 m[1]. Song is heard from late March to August, with peak activity apparently in mid-April to mid-May. An adult with two juveniles was seen at 700 m on 20 July[52]. It is rather sparsely distributed, with a max. 8 reported in a day[28].

# Grey-breasted Prinia
*Prinia hodgsonii*                                    N=10(7). R 200-800

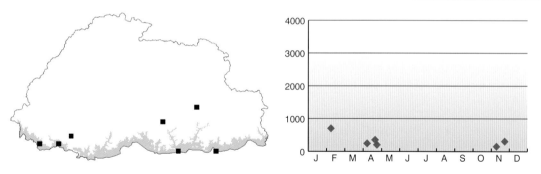

The Grey-breasted Prinia is a widespread resident of the Indian subcontinent, being absent only from a few areas in the north-west, north-east, south-east and the Himalayas. Further east its range covers most of mainland south-east Asia. It occurs in typical prinia habitat, in bushes at forest edge and in cultivated areas.

In Bhutan this prinia is uncommon, with scattered records in the western, central and eastern valleys, and a more regular presence in the western and eastern foothills. It has been found at 200–800 m and appears to be present particularly in winter, with all records in November–April. A max. 20 was reported between Deothang and Samdrup Jongkha on 24 January[28]. As it is usually conspicuous in its breeding areas, a possible explanation for winter presence in Bhutan is dispersal from nearby breeding areas in India. There are no records suggesting breeding in Bhutan.

# Jungle Prinia
## Prinia sylvatica
N=2(2)

The Jungle Prinia is endemic to the Indian subcontinent and is widespread. However, it is absent from the north-east, except for a population in the Himalayan foothills from eastern Nepal to Bhutan. Habitat consists of scrub and tall grass in dry stony country.

In Bhutan the Jungle Prinia is a rare summer visitor, with only two records: in the eastern valleys at 800 m on 23 March 1966[1], and a singing bird in the western foothills at 800 m on 23 March 2002[52].

# Plain Prinia
## Prinia inornata
N=5(5)

The Plain Prinia is the commonest *Prinia* in the Indian subcontinent, but is absent from parts of the north-west, the north-east and the Himalayas. Its range extends east to central China, Taiwan, and over much of mainland south-east Asia and Java. It occurs in a variety of habitats including tall crops, paddyfields and scrub jungle.

In Bhutan the Plain Prinia is a rare visitor, with scattered records in the western foothills and the central and eastern valleys. It has been found mostly in March, suggesting that its presence derives from pre-breeding dispersal from its main range in India. It has been found at 800–1,800 m.

# Oriental White-eye
## Zosterops palpebrosus
N=436(74). R 400-2200

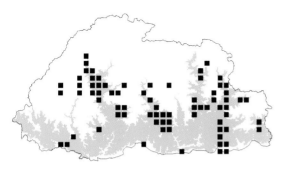
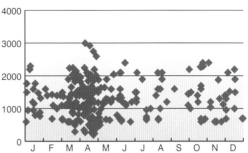

The Oriental White-eye occurs over most of the Indian subcontinent, reaching its westernmost limits in the north-west. Elsewhere, it is found through mainland south-east Asia south to the Sundas. Habitat is open broadleaf forest, often near settlements, where it feeds particularly in flowering shrubs and trees.

In Bhutan the Oriental White-eye is an abundant resident throughout the temperate zone and foothills, although it is apparently less common in the western valleys (perhaps due to limited coverage). Its regular altitudinal range spans 400–2,200 m, with occasional records to 200 m and 3,000 m[14]. From August to February it is usually found in flocks of up to 20, regularly associated with mixed-species flocks of small babblers. A nest with young was found at 1,900 m on 13 July[52], which confirms it as a breeder in Bhutan.

# Chestnut-headed Tesia
## *Tesia castaneocoronata*

N=319(76). S 2200-3400 (May-mid-Oct); W 800-3000

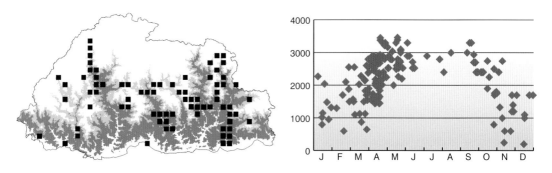

The Chestnut-headed Tesia is distributed along the Himalayas from Himachal Pradesh to Arunachal Pradesh, as well as in north-east India. Its range extends east to northern Vietnam. It inhabits dense undergrowth in broadleaf and mixed forests. Among *Tesia* species it occupies the highest altitudinal range.

The Chestnut-headed Tesia is common in Bhutan and relatively easy to see, compared to other *Tesia* species. It has been found in all zones except the high east, where it may have been overlooked. It is an altitudinal migrant, occupying 2,200–3,400 m in summer. In winter it is found at 800–2,600 m and up to 3,000 m on migration. There are occasional summer records to 3,600 m[52] and winter records from 200 m. Movement to the breeding areas occurs in April, while birds descend between October and mid-November. Song is heard mostly mid-April to June, and occasionally in winter. Breeding is confirmed by the observation of a recently fledged juvenile at 2,800 m on 26 July[52]. Considerable densities can occur, with a mean 0.6 birds heard per km[14,28] in forest above Namling, Mongar district. A max. 15 was heard there along 5 km of road on 19 April[14]. In winter up to five can be present at a site, skulking in low bushes.

# Slaty-bellied Tesia
## *Tesia olivea*

N=184(37). S 1400-2000 (Apr-Oct); W 800-1800

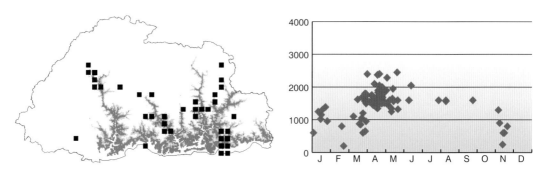

The Slaty-bellied Tesia occurs in the Himalayas from eastern Nepal to Arunachal Pradesh and in north-east India, its range reaching east to Yunnan and northern Vietnam. It occupies the lowest altitudinal zone of the three *Tesia* species, affecting dense undergrowth in moist tropical and subtropical forests.

In Bhutan the Slaty-bellied Tesia is frequently recorded throughout the temperate zone and in the central and eastern foothills, with one record from the western valleys and none in the western foothills, it being scarcer at its westernmost limits. It is an altitudinal migrant, found in summer at 1,400–2,000 m, reaching to 2,400 m occasionally. In winter it descends to 800–1,800 m, occasionally 200 m. Movement to the breeding areas occurs in the second half of March, when the first singing birds are noted. Birds can be heard as late as September, but peak territorial activity is in April. Movement to lower altitudes is noted in November. A regular site is the Mo Chhu valley between Rimchu and Tashithang, Punakha district, where 10–30 singing birds are located annually in spring along c.10 km of road[5,14,19,28]. In winter it occurs dispersed in undergrowth, with a max. 3 at a site.

# Grey-bellied Tesia
## *Tesia cyaniventer*

N= 182(45). S 1400-2600 (Apr-Oct); W 200-1800

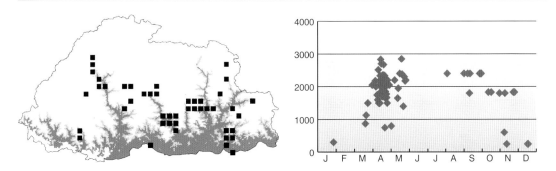

The western range limit in the Himalayas of the Grey-bellied Tesia falls between those of Chestnut-headed and Slaty-bellied Tesias, it being found from Uttar Pradesh east, and in north-east India to Yunnan and Vietnam. It occupies a somewhat intermediate altitude zone between the other two species, but in similar habitat of dense undergrowth in cool broadleaf forest.

In Bhutan this tesia is a frequently recorded altitudinal migrant throughout the temperate zone and in the central and eastern valleys. Remarkably, its summer range of 1,400–2,600 m largely overlaps with that of Slaty-bellied Tesia, although the two species rarely occur together in the same habitat. Closer inspection reveals that there is a gradual transition between them: Grey-bellied Tesia is more numerous above 1,700 m, whilst Slaty-bellied Tesia becomes the commoner of the two below this altitude. The winter range of Grey-bellied Tesia spans 200–1,800 m. Birds appear in the summer range by late March, when they are mostly detected by song. Peak vocal activity appears to occur in the second half of April, and birds can be heard until at least August. In April a mean 0.2 singing birds has been noted per km in forest between Namling and Yonkhola, Mongar district[5,14,28], with up to 15 encountered in a day[14]. In winter up to three can be found at a site. However, it is secretive and most winter records concern specimens. Timing of descent to wintering areas is unclear, but birds are noted in the lowest part of the winter range in November–January.

Grey-bellied Tesia
*Dan Cole*

# Pale-footed Bush Warbler
## Cettia pallidipes

N=14(5). R 1400-2000

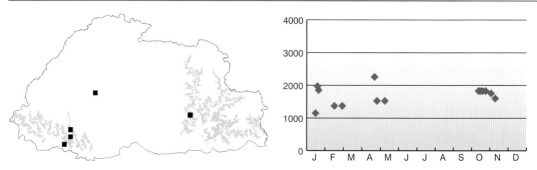

In the Indian subcontinent the Pale-footed Bush Warbler is patchily distributed in the Himalayan foothills and the Andamans. Further east its range extends to northern Vietnam. Habitat is tall grass and shrubs at forest edge.

In Bhutan the Pale-footed Bush Warbler is a rare resident, its distribution rather unclear, as it probably tends to be overlooked. Most records derive from the expeditions of the 1960s and 1970s. It has been found in the western and eastern valleys, with an isolated record from the Sunkosh Valley[1], at altitudes of 1,400–2,000 m, with the lowest record from 1,200 m[22] and the highest at 2,300 m[1]. Most records are in winter, with observations amongst others from scrub in cultivated areas[22]. The few spring records in April–May are from 1,500 m and 2,300 m[1], and may concern birds in the breeding range. However, there are no observations of territorial birds or other evidence that would establish it as a breeder in Bhutan. It may have a very localised distribution as a breeder and could therefore be overlooked, particularly in the less explored western valleys.

# Brownish-flanked Bush Warbler
## Cettia fortipes

N=391(65). S 1400-2800 (Apr-Oct); W 600-2200

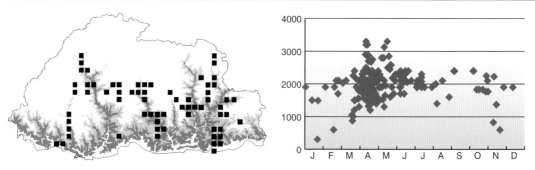

The Brownish-flanked Bush Warbler ranges widely in mainland south-east Asia, reaching Taiwan and Vietnam. In the Indian subcontinent it has a scattered distribution in the Himalayas from Pakistan to Arunachal Pradesh and in north-east India. It inhabits open areas, affecting scrub, open forest with dense undergrowth and edges of cultivation. Like other *Cettia* it skulks and is most frequently located by voice.

In Bhutan the Brownish-flanked Bush Warbler is a common altitudinal migrant throughout the temperate zone and foothills. Its summer range spans 1,400–2,800 m, with occasional presence to 3,300 m. At these altitudes its song is commonly heard in mid-February to late July. In winter it descends below 2,200 m, reaching 600 m and occasionally lower, as evidenced by a specimen taken at 300 m[1]. There is no breeding evidence other than territorial birds. Singing birds are well spaced, with generally several hundred metres between territories. Up to ten have been found at favoured sites in spring. It occurs in open broadleaf and pine forests, and *Artemisia* thickets in cultivated areas.

# Chestnut-crowned Bush Warbler
## *Cettia major*

N=10(6). S 3400-4000

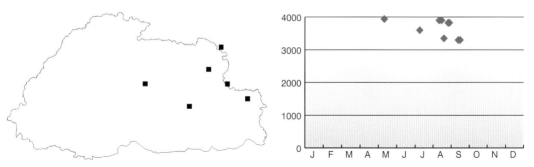

The Chestnut-crowned Bush Warbler is locally distributed in the Himalayas from Uttar Pradesh to Arunachal Pradesh. Further east it reaches Yunnan and Sichuan. It is the highest-ranging *Cettia* in the region and has rather poorly known habits and distribution. It is a long-distance altitudinal migrant, breeding in rhododendron scrub near the treeline and wintering in reedbeds in the plains.

In Bhutan the Chestnut-crowned Bush Warbler is an uncommon summer visitor to the eastern valleys, with a single record from the central valleys, where it was noted near the Yotong La in August[52]. Most records are from the ridge separating the Kuri Chhu and Kulong Chhu valleys, where it was first collected by Ludlow in the 1930s[31] and reconfirmed in May 2000[49]. Its summer range appears well defined, situated at 3,400–4,000 m. Within this range, Ludlow collected juveniles in August, which indicates the presence of a breeding population. It appears to arrive late, with almost all records in May–September, despite peak birding activity being earlier in the season. A record from April between Namling and Sengor, Mongar district[5], probably concerned a migrant en route to its summer range.

# Aberrant Bush Warbler
## *Cettia flavolivacea*

N=65(33). S 1800-3400 (Apr-Sep); W 600-2400

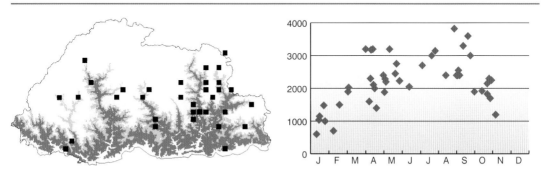

The Aberrant Bush Warbler occurs in the Himalayas from Uttar Pradesh east to Arunachal Pradesh and in the hills of north-east India. It reaches central China and northern Vietnam in the east. Habitat consists of bushes at the edges of forest clearings and scrub in pine forest.

In Bhutan the Aberrant Bush Warbler is an uncommon altitudinal migrant throughout the temperate zone, with one record from the high west. Its summer range spans 1,800–3,400 m. From October to March it retreats to 600–2,400 m, where it is regular in scrub in and around cultivation. Ludlow collected several juveniles in August–early September[31], which indicates the presence of a breeding population. One of these was from 3,800 m[31], the highest recorded altitude. In the breeding season it is rather sparsely distributed, with rarely more than one singing bird reported from a site. However, compared to other *Cettia* there are rather more winter records, indicating that it is not particularly elusive and is easily located by call.

# Yellowish-bellied Bush Warbler
## *Cettia acanthizoides*

N=96(23). S 2200-3400 (Mar-Aug); W 800-3000

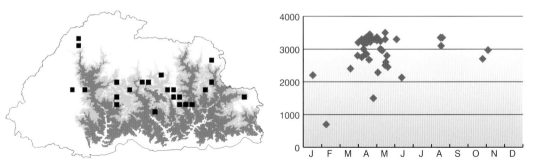

The Yellowish-bellied Bush Warbler occurs patchily in the Himalayas from Uttar Pradesh to Arunachal Pradesh, thence through southern China to Taiwan. It inhabits bamboo thickets at mid-elevations. Due to its skulking behaviour its winter range is poorly known.

In Bhutan the Yellowish-bellied Bush Warbler is a frequently recorded altitudinal migrant, found in the Sunkosh, central and eastern valleys, with one record from the western valleys[26]. The Dochu La ridge is probably its western limit. In summer it ranges at 2,200–3,400 m. The sparse records outside the breeding season indicate some altitudinal migration, with the lowest record from 700 m in February[29]. However, there are November records from close to 3,000 m[22], indicating that some may be resident. Singing birds occupy territories April–August, which is the only indication of breeding. Preferred habitat appears to be open fir forest with a dense bamboo understorey, such as around the Pele La, Yotong La and Thrumshing La passes. In these areas it is relatively common with up to three at a site. Below 3,000 m it occurs more sparsely in cool broadleaf forest.

# Grey-sided Bush Warbler
## *Cettia brunnifrons*

N=371(79). S 2400-3800 (mid-May-Sep); W 1000-3200

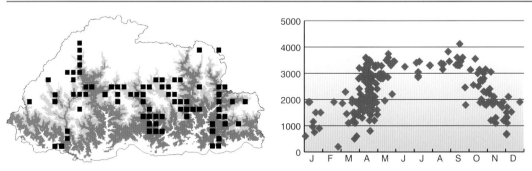

The Grey-sided Bush Warbler occurs in the Himalayas from Pakistan to Arunachal Pradesh and in north-east India. It extends further east through Myanmar to Yunnan. It is a high-altitude species, summering in shrubs and thickets at forest edge and in open alpine areas. In winter it is common in dense undergrowth of a variety of habitats.

The Grey-sided Bush Warbler is the commonest *Cettia* in Bhutan, being abundant throughout the alpine and temperate zones, with isolated records from the foothills. In summer (May–September) it ranges at 2,400–3,800 m, with 4,100 m[1] the highest recorded altitude. Outside the breeding season it is mainly noted at 1,000–3,200 m, with the winter range situated below 2,000 m, occasionally reaching 200 m. It passes through intermediate areas between the breeding and wintering areas in April and October, and is very common during these periods, particularly in spring, with 10–20 noted at some sites. From the last week of April numbers decrease, signifying arrival in the high-altitude breeding areas. Breeding is confirmed by the observation of a bird carrying nest material at 3,000 m on 3 May[22].

# Spotted Bush Warbler
*Bradypterus thoracicus*                                                    N=7(5)

The Spotted Bush Warbler is distributed from Kashmir through the Himalayas to southern China, north to Amur and west to Lake Baikal. In the Himalayas it is rather localised. It breeds in scrub in grasslands around the treeline, wintering in reedbeds and tall grass in the plains.

In Bhutan the Spotted Bush Warbler is a rare summer visitor to the eastern valleys and high east, primarily known from specimens taken in the 1930s on both sides of the Dib La ridge separating the Kulong Chhu and Kuri Chhu valleys, as well as at Sakten, Trashigang district. Birds were collected in July–September in what is presumed to be its breeding range at 3,200–4,400 m[31]. It has not been reconfirmed from these areas in recent years. The only recent record is of one between Namling and Yonkhola, Mongar district, on 6 April 1995[5], which probably concerned a bird en route to its breeding quarters. Ludlow collected a juvenile at 3,300 m in September, which indicates the presence of a breeding population[31].

# Brown Bush Warbler
*Bradypterus luteoventris*                                                  N=7(6)

The Brown Bush Warbler occurs sparsely in the Indian subcontinent, in the Himalayas east from Sikkim and in north-east India, with relatively few recent records. Further east it is found in central and southern China, northern Myanmar and northern Vietnam. It occurs in grassland, bracken, but also undergrowth in pine forest.

In Bhutan the Brown Bush Warbler is a rare resident, with scattered records from the western[25,11] and eastern valleys[1,5,28]. Records are from 1,600 m to 3,300 m and show no clear seasonal pattern, with spring, summer and autumn records throughout this range. It appears very localised, the few records being clustered around Gedu, Chhukha district, the middle Kuri Chhu valley and the ridges either side of the Drangme Chhu valley.

# Russet Bush Warbler
*Bradypterus seebohmi*                                          N=36(9). S 1200-2800

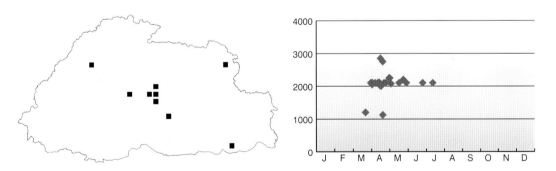

The Russet Bush Warbler has only recently been found in the Indian subcontinent, in West Bengal and central Bhutan. Further east its range reaches central China, northern Vietnam and the Philippines. Like other bush warblers, it is a skulking, inconspicuous species mostly located through knowledge of its song.

In Bhutan the Russet Bush Warbler is an uncommon summer visitor and the most regular of the *Bradypterus*, despite being discovered in Bhutan only recently. The first record came to light only when an observer analysed his tape-recordings from Bhutan, made in spring 1994, and noted the species singing in the background of another species's recording[55]. Subsequently it has been found at more than ten sites in the Sunkosh, central and eastern valleys, and the eastern foothills, at 1,200–2,800 m. Regular localities are the Damji area, Punakha district, where it was first found, and around Trongsa. Records are thus concentrated at 2,100–2,200 m. The first spring record is from 21 March[52], the last 11 July[52]. Peak vocal activity appears to be in April, with a max. 3 noted in the Trongsa area[19].

# Blyth's Reed Warbler
## *Acrocephalus dumetorum*

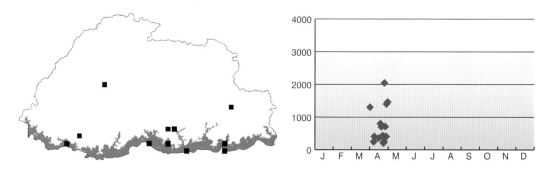

Blyth's Reed Warbler breeds in the central parts of Eurasia, from Eastern Europe to Lake Baikal. Its main winter range is in the Indian subcontinent, where it is abundant in September–April.

In Bhutan this species is an uncommon passage migrant, with scattered records throughout the temperate zone and foothills. Apparently migration across the Himalayas is very rapid, as all records are from April, with the earliest on 1 April[53] and the last on 30 April[22]. In particular, in the latter half of the month significant numbers occur, with a concentration of six noted at Phuntsholing, at 200 m on 26 April[19], and birds seen almost daily during a survey of low altitudes in this period[22]. It has been found at 200–1,400 m, with one record at 2,000 m[14]. The absence of records at higher elevations perhaps indicates movement along the base of the Himalayas, skirting the main range west of Bhutan, as suggested by Inskipp and Inskipp (1985). The lack of autumn records also points to a migration route that bypasses the main Himalayan range.

Blyth's Reed Warbler
*Ren Hathway*

# Thick-billed Warbler
## *Acrocephalus aedon*
N=4(3)

The Thick-billed Warbler breeds from southern and south-east Siberia to north-east China and Japan. In winter it migrates to the Indian subcontinent and to most of mainland south-east Asia.

In Bhutan the Thick-billed Warbler is a rare passage migrant found both in spring and autumn, with a total of four records in March[5], April[14], September[52] and November[22]. A maximum of two birds was noted in November at Phuntsholing[22]. Other records are of singles, at Phuntsholing[5], Samdrup Jongkha[14] and Zhemgang[52]. With records confined to 200–2,000 m and occurrence in both spring and autumn, the pattern appears similar to that of Siberian Rubythroat and Red-throated Flycatcher, the birds possibly moving along the base of the Himalayas in order to skirt the main range further east.

# Booted Warbler
## *Hippolais caligata*
N=1(1)

The Booted Warbler breeds in western Russia and Siberia, south through Central Asia and reaching the north-west Indian subcontinent. It winters in the Indian subcontinent, mostly in the west.

In Bhutan the Booted Warbler is a rare passage migrant which was noted in spring 2000 near Wangdue Phodrang. On 14 April two were present in scrub near the Puna Sang Chhu at two sites at 1,300 m[27], where they were first seen a few days earlier[23]. They were identified as the form *caligata*, which breeds in western Russia and Siberia. The date is within the regular migration period from the Indian wintering grounds.

# Mountain Tailorbird
## *Orthotomus cuculatus*
N=61(18). S 1400-2000 (Mar-Oct); W 600-2200

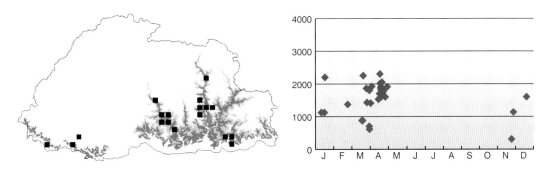

The Mountain Tailorbird is an uncommon resident of the Himalayas from Bhutan east, and in north-east India. Further east its range extends through mainland south-east Asia, the Philippines and most of Indonesia. Habitat is evergreen broadleaf forest including second growth.

In Bhutan the Mountain Tailorbird is an uncommon altitudinal migrant with its stronghold in the eastern valleys and more occasional presence in the central valleys, and isolated winter records in the western valleys and foothills. The Black Mountain range constitutes its main western limit in the subcontinent. Song is heard from late March to mid-May, providing the only evidence for breeding. In this period it is found at 1,400–2,000 m, with occasional records to 2,200 m, which is probably its breeding range. Beyond mid-May it is completely unnoticed until November. Thereafter, until March, there are occasional records of singles at 600–2,200 m, with the lowest record at 300 m in November[1]. Summer range largely overlaps that of Common Tailorbird, the birds being separated mostly by habitat. Mountain Tailorbird is clearly confined to areas of well-developed broadleaf forest, e.g. around Yonkhola, Mongar district, where it is recorded annually in April, with 1–3 noted in a day and a max. 5[28].

# Common Tailorbird
*Orthotomus sutorius*

N=220(45). R 200-2000

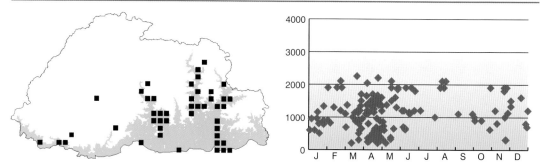

The Common Tailorbird is widespread in southern and south-east Asia, reaching south to Java. It occurs throughout the Indian subcontinent, except parts of the north-west. Habitat consists of scrub on dry hill slopes, at the edges of cultivated areas and in forest clearings. It constructs its nest in a large leaf, sewn together with grass strands to form a cup shape.

In Bhutan this tailorbird is a common resident of the foothills and the central and eastern valleys, with a considerable gap in its distribution in the western and Sunkosh valleys, despite apparent abundant suitable habitat. The few records from these valleys contrast strongly with its widespread occurrence further east. Its main altitudinal range spans 200–2,000 m, with occasional records to 2,200 m[52]. Although mostly resident, in midwinter there is some tendency to retreat below 1,400 m. However, this movement appears to be confined to December/January. Song is heard year-round, but mostly in May–August, which is probably the main breeding season as vegetation is densest and conditions best for nest-building. However, there is no direct evidence of breeding in Bhutan. Although common, territories appear to be well spaced, with mostly only a few birds encountered in a day. A max. 20 was reported between Samdrup Jongkha and Deothang in May[28].

Common Chiffchaff
*Dan Cole*

# Common Chiffchaff
*Phylloscopus collybita*

N=4(4)

The Common Chiffchaff's breeding range comprises most of Europe and reaches east to the Kolyma River in Siberia. It is a common winter visitor to the northern Indian subcontinent, but is mostly a passage migrant in the Himalayas. It winters in forests and bushes, often near water.

In Bhutan the Common Chiffchaff is a rare passage migrant and the least-recorded *Phylloscopus*. The four records are: on 4 October 2000 near Thimphu at 2,600 m[43], on 10 October 2000 one near Lingshi, Thimphu district at 4,000 m[51], on 6 February 2001 one near Wangdue Phodrang at 1,300 m[52], and on 21 April 2002 one near Trongsa at 2,100 m[52].

# Dusky Warbler
## *Phylloscopus fuscatus*

N=41(19). W 200-3600

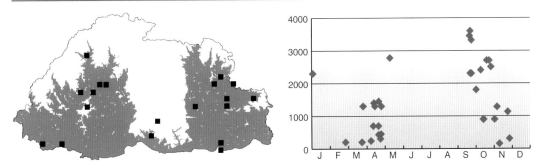

The Dusky Warbler breeds in eastern and south-east Siberia and northern China, its range reaching south to Sichuan and eastern Tibet. It winters in south-east Asia and the north-east Indian subcontinent, west to western Nepal and Bangladesh. Winter habitat consists of bushes, often close to water.

In Bhutan the Dusky Warbler is an uncommon passage migrant throughout the temperate zone and foothills. It is probably also a winter visitor in small numbers, as there is a January record from 2,300 m[22,49] and a February record from 200 m[19]. The foothills are presumed to be its main wintering area, but have been insufficiently explored by ornithologists to refute or prove this. However, four birds in riverine scrub along the Torsa Chhu, Phuntsholing, in February[19] suggest that it is relatively common in suitable habitat. The January record comes from the relatively warm winter of 1999/2000. In autumn the first arrivals are noted by late September, initially at higher elevations and gradually lower, reaching 200 m in November. The earliest autumn record is 19 September[31]. Spring passage appears to commence late March and continues until the first week of May, with the last record on 9 May[44]. During passage periods, birds have been noted at 200–3,600 m[44], suggesting direct Himalayan crossing, rather than a movement along the base of the range.

# Smoky Warbler
## *Phylloscopus fuligiventer*

N=14(6). S 4000-4200 (May-Oct); W 2400

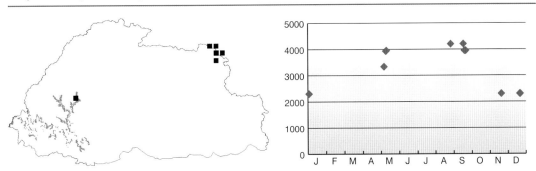

The Smoky Warbler breeds in the southern part of the Tibetan Plateau and south of the Himalayas in Nepal and Bhutan. Breeding habitat consists of scrub above the treeline. In winter it descends to the foothills and adjacent plains, where it is found in dense undergrowth and tall grass near water.

In Bhutan the Smoky Warbler is generally uncommon and possibly overlooked. It has been found in the high west and east, and in the western valleys. Records in the high west have not been mapped due to imprecise localities being reported. Records from August and September[31,49] plausibly concern birds in the breeding areas, as they were from 4,000–4,200 m, which is probably the lower end of its range. As a winter visitor it is known from riverine scrub at Babesa, Thimphu district (2,300 m), where it was present at least in 1999/2000[22,49] and 2001/2002[43,52]. Its winter range is otherwise unclear, as surveys have not yet covered the majority of lower altitudes and many birders are unfamiliar with its call.

# Tickell's Leaf Warbler
## *Phylloscopus affinis*

N=294(80). S 2800-4000 (mid-May-mid-Sep); W 1200-3200

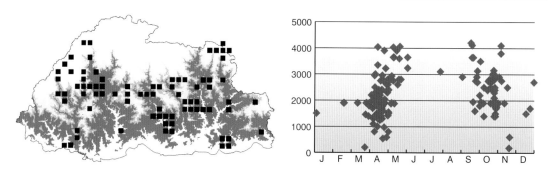

Tickell's Leaf Warbler's breeding range comprises south-east Tibet and Sichuan, as well as the Himalayas from Pakistan to Bhutan. It breeds in bushes in the subalpine and alpine zones, and winters in the foothills and plains, reaching south to the hills of south-west India. Winter habitat consists of forest edge and clearings.

In Bhutan Tickell's Leaf Warbler is a common altitudinal migrant, recorded in all biogeographic units, except the insufficiently explored central foothills. Summer records are few, suggesting that the large numbers passing through mid-elevations in spring and autumn are primarily moving to breeding areas north of Bhutan. Breeding has, however, been confirmed by the observation of one carrying nest material at 4,050 m on 20 May[22]. Based on the few records, its summer range appears to span 2,800–4,000 m, with the highest record from 4,200 m[31]. Winter records are also scarce, and limited to the mild winter of 2001/2002 when birds were found in December–January at three sites in the western, Sunkosh and central valleys at 1,300–2,300 m, with a maximum of two birds present[43,52]. Although this clearly points to an occasional widespread winter presence at mid-elevations, the main wintering areas are probably located south of Bhutan, as there are virtually no winter records from the foothills. Following a few early records from mid-February[52], spring passage commences in earnest in the third week of March and continues to mid-May, being widespread at 1,200–3,200 m, with flocks of up to five. Occurrence is more occasional to 200 m. Peak passage appears to occur around mid-April, with flocks of up to 20 reported. Large-scale autumn passage starts in the second half of September and continues to mid-November, with a peak in mid-October. Autumn numbers are comparable to those in spring.

# Buff-barred Warbler
## *Phylloscopus pulcher*

N=242(65). S 2600-4000 (May-Oct); W 1400-3400

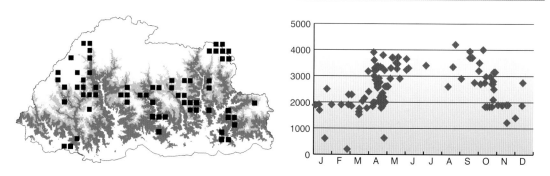

The Buff-barred Warbler ranges from montane western China, west through the Himalayas from Himachal Pradesh to Bhutan, and in the hills of north-east India. Further east it reaches northern Vietnam. It summers in various forest types and shrubs at the treeline, descending to the broadleaf forest zone in winter.

In Bhutan the Buff-barred Warbler is a common altitudinal migrant in all biogeographic units, except the eastern foothills. It summers in fir and hemlock forests at 2,600–4,000 m, reaching the treeline, with the highest record from 4,200 m[31]. In winter and on migration it is found mainly at 1,400–3,400 m, although its winter range is 1,400–2,600 m, where it occurs in cool and warm broadleaf forests. There are a few winter records at lower elevations down to 200 m and most records at this season concern singles in mixed flocks of warblers and small babblers. Movement to the breeding quarters starts in late March and is characterised by the occurrence of larger flocks of up to 20, which feed particularly on flowering shrubs such as rhododendron. Spring migration continues to early May, after which there are occasional records from the breeding areas. There are no confirmed breeding records for Bhutan, with only the presence of singing birds as evidence for nesting. Descent to the winter range takes place in October and the first half of November, and is much less conspicuous than spring passage, as birds are dispersed and associated with mixed flocks.

Buff-barred Warbler
*Dan Cole*

# Ashy-throated Warbler
## *Phylloscopus maculipennis*

N=479(81). S 2000-3400 (May-Oct); W 1200-3200

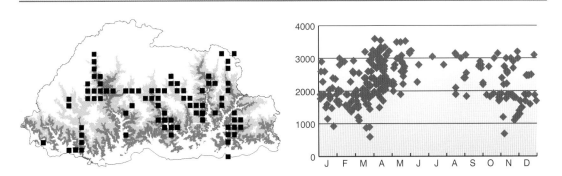

The Ashy-throated Warbler is distributed along the Himalayas from Himachal Pradesh to Arunachal Pradesh, extending east and north to Sichuan, Yunnan and northern Vietnam. It is an altitudinal migrant, but is partial to broadleaf forest in summer as well as winter.

In Bhutan the Ashy-throated Warbler is an abundant altitudinal migrant throughout the temperate zone, with more occasional presence in the alpine zone and the western and eastern foothills. Its summer range spans 2,000–3,400 m, occasionally reaching 3,600 m. Its main range appears to be above 2,800 m, occurrence lower mostly relating to late-spring and early-autumn passage. In winter it remains present up to 3,200 m, but reaches 1,200 m and occasionally 600 m[40,52]. Outside the breeding season, in August–April, it occurs in flocks of up to ten, but most frequently in small numbers with mixed-species flocks of warblers and small babblers. Several tens can be found in a day during this period. From May birds are dispersed in the breeding habitat, which consists of hemlock, temperate broadleaf and mixed forests. There are no confirmed breeding records and very few of singing birds. Autumn migration starts in August with birds gradually dispersing lower, reaching the lowest part of the winter range in November.

# Lemon-rumped Warbler
*Phylloscopus chloronotus*                N=613(103). S 2400-3600 (May-mid-Oct); W 800-3200

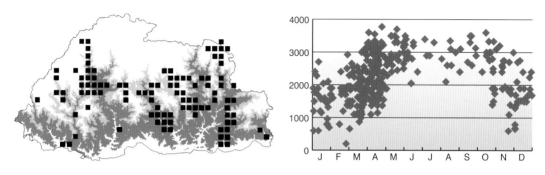

The Lemon-rumped Warbler occurs in the Himalayas from Pakistan to Arunachal Pradesh, in the hills of north-east India, and further north-west in south-west and western China. In summer it is found in coniferous or mixed forest at high altitudes. In winter it descends to lower altitudes.

In Bhutan the Lemon-rumped Warbler is an abundant altitudinal migrant in the alpine and temperate zones, with isolated records from the western and eastern foothills. It occurs at similar elevations as Ashy-throated Warbler, although reaching slightly higher in summer and lower in winter. In habitat choice it is more associated with conifer forest than the latter, also occurring in relatively poor Blue Pine forest. In summer it is found at 2,400–3,600 m, occasionally to 3,800 m[22]. In winter and on migration it is common at 800–3,600 m, retreating below 2,600 m in midwinter. Occurrence is more occasional below 800 m, with the lowest record at 200 m[19]. In March–April it gradually moves upslope to the breeding areas, descending again in October to mid-December, with a widespread presence throughout its altitudinal range. Outside the breeding season it generally occurs in smaller flocks than Ashy-throated Warbler, with rarely more than ten together. Day totals can, however, amount to several tens of birds, mostly found in mixed-species flocks with other warblers and small babblers. In the breeding season birds are heard mostly in May–July, with normally several present at a site. Despite its abundance, there are no confirmed breeding records.

# Yellow-browed Warbler
*Phylloscopus inornatus*                          N=89(32). W 200-2800

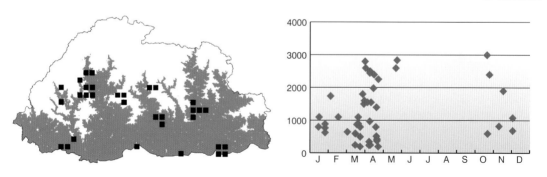

The Yellow-browed Warbler breeds in Siberia east of the Urals, south to north-east China. It winters in south-east Asia, reaching east to central Nepal, Bangladesh and southern India. Winter habitat consists of open forest.

In Bhutan the Yellow-browed Warbler is a common winter visitor throughout the temperate zone and foothills. The main winter range appears to be at 200–1,200 m, where it is common in open subtropical forest. Several tens were found between Phuntsholing and Kamji in January[53]. Migration is marked by records at higher elevations, up to 2,800 m, the highest being at 3,000 m in October[22]. Arrivals occur in the second half of October and birds depart in April to late May. The species is invariably found singly or a few together, sometimes with mixed flocks of other insect-hunters.

# Hume's Leaf Warbler
## *Phylloscopus humei*

N=78(49). S 3000-4000 (May-Sep); W 800-3200

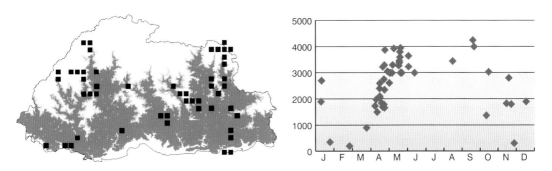

Hume's Leaf Warbler breeds in montane Turkestan and the Altai, the Himalayas from Pakistan to Bhutan (subspecies *humei*), and montane China (*mandellii*). It winters in the north, east and central Indian subcontinent and east to northern Vietnam. It breeds in conifer forest and subalpine scrub, and winters in open forest and second growth.

Hume's Leaf Warbler
*Ren Hathway*

    In Bhutan Hume's Leaf Warbler is frequently recorded and widespread, found in all biogeographic units except the central foothills. Both above-mentioned subspecies have been confirmed from Bhutan: nominate *humei* from a specimen taken in November[1], with records at 3,000–4,000 m in May to September relating to breeders of this subspecies, although there is no direct evidence of breeding as yet. Summer habitat comprises fir and hemlock forests. The majority of specimens collected in the 1960s and 1970s are of *mandellii*, and are from October, November and April, suggesting that it is a passage migrant. Passage is evident particularly in April and probably includes some numbers of *mandellii*. Occurrence of this subspecies on spring passage is further confirmed by a flock of five at *c*.2,400 m on 23 April[14]. Autumn passage is much less marked and winter occurrence is rather diffuse, with no indication of the subspecies involved. General altitudinal range in winter and on migration is 800–3,200 m, with occasional records to 200 m. Most records concern singles, often with mixed-species flocks of other warblers and small babblers.

# Greenish Warbler
*Phylloscopus trochiloides*    N=167(63). S 1800-4000 (May-Nov); W 200-3200

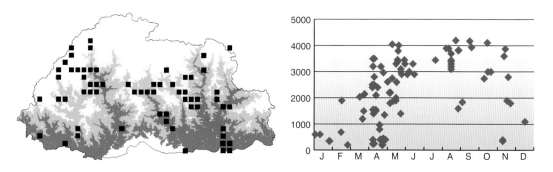

The Greenish Warbler breeds from Eastern Europe to eastern Siberia, discontinuously from the Caucasus to Pakistan, and in montane Central Asia from Turkestan to the Himalayas and the mountains of western China. In the Indian subcontinent it breeds throughout the entire Himalayan range and in north-east India. It winters in south-east Asia and over the Indian subcontinent. Summer habitat consists of birch and coniferous forests, as well as shrubs, descending to winter in a variety of forest habitats.

In Bhutan the Greenish Warbler is common and has been found in all biogeographic units except the central foothills. It occurs over a large range, roughly 1,800–4,000 m in summer and 200–3,200 m in winter and on migration. The main summer range appears to be above 3,000 m, lower records probably involving late-spring and early-autumn migrants. The highest record is from 4,200 m[31]. Pairs appear to be well spaced, with never more than 2–3 found singing at a site. Breeding is confirmed by a record of a nest at 3,800 m on 27 August[31]. In midwinter it descends below 1,200 m, with movement to the breeding areas noted from mid-March, although passage at mid-elevations is still evident in mid-May. In autumn dispersal to lower areas commences in September, but higher areas are only entirely vacated in December. In its winter range it is regularly found in mixed flocks of warblers and small babblers, with one to a few birds present in such groups.

# Large-billed Leaf Warbler
*Phylloscopus magnirostris*    N=295(78). S 1200-3400

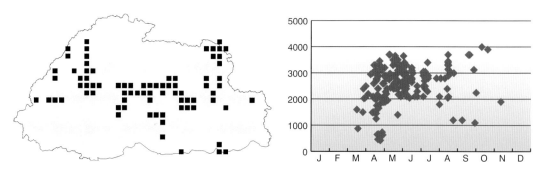

The Large-billed Leaf Warbler is the largest representative of the genus in the region. It breeds in the Himalayas from Pakistan to Bhutan, and extends north to montane western China. It winters in southern India and Sri Lanka. Breeding habitat comprises both coniferous and broadleaf forests.

In Bhutan the Large-billed Leaf Warbler is a common summer visitor and the only *Phylloscopus* to vacate the country completely in winter. It has been found in all biogeographic units, except the central foothills. The regular altitudinal range spans 2,000–3,400 m, with occasional records to 4,000 m. However, on migration it is regularly found at 1,200 m and occasionally as low as 400 m. It arrives in Bhutan from mid-March, with the earliest record on 16 March[46]. Arrivals are first noted at lower elevations, but it rapidly occupies its entire range during April. The bulk arrives in the second half of April, when its song is heard everywhere in mid-elevation forests. Passage at low elevations is noted until early May. In August departure is noted by the appearance of birds below the summer range, with records generally sparser, although this might also reflect reduced vocal activity. By mid-October it has departed Bhutan, with a single late record on 10 November at 1,900 m[52]. Breeding is confirmed by a record of a nest with eggs on 13 June at 2,700 m[31].

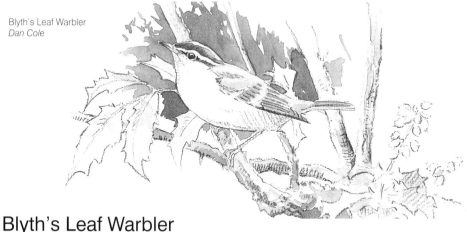

Blyth's Leaf Warbler
*Dan Cole*

# Blyth's Leaf Warbler
## *Phylloscopus reguloides*

N=673(93). S 1600-3200 (Apr-Oct); W 400-2600

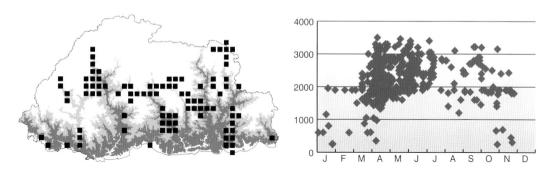

Blyth's Leaf Warbler breeds in the Himalayas from Pakistan to Arunachal Pradesh and in the hills of north-east India. In winter it descends to adjacent foothills and plains, and Bangladesh. Its range extends north-east to southern China and northern Vietnam. It breeds in coniferous as well as broadleaf forests.

In Bhutan Blyth's Leaf Warbler is an abundant altitudinal migrant, found in all biogeographic units, although primarily in the temperate zone. Summer range spans 1,600–3,200 m, occasionally to 3,500 m. In winter it descends to 400–2,600 m, reaching 200 m occasionally. The relative paucity of winter records suggests that important numbers winter outside Bhutan. The complete absence of records in December is remarkable, and the bird is undoubtedly overlooked outside the breeding season. Singing birds appear in their breeding areas from mid-March, with the entire summer range occupied during the first half of April. This month also witnesses peak territorial activity, and is followed by observations of birds carrying nest material, at 2,100, 2,800 and 2,600 m, on 1, 10 and 22 May respectively [22,43,52]. Birds carrying food have been noted at 2,900 m on 6 June and at 2,500 m on 14 June[43,52]. Near Zhemgang a density of 1.6 territories per km was found at 1,600–1,900 m[52]. This appears to be just a fraction of densities attained above 2,000 m, where it replaces Grey-hooded Warbler as the commonest warbler. Singing birds are still commonly heard in July–August, when it also regularly joins mixed-species flocks. While, in August and September, up to 20 can be present in such flocks, numbers decline from late September, with only a few birds per flock thereafter. From mid-October it is again noted in the lower part of its winter range. In peak season several tens can be found at a site.

# Yellow-vented Warbler
## Phylloscopus cantator

N=390(45). S 600-1800 (Mar-Oct); W 600-1000

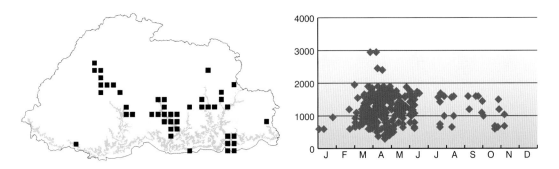

The Yellow-vented Warbler occupies the lowest altitudinal range of the region's *Phylloscopus* and is found in a restricted area from eastern Nepal to Arunachal Pradesh, the hills of north-east India and Bangladesh. It inhabits dense moist broadleaf forest in the subtropical zone.

In Bhutan the Yellow-vented Warbler is an abundant altitudinal migrant, found in the Sunkosh, central and eastern valleys, and in the foothills. In the temperate zone it is absent only from the western valleys, which lie close to the species's westernmost limits. Its summer range spans 600–1,800 m, with occasional presence down to 300 m and a few records up to 3,000 m[19]. In November–February it retreats below 1,000 m and the paucity of records suggests that a large part of the population winters outside Bhutan. Singing birds occupy territories from early March and are heard until June. Peak vocal activity appears to be in May, although in the lower part of its range some numbers are already noted in March. In the central and eastern valleys it is amongst the commonest warblers below 1,500 m and several tens can be found at a site. Around five singing birds per km have been found in March along trails at *c*.800 m in the Kuri Chhu[14] and Mangde Chhu valleys[40,52], which corresponds well with the maximum number of 28 found in the Mo Chhu valley between Tashithang and Rimchu along 4 km of road at *c*.1,500 m in April[19], as well as a density of 5.1 territories per km at 1,600–1,800 m near Zhemgang. These data suggest that densities are relatively constant throughout the range. It appears to reach highest densities in well-developed warm broadleaf forest, but tolerates secondary forest and scrub. From August it is mostly found in mixed-species flocks with other passerines of low elevations, with regularly up to ten in a flock.

# Golden-spectacled Warbler
## Seicercus burkii

N=434(88). S 1400-2600 (mid-Mar-Nov); W 400-1600

# Whistler's Warbler
## Seicercus whistleri

N=197(39). S 2600-3400 (mid-Mar-Nov); W 400-1600

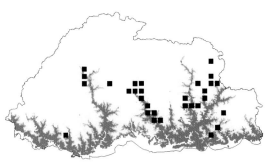

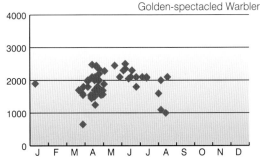

Golden-spectacled Warbler

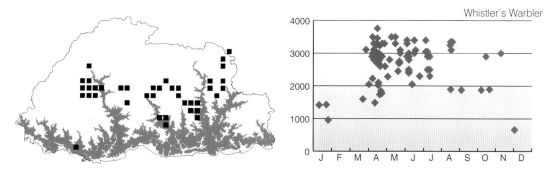

Whistler's Warbler

Golden-spectacled Warbler has recently been considered to involve six species and thus the precise distribution of each of these 'new' species is still unclear. The range of the species complex extends along the Himalayas from Pakistan to Arunachal Pradesh and north-east India, and further east through southern China and northern mainland south-east Asia. In Bhutan two species occur, with Golden-spectacled Warbler found at lower elevations and Whistler's Warbler at higher elevations. Of the *Seicercus* species, Whistler's Warbler reaches the highest altitudes. The species are treated together here, as birders in Bhutan have only started to separate them since early 2000.

From the limited records, both species appear common throughout the temperate belt. They have also been found in the alpine zone and the foothills, but it is unclear whether both or only one species is involved. In summer there is a clear altitudinal divide between them, Golden-spectacled Warbler dominating at 1,400–2,500 m and Whistler's Warbler at 2,500–3,400 m and occasionally reaching 3,800 m. This corresponds well with the reported ranges (Alström and Olsson 1999) from Uttar Pradesh (*burkii* 2,085–2,600 m; *whistleri* 2,775–3,050 m), Darjeeling (*whistleri* 2,300–3,500 m) and north-east India (*burkii* 1,700–2,050 m; *whistleri* 2,000–2,300 m). Winter altitudinal ranges are still unclear, but records point at presence of both species in an altitudinal range between 400 m and 1,600 m in November to mid-March, with occasional records at 200 m. This has been mapped for both species as probable winter range, even though only few of the confirmed records could be assigned with certainty to one species or the other. Golden-spectacled Warbler establishes breeding territories from mid-March and is heard until June. Peak vocal activity appears to be in April. Within its range the species can be very common locally, e.g. in the Trongsa area, with up to 20 found at a site[19]. Whistler's Warbler starts singing somewhat later, from the first week of April, but is heard until August. Densities are apparently lower than for Golden-spectacled Warbler, with no more than five found at a site, but the species is widespread in a variety of forest habitats. Nests with eggs found at 2,700 m and 3,000 m on 10 and 12 June[31] could be ascribed to *whistleri*, given the altitude. Outside the breeding season both species are occasionally found, mostly as singles, in mixed-species flocks of warblers and small babblers.

Whistler's Warbler
*Ren Hathway*

# Grey-hooded Warbler
*Seicercus xanthoschistos*
N=756(82). R 600-2200

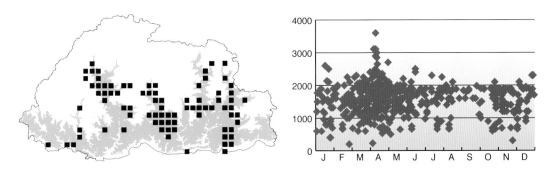

The Grey-hooded Warbler is a common resident of the Himalayas from Pakistan to Arunachal Pradesh and in north-east India. Its range extends further east into Myanmar. It inhabits open forest.

In Bhutan the Grey-hooded Warbler is abundant throughout the temperate zone and foothills. It is resident at 600–2,200 m, with occasional records to 200 m and 3,100 m, with one record from 3,600 m[1]. High-altitude records are mostly from the first half of April, prior to the start of breeding in the second half. The first singing birds are heard in mid-February, but most territories are established in early April. A second peak in territorial activity is noted in June, probably indicating second broods. Although song is heard until August, from July birds are frequently seen in mixed-species flocks with other small insectivores. It is one of the most regular members of such flocks until March, with up to five individuals present. In the breeding season several tens can be present at a site. Near Zhemgang a density of 9.5 territories per km was found at 1,600–1,900 m[52], where it is the commonest warbler. Breeding is confirmed by the observation of birds carrying nest material in April[5].

# White-spectacled Warbler
*Seicercus affinis*
N=101(34). S 1000-2800 (Mar-Sep); W 800-1800

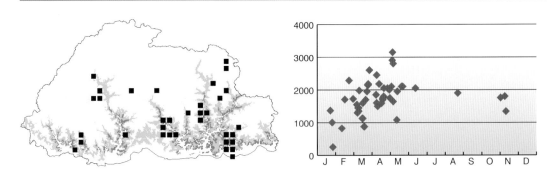

The White-spectacled Warbler occurs in the Eastern Himalayas from Darjeeling east and in north-east India. Further east it reaches northern Vietnam and south-east China. It affects dense, moist broadleaf and conifer forests.

In Bhutan the White-spectacled Warbler is a frequently recorded altitudinal migrant found throughout the temperate zone, although comparatively scarcer in the western and central valleys, and with a few records from the central and eastern foothills. In summer it is found at 1,000–2,800 m, descending in winter to 800–1,800 m, with one record from 200 m[28]. In the breeding season it occurs in broadleaf and in hemlock forests. Those between Namling and Yonkhola, Mongar district, constitute a regular site, with a max. of 12 birds reported[19]. The presence of singing birds is the only indication of breeding in Bhutan.

# Grey-cheeked Warbler
## *Seicercus poliogenys*

N=185(38). S 1400-2400 (Mar-Sep); W 800-2400

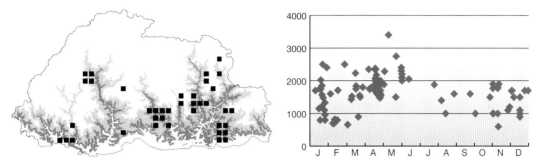

The Grey-cheeked Warbler inhabits the Himalayas from central Nepal to Arunachal Pradesh in north-east India, then east to Yunnan and northern Vietnam. Habitat is evergreen broadleaf forest and bamboo jungle.

In Bhutan the Grey-cheeked Warbler is frequent throughout the temperate zone, with isolated records in the foothills. It is scarcer further west, where it approaches its westernmost limits. Some altitudinal movements have been noted, it being found at 1,400–2,400 m in summer, with occasional records to 2,600 m. There is one record from 3,400 m in May[10]. In winter it remains present throughout this range whilst dispersing down to 800 m, occasionally 600 m. While occurring over a similar altitudinal range as Grey-hooded Warbler, in the breeding season it is segregated by habitat choice, preferring mature forest, where it keeps to the mid-storey. Song has been noted from mid-March–May, the species apparently having a relatively short breeding season. In July–March it disperses lower and to other habitats including secondary forest. It is then a regular, albeit rather inconspicuous, member of mixed-species flocks. In such flocks it moves especially in scrub low above ground, often with fulvettas, the number of birds per flock never exceeding five.

# Chestnut-crowned Warbler
## *Seicercus castaniceps*

N=442(57). S 1400-2800 (Apr-Nov); W 600-2600

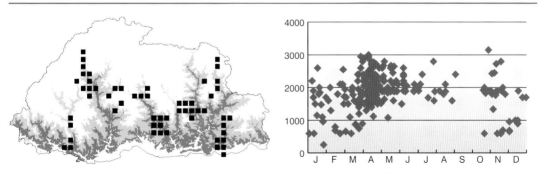

The Chestnut-crowned Warbler's main range includes central China, much of mainland south-east Asia and Sumatra, reaching the Indian subcontinent in north-east India and the Himalayas to eastern Nepal, and more patchily east to Arunachal Pradesh. Habitat consists of bamboo and undergrowth in dense broadleaf forest.

In Bhutan the Chestnut-crowned Warbler is a common altitudinal migrant throughout the temperate zone, with a few records from the high west and the western and eastern foothills. Its summer range spans 1,400–2,800 m, occasionally to 3,000 m. In winter it remains at 2,600 m, but disperses to 600 m, with one record at 200 m in January[28]. Dispersal to lower areas is noted by late October, with a gradual return in mid-March to late April. Singing birds occupy territories in the summer range from mid-March and are heard until August. At 1,900 m peak territorial activity is in late May. Near Zhemgang a density of 0.9 territories per km was found at 1,600–1,900 m[52]. A pair carrying nest material was observed at 2,700 m on 4 May[52]. From mid-July it regularly joins mixed-species flocks, and is invariably present in larger ones, with a max. 10.

# Broad-billed Warbler
## *Tickellia hodgsoni*

N=69(17). S 1600-2600 (Mar-Sep); W 600-1800

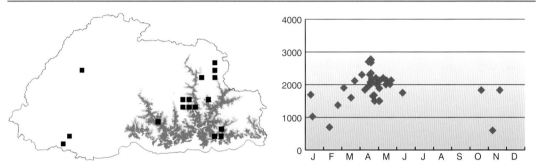

The Broad-billed Warbler is a scarce resident of the Eastern Himalayas, from Nepal to Arunachal Pradesh and in the hills of north-east India. Further east its range reaches Yunnan and northern Vietnam. It inhabits dense forest undergrowth and is generally little known.

In Bhutan the Broad-billed Warbler is an uncommon altitudinal migrant, recorded primarily from the eastern valleys, with scattered records elsewhere in the temperate zone, and is strongly associated with bamboo. In summer it is found mainly in cool broadleaf forest, at 1,600–2,600 m, descending in winter to the warm broadleaf forest zone, at altitudes of 600–1,800 m in November–March. It occurs annually in spring in forests between Sengor and Yonkhola, Mongar district, where up to eight have been seen[14]. Largest numbers are present here in the second half of April, when vocal activity appears to peak. In winter it is relatively difficult to locate and mostly encountered singly in mixed flocks of warblers and small babblers.

# Rufous-faced Warbler
## *Abroscopus albogularis*

N=42(7). S 600-1400 (Mar-Sep); W 600-800

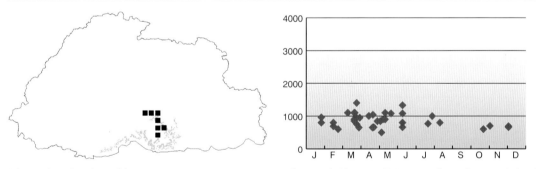

The Rufous-faced Warbler's main range spans western and central China to Taiwan and northern mainland south-east Asia, reaching the Indian subcontinent in the west. In the subcontinent its distribution appears patchy, with seemingly separate populations in north-east India, eastern Nepal and Bhutan. Habitat comprises more open patches in moist deciduous and evergreen broadleaf forest, with bamboo clumps and scrub.

In Bhutan the Rufous-faced Warbler occurs in a relatively restricted area in the southern central valleys and in the central foothills. Its status is that of a frequently recorded but local resident, largely within Royal Manas and Jigme Singye Wangchuck National Parks, and the adjacent buffer zone. In the breeding season it occurs at 600–1,400 m. In winter, in October–February, it appears to retreat slightly lower and is found mostly at 600–800 m. Territorial birds in March[40,52] and April[5,52] provide evidence for possible breeding in Bhutan, with apparently a relatively early breeding season. Its song is, however, rarely heard. The species is most frequently found in small flocks of 5–10. In December–March it regularly joins mixed feeding flocks of fulvettas and warblers, but usually not more than 1–2 birds are present in a flock.

# Black-faced Warbler
## *Abroscopus schisticeps*

N=213(31). R 1400-2400

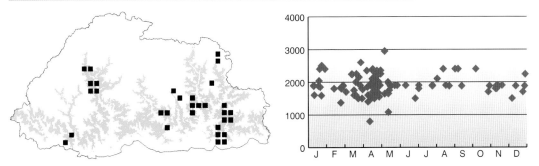

The Black-faced Warbler has a limited range in southern and south-east Asia, over a relatively narrow zone from Nepal to northern Vietnam. Habitat is moist oak and mixed broadleaf forest, with dense undergrowth of bushes and bamboo patches.

In Bhutan the Black-faced Warbler is a common resident throughout the temperate zone and in the eastern foothills, but is relatively scarce in the western valleys. It is found at altitudes of 1,400–2,400 m, with occasional records to 800 m[5] and 3,000 m[49]. There are no confirmed breeding records, although a pair maintained a territory in spring 1999 near Zhemgang at 1,900 m, with a bird singing on two dates in May[52]. However, like other *Abroscopus*, it appears to sing rarely and its vocalisations are poorly known. From late April to June records of singles and pairs dominate, which is the main indication for the timing of breeding. Based on the presence of singles in May/June, near Zhemgang a density of 0.4 breeding pairs per km was found at 1,600–1,900 m[52], suggesting that it is relatively scarce. From July it occurs in flocks, presumably family groups. During autumn and winter these assemble into flocks of up to 20. These are often single-species flocks, but they also associate with other birds of similar size in mixed flocks. The largest winter flock recorded involved 30 birds[22].

# Yellow-bellied Warbler
## *Abroscopus superciliaris*

N=18(8). R 200-2000

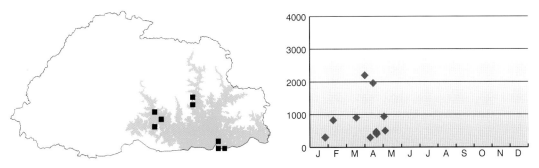

The Yellow-bellied Warbler occurs over much of mainland south-east Asia, reaching the Greater Sundas in the south, and extending to the Indian subcontinent in north-east India and the Himalayas west to central Nepal. It is particularly associated with bamboo.

In Bhutan the Yellow-bellied Warbler is an uncommon resident, found mostly in the eastern foothills, with scattered records from the central and eastern valleys. It appears very thinly distributed at altitudes of 200–2,000 m, which probably reflects the patchy nature of large bamboos. It is regular above Samdrup Jongkha, where up to five have been found[19,28]. As records are scant, there is no clear indication of possible altitudinal movements and the preferred altitudinal zone, which according to Ali and Ripley (1987) is 600–1,200 m. There are no confirmed breeding records, but singing birds have been heard in April[5,14].

# Striated Grassbird
## *Megalurus palustris*

The Striated Grassbird is resident in plains at the foot of the Himalayas, from Pakistan to Arunachal Pradesh and in north-east India and Bangladesh. Further east its range extends from southern China to the Philippines and parts of Indonesia. It inhabits tall grassland, reedbeds and tamarisk scrub along rivers and near cultivation.

The Striated Grassbird is a vagrant that has been recorded only once in Bhutan. On 23 April 2002 a single bird was present near Phuntsholing at 200 m[19].

Striated Grassbird
*Clive Byers*

# White-throated Laughingthrush
## *Garrulax albogularis*

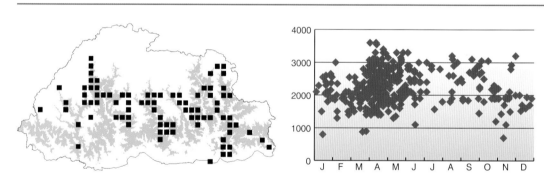

The White-throated Laughingthrush occurs in the Himalayas from Pakistan to western Arunachal Pradesh. Elsewhere it is found in Sichuan, Yunnan, northern Vietnam and Taiwan, affecting varied habitats including relatively poor open pine forest and scrub.

In Bhutan the White-throated Laughingthrush is an abundant altitudinal migrant, mainly in the temperate zone, with occasional records in the high west and central and eastern foothills. It is probably one of the most numerous birds in many forest areas and definitely amongst the most obvious due to its forming large noisy flocks. In summer it is found at 1,400–3,200 m, while in November–March it retreats below 2,800 m, with occasional records to *c.*800 m and 3,600 m, the former particularly in winter. Below 2,000 m it is generally scarce and is replaced by White-crested Laughingthrush. At 1,900 m near Zhemgang it was present in the breeding season in only one year of three[52]. In the upper Mo Chhu valley, Punakha district, where White-crested Laughingthrush is largely absent, the species is common down to 1,500 m. In winter it gathers in large noisy flocks, which can number up to 150. Mean flock size during this period is *c.*60. By March–April these flocks start to disband, and the average falls to *c.*20. However, even during the breeding season, birds remain gregarious, and in May–November flocks still number 12 on average. One was photographed at a nest in June[52], proving breeding.

# White-crested Laughingthrush
## *Garrulax leucolophus*
N=504(60). R 600-2000

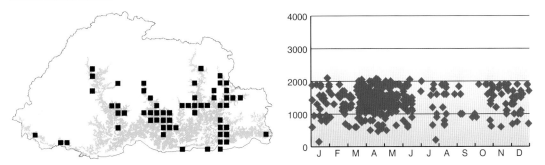

The White-crested Laughingthrush is distributed along the Himalayas from Himachal Pradesh to Arunachal Pradesh and in north-east India. Further east its range spans mainland south-east Asia and south to Sumatra. Habitat consists of warm broadleaf forest with dense undergrowth.

In Bhutan the White-crested Laughingthrush is an abundant resident in the Sunkosh, central and eastern valleys, and in the foothills. Its range spans 600–2,000 m, with occasional records to 200 m. It is largely absent from upper parts of the Sunkosh Chhu valley, possibly because broadleaf forests here is relatively isolated from other such tracts in the south. It generally occupies lower altitudes than White-throated Laughingthrush and higher areas than the necklaced laughingthrushes. Between the ranges of these species, roughly at 1,000–1,600 m, numbers of White-crested Laughingthrush appear highest. Flocks are considerably smaller than those of White-throated Laughingthrush. In December–February up to 20 can assemble in a flock, whereas in March–July flock size is typically less than five. From August up to ten are again found in a flock, probably through young birds reinforcing the ranks. In winter it occasionally associates with other laughingthrushes in mixed flocks, particularly necklaced laughingthrushes. There are no confirmed breeding records. Based on the presence of calling birds or flocks, near Zhemgang a density of 1.0 breeding pair per km of road was found at 1,600–1,900 m[52].

# Lesser Necklaced Laughingthrush
## *Garrulax monileger*
N=57(16). R 200-1400

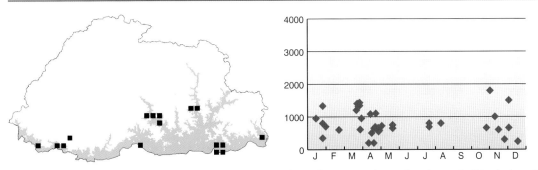

The Lesser Necklaced Laughingthrush occurs in the Himalayas from central Nepal to Arunachal Pradesh and in north-east India. Further east its range continues to Vietnam. Habitat consists of dense broadleaf forest at low elevations, with dense undergrowth. It is rather secretive in its behaviour.

In Bhutan the Lesser Necklaced Laughingthrush is a frequently recorded resident in the foothills, as well as higher in the central and eastern valleys. There is a single record from the western valleys, where it has been ringed at Gedu[36]. It occurs at 200–1,400 m, with occasional records to 1,800 m, and is found in flocks of up to 10–20 during most of the year. In May–August flocks appear to be smaller, with at most five birds. In winter it occasionally associates with White-crested Laughingthrushes.

# Greater Necklaced Laughingthrush
## Garrulax pectoralis

N=43(16). R 200-1200

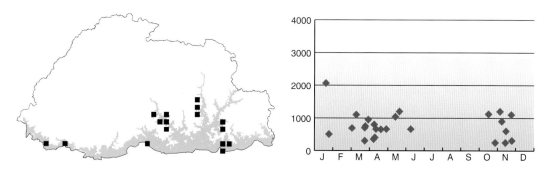

The Greater Necklaced Laughingthrush occurs over a very similar range and habitat to Lesser Necklaced Laughingthrush (which see). Often they also mix in the same flock, rustling between dry leaves on the forest floor in search for food.

In Bhutan the Greater Necklaced Laughingthrush is an occasionally reported resident, resembling the Lesser Necklaced Laughingthrush not only in appearance but also in occurrence. It is found in the foothills and in the central and eastern valleys, at 200–1,200 m. Compared with Lesser Necklaced Laughingthrush, it has less tendency to disperse to higher elevations. There is, however, a record from 2,000 m in the Kuri Chhu valley[22,49]. Flock size is smaller than that of Lesser Necklaced Laughingthrush, birds generally being encountered singly or in pairs. In October–April it gathers in flocks of up to five, with rarely up to 20 found together.

# Rufous-necked Laughingthrush
## Garrulax ruficollis

N=103(28). R 600-2000

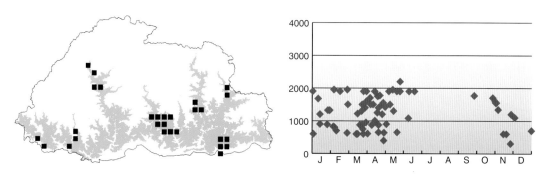

The Rufous-necked Laughingthrush has a relatively small range, with an isolated population in central Nepal, also occurring from Sikkim to Arunachal Pradesh and in north-east India and Bangladesh. Further east its range reaches Myanmar and south-west China. Habitat consists of dense scrub, particularly around cultivation.

In Bhutan the Rufous-necked Laughingthrush is frequent in the temperate zone, from the Sunkosh Valley east and in the western and eastern foothills. There are only two records from the western valleys, where it is apparently scarce. It is resident at 600–2,000 m, with occasional presence to 300 m[1] and 2,200 m[55]. In winter it is mostly found in flocks of 10–20, sometimes up to 30. By mid-April these disband and birds are noted in pairs or singly, located mostly by their call. Later in the breeding season the species is silent and appears to be extremely secretive. Reports cease completely after June and only in November is it noted again. The single September record concerns a specimen, and most of the November records were also made during the surveys of the 1960s and 1970s[1,31]. Only in December does it gather again in noisy flocks.

# Striated Laughingthrush
*Garrulax striatus*

N=809(76). R 1200-2600 (broadleaf forest)

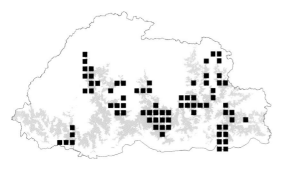

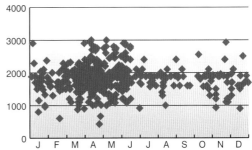

The Striated Laughingthrush occurs in the Himalayas from Himachal Pradesh to Arunachal Pradesh and in north-east India, its range penetrating east to Myanmar and south-west China. It inhabits dense broadleaf forest, particularly the midcanopy.

The Striated Laughingthrush is abundant and widespread in Bhutan, being found throughout the temperate zone and foothills, and is resident at 1,200–2,600 m, with occasional presence to 400 m and 2,900 m, the latter coinciding with the upper limit of cool broadleaf forest. As it is closely associated with broadleaf forest, the species is absent from middle western valleys, which are dominated by Blue Pine forest. Locally it may, however, venture into scrub around villages. Year-round it is mostly found in pairs or small flocks. In January–December it may concentrate in areas with supplies of berries, with up to 50 present at some sites. It reaches considerable densities and in spring up to 30 can be found in a morning. Near Zhemgang a density of 5.0 territories per km was found at 1,600–1,900 m[52]. Pairs maintain territories March–August, with peak territorial activity noted in April–June. There are no confirmed breeding records.

Striated Laughingthrush
*Ren Hathway*

# Rufous-vented Laughingthrush
*Garrulax gularis*

N=7(3)

The Rufous-vented Laughingthrush is endemic to the Indian subcontinent, in the Himalayas from eastern Bhutan to Arunachal Pradesh and in north-east India. It is a bird of dense undergrowth in warm broadleaf forest.

The Rufous-vented Laughingthrush is rare in Bhutan, being known from only two localities. It was collected in the 1930s and 1960s at Deothang, Samdrup Jongkha district, at *c*.600 m[1,31], and in recent years has been seen in the Nubji-Korphu Valley, a side valley of the Mangde Chhu valley, Trongsa district. Whereas the first observation at the latter site was unconfirmed[55], subsequently the species has been observed higher in the same valley[52], in both cases at 1,300 m, in scrub in secondary forest. Including the probable identification, it has been found in May, November and December. It appears to be very skulking and is probably much overlooked.

# Rufous-chinned Laughingthrush
## *Garrulax rufogularis*

N=126(28). R 1000-2000

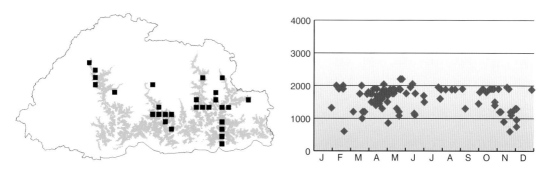

The Rufous-chinned Laughingthrush is patchily distributed in the Himalayas from Pakistan to Arunachal Pradesh and in north-east India to northern Vietnam. It is less gregarious than most laughingthrushes and easily overlooked as it keeps to dense scrub in warm broadleaf forest.

In Bhutan the Rufous-chinned Laughingthrush is frequently recorded in the eastern foothills and in the temperate zone from the Sunkosh Valley east. It is resident at 1,000–2,000 m, more erratically to 600 m and 2,200 m[55]. Records below 1,000 m are all in winter, suggesting some dispersal at this season. It is typically encountered in pairs or singly, although in December–February it sometimes forms small flocks of up to five. Calling birds maintain territories from early April to late August. Near Zhemgang a density of 1.0 territory per km was found at 1,600–1,900 m[52]. In habitat choice it favours forest edge and regrowth on abandoned fields, being a regular constituent of the bird community of shifting-cultivation areas.

# Spotted Laughingthrush
## *Garrulax ocellatus*

N=115(29). S 2800-3200 (May-Oct); W 2400-3800

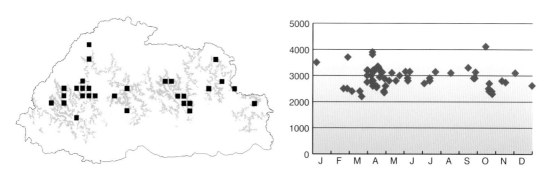

The Spotted Laughingthrush occurs in the Himalayas from Uttar Pradesh to Arunachal Pradesh, its range continuing to Myanmar and western and central China. It is a bird of undergrowth in high-altitude forest.

In Bhutan the Spotted Laughingthrush is frequently recorded throughout the temperate zone and in the high west. In summer, May–October, it appears to occupy a relatively narrow altitudinal range of 2,800–3,200 m, where it favours particularly fir forest. In winter it is more widespread, at 2,400–3,800 m, and in a wider range of conifer forest habitats, also appearing in Blue Pine forest, particularly in the Paro and Thimphu valleys. The lowest recorded altitude is 2,200 m[10], the highest 4,100 m[51]. Vocalising birds are active May–September. At all seasons it is typically found singly, or with a few together in the same area. As it occurs dispersed in its conifer forest habitat, numbers encountered are always small, with a max. 15 in a morning[57].

# Grey-sided Laughingthrush
## *Garrulax caerulatus*

N=97(27). R 1600-2400

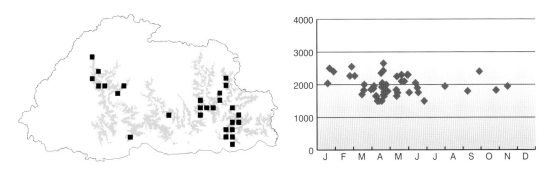

The Grey-sided Laughingthrush occurs in the Himalayas from eastern Nepal to Arunachal Pradesh, and in north-east India to northern Myanmar and south-west China. Habitat consists of dense undergrowth in humid forest and bamboo thickets.

The Grey-sided Laughingthrush is frequently recorded in Bhutan, in the temperate zone from the Sunkosh Valley east, with most records from the eastern valleys where it appears more widespread. Year-round it occupies a narrow altitudinal range (1,600–2,400 m), with no records below 1,500 m or above 2,500 m, probably reflecting a degree of habitat specialisation, as further suggested by its scattered presence within this range. Near Zhemgang inventories yielded a single pair over *c*.4.5 km at 1,600–1,900 m[52]. Here the species occupied dense, stunted broadleaf forest on a steep slope with some bamboo in the undergrowth. Calling pairs are noted particularly in May–June. Outside the breeding season, in December–April, it assembles in small flocks normally of fewer than ten.

# Streaked Laughingthrush
## *Garrulax lineatus*

N=369(56). R 1400-2400

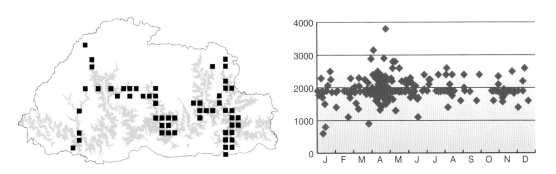

The Streaked Laughingthrush occurs from Afghanistan and Tajikistan along the Himalayas to south-east Tibet. In the Eastern Himalayas habitat consists of scrub in cultivated areas and secondary forest.

In Bhutan the Streaked Laughingthrush is common throughout the temperate zone and in the eastern foothills. It is, however, relatively scarce in the western and Sunkosh valleys and, for example, rarely recorded in the Thimphu and Paro valleys. It is resident at 1,400–2,400 m, more occasionally to 600 m and 2,900 m, with one record from the west at 3,800 m[22]. It usually occurs singly or in small flocks, or in pairs during the breeding season. In November–March it occasionally forms flocks of up to 10–20. It has been noted carrying nest material on 17 April[22] and 18 April[52] at *c*.1,900 m, establishing it as one of the few laughingthrushes with evidence of breeding in Bhutan. Near Zhemgang a density of 0.8 breeding pairs was found per km at 1,600–1,900 m[52]. Here, birds were confined to scrub where tree-felling had created canopy openings in broadleaf forest, and they quickly occupied newly created openings. In scrub outside broadleaf forest densities are probably considerably higher.

# Blue-winged Laughingthrush
## Garrulax squamatus

N=180(26). R 1000-2000

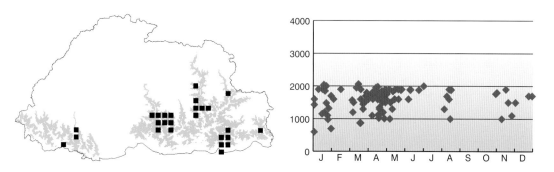

The Blue-winged Laughingthrush occurs in the Himalayas from central Nepal to Arunachal Pradesh and in north-east India. It is uncommon and local in the west of this range. Further east it reaches northern Vietnam. Habitat is dense undergrowth in humid broadleaf forest.

In Bhutan the Blue-winged Laughingthrush is frequently recorded. The central and eastern valleys and the eastern foothills are its core range, whilst it is scarce in the western valleys and foothills, with one record from the Sunkosh Valley[19]. This record has not been mapped due to an imprecise locality being reported. It is resident at 1,000–2,000 m, with occasional records to 600 m, particularly in midwinter. Most observations concern singles or pairs, but in January–April it also occurs in small flocks of up to ten. Calling birds occupy territories March–August. Near Zhemgang a density of 0.6 territories per km was found at 1,600–1,900 m[52].

# Scaly Laughingthrush
## Garrulax subunicolor

N=99(29). S 2000-3400 (Apr-Oct); W 1400-2400

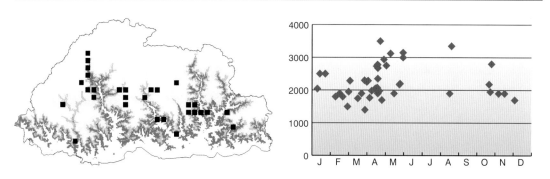

The Scaly Laughingthrush is found along the Himalayas from central Nepal east to Arunachal Pradesh, and thence to Myanmar, Yunnan and northern Vietnam. Habitat consists of dense scrub in broadleaf and mixed forests at higher altitudes.

In Bhutan the Scaly Laughingthrush is reported occasionally throughout the temperate zone. It is scarce in the western valleys and, on the whole, its distribution appears relatively scattered, being most regularly found in the Sunkosh Valley and above Yonkhola, Mongar district. It shows clear altitudinal movements, summering at 2,000–3,400 m, descending in winter to 1,400–2,400 m. It occupies the breeding range by mid-April, remaining there until October. Whereas it is found singly or in pairs in the breeding season, in winter it may form small flocks of up to ten.

# Black-faced Laughingthrush
## *Garrulax affinis*  N=360(75). S 2200-3800 (Apr-Nov); W 1800-3800

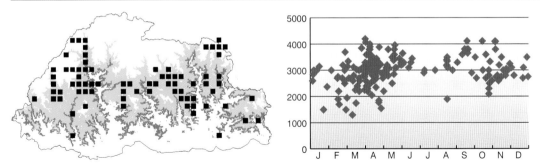

The Black-faced Laughingthrush occurs in the Himalayas from central Nepal to Arunachal Pradesh, thence further east to western and south-west China, northern Myanmar and northern Vietnam. It is amongst the highest-ranging laughingthrushes, inhabiting high-altitude forest and scrub above the treeline.

In Bhutan the Black-faced Laughingthrush is abundant throughout the alpine and temperate zones. In summer it occurs at 2,200–3,800 m, occasionally to 4,200 m. Its breeding range is perhaps above 3,000 m, lower-elevation records probably concerning late migrants. In the non-breeding season it occurs to 1,800 m, more occasionally 1,300 m. It appears largely to retreat from higher areas in winter, birds being noted at lower elevations from October and apparently absent above 3,200 m in December–February. In March–April slow but steady movement to the breeding areas is evident, at which season it occurs over the broadest altitudinal range. Winter flocks can number up to 30, with up to 70 birds at a site[5].

# Chestnut-crowned Laughingthrush
## *Garrulax erythrocephalus*  N=540(88). S 1600-3400 (mid-Apr-mid-Oct); W 1200-3000

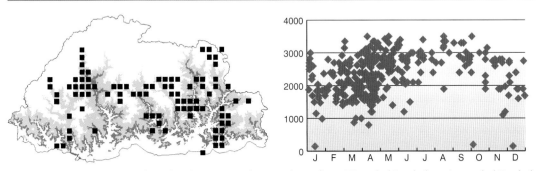

The Chestnut-crowned Laughingthrush occurs in the Himalayas from Himachal Pradesh to Arunachal Pradesh and in north-east India. Further east its range extends to Vietnam and the Malay Peninsula. Habitat is dense undergrowth in broadleaf forest.

In Bhutan the Chestnut-crowned Laughingthrush occurs in all biogeographic units, except the poorly explored central foothills. Its core range lies in the temperate zone, where it is abundant throughout. The regular summer range spans 1,600–3,400 m, not extending above 3,500 m where it is entirely replaced by Black-faced Laughingthrush. In winter it retreats to 1,200–3,000 m, with occasional records to 200 m. It is present here from November to February. In March–May there is a gradual movement to the breeding areas, but as some linger at low elevations late into spring the breeding range is probably above 2,000 m, its summer distribution coinciding with that of cool broadleaf forest. When breeding it is mostly found singly or in pairs, forming flocks in autumn, which can number up to 30 and regularly mix with other laughingthrush species, particularly Black-faced Laughingthrush. Despite its abundance, there is an absence of confirmed breeding records for Bhutan.

Chestnut-crowned Laughingthrush
*Jan Wilczur*

# Red-faced Liocichla
## *Liocichla phoenicea*

N=124(17). R 1200-2000 (broadleaf forest)

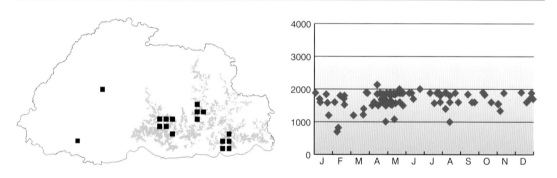

The Red-faced Liocichla is distributed along the Himalayas from Sikkim to Arunachal Pradesh and in north-east India. Further east it reaches northern Vietnam. It is found in dense undergrowth in broadleaf forest.

In Bhutan the Red-faced Liocichla is frequently recorded in the central and eastern valleys and foothills, with isolated records in the western and Sunkosh valleys. It is resident at 1,200–2,000 m, but occasionally reaches 700 m, particularly in winter. Presence is clearly dictated by the availability of large areas of intact broadleaf forest, such as in the Zhemgang area, around Yonkhola, Mongar district, and the Deothang area, Samdrup Jongkha district. There are no records from more fragmented forests higher in the Drangme Chhu and Kuri Chhu valleys. Singing birds occupy territories by mid-April and are vocal until late autumn. Peak song activity is from mid-May to July. Near Zhemgang a density of 1.8 territories per km was found at 1,600–1,900 m[52], with remarkably stable numbers between years. From July it gathers in small flocks of up to five, although on the whole it is most frequently encountered singly.

# Abbott's Babbler
## *Malacocincla abbotti*

N=8(2)

Abbott's Babbler is found in the Himalayan foothills from eastern Nepal to Arunachal Pradesh and in north-east India, its range continuing to Thailand and through parts of mainland south-east Asia to Sumatra and Borneo. Habitat consists of dense thickets in moist broadleaf forest.

In Bhutan Abbott's Babbler is a rare resident, primarily known from specimens taken in the 1960s and 1970s. Ali *et al.* (1996) noted it as 'quite common' in the Gelephu area in 1967, but on their return in 1973 it had become scarce due to loss of forest habitat in the area[1]. The present status of the species and of its habitat is unclear due to limited survey work in the lower foothills, with the only recent record being from the extreme south-east, near Daifam, Samdrup Jongkha district[48].

# Spot-throated Babbler
## *Pellorneum albiventre*
N=1(1)

The Spot-throated Babbler occurs in the hills of north-east India and from the Himalayan foothills in eastern Bhutan. Further east its range extends to northern Vietnam. It inhabits scrub and thickets in open forest.

In Bhutan the Spot-throated Babbler is rare, being known only from five specimens (exact date and sites unknown) taken in the Deothang area, Samdrup Jongkha district, by Ludlow in the 1930s[31], when it was perhaps relatively common in the area.

# Puff-throated Babbler
## *Pellorneum ruficeps*
N=46(11). R 200-1000

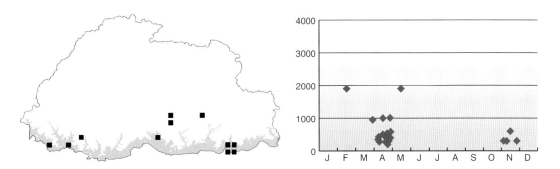

The Puff-throated Babbler is widespread in mainland south-east Asia. In the Indian subcontinent it is found along the Himalayan foothills from Himachal Pradesh to Arunachal Pradesh, in north-east India and other hill areas in central and southern India. Habitat consists of undergrowth, bamboo and thickets in broadleaf forest.

In Bhutan the Puff-throated Babbler is a frequently recorded resident of the foothills, between 200 m and 1,000 m, with isolated records from higher in the western, central and eastern valleys, the highest being from the Gedu area, Chhukha district at 1,900 m[36,44]. In suitable habitat it is regularly encountered, with several in the forests above Samdrup Jongkha noted annually in spring, mostly located by voice. A max. 15 has been found in this area in April[19].

# Spot-breasted Scimitar Babbler
## *Pomatorhinus erythrocnemis*
N=2(1)

The Spot-breasted Scimitar Babbler replaces Rusty-cheeked Scimitar Babbler in north-east India, its range extending east to western and central China, Taiwan and northern Vietnam and Taiwan. Habitat consists of scrub and forest undergrowth.

In Bhutan the Spot-breasted Scimitar Babbler is a rare resident in the east of the country, having been found twice in the eastern valleys, along the road between Trashigang and Deothang, firstly in April 1997[28] and then in April 2000[27], the latter between 1,200 m and 1,800 m.

# Rusty-cheeked Scimitar Babbler
*Pomatorhinus erythrogenys*                  N=309(58). R 600-2000

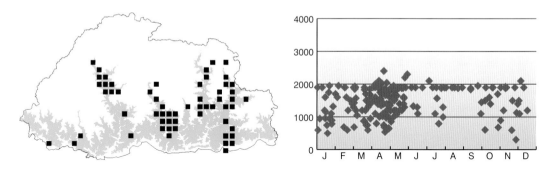

The Rusty-cheeked Scimitar Babbler is found along the Himalayas from Pakistan to Bhutan, its range extending to northern Myanmar and north-west Thailand. It is a bird of dense undergrowth at forest edge and in scrubby vegetation.

In Bhutan the Rusty-cheeked Scimitar Babbler is common throughout the temperate zone and foothills. Contrary to expectations, it is relatively scarce in the western and Sunkosh valleys, but common in the east, although it reaches its easternmost limits there. Apparently, there is a sharp divide with Spot-breasted Scimitar Babbler, the sister species which replaces it east of Bhutan. The present species is resident at 600–2,000 m, with occasional records to 300 m and 2,400 m. It is widespread, particularly encountered in scrub around villages. Year-round it occurs singly or in pairs, never forming flocks and only occasionally associating with mixed-species flocks of babblers. Vocalising birds and duetting pairs occupy territories in March–September. A pair was observed carrying food on 24 May[52] at 1,600 m. Near Zhemgang a density of 2.0 territories per km was found at 1,600–1,900 m[52].

# White-browed Scimitar Babbler
*Pomatorhinus schisticeps*                   N=74(14). R 400-1400

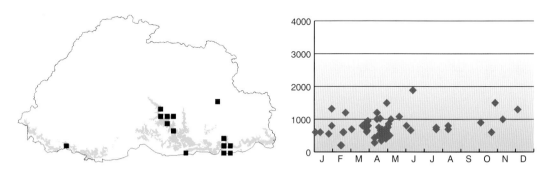

The White-browed Scimitar Babbler occurs in the Indian subcontinent along the Himalayan foothills from Himachal Pradesh to Arunachal Pradesh and in the hills of north-east India. Further east its range continues to Vietnam. Habitat is dense undergrowth in broadleaf forest, occupying the lowest altitudinal range of the scimitar babblers found in the Himalayas.

The White-browed Scimitar Babbler is local in Bhutan but frequently recorded. It has been found in the western and eastern foothills, and in the central and eastern valleys, strongholds being the Zhemgang and Deothang areas. There is an isolated record from the eastern valleys[49], from 1,850 m, the highest altitude at which it has been recorded. It is generally encountered singly or in pairs, but in winter also in small flocks of up to ten. The latter regularly associate with flocks of necklaced laughingthrushes.

# Streak-breasted Scimitar Babbler
## *Pomatorhinus ruficollis*
N=312(55). R 1600-2600

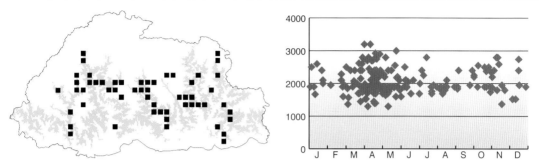

The Streak-breasted Scimitar Babbler is patchily distributed in the Himalayas from Uttar Pradesh to Arunachal Pradesh and in north-east India. Further east its range extends to western and central China, Taiwan and northern Vietnam. It inhabits dense scrub on hillsides and dense undergrowth in open forest.

In Bhutan the Streak-breasted Scimitar Babbler is common at mid-elevations in the temperate zone, being resident at 1,600–2,600 m, with occasional records to 1,300 m and 3,200 m. In the lower part of this range, it partially overlaps with Rusty-cheeked Scimitar Babbler, but differs in habitat choice, being more closely associated with forest in this zone. In higher parts of its range it keeps more to scrub and open conifer forest. Year-round it is mostly found singly or in pairs, occasionally in groups up to five, particularly in March–April, sometimes associated with laughingthrushes. Near Zhemgang inventories at 1,600–1,900 m revealed low densities in this part of its range, with 0.5 pairs per km[52]. Its optimal altitude therefore appears to be higher, above Rusty-cheeked Scimitar Babbler. Although common and widespread, there are no confirmed breeding records.

# Coral-billed Scimitar Babbler
## *Pomatorhinus ferruginosus*
N=60(17). R 1000-2000 (broadleaf forest)

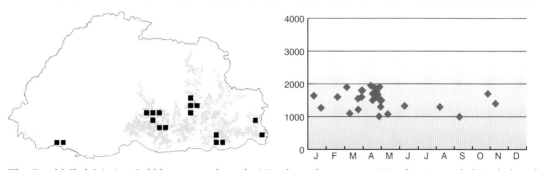

The Coral-billed Scimitar Babbler occurs along the Himalayas from eastern Nepal to Arunachal Pradesh and in north-east India, its range extending east to northern Vietnam. It inhabits dense undergrowth and bamboo in subtropical broadleaf forest.

In Bhutan the Coral-billed Scimitar Babbler is an uncommon resident with a localised distribution in the central and eastern valleys, with scattered records throughout the foothills, where it may have been overlooked. It is associated with areas of largely continuous forest cover below 2,000 m and is absent from more fragmented broadleaf forests in the Drangme Chhu and upper Kuri Chhu valleys. Its altitudinal range, at 1,000–2,000 m, overlaps with those of Rusty-cheeked and Streak-breasted Scimitar Babblers. It is generally more thinly spread and scarcer than these, and occupies denser forest habitat, of which an important component appears to be extensive bamboo thickets where landslides have created gaps in the forest canopy. In August–March it is mostly found in small flocks of up to five, within mixed flocks particularly of Greater and Lesser Rufous-headed Parrotbills. In April–May mostly pairs and individual birds are encountered.

291

# Slender-billed Scimitar Babbler
## Xiphirhynchus superciliaris
N=97(30). S 1600-3400 (mid-Apr-mid-Oct); W 1400-2200

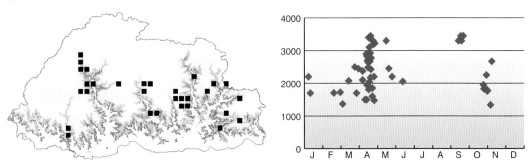

The Slender-billed Scimitar Babbler is found in the Himalayas from eastern Nepal to Arunachal Pradesh and in north-east India, thereafter extending to Yunnan and northern Vietnam. It is the highest-ranging of the scimitar babblers in the Himalayas, associated particularly with bamboo thickets in temperate forest.

In Bhutan the Slender-billed Scimitar Babbler is recorded throughout the temperate zone, where it is commonesst in the east, becoming scarcer further west where it approaches its westernmost limits. It is the only scimitar babbler in Bhutan to exhibit clear altitudinal movements, summering at 1,600–3,400 m, where largely segregated from Streak-breasted Scimitar Babbler by its preference for bamboo and denser broadleaf forest, and descending in winter to 1,400–2,200 m. It occurs singly, in pairs or in small parties. Densities in the breeding range appear low, less than 0.1 pair per km. A maximum of three pairs was found between Sengor and Yonkhola, Mongar district[5], and on the west slope of Yotong La, Trongsa district[52].

# Long-billed Wren Babbler
## Rimator malacoptilus
N=7(3)

The Long-billed Wren Babbler is a rare resident in the Himalayan foothills from Bhutan to Arunachal Pradesh and the hills of north-east India, thence into northern Myanmar, Yunnan and northern Vietnam. Habitat consists of forest undergrowth on rocky ground and in steep ravines.

In Bhutan the Long-billed Wren Babbler is rare in the western and eastern valleys at 1,800–2,000 m. Apparently, it is resident in this narrow altitudinal range, with records from April and October/November. Those from the western valleys concern specimens taken in the 1960s[1]. In April 2002 singing birds were discovered in the Kuri Chhu valley, at two separate sites[14,19].

# Eyebrowed Wren Babbler
## Napothera epilepidota
N=1(1)

The Eyebrowed Wren Babbler is a rare resident of the Himalayas, from Bhutan east, and in the hills of north-east India. Further east, it reaches Vietnam south to the Malay Peninsula and Greater Sundas. Habitat consists of mossy and fern-covered boulders and fallen logs in dense, moist and shady broadleaf forest.

In Bhutan the Eyebrowed Wren Babbler is a rare and possibly overlooked resident, having been collected by Ludlow, at 600 m near Deothang, on 21 November 1936[31].

# Scaly-breasted Wren Babbler
## Pnoepyga albiventer
N=250(62). S 2000-3600 (mid-Apr-Oct); W 1200-2800

The Scaly-breasted Wren Babbler occurs in the Himalayas from Himachal Pradesh to Arunachal Pradesh and in north-east India. Further east its range extends to northern Myanmar, Yunnan and northern Vietnam. It is found in moist, shady broadleaf forest, where it particularly affects ravines and edges of streams.

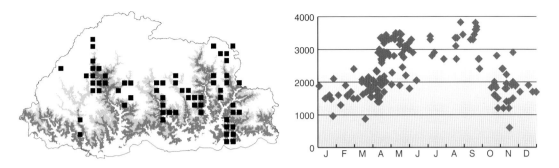

In Bhutan the Scaly-breasted Wren Babbler is a common altitudinal migrant throughout the temperate zone. Its summer range spans 2,000–3,600 m, reaching close to the treeline and frequenting cool broadleaf, fir and hemlock forests, with the highest record from 3,800 m[31]. In winter it is found at 1,200–2,800 m in broadleaf forest, more occasionally to 600 m[31]. Birds reach the breeding areas in April, with most having vacated lower elevations by the end of the month. In October and the first half of November a gradual downslope movement is noted. Song is heard almost year-round, both in summer and winter quarters, but with a peak in April–May. Apart from altitudinal movements, the only indication of the timing of the breeding season is provided by Ludlow, who collected juveniles in late July–August[31]. Territorial birds in the breeding areas are well spaced at low densities, with not more than 1–3 encountered at a site. In winter its occurrence in the warm broadleaf zone is more concentrated and up to ten can be found spread over an area of 1–2 km².

# Pygmy Wren Babbler
## *Pnoepyga pusilla*

N=297(56). S 1000-2600 (mid-Apr-Oct); W 400-2200

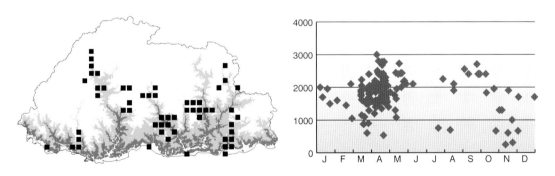

The Pygmy Wren Babbler ranges widely in eastern and south-east Asia, from central China south over much of Indonesia. In the Indian subcontinent it reaches the Himalayas west to central Nepal and the hills of north-east India. It occurs at lower elevations than the similar Scaly-breasted Wren Babbler, affecting similar habitat.

In Bhutan the Pygmy Wren Babbler is common throughout the temperate zone and foothills, being closely associated with densely vegetated ravines in broadleaf forest. Altitudinal movements are much less marked than those of Scaly-breasted Wren Babbler. In winter it occurs at 400–2,200 m and in summer it moves to 1,000–2,600 m, with occasional presence down to 600 m and up to 3,000 m. Its main range appears to be the upper warm broadleaf forest zone, at 1,500–2,000 m. Movement to the upper part of its range is noted from mid-March to mid-April, it retreating again by mid-October. Song is heard from mid-March to late April, with occasional records later and in autumn until December. Ludlow collected juveniles in late July and September[31]. Up to five singing birds have been found at a site, although it generally appears to be widespread at low densities. However, like other wren babblers it appears to sing quite infrequently and numbers might easily be under-estimated.

# Rufous-throated Wren Babbler
*Spelaeornis caudatus*                    N=96(20). R 1600-2400 (broadleaf forest)

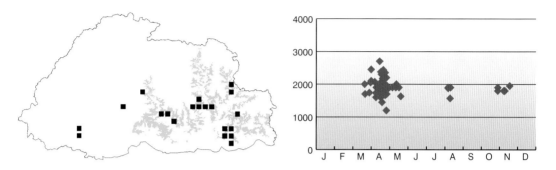

The Rufous-throated Wren Babbler occurs in the Himalayas from eastern Nepal to Arunachal Pradesh. It is endemic to the subcontinent and listed as Near Threatened by BirdLife International, due to its small population and habitat loss to shifting cultivation and logging. It occurs in typical wren babbler habitat of undergrowth with ferns, mossy rocks and fallen trees, in moist, dense broadleaf forest.

In Bhutan the Rufous-throated Wren Babbler is a frequently recorded resident, found mostly in moist parts of the central and eastern valleys, with isolated records from the western[1,19] and Sunkosh valleys[22], where it approaches it westernmost limits. It is mostly noted by its song, thus most records are in spring. The few late-autumn records appear to indicate only minor altitudinal movements. It occupies a narrow altitudinal range at 1,600–2,400 m, occasionally to 1,400 m, and is thus closely linked to the ecotone between the warm and cool broadleaf forest zones. It prefers moist, secluded valleys, often with a western or northern aspect. Song is mostly heard mid-March to mid-May, marking the breeding season. However, there appears to be a second period of vocal activity in early August[52]. Forests between Namling and Yonkhola in Thrumshingla National Park are a stronghold, several territories being noted annually and a maximum of seven birds in April 1996[28]. As vocal activity appears to be rather capricious, it is difficult to estimate the number of territories in this area over different years. Based on peak numbers in 1997–2002, the number of territories was estimated at 4–8 along 24 km of road at suitable altitudes. The years 1997 and 2002 witnessed highest numbers. Occurrence elsewhere appears less regular and there is only one other site in a protected area, on the west side of the Jigme Singye Wangchuck National Park. However, further surveys will probably identify additional sites, particularly in protected areas harbouring important stretches of warm broadleaf forest. Considering the bird's restricted range and the specific ecological conditions necessary to the species, Bhutan probably harbours key sites for its conservation.

# Bar-winged Wren Babbler
*Spelaeornis troglodytoides*                    N=42(12). R 2600-3400

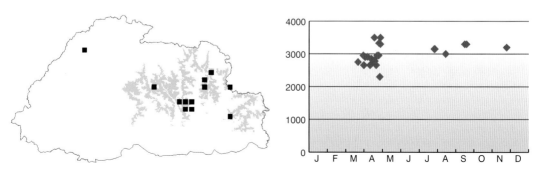

The Bar-winged Wren Babbler is a rare resident of the Eastern Himalayas, in Bhutan and Arunachal Pradesh, and thence through Myanmar to western and central China. Habitat consists of undergrowth and bamboo in moist temperate forest, and rhododendron scrub.

The Bar-winged Wren Babbler is an uncommon resident in Bhutan. It occupies a narrow altitudinal range at 2,600–3,400 m, where it inhabits rhododendron and bamboo scrub in mixed hemlock–broadleaf and fir forests. Occasional records are available at 2,300 m and 3,500 m. It is primarily known from forest between Sengor and Namling, Mongar district, where a maximum of four singing birds has been found[28]. In the 1930s it was collected at two different sites on the ridges either side of the Kulong Chhu valley, Trashi Yangtse district[31], with a

Bar-winged Wren Babbler
*Dan Cole*

third site located during the 1970s. Another five sites have been found in recent years in the Sunkosh[22,28], central[14,28,52] and eastern valleys[49,27], although at each occurrence appears rather unpredictable, with variation between seemingly considerable, and 2001 standing out as a relatively good year. Most records are in mid-March to late April when birds are vocal. Outside this season it is only known only from specimens. The few late-autumn records suggest that the species is mostly resident within its altitudinal range. Most sites are within protected areas, demonstrating it to be a useful indicator species of habitat quality.

# Spotted Wren Babbler
## *Spelaeornis formosus*

N=172(44). R 800-2200

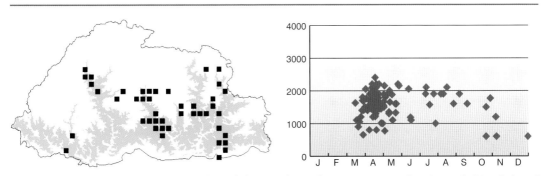

The Spotted Wren Babbler is a rare resident of the Himalayas, from eastern Nepal to Arunachal Pradesh and in north-east India, thence east to northern Vietnam. It occurs in the undergrowth of moist temperate and subtropical broadleaf forest.

In Bhutan the Spotted Wren Babbler is a widespread, albeit occasionally recorded, resident throughout the temperate zone, with isolated records from the western and eastern foothills. It is significantly commoner in Bhutan than elsewhere in its range. Altitudinally it spans 800–2,200 m, more occasionally reaching 600 m and 2,400 m[5]. The limited data suggest some retreat lower in winter, with records at 600–1,800 m. It is almost invariably located by its thin, faltering song, thus most records are in spring. Song is mostly heard mid-March to May, with occasional records later in spring, summer and autumn, until December. Up to nine singing birds have been heard at a site[19]. Well-developed warm broadleaf forest from the Sunkosh Valley east invariably harbours this species, although it is easily overlooked as it sings rather infrequently. In the western valleys the species appears scarcer, as it approaches its westernmost limits in this region. Near Zhemgang a density of 0.6 territories per km was found at 1,600–1,900 m[52], with remarkably large 'between-year' fluctuations. At other regular sites, e.g. the forested section of the Mo Chhu, Punakha district, and the forests above Yonkhola, Mongar district, numbers and fluctuations are similar.

# Wedge-billed Wren Babbler
## *Sphenocichla humei*

N=11(4). S 1600-2000 (Mar-Sep); W 1200

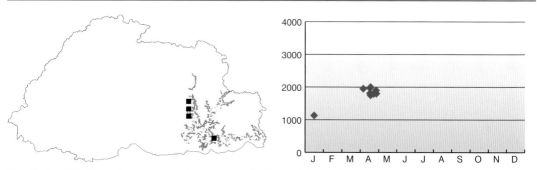

The Wedge-billed Wren Babbler is another rare wren babbler of the north-east Indian subcontinent. It occurs in the Himalayas from Sikkim to Arunachal Pradesh and in the hills of north-east India, thence east to south-west China and northern Myanmar. Habitat consists of broadleaf forest with large trees and bamboo. It is more arboreal than other wren babblers, sometimes foraging on branches like a treecreeper. It is listed by BirdLife International as Near Threatened, due to its small population in habitat affected by shifting cultivaton and logging.

In Bhutan the Wedge-billed Wren Babbler is rare, being initially discovered only in January 2000, when a flock of 12 was encountered in the Kuri Chhu valley at 1,100 m[22,49]. These were most likely in their winter range, as elsewhere it winters down to 800 m. A singing bird was subsequently discovered in the Deothang area, Samdrup Jongkha district, at 1,600 m[14]. A second site with singing birds was found in the Kuri Chhu valley at 1,950 m[19], where it was present in both spring 2001 and 2002. Up to three have been found singing there, suggesting considerable densities in suitable habitat. Summer habitat appears to consist of tall broadleaf forest with a western aspect. Records from the Kuri Chhu valley are from within Thrumshingla National Park, which may harbour a significant population. However, most of its probable range is situated outside protected areas, and the species's fortunes in Bhutan will depend on future forest management practices within its habitat.

# Rufous-fronted Babbler
## *Stachyris rufifrons*

N=53(27). R 600-2600

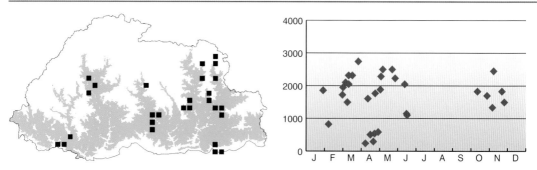

The Rufous-fronted Babbler is found in the Himalayas from Sikkim east, as well as in north-east India and locally in eastern India. Further east it reaches northern Vietnam, and south to the Malay Peninsula, Sumatra and Borneo. It inhabits dense undergrowth and bamboo in open forest and forest clearings.

In Bhutan the Rufous-fronted Babbler is an occasionally recorded resident throughout the temperate zone and foothills. Its principal stronghold is above Samdrup Jongkha, where up to 15 have been found in spring[28] and where it occupies an altitudinal range largely below that of Rufous-capped Babbler, roughly at 200–800 m. Elsewhere it is scarce and unpredictably recorded, with a maximum of three at a site. It occurs, however, over a relatively broad altitudinal range, which overlaps that of Rufous-capped Babbler, from 600–2,600 m and occasionally reaching 2,800 m.

# Rufous-capped Babbler
*Stachyris ruficeps*                                         N=354(60). R 1200-2800

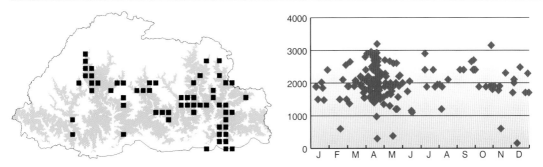

The Rufous-capped Babbler occurs in the Himalayas from eastern Nepal to Arunachal Pradesh and in the hills of north-east India and northern Orissa. Its range extends further north and east to Sichuan, Taiwan and central Vietnam. It inhabits dense undergrowth and bamboo in humid broadleaf forest, generally at higher altitudes than Rufous-fronted and Grey-throated Babblers.

In Bhutan it is common in the temperate zone, but scarce in the western valleys. It also reaches the eastern foothills and is resident at 1,200–2,800 m, occasionally to 200 m and 3,200 m. As it approaches its western limits west of Bhutan, its lower altitudinal limit shifts higher, from 200 m in the eastern foothills, to 1,200 m in the central-east, 1,400 m in the Sunkosh and 1,800 m in the western valleys. Year-round it is noted in small numbers, widely dispersed and rarely in flocks. However, up to 30 have been reported per day in January[28] and up to 15 in the breeding season. Outside the breeding season, in October–March it regularly associates with mixed flocks of babblers, but with only one or a few noted per flock. Song is noted mid-April to July and breeding confirmed by the observation of a bird carrying faeces away from the nest, at 1,900 m on 8 May[52].

# Golden Babbler
*Stachyris chrysaea*                                          N=271(38). R 800-2000

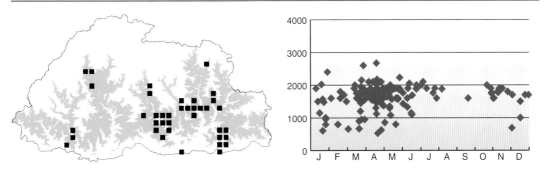

In the Himalayas and north-east India the Golden Babbler has a similar range to Rufous-capped Babbler, being found from eastern Nepal and thence east to Vietnam and south to Sumatra. Also, in habitat and altitudinal range it closely resembles Rufous-capped Babbler, affecting undergrowth in humid broadleaf forest.

In Bhutan the Golden Babbler is a frequently recorded resident of the temperate zone and foothills. It is relatively uncommon in the western and Sunkosh valleys and western foothills, as it approaches its westernmost limits there. It occurs at 800–2,000 m, occasionally reaching 500 m[22] and 2,500 m. Song is heard as early as mid-February, but mostly late March to July. Peak territorial activity is in the second half of May and June. From August it joins mixed flocks of babblers and warblers, often with Grey-throated Warbler. Up to ten are present in a flock, with a max. 20[52]. In particular, from January to March, pre-breeding, it can be numerous, with a max. 40 reported in a day[46]. There are no confirmed breeding records, but near Zhemgang a density of 3.4 territories per km was found at 1,600–1,900 m[52], thus one of the commonest birds in warm broadleaf forest.

# Grey-throated Babbler
*Stachyris nigriceps*

N=206(32). R 400-1800

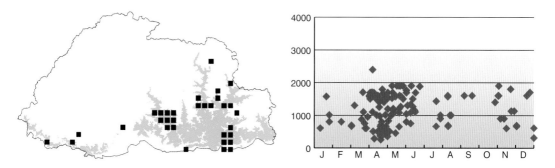

The Grey-throated Babbler is distributed from central Nepal to Arunachal Pradesh and north-east India. Further east its range extends to Vietnam, the Malay Peninsula, Sumatra and Borneo. Habitat consists of low scrub in forest clearings and at forest edge.

In Bhutan the Grey-throated Babbler is a common resident in the central and eastern valleys and the eastern foothills, with a few records further west in the temperate zone and western foothills. It occurs at 400–1,800 m, with occasional records to 200 m and 1,900 m, and one at 2,400 m in April[19]. From August to early March it is regularly found in mixed-species flocks of babblers, often forming the core of the flock. Numbers are highest after December, when up to 20 can be present in such groups. From March the flocks disband and singing birds dominate. Its song is heard March to mid-August, without any clear peak in activity. Due its secretive behaviour in the breeding season, there are no confirmed breeding records. Near Zhemgang a density of 0.9 territories per km was found at 1,600–1,900 m, the species being commoner at lower elevations.

# Striped Tit Babbler
*Macronous gularis*

N=61(8). R 200-800

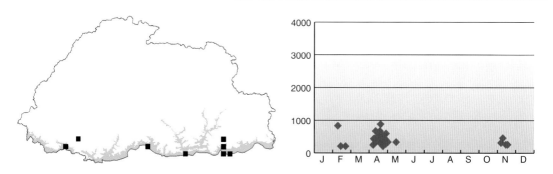

The Striped Tit Babbler is widespread in south-east Asia, reaching its westernmost limits in the Indian subcontinent, where it occurs in the Himalayas from eastern Nepal to Arunachal Pradesh, and south through north-east India, Bangladesh and eastern India. It inhabits forest undergrowth at low elevations.

In Bhutan the Striped Tit Babbler is a frequently recorded resident of the foothills, with isolated records from the western and Sunkosh valleys. The record in the Sunkosh valley has not been mapped due to an imprecise locality being reported. It is most regular in the eastern foothills, where it is found annually above Samdrup Jongkha, with up to 35 encountered in a day[19]. It is usually found at elevations up to 800 m, but has been ringed at Gedu, Chhukha district, presumably at *c*.1,800 m[36]. It mostly moves in flocks, with records of singles and pairs in April–May.

# Jungle Babbler
*Turdoides striatus*                                              N=12(6). R 200-400

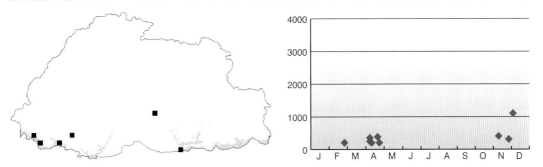

The Jungle Babbler is endemic in the Indian subcontinent, being a common resident in most parts including the Himalayan foothills. It occurs at edges of cultivation, plantations and other man-modified habitats. It is highly gregarious, being known in India as 'the seven brothers' through its habit of always moving in parties.

In Bhutan the Jungle Babbler is an uncommon resident, found primarily in the western foothills, with scattered records in the central valleys[4,52] and the adjacent eastern foothills at Manas[22]. Its regular altitudinal range spans 200–400 m, but it has been found once at 1,100 m, in the Mangde Chhu valley in December[52]. In the Phuntsholing area it is relatively common, with up to ten reported[19].

# Silver-eared Mesia
*Leiothrix argentauris*                           N=137(27). R 600-1800 (broadleaf forest)

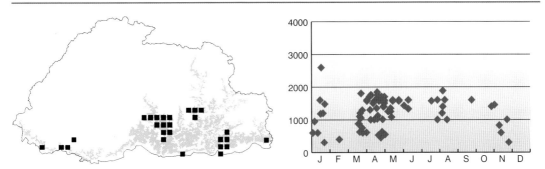

The Silver-eared Mesia occurs in the Himalayas from Sikkim to Arunachal Pradesh and in north-east India, more patchily west to Uttar Pradesh. Further east it reaches Vietnam and south through the Malay Peninsula to Sumatra. It affects undergrowth in evergreen forest, notably more open patches and edges.

In Bhutan the Silver-eared Mesia is a common resident throughout the foothills and the central and eastern valleys, with isolated records from the western valleys. It appears to be rather scattered in its distribution, being associated with areas where broadleaf forest cover is largely intact, and is nearly absent from the cultivated and Chir Pine zones of the Drangme Chhu valley. This seems to contradict its association with edge habitats, but a key feature is apparently the alternation between well-developed broadleaf forest and open patches created by natural forest regeneration. A similar pattern is evident in other babblers, such as Grey-throated Babbler, Coral-billed Scimitar Babbler and Greater Rufous-headed Parrotbill. Its altitudinal range spans 600–1,800 m, with occasional records to 300 m. There is one record of a flock of 20 at 2,600 m in January[13]. Song is noted early April to August, with peak activity in the second half of April. There is no clear evidence of breeding other than the presence of birds on territory. From September it is mostly found in flocks, which reach maximum numbers in January–March, when up to 20 occur together. These flocks only occasionally join mixed flocks with other babblers. In April they disband, the birds forming clusters of breeding territories. Near Zhemgang a density of 2.1 territories per km was found at 1,600 m[52].

# Red-billed Leiothrix
## *Leiothrix lutea*

N=227(61). S 1800-3200 (May-Sep); W 1000-2800

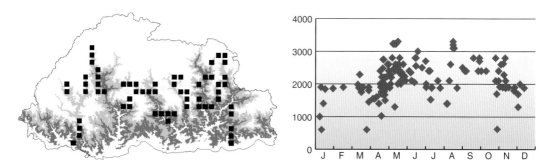

The Red-billed Leiothrix has a somewhat scattered distribution in the Himalayas, from Himachal Pradesh to Uttar Pradesh, and thence through north-east India to northern Vietnam and north to Sichuan. Habitat consists of dense undergrowth in broadleaf forest.

In Bhutan the Red-billed Leiothrix is a common altitudinal migrant throughout the temperate zone, with one record from the eastern foothills. Its summer range spans 1,800–3,200 m. Records above 2,800 m are all from the central valleys, where it is common in the Ura Valley, regularly reaching 3,400 m. Breeding habitat includes cool broadleaf and coniferous forests, amongst others Blue Pine forest in the Thimphu and Bumthang valleys, and fir at Ura, Bumthang district. Outside the breeding season it descends to 1,000–2,800 m, occasionally reaching 600 m. Its winter range is situated in the warm broadleaf forest zone below 2,000 m, where it is present mid-November to mid-April. Movement to and from the breeding areas is relatively rapid in the second half of April and the first half of November, when birds are reported over a broad altitudinal range. Song is noted mid-May to August but, despite its nest being reputedly easy to find, there are no confirmed breeding records. From August birds associate in flocks of up to 20. These are invariably single-species flocks, moving rapidly through the undergrowth in characteristic manner.

# Cutia
## *Cutia nipalensis*

N=208(34). R 1200-2400

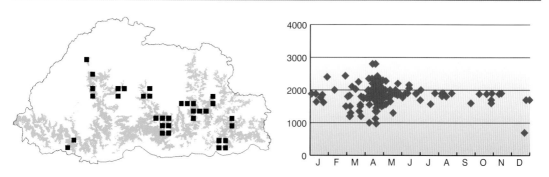

The Cutia is patchily distributed in the Himalayas from Uttar Pradesh to Nepal, and in a continuous band from Bhutan east to Arunachal Pradesh and north-east India. Its range reaches south to the Malay Peninsula and east to Vietnam. It inhabits dense, humid broadleaf forest with a well-developed upper canopy and abundant epiphytes. It forages mostly in the canopy on mossy branches.

In Bhutan the Cutia is a frequently recorded resident throughout the temperate zone and foothills. However, its distribution is scattered, with most records from those parts of the central and eastern valleys harbouring old-growth forest with a well-developed canopy. It is particularly regular in the Zhemgang area, where it can be numerous, with once a flock of several tens reported[5]. Its altitudinal range spans 1,200–2,400 m, occasionally to 700 m and 2,800 m. In October–March it is found in small flocks of up to ten, which only occasionally join mixed flocks of other babblers. In April these flocks disband and the birds occupy territories. Singing birds are evident until early August[52]. Near Zhemgang a density of 1.3 territories per km was found at 1,600–1,900 m[52]. Densities appeared to vary considerably between years, with particularly high numbers following the mild winters of 1999/2000 and 2000/2001. Nests have never been observed in our region or in Bhutan.

# Black-headed Shrike Babbler
## *Pteruthius rufiventer*

N=26(12). R 1600-2400

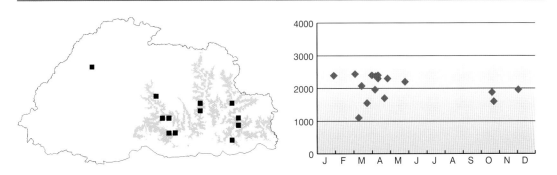

The Black-headed Shrike Babbler is a scarce resident of the Eastern Himalayas from central Nepal to Arunachal Pradesh and the hills of north-east India. Its range continues east through Myanmar and Yunnan to northern Vietnam. Habitat comprises dense humid broadleaf forest, where it feeds in the undergrowth and on mossy branches in the canopy.

In Bhutan the Black-headed Shrike Babbler is uncommon, found primarily in the eastern valleys, with increasingly sparse records further west in the central valleys and just one record from the Sunkosh Valley[55]. It is resident at 1,600–2,400 m, with its occurrence being dictated by the presence of mature, undisturbed forest. Its scarcity is accentuated by the fact that most records concern singles, with a max. 3 reported at a site. A singing bird was found at 2,300 m on 10 April, which is the only evidence of breeding in Bhutan[5].

White-browed Shrike Babbler
*Dan Cole*

# White-browed Shrike Babbler
## Pteruthius flaviscapis

N=398(62). S 1400-2400 (May-Sep); W 800-2400

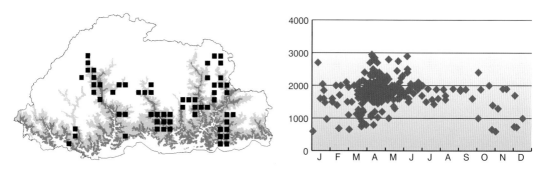

The White-browed Shrike Babbler is the commonest of the shrike babblers in the Himalayas and has the most extensive range. It occurs from Pakistan to Arunachal Pradesh, and in north-east India east through mainland south-east Asia to the Greater Sundas. Habitat is broadleaf forest and, to a lesser extent, conifers, where it affects the top canopy, often accompanying other similar-sized insectivores.

In Bhutan the White-browed Shrike Babbler is a common resident of the temperate zone, with a more occasional presence in the western and eastern foothills. It is an altitudinal migrant, breeding at 1,400–2,400 m, occasionally to 2,900 m, and in winter present throughout the main range but also dispersing to 600 m. It moves upslope during April, descending in October. In August–March it forms small groups, sometimes of up to 15, which frequently associate with mixed-species flocks of other larger babblers. Song is heard mostly April–July, occasionally earlier or in autumn. Near Zhemgang a density of 3.9 territories per km was found at 1,600–1,900 m[52], making it among the commonest birds in forest at this altitude. Breeding is confirmed by a record of a nest with young at 2,100 m[20]. In Bhutan it primarily inhabits cool and warm broadleaf forests, rarely conifers.

# Green Shrike Babbler
## Pteruthius xanthochlorus

N=107(42). R 1800-3200

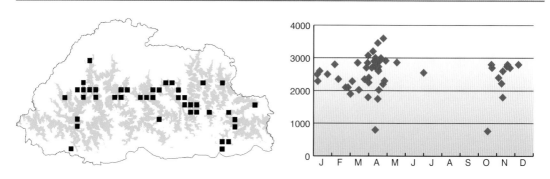

The Green Shrike Babbler has a scattered distribution through the Himalayas, from Pakistan to Arunachal Pradesh, and in north-east India east to northern Myanmar and southern China. Habitat is temperate broadleaf and conifer forests, occupying the highest altitudinal range of the *Pteruthius*.

In Bhutan the Green Shrike Babbler is common in the temperate zone, with one record from the eastern foothills. It is resident at 1,800–3,200 m, with isolated records at 700 m[5,20] and 3,500 m[5,19]. Year-round it is mostly encountered singly or in pairs, often in mixed-species flocks with tits and *Phylloscopus* warblers. Numbers are generally low, with a max. 12 reported in January[28]. There are very few records in summer, when mixed-species flocks disband and this unobtrusive species is more difficult to locate.

# Black-eared Shrike Babbler
## *Pteruthius melanotis*

N=190(44). S 1600-2400 (Apr-Oct); W 600-2400

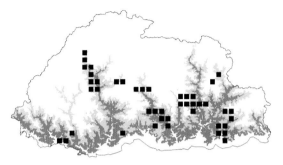

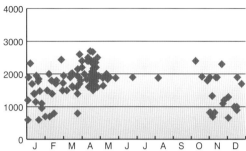

The Black-eared Shrike Babbler ranges in the Himalayas from eastern Nepal to Arunachal Pradesh and in north-east India, with a more localised presence west to central Nepal. Further east its range reaches northern Vietnam and the Malay Peninsula. It is a bird of humid broadleaf forest.

In Bhutan the Black-eared Shrike Babbler is a common altitudinal migrant throughout the temperate zone and the western foothills. Its summer range spans 1,600–2,400 m, occasionally 2,500 m. In winter it remains present in this zone but spreads to 600 m. Altitudinal ranges and habitat choice of White-browed Shrike Babbler, Black-eared Shrike Babbler and, to a lesser extent, Black-headed Shrike Babbler largely overlap and it is probably their different sizes that permit them to occupy complementary niches.

Black-eared Shrike Babbler
*Jan Wilczur*

In autumn and winter, in August–March, it is typically found in mixed-species flocks, with one or a few present in these. From late March it occupies territories and singing birds are heard until July. A max. 12 has been found in a day[46], in March just prior to the breeding season.

# White-hooded Babbler
## *Gampsorhynchus rufulus*

N=7(3)

The White-hooded Babbler occurs in the Himalayan foothills from eastern Nepal to Arunachal Pradesh and in north-east India. Further east it ranges over much of mainland south-east Asia. Habitat consists of bamboo jungle and undergrowth in moist subtropical forest.

In Bhutan the White-hooded Babbler is uncommon, being known from only two localities in the central and eastern valleys: the Samdrup Jongkha–Deothang road and the Tingtibi–Gomphu road near Zhemgang. Records are from 200–900 m. Apparently it is more easily located in winter, when it occurs in more open habitat, scrub and bamboo at forest edge. Stands of large *Dendrocalamus* bamboo appear to be a key habitat component. It is invariably found in small flocks, mostly numbering *c*.5, but up to 20[28].

# Rusty-fronted Barwing
*Actinodura egertoni*                                              N=259(35). R 1000-2000

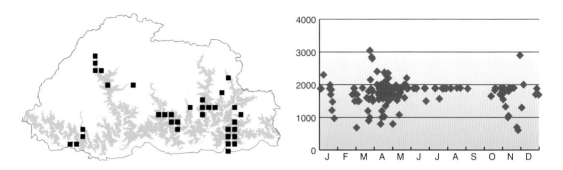

The Rusty-fronted Barwing occurs from central Nepal, where it is rare, east to Arunachal Pradesh, south-west China and northern Myanmar. It occurs at lower altitudes than its congeners in the subcontinent, Hoary-throated Barwing and Streak-throated Barwing. Habitat is dense undergrowth in warm broadleaf forest and dense second growth.

In Bhutan this barwing is a frequent resident of the temperate zone and the western and eastern foothills. It appears less common in the west, closer to the periphery of its range. It occurs at 1,000–2,000 m, occasionally to 600 m and 2,400 m, the latter particularly in the Mo Chhu valley, Punakha district, and Kori La, Mongar district. In autumn and winter it forms flocks of 5–20, which move within a well-defined home range. It mostly forms single-species flocks but also associates with the rarer Greater Rufous-headed Parrotbill. From late April the flocks separate as pairs and territories are established. Song activity continues until August. Near Zhemgang a density of 1.6 territories per km was found at 1,900 m [52]. No nests or feeding birds have been observed, but in the 1960s a female in laying condition was collected at 1,500 m on 8 May [1].

# Hoary-throated Barwing
*Actinodura nipalensis*                                            N=173(46). R 1800-3200

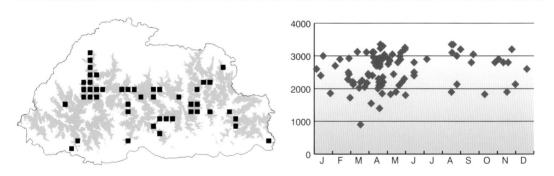

The Hoary-throated Barwing is a restricted-range species of the Eastern Himalayas that is endemic to the Indian subcontinent. It occurs in a narrow band from central Nepal to eastern Bhutan. There is thought to be some ecological separation between this species and Rusty-fronted Barwing, with Hoary-throated Barwing foraging more in the tree canopy, whereas Rusty-fronted Barwing keeps to bushes and undergrowth. Despite this difference, there appears to be very little overlap between them, Hoary-throated Barwing occurring at higher altitudes.

In Bhutan the Hoary-throated Barwing is an occasionally recorded resident throughout the temperate zone, at 1,800–3,200 m, in oak and conifer forests. It is commonest in the western and Sunkosh valleys, and becomes somewhat scarcer in the east, with relatively few records from the Drangme Chhu valley at the easternmost edge of its range. In the western and Sunkosh valleys, where Rusty-fronted Barwing is scarce, it occurs well below its regular altitude range to 1,400 m, whilst in the east it is clearly confined above the upper altitude limit of its sister species. There is one record from 900 m[10], while the highest recorded altitude is 3,400 m. In autumn and winter it forms flocks of up to ten, which do not readily mix with other species. From April these flocks disband and singing birds occupy territories, maintained until August. It does not seem to associate regularly with mixed-species flocks, and there are no confirmed breeding records. Song has been noted in June–July. Bhutan probably holds important populations of this restricted-range species, given the largely intact forest cover within its altitudinal range, including important stretches within protected areas.

Hoary-throated Barwing
*Ren Hathway*

# Blue-winged Minla
## *Minla cyanouroptera*

N=318(53). S 1600-2400 (May-Sep); W 600-2000

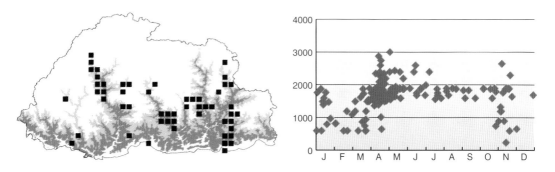

The Blue-winged Minla occurs in the Himalayas from Uttar Pradesh to Arunachal Pradesh and in north-east India, its range extending east to western China and over much of mainland south-east Asia. It inhabits broadleaf and mixed forests.

In Bhutan the Blue-winged Minla is a common altitudinal migrant, occupying the lowest altitudinal range of the minlas. It is found throughout the temperate zone and the foothills, becoming progressively commoner further east. Its summer range spans 1,600–2,400 m, with occasional records to 3,000 m. In winter it largely retreats below 2,000 m and down to 600 m, with one record at 200 m[1]. Birds reach the breeding areas by mid-April, descending by November. Singing birds occupy territories from mid-April to August and birds carrying nest material were observed on 17 April, with adults carrying faeces on 8 May, both at 1,900 m, but involving different pairs[52]. Near Zhemgang a density of 1.2 territories per km was found at 1,600–1,900 m[52]. From August birds form flocks of up to 10–20, which commonly join mixed flocks of other species, particularly other minlas, similar-sized babblers and tits. An exceptionally large flock of 180, with Red-tailed Minlas, was observed at Namling, Mongar district, in April[5]. Flocks remain in evidence until mid-April, when pairs form and territories are occupied.

# Chestnut-tailed Minla
*Minla strigula*　　　　　　　　N=359(73). S 2000-3400 (May-Sep); W 1800-3200

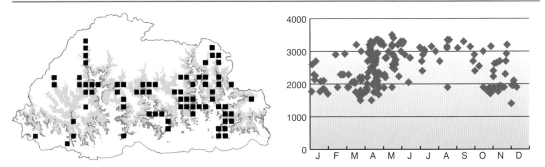

The Chestnut-tailed Minla is found in the Himalayas from Himachal Pradesh to Arunachal Pradesh and locally in north-east India. Further east it reaches western China, northern Vietnam and the Malay Peninsula. It is a bird of oak–rhododendron and mixed conifer–broadleaf forest.

In Bhutan this minla is a common altitudinal migrant throughout the temperate zone, and is the highest ranging of the minlas, but shows the least-pronounced altitudinal movements. In summer it is found at 2,000–3,400 m and in winter only retreats from the upper part of this range, to 3,200 m and down to 1,800 m. More occasionally it is found at 1,400 m and 3,500 m. In the breeding season it occurs in cool broadleaf, fir and hemlock forests, but in winter it keeps to cool broadleaf and adjacent scrub forests. Outside the breeding season it is found in flocks of up to ten, which regularly associate with mixed flocks, particularly of other minlas. Flocks appear to disband only by late April, with singing birds heard in this period, coinciding with the move to higher elevations. Flocks form again in October, when the species reoccupies the lower part of its range. There are no confirmed breeding records.

# Red-tailed Minla
*Minla ignotincta*　　　　　　　　N=358(82). S 1800-3200 (mid-Apr-mid-Oct); W 800-2800

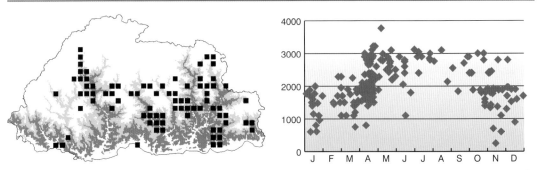

The Red-tailed Minla is distributed along the Himalayas from central Nepal to Arunachal Pradesh, and in north-east India east to western China and northern Vietnam. Habitat consists of moist broadleaf and mixed forests.

In Bhutan the Red-tailed Minla is common in the temperate zone and foothills, but relatively scarce in the western valleys, where conifer forest dominates much of its altitudinal range. It shows pronounced altitudinal movements, summering at 1,800–3,200 m and wintering at 800–2,800 m, when it is occasionally found to 600 m, with the lowest record at 200 m[1]. The highest record is one at 3,800 m in the central valleys[22]. It is present in its winter range April–October, when it is mostly found in flocks, which commonly number up to ten but are occasionally larger, with an exceptional 120 with Blue-winged Minlas near Namling, Mongar district, in April[5]. It is among the most regular members of mixed-species flocks with other minlas, yuhinas and tits. Evidence of breeding is limited to occasional observations of singing birds.

# Golden-breasted Fulvetta
## *Alcippe chrysotis*
N=98(32). S 2000-2800 (mid-May-Oct); W 1600-2800 (broadleaf forest)

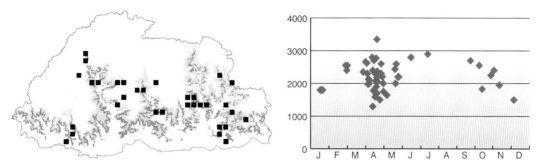

The Golden-breasted Fulvetta occurs in the Indian subcontinent from central Nepal to Arunachal Pradesh. Further east its range reaches western China and northern Vietnam. Of the fulvettas, it is most associated with bamboo stands and undergrowth in temperate forest.

In Bhutan the Golden-breasted Fulvetta is a frequently recorded altitudinal migrant, found throughout the temperate zone but remarkably scarce in the western and central valleys. Apparently its specific habitat requirements are a factor. It summers at 2,000–2,800 m, where it is partial to bamboo stands in cool broadleaf and mixed forests, a habitat rather scarce in these valleys. It is present at these altitudes from mid-May to October, but outside the breeding season reaches 1,600 m and occasionally 1,300 m. There is one record from *c.*3,300 m in April[19]. In winter it gathers in small flocks, mostly of fewer than five. Observations of up to 30 are clearly linked to a few strongholds: the forested section of the Mo Chhu, Punakha district, forests between Khelakha and Nobding, Wangdue Phodrang district, and forests around Namling, Mongar district. There are no confirmed breeding records.

# Yellow-throated Fulvetta
## *Alcippe cinerea*
N=141(24). R 1400-2400 (broadleaf forest)

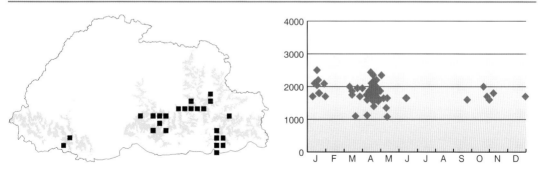

The Yellow-throated Fulvetta is distributed in the Himalayan foothills from Sikkim in the west, to Arunachal Pradesh and the hills of north-east India, thence further east to northern Vietnam. It inhabits undergrowth in dense warm broadleaf forest.

In Bhutan this fulvetta is a frequently recorded resident, found mostly in the central and eastern valleys and the eastern foothills. It is apparently absent from the Sunkosh Valley and scarce in the western valleys, with only one recent record[19]. The Black Mountain range constitutes the limit of its core range in Bhutan. It is found at 1,400–2,400 m, occasionally to 1,100 m and 2,500 m. Outside the breeding season, in October–February, it gathers in flocks of 10–30. The breeding season is unclear, as birds are regularly seen in small flocks of 5–10 throughout March–May. On 19 April one was carrying nest material, near Thekpaling, Thrumshingla National Park, between 1,600 m and 1,800 m[22].

# Rufous-winged Fulvetta
*Alcippe castaneceps*  N=362(72). S 1800-3200 (May-mid-Oct); W 1400-3000

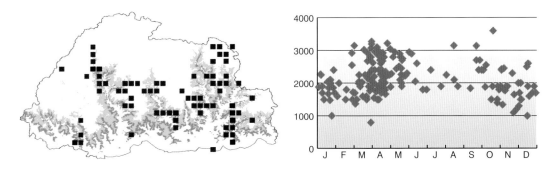

The Rufous-winged Fulvetta occurs in the Himalayas from central Nepal east to Arunachal Pradesh, and in north-east India and Bangladesh east to northern Vietnam and the Malay Peninsula. Among fulvettas, it has a relatively large altitudinal range, occurring in the undergrowth of warm as well as cool broadleaf forest.

In Bhutan the Rufous-winged Fulvetta is a common altitudinal migrant throughout the temperate zone and in the western and eastern foothills, but is scarce in the western valleys, where conifers dominate its altitudinal range. In summer it spans 1,800–3,200 m, the highest record being *c*.3,600 m[51]. In winter it spreads lower, occurring at 1,400–3,000 m, and being confined below 2,400 m for most of this season. In particular, in autumn it may occasionally disperse as low as 800 m. In September–March it gathers in large flocks of typically 20–40, sometimes up to 70. Often these form the core of a mixed flock of small babblers and warblers. From April records of individuals and pairs in breeding habitat dominate, followed subsequently by family groups. A nest was found at 2,100 m on 17 May[1].

# White-browed Fulvetta
*Alcippe vinipectus*  N=366(50). S 2400-3600 (Apr-Oct); W 2000-3200

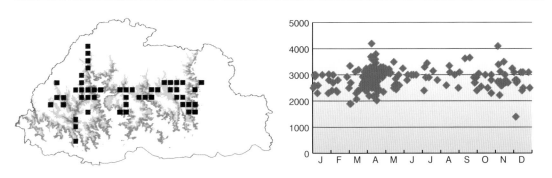

The White-browed Fulvetta has the most westerly distribution of the fulvettas in the region, occurring from the Western Himalayas east to central Bhutan and again in north-east India and adjacent northern Myanmar, continuing over southern Tibet, western and south-west China and northern Vietnam. It is a high-altitude babbler affecting juniper, willow, birch and rhododendron scrub in the alpine zone, as well as open forest with a well-developed scrub layer at lower levels.

In Bhutan the White-browed Fulvetta is an abundant altitudinal migrant throughout the temperate zone from the Kuri Chhu valley west, gradually becoming commoner. East of the Kuri Chhu it appears to be replaced by Brown-throated Fulvetta, which occurs at similar altitudes and in similar habitat. This sharp divide is remarkable as the two occur sympatrically in northern Myanmar (King *et al.* 2001). It summers at 2,400–3,600 m and probably higher, as evidenced by records at 4,200 m[52]. In winter it descends slightly, reaching

2,000 m and retreating below 3,200 m. Two at 1,400 m in December were exceptionally low[53]. Winter flocks appear smaller than those of Rufous-winged Fulvetta, usually numbering 10–20. However, it associates less frequently with mixed-species flocks. During April, gradually records of pairs and individual birds dominate. One was observed carrying nest material at 3,300 m on 23 April[52], the only evidence of breeding in Bhutan.

# Brown-throated Fulvetta (Ludlow's Fulvetta)
## *Alcippe ludlowi*

N=31(10). S 3000-4000 (May-Sep); W 2200-3200

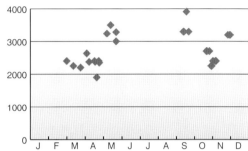

The Brown-throated Fulvetta was described from specimens taken by Frank Ludlow in Bhutan in 1933. It is a restricted-range species, occurring in the Eastern Himalayas from eastern Bhutan, adjacent south-east Tibet and northern Myanmar (King *et al.* 2001) to Arunachal Pradesh. Habitat consists of low bushes and bamboo in rhododendron forest.

In Bhutan the Brown-throated Fulvetta is uncommon, replacing White-browed Fulvetta in the temperate zone east of the Kuri Chhu and in the high east. Like the latter it is an altitudinal migrant, occurring at 3,000–4,000 m in summer and descending to 2,200–3,200 m in winter (October–April). In this period it appears to prefer well-developed stands of cool broadleaf forest, where it is invariably found in small numbers, with a maximum of just two birds per sighting. Larger flocks of up to 16 have been observed in its breeding range in May–September[49].

Brown-throated Fulvetta
*Phil Jones*

# Rufous-throated Fulvetta
## *Alcippe rufogularis*

N=2(1)

The Rufous-throated Fulvetta is distributed in the Himalayan foothills from Bhutan to Arunachal Pradesh, and in north-east India and Bangladesh east to northern Vietnam. It inhabits low elevations, affecting undergrowth in tropical forest, secondary forest and bamboo stands.

In Bhutan the Rufous-throated Fulvetta has been recorded just twice, both times in Royal Manas National Park. It was initially reported there during one of the early bird tours, without much detail (Inskipp 2001). The second record concerned a single seen very briefly within a mixed flock at 1,600 m in March[40,52]. Considering its range elsewhere in the subcontinent, this is an exceptionally high altitude and more data are needed to confirm its status in the Manas area.

# Rusty-capped Fulvetta
## Alcippe dubia

N=2(1)

The Rusty-capped Fulvetta is rare in the Indian subcontinent, known only from Bhutan and north-east India. Its main range is in Myanmar and southern China east to northern Vietnam. Habitat consists of fern and bramble understorey in open broadleaf forest.

In Bhutan the Rusty-capped Fulvetta is a rare resident, with just a single record. On 25 February 1995 three were observed between Gedu and Phuntsholing[19].

# Nepal Fulvetta
## Alcippe nipalensis

N=323(50). R 600-2000

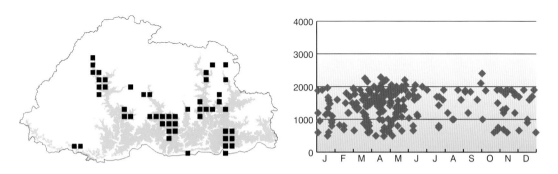

The Nepal Fulvetta has a similar distribution in the Indian subcontinent as Rufous-winged Fulvetta, from central Nepal east to Arunachal Pradesh and in north-east India and Bangladesh, thence to Myanmar. Also, in habitat choice it is very close to Rufous-winged Fulvetta, affecting undergrowth in moist broadleaf forest, albeit principally at lower altitudes.

In Bhutan this fulvetta is a common resident throughout the foothills and in the Sunkosh, central and eastern valleys, with one record from the western valleys[52,53]. It occurs at 600–2,000 m, with no obvious altitudinal movements. The highest record is from 2,400 m in October[29]. In September–March it occurs in flocks of up to 20 and is one of the most regular members of mixed-species flocks, with a few present in most of these. As a breeder it is rather inconspicuous, due to its skulking behaviour and rarely noticed song. In consequence there are no confirmed breeding records. Based on the presence of pairs, a density of 1.4 territories per km was found near Zhemgang at 1,600–1,900 m[52].

# Rufous-backed Sibia
## Heterophasia annectans

N=18(4). R 600-1400 (broadleaf forest)

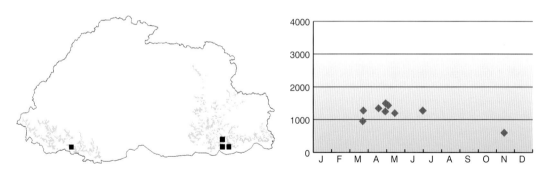

The Rufous-backed Sibia is a scarce resident of the Himalayas from eastern Nepal to Arunachal Pradesh and the hills of north-east India, as well as further east to northern Vietnam. It inhabits dense, moist broadleaf forest in the subtropical and temperate zones, where it frequents the top canopy.

In Bhutan the Rufous-backed Sibia is uncommon and local in the western and eastern valleys and the eastern foothills, where it occurs at 1,000–1,400 m, in areas with well-developed broadleaf forest. Its range is complementary to that of Rufous Sibia, which occupies higher levels. Possibly some altitudinal movement occurs, as suggested by a winter record at 600 m[31]. Occurrence in the above areas is rather irregular and a maximum of just two has been found in spring. However, at least ten were observed between Kamji and Phuntsholing in December[53], suggesting that it is commoner and generally overlooked because of its habit of keeping to the tops of large trees. Breeding was confirmed by the collecting of an egg-laying female at 1,400 m on 28 April[1].

# Rufous Sibia
## *Heterophasia capistrata*

N=1149(97). S 1600-3000 (May-mid-Nov); W 800-3000

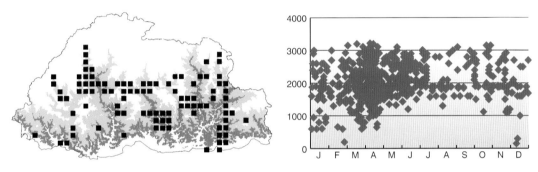

The Rufous Sibia is distributed in the Himalayas from Pakistan to western Arunachal Pradesh. It inhabits temperate forest, with a preference for oak, and frequents the midstorey.

In Bhutan this sibia is abundant throughout the temperate zone, where it is probably the commonest forest bird, although associated with areas of good forest cover. In the east it approaches the eastern limit of its range, but is apparently no less common than in the west. Its summer range spans 1,600–3,000 m, with occasional records to 3,200 m, largely coinciding with the extent of oak. In winter it is present throughout the same range, and disperses to 800 m into the foothills, occasionally to 200 m. However, numbers descending below 1,600 m are small and only a fraction of the population. The summer range is occupied from late March, while birds descend to lower elevations in November. Song is heard year-round occasionally, but most vocal activity is in April–August, when birds occupy territories, with a clear peak around mid-May. Near Zhemgang a density of 13 territories per km was found at 1,600–1,900 m[52], the highest density of all species in the area. Birds carrying nest material were seen at *c*.2,200 m on 15 April[1] and at 2,900 m on 13 May[22], which could suggest later breeding at higher altitudes. A recently fledged juvenile was noted at 2,000 m on 24 June[52]. In October–March it forms flocks ranging from several to 20 birds. These occasionally join mixed flocks of warblers and babblers, although generally the association is rather loose and mostly a result of the bird's omnipresence. It frequently joins feeding flocks at fruiting or flowering trees, e.g. *Bombax*, in January.

Rufous Sibia
*Jan Wilczur*

# Long-tailed Sibia
## *Heterophasia picaoides*

N=69(18). S 400-1600 (Mar-Sep); W 400-1000 (broadleaf forest)

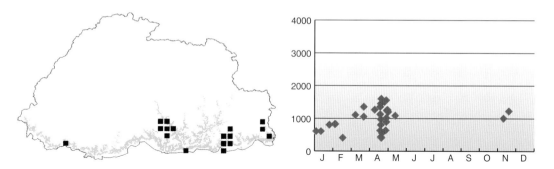

The Long-tailed Sibia occurs in the Himalayas from Sikkim to Arunachal Pradesh and in north-east India, its range continuing east to Vietnam and south through the Malay Peninsula to Sumatra. It inhabits tropical and subtropical forests, keeping mostly to the top canopy and frequently visiting flowering trees.

In Bhutan the Long-tailed Sibia is a common altitudinal migrant throughout the foothills and the central and eastern valleys. Occurrence is, however, limited to large areas of continuous broadleaf forest, particularly in the Deothang area, Samdrup Jongkha district, and the western slope of the Mangde Chhu valley near Zhemgang (Royal Manas and Jigme Singye Wangchuck National Parks). It is absent from higher parts of the Kuri Chhu valley, where low-altitude broadleaf forest is fragmented by Chir Pine and cultivation. The western foothills are close to its westernmost limits and it is scarce there, with only a single record from the Phuntsholing area[22]. In spring it occurs at 400–1,600 m, but in winter appears to withdraw largely below 1,000 m. In January it occasionally joins feeding flocks at flowering *Bombax*. Flocks may number up to 20, with a mean of eight and lacking a noticeable seasonal pattern. Presence of flocks until mid-May suggests a relatively late breeding season. However, there are no records of individuals or pairs from the period mid-May and October.

# Striated Yuhina
## *Yuhina castaniceps*

N=144(27). R 600-1400

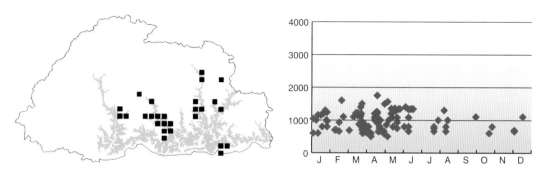

The Striated Yuhina is mostly found in fast-moving flocks working their way through the midstorey of forest. Its range includes the Himalayan foothills from Sikkim and north-east India east to northern Vietnam, as well as in Borneo. It occurs in various forest types in the tropical and subtropical zones.

In Bhutan the Striated Yuhina is an occasionally recorded resident of the central and eastern valleys and foothills. Further west it is scarce, with only a few records from the western valleys where it approaches its westernmost limits. It occurs at 600–1,400 m, occasionally to 1,600 m, and is extremely gregarious year-round, being primarily found in flocks larger than ten. The largest flocks are noted in August–February (mean 20), which disband in March–April (mean 15), reaching lowest numbers in May–July, the presumed breeding season (mean eight). The largest flocks number *c*.40. They rarely join mixed flocks of warblers and small babblers. No breeding evidence is available.

# White-naped Yuhina
## *Yuhina bakeri*

N=185(29). S 1400-2000 (May-Oct); W 600-2000 (broadleaf forest)

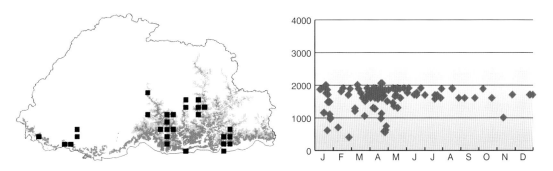

The White-naped Yuhina has a restricted range in the Himalayas from eastern Nepal to Arunachal Pradesh, north-east India, south-west China and northern Myanmar. Habitat comprises broadleaf subtropical forest.

White-naped Yuhina
*Craig Robson*

In Bhutan the White-naped Yuhina is only occasionally recorded, mainly in the foothills and central and eastern valleys, with isolated records from the western valleys. It occupies a relatively narrow altitudinal range in summer (1,400–2,000 m), where it particularly prefers mature broadleaved forest. In winter it remains present in this range, but disperses to 600 m, occasionally 400 m. From mid-October to late March it occurs in flocks of 5–10, with occasionally larger flocks of up to 30. Maximum flock size is 35[22,49]. It rarely associates with mixed flocks of warblers and babblers. Largest concentrations are noted in January, with a max. 80 in a day[28]. During April flocks gradually disband and pairs form, whilst birds largely withdraw from lower elevations. A pair carrying nest material was noted at 600 m on 26 April[22]. Near Zhemgang a density of 0.6 breeding pairs per km was found at 1,600–1,900 m[52]. Highest numbers are noted in protected areas, revealing the species to be a good indicator of habitat quality. Bhutan probably holds an important population of this restricted-range species, given the vast areas of intact forest over its altitudinal range, some within protected areas.

# Whiskered Yuhina
## *Yuhina flavicollis*

N=852(83). S 1600-2800 (May-Oct); W 1000-2800

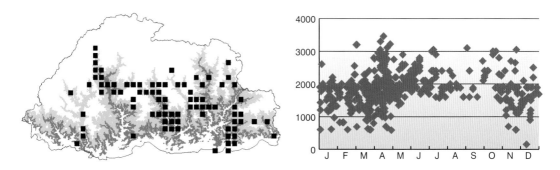

The Whiskered Yuhina is the commonest *Yuhina* in the Himalayas. It ranges from Himachal Pradesh to Arunachal Pradesh and north-east India to northern Vietnam. It inhabits broadleaf forest and second growth in the subtropical and temperate zones.

In Bhutan the Whiskered Yuhina is abundant and one of the commonest birds in broadleaf forest in the temperate zone, where it occurs throughout, as well as in the foothills. In summer it occurs at 1,600–2,800 m, occasionally to 3,200 m, with the highest record from 3,450 m in April[19]. In winter it remains present in the main range but also reaches 1,000 m from early November, occasionally 600 m. Birds move to the summer range during April, with the last gone from lower elevations by early May. In April winter flocks gradually disband and pairs form, the first carrying nest material noted at 1,900 m on 17 April, with subsequent records throughout May[52]. On 8 May faeces being carried from the nest was observed at the same altitude[52], thus confirming breeding. By mid-August family groups form larger flocks, which are noted throughout autumn and winter, until March. These regularly number 5–10, but can be as large as 50. They usually do not form mixed flocks with other species. Abundance is shown by day totals regularly in excess of 50 in spring, with up to 200 in the forests between Namling and Yonkhola, Mongar district[28]. Near Zhemgang a density of 2.3 breeding pairs per km was found at 1,600–1,900 m[52], with highest numbers in the upper part of this range.

# Stripe-throated Yuhina
## *Yuhina gularis*

N=401(68). S 2400-3400 (mid-May-mid-Oct); W 1600-3400

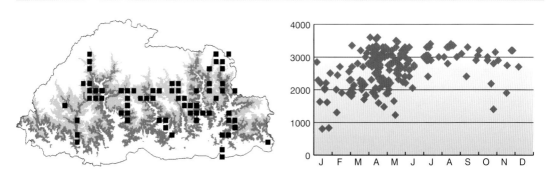

The Stripe-throated Yuhina is found in the Himalayas from Uttar Pradesh to Arunachal Pradesh and into north-east India. Its range extends east to Sichuan and northern Vietnam. Habitat is temperate forest, where it feeds on the nectar of rhododendrons, amongst other sources.

In Bhutan this yuhina is an abundant altitudinal migrant in the temperate and alpine zones and the eastern foothills. Its summer range spans 2,400–3,400 m, occasionally to 3,600 m. In winter it remains present in this range and also moves lower, reaching 1,600 m and occasionally 800 m. The first records at such altitudes are in October, but mostly after January. From lower elevations it gradually moves upslope, following the season of flowering of rhododendrons at progressively higher altitudes. In February it also feeds on sugar-rich saps from bark, together with Whiskered and Rufous-vented Yuhinas. In winter flocks it usually occurs with Rufous-vented Yuhina, being outnumbered by the latter, although up to 20 occur in these flocks, which form in January and disband by mid-April. The rest of the year birds are more dispersed in high-elevation forests, where the species is one of the commonest birds, with several tens sometimes found in a morning. Breeding is confirmed by the observation of a bird attending a nest with young at 3,300 m on 8 August[52].

Stripe-throated Yuhina
*Chris Orgill*

# Rufous-vented Yuhina
## *Yuhina occipitalis*

N=332(69). S 2400-3400 (May-Oct); W 1600-3400

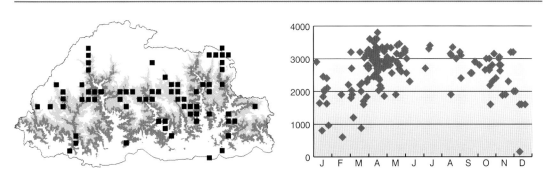

The Rufous-vented Yuhina is a bird of temperate forest, distributed in the Himalayas from central Nepal to Arunachal Pradesh, and ranging east to northern Myanmar. It favours oak–rhododendron forest, and like Stripe-throated Yuhina it frequently feeds on flower nectar.

The distribution of the Rufous-vented Yuhina is an exact copy of that of Stripe-throated Yuhina. It is a common altitudinal migrant throughout the temperate and alpine zones and the eastern foothills. It also shows similar altitudinal movements. The main range spans 2,400–3,400 m, with occasional records to 3,800 m[19]. From late October to late April it is also noted down to 1,600 m, with occasional records even lower, exceptionally at *c.*400 m in December[52]. In winter it frequently associates with Stripe-throated Yuhina, feeding on rhododendron and other flowering trees, and makes a similar gradual movement to higher altitudes, following the flowering season of rhododendron. Numbers in flocks are generally larger than those of Stripe-throated Yuhina, with up to 40 present. Winter flocks disband in mid-April and birds are subsequently found in pairs. Only in December do family groups aggregate in larger flocks again. In the breeding areas it appears somewhat more thinly distributed than Stripe-throated Yuhina, although several tens are noted in a day. There are no confirmed breeding records.

# Black-chinned Yuhina
## Yuhina nigrimenta

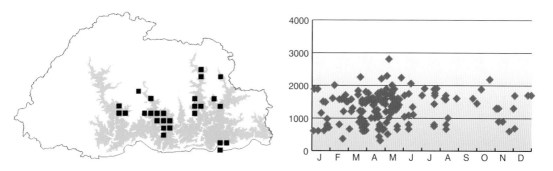

The Black-chinned Yuhina occurs mainly in the Himalayas east of Sikkim, as well as in north-east India. It is found west to Uttar Pradesh but is scarce and local in this part of its range. Further east it reaches northern Vietnam. It occurs in subtropical broadleaf forest and second growth.

In Bhutan the Black-chinned Yuhina is a common resident throughout the temperate zone and foothills, but scarcer in the west, which is already noticeable in the relatively small number of records from the Sunkosh Valley. In the western valleys and foothills, where it is very close to its westernmost limits, there are only single records. It is resident at 400–2,000 m, with more occasional presence to 300 m and 2,300 m, with one record at 2,800 m in May[49]. In August–March it occurs in flocks of 5–20, the largest numbering 30. In April these flocks disband and its remarkable song is heard. However, already by the end of the month records of flocks dominate again, probably of adults with fledged young. The same pattern, including the observation of singing birds, is repeated in May and July, pointing to multiple broods with well-synchronised timing. A pair with recently fledged young was observed at 1,600 m on 9 August[52].

# White-bellied Yuhina
## Yuhina zantholeuca

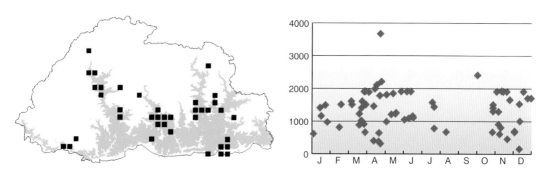

The White-bellied Yuhina is distributed in the Himalayas from Nepal to Arunachal Pradesh and in the hills of north-east India. It has a vast range in south-east Asia, from Taiwan to Borneo. Habitat is broadleaf forest, where it particularly affects the edge and open patches. It is less gregarious than other yuhinas.

In Bhutan the White-bellied Yuhina is occasionally recorded throughout the temperate zone and the foothills. It is resident at 400–2,000 m, with occasional presence to 200 m and 2,400 m, and one record at 3,650 m in May[22], exceptionally far from its normal altitudinal range. Year-round, it is mostly found singly. Unlike other yuhinas it is a frequent member of mixed-species flocks of small babblers and warblers, typically with a single bird present in a flock. The maximum number in a mixed flock is ten. A pair was observed carrying nest material at 1,800 m on 2 May[20].

# Fire-tailed Myzornis
*Myzornis pyrrhoura*                    N=89(30). S 2800-3600 (mid-Apr-Sep); W 1800-3000

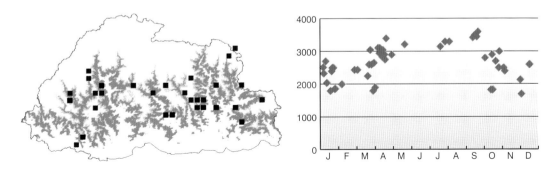

The Fire-tailed Myzornis occurs in the Himalayas from central Nepal to Arunachal Pradesh, its range extending east to northern Myanmar and south-west China. Summer habitat is rhododendron and juniper shrub and oak–rhododendron forest. It particularly feeds on flower nectar and insects attracted to it.

In Bhutan the Fire-tailed Myzornis is a frequently recorded altitudinal migrant, sparsely distributed throughout the temperate and alpine zones. Its summer altitudinal range spans 2,800–3,600 m, descending in winter to 1,800–3,000 m. It gradually ascends upslope again in March and appears to follow the season of rhododendron flowering, which touches progressively higher elevations during spring. There are relatively few records from its breeding areas, but the observation of a pair with two juveniles at 3,400 m on 12 September[49] suggests a relatively late breeding season. Downslope movement is apparent in October. It is mostly seen in small flocks of up to five. Larger flocks of 10–30 have been noted only at Dochu La, Thimphu district, in April and October. Remarkably, such concentrations are not noted elsewhere or in other months, and they possibly relate to the presence of an abundant seasonal food resource encountered during the course of their altitudinal migrations.

# Great Parrotbill
*Conostoma oemodium*                    N=44(18). R 2800-3400

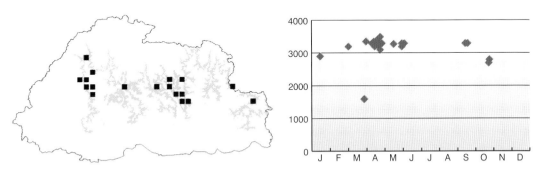

The Great Parrotbill occurs in the Himalayas between central Nepal and Arunachal Pradesh, though mostly from eastern Nepal to Bhutan. Its range continues further east to Yunnan and Sichuan. It is a specialist of ringal bamboo stands in fir or oak forests.

In Bhutan the Great Parrotbill is an uncommon resident of the Sunkosh, central and eastern valleys, with one record in the western valleys[22]. It occupies a rather narrow band between 2,800 m and 3,400 m, with a single record from 1,600 m[44]. The limited data suggest some degree of movement, with records below 3,000 m all in October–March. It is invariably encountered in small numbers, with 1–4 at a site. In habitat choice it shows a preference for open fir forest, dominated by extensive undergrowth of bamboo, such as is found around the Pele La and Yotong La passes.

317

# Brown Parrotbill
*Paradoxornis unicolor*

N=91(14). S 2000-3400 (Mar-Sep); W 2000-3000

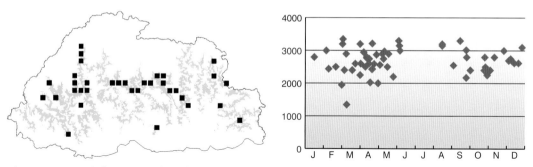

The Brown Parrotbill occurs in the Indian subcontinent in the Himalayas, mostly from eastern Nepal to Bhutan, with a more scattered presence in central Nepal and Arunachal Pradesh. Further east its range reaches northern Myanmar, Yunnan and Sichuan. Preferred habitat is dense bamboo at higher elevations, but it also occurs in scrub.

In Bhutan this parrotbill is frequently recorded but has a rather patchy distribution throughout the temperate zone. Its summer altitudinal range spans 2,000–3,400 m. In October–March it withdraws below 3,000 m, with a single record from 1,400 m in March[44]. In habitat choice it appears to favour open areas with patches of higher, ungrazed bamboo, and is found in such habitat particularly in the Bumthang Valley and on Pele La, Wangdue Phodrang district. Elsewhere it also occurs in scrub in open forest, particularly in winter when its distribution appears somewhat wider. Year-round it is mostly found in small flocks of up to five, but in winter, particularly December–March, up to 25 may occur together. From late April to June there are regular records of singles or pairs, which is the only evidence for its breeding season.

# Grey-headed Parrotbill
*Paradoxornis gularis*

N=25(8). R 1000-1800

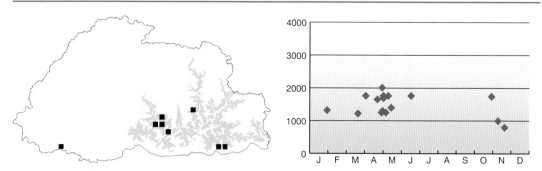

The Grey-headed Parrotbill occurs in the Himalayas from West Bengal to Arunachal Pradesh and in north-east India, continuing east to northern Vietnam. It is a bird of the lower strata of broadleaf forest in the subtropical zone, less associated with bamboo and more arboreal than other parrotbills.

In Bhutan the Grey-headed Parrotbill is uncommon and erratic, with records spread over the central and eastern valleys and the western and eastern foothills, but rarely from the same sites in multiple years. It has been found at 1,000–1,800 m, with the limited data suggesting some altitudinal movements. The lowest record is from 800 m[31] and the highest at 2,000 m[22]. In winter it is mostly noted in flocks of up to ten. Observations near Zhemgang in 2001 illustrate the species' erratic nature. From early April a flock of *c*.10 was present in the area at *c*.1,700 m, followed by the observation of a pair carrying nest material on 1 May. In October a flock of 30 was present, suggesting that the birds had bred at the site in a cluster of around five pairs that year[52]. There are, however, no records from this site in other years, despite regular observations. The habitat consisted of dry, but well-developed broadleaf forest on a steep slope, with dense scrub undergrowth and some bamboo.

# Fulvous Parrotbill
## *Paradoxornis fulvifrons*

N=26(11). R 3000-3400

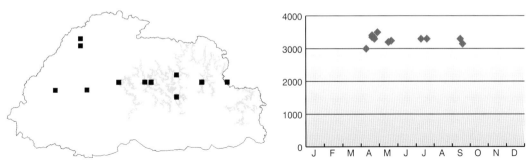

The Fulvous Parrotbill is a small, high-altitude parrotbill, closely associated with stands of dense bamboo. It has a scattered distribution in the Himalayas from central Nepal to Arunachal Pradesh, its range continuing north-east to Sichuan and Yunnan.

In Bhutan the Fulvous Parrotbill is uncommon, known from scattered localities in the high west and the central and eastern valleys, with occasional records from the Sunkosh and western valleys. It appears to be resident in an extremely narrow altitude band (3,000–3,400 m), affecting dense bamboo in open fir forest. Regular sites appear to be the trail between Gasa and Koina in Punakha district, the Yotong La pass, and the ridge between the Lhuntse and Trashi Yangtse valleys. At the former a pair was found carrying nest material on 24 April[39]. Its scarcity contrasts with the large numbers in winter flocks in November–April, when almost all records concern flocks of 25–40. From mid-April to May there are records of pairs and singles, indicating the onset of breeding.

# Black-throated Parrotbill
## *Paradoxornis nipalensis*

N=87(33). S 1600-2800 (Mar-Oct); W 1200-2400

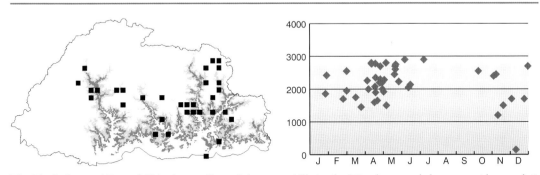

The Black-throated Parrotbill is the smallest of the parrotbills in the Himalayas and the most widespread. It occurs from eastern Nepal to Arunachal Pradesh, in north-east India, and more patchily west to Uttar Pradesh. Further east its range reaches south-west China and central Vietnam. Habitat comprises bamboo and dense undergrowth in cool broadleaf forest.

In Bhutan this parrotbill is a frequently recorded altitudinal migrant, found mainly in the temperate zone from the Sunkosh Valley east. There is an isolated record from the western valleys[43], where the species approaches its westernmost limits. Regular sites holding winter flocks of up to 50 are the Dochu La pass, the Zhemgang area and the forests between Namling and Yonkhola, Mongar district. The summer range is largely located in the cool broadleaf forest zone, at 1,600–2,800 m, but it also occurs in hemlock and mixed forests at these altitudes. In winter it is found at 1,200–2,400 m, with one record from the eastern foothills at *c*.200 m in December[44]. Altitudinal movements appear gradual and little pronounced, birds vacating lower areas by April and dispersing down in November. In November–April it is usually found in flocks of 5–20, which restlessly move through bamboo patches and forest undergrowth. It rarely associates with mixed flocks.

# Lesser Rufous-headed Parrotbill
*Paradoxornis atrosuperciliaris*                          N=11(6). R 600-1800

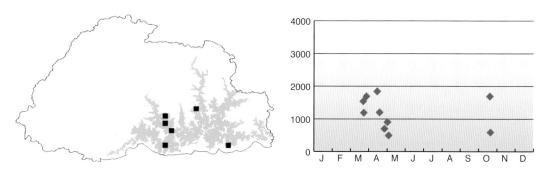

The Lesser Rufous-headed Parrotbill is a scarce and localised resident of the Himalayan foothills from West Bengal to Arunachal Pradesh and the hills of north-east India. Further east its range reaches Yunnan and northern Vietnam. Habitat consists of bamboo and scrub in tropical and subtropical forests. In the Indian subcontinent two distinct subspecies occur: *oatesi* was previously known only from Sikkim, from specimens taken in the19th century, but has recently been rediscovered in Bhutan. Subspecies *atrosuperciliaris* occurs in north-east India.

In Bhutan the Lesser Rufous-headed Parrotbill is a rare resident. The subspecies is *oatesi*, and was discovered in Bhutan in spring 1993[22,26]. However, a bird showing a black eyebrow, diagnostic of *atrosuperciliaris*, was observed together with two birds lacking such an eyebrow[52], suggesting that Bhutanese birds might, to some degree, be intermediate between the two races. In any case, there appears to be considerable variation and identification is complicated, with a risk of confusion with Greater Rufous-headed Parrotbill. Most records of Lesser Rufous-headed Parrotbill are from the Zhemgang area in the central valleys, where it was intially discovered. There are occasional records from the central foothills[22,29] and the eastern valleys[19]. The altitudinal range spans 600–1,800 m, largely overlapping with that of Greater Rufous-headed Parrotbill. Below 1,000 m, where Greater Rufous-headed Parrotbill is absent, it appears to be associated with extensive stands of large bamboo *Dendrocalamus* spp. In this habitat it is reported in mixed flocks with White-hooded Babbler. At higher elevations it also tends to associate with mixed flocks, particularly of Coral-billed Scimitar Babbler. It is rather gregarious, being mostly found in flocks of 3–20.

# Greater Rufous-headed Parrotbill
*Paradoxornis ruficeps*                     N=75(11). R 1000-2000 (broadleaf forest)

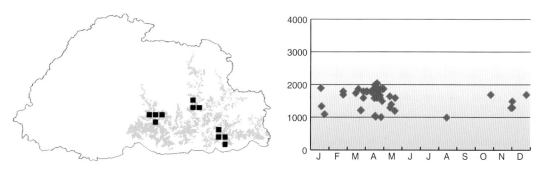

The Greater Rufous-headed Parrotbill occurs in the Himalayas from Darjeeling to Arunachal Pradesh and in north-east India. Further east its range reaches northern Vietnam. It inhabits the tropical and subtropical zones, affecting bamboo and undergrowth in forest.

In Bhutan the Greater Rufous-headed Parrotbill is uncommon and is localised in the central and eastern valleys, being known from just three localities: the Zhemgang area, between Namling and Yonkhola, Mongar district, and the Deothang area, Samdrup Jongkha district. It is resident at 1,000–2,000 m, preferring patches of bamboo dominated by smaller species, but contained within extensive stretches of old-growth forest. During most of the year it occurs in flocks of 5–20, which often form mixed-species flocks, particularly with Rufous-fronted Barwing and Coral-billed Scimitar Babbler. In May singles are seen, which is the only indication of timing of the breeding season. The maximum encountered in a day is 45[28].

# Lesser Whitethroat
## Sylvia curruca

N=1(1)

The Lesser Whitethroat has a vast breeding range from Europe to East Asia, occurring primarily as a winter visitor to the western Indian subcontinent.

In Bhutan the Lesser Whitethroat is a vagrant recorded just once: on 16 May 2002 a single near Dorji Gompa, Trongsa district at 2,500 m[52].

# Rufous-winged Bushlark
## Mirafra assamica

N=2(1)

The Rufous-winged Bushlark is distributed along the northern, and north-east to southern edge of the Indian subcontinent. Further east its range reaches Myanmar. It is a bird of open grassy areas.

In Bhutan the Rufous-winged Bushlark has only been found in the foothills at Phuntsholing, in February 1995 and April 1998, when 2–3 were present[19].

# Greater Short-toed Lark
## Calandrella brachydactyla

N=5(5)

The Greater Short-toed lark breeds from southern Europe in a broad band across Central Asia to northern China, reaching the Tibetan Plateau in the south. It is a common winter visitor to northern and western India, and is less widespread in the north-east. It is a bird of open grassland and fields, forming flocks in winter.

In Bhutan the Greater Short-toed Lark is a rare passage migrant, with five records from April[19,52,53] and October[17,22]. Spring passage appears concentrated in the second week of April, while autumn records are from the last week of October. It has occurred in Thimphu, Wangdue Phodrang and Bumthang valleys. Two records concerned a flock of c.30[17,19], showing that larger numbers sometimes reach Bhutan. However, the main axis of migration into the Indian peninsula appears to be further west in the Himalayas and through the Indus Valley.

# Hume's Short-toed Lark
## Calandrella acutirostris

N=2(2)

Hume's Short-toed Lark breeds from northern Iran east through Pakistan to the Tibetan Plateau, and in winter migrates to the northern Indian subcontinent, primarily to Madhya Pradesh and southern Nepal.

In Bhutan Hume's Short-toed Lark is a rare passage migrant, with two records from October 1973[1] and May 1996[22], respectively from Jangothang, Paro district, and Gyetsa, Bumthang district. The former concerned a flock of c.20.

# Sand Lark
*Calandrella raytal*                                                    N=5(1)

The Sand Lark occurs along the Indus and Ganges river systems of Pakistan, India and Bangladesh, as well as in the Assam plains. Further east it occurs along large rivers in Myanmar, and in the west reaches eastern Iran. It inhabits sand and mudbanks of large rivers.

In Bhutan the Sand Lark is an uncommon resident, localised along the Torsa Chhu at Phuntsholing[1,19,22], where it has been found in March, April and November, with up to 20 present. These are probably part of a larger resident population in northern India.

# Oriental Skylark
*Alauda gulgula*                         N=177(40). S 2200-3600 (mid-Apr-Oct); W 1400-3200

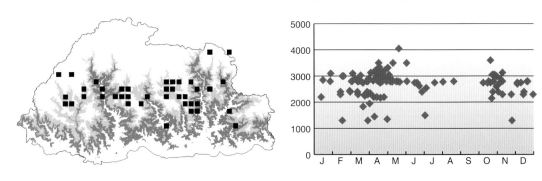

The Oriental Skylark is widespread in southern Asia, from the Central Asian republics and Iran eastwards to most of China and Taiwan. It is a resident throughout the Indian subcontinent, the numbers augmented in winter by birds from southern Tibet and southern China. Habitat is upland pasture and cultivation.

In Bhutan the Oriental Skylark is common both as a breeder and winter visitor. The ornithological expeditions of the 1960s and 1970s collected two subspecies in Bhutan: *inopinata* and *vernayi*, both originating from southern and south-east Tibet. The former is from October/November in the Bumthang Valley, the latter from the Trashigang area in February/March[1]. Both are probably winter visitors to Bhutan. However, there are summer records throughout the temperate zone, indicating the presence of breeders. These birds are, however, unidentified to subspecies. In summer it is found at 2,200–3,600 m, with the highest record from 4,000 m[22]. In winter it occurs at 1,400–3,200 m. It probably breeds throughout the temperate zone where there is suitable grassland. The open Phobjikha and Bumthang valleys at *c.*2,800 m are well-known sites, where singing birds can be heard in spring and summer. The first birds are heard in the second half of March and remain regular in these valleys until July. The presence of singing birds establishes it as a probable breeder in Bhutan. Winter flocks regularly number more than 50 between late October and mid-March, when such flocks are frequent in the Phobjikha Valley, the Bumthang area, Thimphu Valley and near Wangdue Phodrang.

# Yellow-vented Flowerpecker
*Dicaeum chrysorrheum*                                                  N=5(3)

The Yellow-vented Flowerpecker occurs throughout mainland south-east Asia to the Greater Sundas in the south, its range just reaching the Indian subcontinent, where it is common in the hills of north-east India south of the Brahmaputra, with a few records from the Himalayan foothills between central Nepal and Bhutan. Habitat is open forest, forest edge and orchards.

In Bhutan the Yellow-vented Flowerpecker has been recorded five times. Singles have been found near Samdrup Jongkha at 200–400 m[14,28]. Near Zhemgang three were found in the village of Zurphey at 1,200 m[52] in mandarin trees within a mixed flock of Oriental White-eyes. The timing of records, in January and April, suggests that its presence involves strays dispersing along the foot of the Himalayas in the non-breeding season.

# Yellow-bellied Flowerpecker
## Dicaeum melanoxanthum

N=20(14). R 600-3000

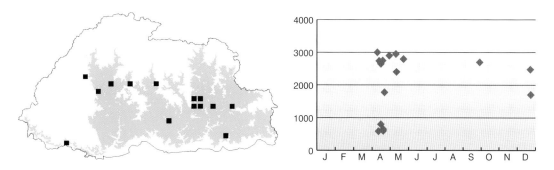

The Yellow-bellied Flowerpecker occurs in the Himalayas from central Nepal to Arunachal Pradesh and in the hills of north-east India, but is generally scarce and local. Its range extends east in a narrow band to northern Vietnam. It is a bird of broadleaf forest, subject to altitudinal migration.

In Bhutan this flowerpecker is uncommon, occurring thinly but widely, in the Sunkosh, central and eastern valleys, and the western foothills, with an isolated record from the western valleys[22]. Given the limited number of records, its altitudinal movements are difficult to assess. However, the concentration of records in mid-April at 600–800 m, and from mid-April to May at 2,600–3,000 m, might well indicate marked altitudinal movements, the bird wintering below and summering above the range of the commoner Fire-breasted Flowerpecker. Numbers are invariably low, with mostly singles reported and a max. 4 together.

# Plain Flowerpecker
## Dicaeum concolor

N=39(20). R 200-1600

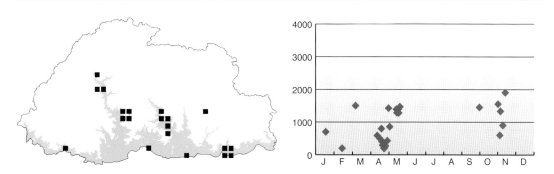

The Plain Flowerpecker ranges widely in south-east Asia, reaching the Indian subcontinent in the west. It occurs in the Himalayas from central Nepal to Arunachal Pradesh and in north-east India, with another population in the hills of south-west India. It occurs at edges and clearings in broadleaf forest, associating particularly with *Loranthus* epiphytes.

In Bhutan the Plain Flowerpecker is uncommon and has a relatively scattered distribution, in the foothills and the Sunkosh and central valleys, with an isolated record from the eastern valleys[28]. It is resident at 200–1,600 m, with the highest record from 1,900 m in November[52]. A max. 4 has been found at a site[19].

# Fire-breasted Flowerpecker
*Dicaeum ignipectus*                    N=523(75). S 1000-2600 (Apr-Oct); W 600-2400

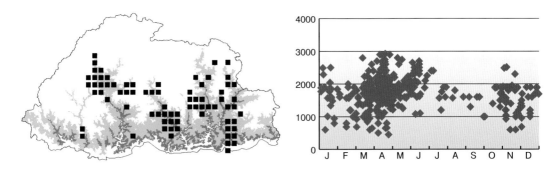

The Fire-breasted Flowerpecker is widespread in south-east Asia, reaching Taiwan and the Philippines in the east and Sumatra in the south. In the Indian subcontinent it occurs in the Himalayas from Kashmir to Arunachal Pradesh and in the hills of north-east India, where it is generally the commonest flowerpecker. Habitat is broadleaf forest, particularly with *Loranthus*-infested trees.

In Bhutan the Fire-breasted Flowerpecker is abundant throughout the temperate zone and in the western and central foothills, but is relatively scarce in the western valleys, where conifer forest dominates the upper part of its altitudinal range. It shows some altitudinal movement, with its summer range at 1,000–2,600 m, occasionally to 2,900 m, and reaching the upper limit of broadleaf forest, and in winter moving slightly lower, to 600–2,400 m. Singing birds are noted from February to early August, but peak vocal activity is in early April to mid-May. Near Zhemgang a density of 3.9 territories per km was found at 1,600–1,900 m[52]. It is usually found singly or a few together, keeping to the treetops, and only occasionally associating with mixed flocks of warblers and sunbirds.

# Scarlet-backed Flowerpecker
*Dicaeum cruentatum*                    N=12(12). R 200-2400

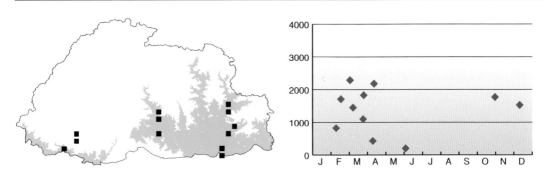

The Scarlet-backed Flowerpecker is found over large parts of south-east Asia south to Sumatra and Borneo. It reaches the eastern Indian subcontinent, where it occurs in north-east India and Bangladesh, and sparsely in the Himalayan foothills in Nepal and Bhutan. Like other flowerpeckers it prefers broadleaf forest with *Loranthus*.

In Bhutan this flowerpecker is rare and mainly known from records in the 1960s and 1970s, since when there is only one record. In April 2001 a pair was observed above Samdrup Jongkha at 400 m[19]. The near lack of recent records suggests a decline since the 1960s, for unknown reasons. In the 1960s it was found to be resident at 200–2,400 m[1] in the western and eastern foothills and the central and eastern valleys, with isolated records in the western valleys. There is an observation of a pair with juveniles in June at 200 m[20], establishing it as a confirmed (but possibly former) breeder.

# Ruby-cheeked Sunbird
## *Anthreptes singalensis*

The Ruby-cheeked Sunbird's main range is in mainland south-east Asia south to parts of Indonesia. In the subcontinent it is found in the Himalayan foothills from central Nepal to Arunachal Pradesh and north-east India. It inhabits open evergreen forest.

In Bhutan this sunbird is rare, with just three records from the central and eastern foothills (Gelephu, Manas and Samdrup Jongkha), where it has been found to 400 m in April[1,22].

# Purple Sunbird
## *Nectarinia asiatica*

The Purple Sunbird is one of the commonest sunbirds in the subcontinent, but absent from the north-east, its range just reaching Bhutan. Outside the subcontinent it occurs in Iran and over most of mainland south-east Asia. In Nepal and India it reaches altitudes of 2,100 m and 1,700 m respectively in the Himalayas in summer.

In Bhutan the Purple Sunbird is rare and records are confined to the western and eastern foothills, with one from the central valleys[29]. The April and May records[5] are mostly from *c*.200 m and possibly concern breeders. In the non-breeding season it apparently disperses higher, with the highest record at 1,400 m in September[29].

# Mrs Gould's Sunbird
## *Aethopyga gouldiae*

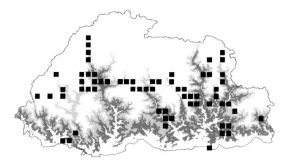
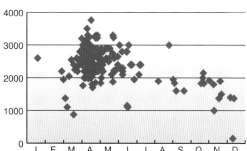

Mrs Gould's Sunbird occurs in the Indian subcontinent only in the Himalayas. Further east it reaches Sichuan and northern mainland south-east Asia. Habitat is forest with flowering trees and shrubs, particularly rhododendron, where it feeds primarily on nectar, supplemented with insects and spiders.

Mrs Gould's Sunbird is frequent in Bhutan, being found throughout the temperate zone and in the western and eastern foothills. It is an altitudinal migrant, occurring at 1,800–3,200 m in summer and 1,000–2,600 m in winter, with single records at *c*.200 m[44] and 3,800 m[19]. Habitat is primarily broadleaf forest. It returns to its breeding range in March, and from August a gradual descent to the winter quarters is noticeable. It is typically found singly or in small flocks, only occasionally associating with mixed flocks. Unlike other sunbirds it does not gather in larger flocks at flowering trees, but probably tends to exploit more scattered food sources in the forest such as flowering rhododendrons. Nevertheless, particularly in April, it can be encountered commonly, with a single-day max. of 40[14]. Evidence of breeding is provided by the observation of a nest at 1,800 m on 2 May[49].

# Green-tailed Sunbird
## *Aethopyga nipalensis*

N=554(78). S 1600-3400 (Apr-Jul); W 1200-2600

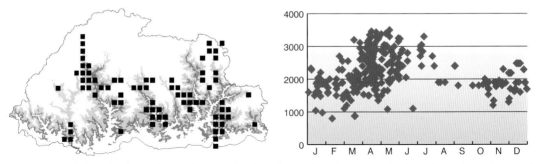

The Green-tailed Sunbird is widespread in mainland south-east Asia, but occurs in the Indian subcontinent only in the Himalayas. It is a bird of oak–rhododendron forest and mixed broadleaf–conifer forest.

The Green-tailed Sunbird is one of the most abundant members of the Bhutan avifauna, being found throughout the temperate zone and in the eastern foothills. It is an altitudinal migrant, occupying much the same range as Mrs Gould's Sunbird. It summers at 1,600–3,400 m and winters at 1,200–2,600, occasionally to 800 m. Unlike Mrs Gould's Sunbird, it gathers in larger flocks in winter, involving 5–10 and sometimes up to 20, normally within mixed flocks of warblers and small babblers. It also appears in numbers at flowering trees, often with yuhinas. An exceptionally large winter flock of 100 was observed in the forests in the east of Thrumshingla National Park[22,49]. In February–April there is a gradual movement to the breeding areas, appearing to follow the rhododendron flowering season, which starts progressively later at higher elevations. In autumn there is a gradual descent commencing around August. Although birds tend to linger at lower elevations throughout spring, the breeding range appears to be at 2,000 m or above. In Zhemgang at 1,900 m it is definitely only a winter visitor[52]. A bird carrying faeces away from a nest was observed at 2,500 m on 16 May[52].

# Black-throated Sunbird
## *Aethopyga saturata*

N=503(65). R 600-2200

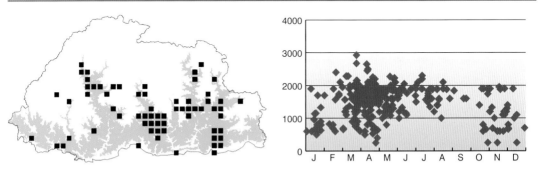

The Black-throated Sunbird has a somewhat more easterly distribution in the Himalayas than other *Aethopyga*. Further east it is found over much of mainland south-east Asia. Habitat is more open secondary forest at lower elevations, particularly shrubs in the undergrowth.

The Black-throated Sunbird is abundant in Bhutan and is found throughout the temperate zone and foothills, but is scarce in the western valleys. It is commonest in the central and eastern valleys, and is resident at 600–2,200 m, with occasional presence to 200 m and 2,800 m. Its breeding range is complementary to those of Mrs Gould's and Green-tailed Sunbirds, with a relatively sharp divide at *c*.2,000 m, at the upper limit of the warm broadleaf forest zone. It is mostly observed singly or in pairs and regularly joins mixed flocks. Territories are established from late March and occupied until late August. Pairs were found nest-building at

1,900 m on 9 April and at 2,100 m on 28 May[52]. Near Zhemgang a density of 3.3 breeding pairs was found at 1,600–1,900 m[52]. Although this establishes it as relatively common in the warm broadleaf forest zone, rarely more than ten are noted in a day, as it is relatively inconspicuous in its habits.

# Crimson Sunbird
## Aethopyga siparaja

N=87(26). R 200-1600

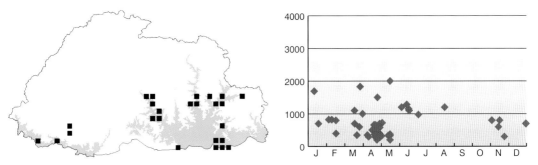

In the Indian subcontinent the Crimson Sunbird mainly occurs in the Himalayas. Among *Aethopyga* it occupies the lowest altitudinal range and is also patchily found in the plains and elsewhere in the subcontinent. It is widespread further east in south-east Asia, reaching the Philippines and Indonesia. It occurs in open habitats, particulary affecting gardens with flowering shrubs.

In Bhutan the Crimson Sunbird is a common resident in the western and eastern foothills and in the central and eastern valleys, with isolated records in the western valleys. The species's altitudinal range is from 200 to 1,600 m, occasionally reaching 2,000 m. It is regular in the forests between Deothang and Samdrup Jongkha, where it is found annually, with a single-day max. of 25[28]. As elsewhere in the subcontinent, it is frequent around habitation.

# Fire-tailed Sunbird
## Aethopyga ignicauda

N=110(46). S 2000-4000 (May-Sep); W 1000-2400

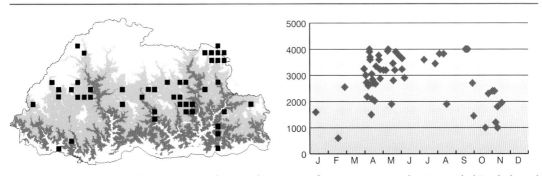

The Fire-tailed Sunbird is distributed over the Himalayan range from western Nepal to Arunachal Pradesh, and in the hills of north-east India to Myanmar and south-west China. Among the sunbirds it reaches the highest altitudes, breeding in scrub above the treeline and in high-altitude open forest.

In Bhutan the Fire-tailed Sunbird is a frequently recorded altitudinal migrant throughout the alpine and temperate zones and in the western and eastern foothills. Its summer range spans 2,000–4,000 m, although the breeding areas appear to be above 2,800 m. Records at low elevations in May probably involve late migrants. In winter it descends to 1,000 m, largely vacating areas above 2,400 m, with one record from *c*.600 m[31]. The ascent in March–April appears very gradual, apparently following the rhododendron flowering season, which starts later at higher altitudes. Flock size is generally small, with typically fewer than three together. In late April and early May larger concentrations of up to 15 are sometimes noted[5]. An exceptionally large gathering of *c*.100 has been noted in Bumdeling Wildlife Sanctuary[49]. As visits by birders to higher elevations in summer are few, the lack of confirmed breeding records is unsurprising.

# Little Spiderhunter
*Arachnothera longirostra*                                      N=18(4). R 400-600

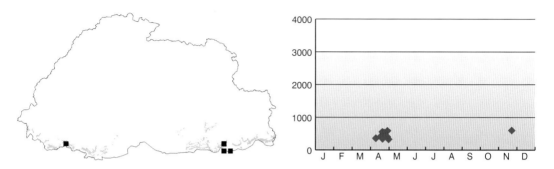

The Little Spiderhunter is extensively distributed in south-east Asia, reaching the Philippines and Greater Sundas. In the Indian subcontinent it is patchy, occurring in the hills of south-west and north-east India, and in the Himalayan foothills. Like Streaked Spiderhunter, it is particularly associated with banana trees, playing an important role in their pollination. It typically keeps to the lower storey of forest.

In Bhutan the Little Spiderhunter is an uncommon resident, found primarily in the eastern foothills, where it is recorded annually in spring between Samdrup Jongkha and Deothang, with a max. 6. There is one record from the western foothills, near Phuntsholing[5]. It occurs in a narrow altitudinal range at 400–600 m. A record from November[31] confirms it as resident in Bhutan.

# Streaked Spiderhunter
*Arachnothera magna*                         N=248(42). S 400-2000 (mid-Mar-Sep); W 200-1600

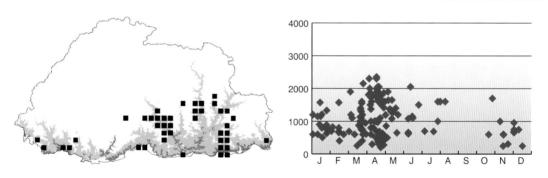

The Streaked Spiderhunter is widespread in mainland south-east Asia, reaching its westernmost limits in the Indian subcontinent, in north-east India and the Himalayas west to central Nepal. Habitat is tropical and subtropical broadleaf forest with dense undergrowth. It has a preference for feeding on the nectar of banana flowers, but also takes insects and spiders, and normally forages in the canopy.

In Bhutan this spiderhunter is a common altitudinal migrant throughout the foothills and the western, central and eastern valleys, with one record from the Sunkosh Valley, where it has probably been under-recorded. In summer it occurs at 400–2,000 m, being commonest below 1,600 m and occasionally reaching 2,400 m[19]. In winter it retreats to 200–1,600 m, but reaches the upper part of its range again during April, gradually descending from August. In January–February it is often found at flowering *Bombax* trees, sometimes in flocks of up to 30. There are no confirmed breeding records.

# House Sparrow
## *Passer domesticus*

N=83(16). R 200-2400 (agricultural areas)

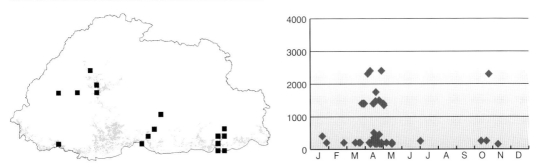

The House Sparrow's natural range stretches from Europe and North Africa to western Siberia, in the south including almost the entire Indian subcontinent and north-west mainland south-east Asia. Introduced populations thrive in many parts of the world. It is strictly commensal, breeding in cities, towns and small settlements.

In Bhutan the House Sparrow is a common resident, mainly in the Indian border towns and adjacent areas to 400 m, where it is the commonest sparrow, although numbers only run into tens of individuals. Indication of breeding is provided by birds carrying nest material in Samdrup Jongkha[1]. It occasionally occurs in towns within the temperate zone, with isolated records from Paro, Thimphu, Trongsa and villages in northern Samdrup Jongkha district, up to 2,400 m. In the Punakha/Wangdue Phodrang area, following initial records in 1994, 1997 and 1999, a total of *c*.20 was noted at various localities in spring 2001[19,33]. Further records in 2002[5] suggest an established breeding population. The frequency of reports from towns in the temperate zone appears to have increased in recent years, and further expansion seems likely.

# Russet Sparrow
## *Passer rutilans*

N=546(74). R 1400-3000

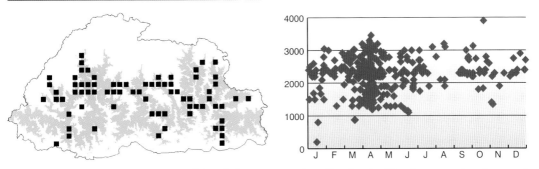

The Russet Sparrow is the most mobile of the sparrows breeding in the Himalayas, performing regular migrations. Its range spans the Himalayas from Pakistan to Arunachal Pradesh. Further north it occurs on the Tibetan Plateau and over large parts of east Asia, north to North Korea and Japan and south to northern Vietnam. Habitat includes habitations, but it also occurs in open forest.

The Russet Sparrow is an abundant resident, occupying the highest altitudinal range of the sparrows found in Bhutan. It is generally the most abundant sparrow in towns and villages above 2,100 m, with several tens often present. It occurs throughout the temperate zone at 1,400–3,000 m, with occasional records to 800 m and 3,400 m, the lowest from 200 m[20] and the highest at 3,900 m[31]. In September–January it gathers in flocks of up to 200, which forage in agricultural fields. In spring these flocks break into smaller ones and the birds appear more widespread, reaching the lower part of the species's altitudinal range. At this season it also appears more associated with open forest and scrub. There are no indications that longer-distance migrants reach Bhutan. Nests have been found in May–June[1,52], by which time the birds are mostly above 2,100 m.

# Eurasian Tree Sparrow
## Passer montanus

N=505(75). R 600-2800 (agricultural areas)

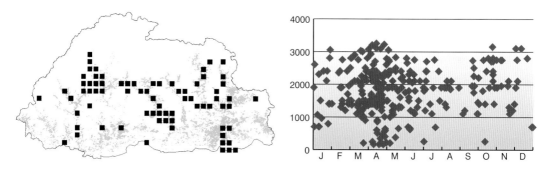

The Eurasian Tree Sparrow is widespread from Europe to East Asia and south to the Sundas. In the Indian subcontinent it occurs in Pakistan, in the Himalayas from Nepal to Arunachal Pradesh, and locally in north-east and eastern India. Like House Sparrow it is entirely associated with habitation but reaching higher altitudes.

The Eurasian Tree Sparrow is the most widespread of the sparrows in Bhutan and is abundant throughout the temperate zone and foothills. It is a numerous breeder in towns and villages in the warm broadleaf forest zone, with several tens even in small villages. Its regular altitudinal range spans 600–2,800 m, with occasional records to 200 m and 3,200 m. In the lower part of its range, it is outnumbered by House Sparrow only in the border towns. Above 2,100 m it is more sparsely distributed and Russet Sparrow starts to dominate. However, there is no sharp limit between the two, and breeding colonies of Tree Sparrows occur well above 2,100 m. Like Common Myna, it reaches highest altitudes in the Sunkosh Valley. It has multiple broods, with the first young fledging by mid-May at 1,900 m[52].

# Forest Wagtail
## Dendronanthus indicus

N=8(8)

The Forest Wagtail breeds in east Asia, from south-east Siberia south to Sichuan and Japan. It winters in mainland south-east Asia, the Philippines, the Greater Sundas and west to the Indian subcontinent, where it has bred in Assam, but is chiefly a winter visitor to north-east and south-west India. Habitat is shady broadleaf forest, where it affects trails and glades.

In Bhutan the Forest Wagtail is a rare passage migrant, with scattered records throughout the temperate zone and in the eastern foothills. It passes through during a short period from late April to late May, with the earliest record 24 April[27] and the latest 24 May[55]. There are no autumn records. It has been found at 400 m[27] to c.3,200 m[22], with a max. 2 at a site.

# White Wagtail
## Motacilla alba

N=531(92). S 1800-4000 (May-Aug); W 600-3000

The White Wagtail occurs throughout Eurasia from Iceland to Sakhalin, also just penetrating North America. Two subspecies breed in the Himalayas from Pakistan to Arunachal Pradesh. Elsewhere in the subcontinent it is a common winter visitor, with six subspecies originating from various parts of its range. Habitat is mainly streams and rivers, although it is less tied to wetland habitats than other wagtails.

In Bhutan the White Wagtail is abundant throughout the alpine and temperate zones and foothills. The subspecies *alboides* breeds and is the commonest subspecies throughout the year. Its summer range spans 1,800–4,000 m. A nest was found at 2,400 m on 27 April[20] and recently fledged young have been observed at 1,900 m on 2 May[49] and at 2,400 m on 20 and 26 June[52]. In the breeding season it is present in open areas near

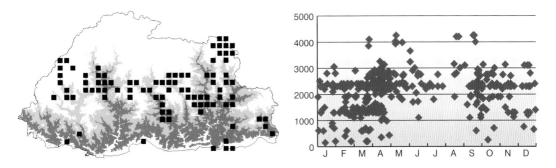

habitation in the Thimphu/Paro, Bumthang, Kuri Chhu and Drangme Chhu valleys, but seems to be largely absent as breeder in the Sunkosh Chhu and Mangde Chhu valleys, possibly occupying higher altitudes where it may have been overlooked. From September it disperses to 600 m, occasionally to 200 m. Migratory movement is marked by the appearance of birds outside their breeding range, such as the Zhemgang area. Numbers at the sewage ponds at Babesa, Thimphu district (2,300 m), increase from September, peaking in November at up to 100[52]. Numbers here are lowest in mid-April to August, during the breeding season. The increase in winter can partially be attributed to the presence of immatures from the local breeding population, but most probably also includes birds from higher areas. Some, however, remain present year-round at up to 3,200 m. Besides *alboides*, four other subspecies have been noted as passage migrants and/or winter visitors. The main passage periods are mid-March to early May and mid-August to October. Most high-altitude records up to 4,200 m in these periods concern passage migrants, although only *leucopsis* has been identified at high elevations[31]. Of the migrant subspecies, *leucopsis*, which breeds in western and northern China, Korea and Amurland, is the commonest. It is has been noted from mid-March to mid-April and mid-August to October. The somewhat rarer *ocularis*, *baicalensis* and *dukhunensis* appear to pass later, both in spring and autumn. Subspecies *ocularis*, breeding in eastern Siberia, passes in mid-September to early October. *Baicalensis*, breeding around Lake Baikal and in Mongolia, has been noted from mid-February to April and late September to October. *Dukhunensis*, breeding in western Siberia, occurs from late March to early May and in October. Thus, there appears to be a trend of subspecies with more easterly breeding ranges passing earlier. In addition, the more easterly breeding subspecies are relatively more frequently recorded in the eastern valleys, although all three are mostly noted in the Thimphu/Paro and Punakha/Wangdue Phodrang areas, where most suitable staging habitat is found. Subspecies *ocularis* has also been noted in winter, in January[43] in the Wangdue Phodrang area.

Forest Wagtail
*Brin Edwards*

# White-browed Wagtail
## Motacilla maderaspatensis

N=26(10). R 200-2400

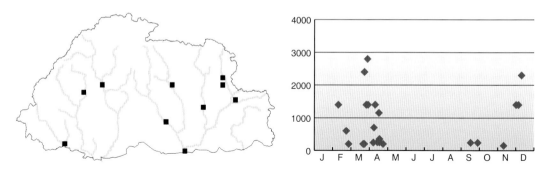

The White-browed Wagtail occurs over much of the Indian subcontinent except parts of the north-west, the north-east, the higher Himalayas and Sri Lanka. Habitats are lakes, rivers and pools.

In Bhutan the White-browed Wagtail is an uncommon resident, mostly noted in the western foothills, near Phuntsholing along the Torsa Chhu, and near Punakha in the Sunkosh Valley, with scattered records in the western, central and eastern valleys and the eastern foothills. It appears to be resident in the Phuntsholing area below 400 m and probably further east in the foothills to Manas, where it has been recorded once. Its presence higher up appears to be related to dispersal outside the breeding season. It reaches the Punakha area on a regular basis, but also moves along the Manas tributaries. At Punakha it is found in December–April, with a max. 4. The highest record is from 2,800 m in the Bumthang region[5]. At Phuntsholing a singing bird was observed[20], which is the only evidence of breeding. It is only ever found in small numbers[22].

# Citrine Wagtail
## Motacilla citreola

N=32(12). W 400-3000

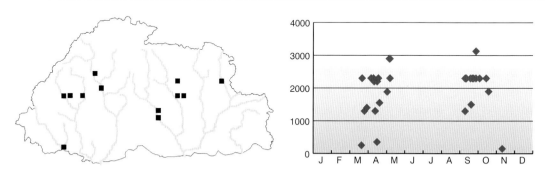

The Citrine Wagtail breeds from Eastern Europe across western and central Siberia from the Arctic Sea south to the Tibetan Plateau. Except for breeders in the north-west, it occurs in the northern Indian subcontinent only as a winter visitor, represented by three subspecies. Habitat consists of marshes and other wetlands.

In Bhutan this wagtail is an uncommon passage migrant, mostly through the western valleys and foothills, becoming gradually scarcer further east, with just one record from the eastern valleys[49]. It has been found over a broad altitudinal range, from 400 m to 3,000 m, suggesting direct crossing of the Himalayas. The highest record is from 3,300 m[3]. Spring passage is noted from the third week of March to the first week of May, and autumn passage from the second week of September to mid-October, with the latest record dated 9 November, at 200 m[22], which perhaps involved a wintering bird. The earliest spring record is from 20 March[1]. Records at this season are mostly of singles, often males in breeding plumage, permitting subspecific identification. The majority are of the subspecies *citreola*, from the north-east of its range, with one record of the more southerly *calcarata*[1]. In autumn it is commoner and found in small flocks at the sewage ponds at Babesa, Thimphu district, with a max. of 20[52].

Citrine Wagtail
*Brin Edwards*

# Yellow Wagtail
## *Motacilla flava*

N=12(6). W 1800-2600

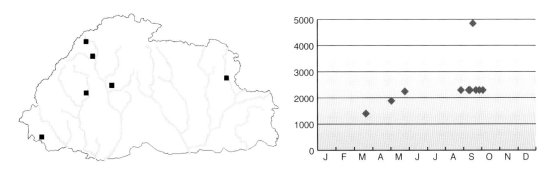

The Yellow Wagtail breeds across a vast zone from Europe to east Asia, and Alaska, its range extending south to Turkestan, Ladakh and Mongolia. It is a long-distance migrant, wintering in sub-Saharan Africa, southern and south-east Asia. In the Indian subcontinent it is a common and widespread winter visitor, represented by at least seven subspecies from various breeding areas between western Siberia and Kamchatka. Winter habitat consists of wetland margins.

In Bhutan the Yellow Wagtail is a rare passage migrant. Like Citrine Wagtail it passes principally through western Bhutan, with most records in the western valleys, followed by the Sunkosh Valley, and isolated records in the eastern valleys. It is found mostly at 1,800–2,600 m, reflecting the presence of favoured staging sites, but has been collected once at 4,850 m, on 16 September[1]. Spring records are few, the earliest being 20 March[26], the last 24 May[55]. In autumn occurrence is more regular, with the sewage ponds at Babesa, Thimphu district, a regular site in September, with a max. 8 there on 8 September[52]. The earliest autumn record is dated 26 August[43], the last 2 October[43,52]. Given the predominance of autumn records, when subspecies are very difficult to differentiate, it is unclear which subspecies pass through Bhutan. The only confirmed record is that of *taivana*, collected during the 1960s[1]. This ironically concerns a vagrant, as its regular winter quarters are outside the Indian subcontinent in eastern and southern parts of south-east Asia. There is one record of a probable *thunbergi*[55]. Passage of birds from different origins is probable as calls of different unidentified races have been noted at sewage ponds[52].

# Grey Wagtail
## Motacilla cinerea

N=273(67). W 400-2800

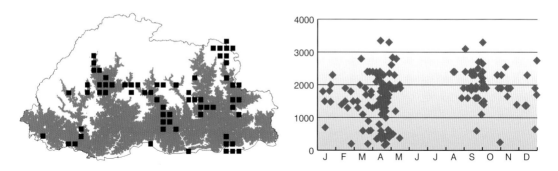

The Grey Wagtail breeds in montane areas from Western Europe to east Asia, including the north-west Indian subcontinent. It winters to the south, including most of the Indian subcontinent. Habitat consists of fast-flowing streams and rivers.

In Bhutan the Grey Wagtail is a common and widespread passage migrant and winter visitor throughout the temperate belt and foothills and in the high east. Its winter range spans 400–2,800 m, with occasional records to 200 m and 3,300 m. It is common along roadside ditches as well as by larger streams and rivers. The first migrants are noted by mid-August, the earliest record being 12 August[52]. Passage is particularly evident in September, with records at higher altitudes and widespread presence. Up to nine have been noted at a single site in this period[52]. In winter it appears to be more sparsely distributed, found particularly at 1,000–2,000 m. However, in this period considerable numbers can occur, e.g. c.10 near Kamji on 10 December[53]. From late March to mid-May spring passage is noted, particularly through observations at higher altitudes. However, it is markedly less common than on autumn passage. The latest spring record is 16 May[52].

# Richard's Pipit
## Anthus richardi

N=8(8)

Richard's Pipit breeds in southern Siberia, Mongolia and China. In the Indian subcontinent it is a widespread winter visitor to open grassland and cultivation.

In Bhutan this species is an uncommon passage migrant, with scattered records in the high west, the western, central and eastern valleys, and the western foothills. Most are noted in autumn, between mid-September and late October, at 2,600 m[22] to 4,800 m[1]. In spring it has been found between 200 m[19] and 2,100 m[19]. While records from 1 April[19] and 6 May[5] fit well into the period of spring migration reported elsewhere in the subcontinent (April–early May), a record at Phuntsholing on 25 February does not and this was probably a wintering bird. Almost all records are of singles, with one record involving three individuals[5].

# Paddyfield Pipit
## Anthus rufulus

N=21(8). R 200-1600

The Paddyfield Pipit is widespread in southern and south-east Asia, reaching the Philippines and Indonesia. It is common over most of the Indian subcontinent. In Nepal and India it is a common resident in the Himalayas up to 1,800 m. Habitat is grassland and cultivation.

In Bhutan the Paddyfield Pipit is an uncommon resident. Records are concentrated in the western and eastern foothills, in respectively the Phuntsholing and Samdrup Jongkha areas, as well as in the Sunkosh Valley around

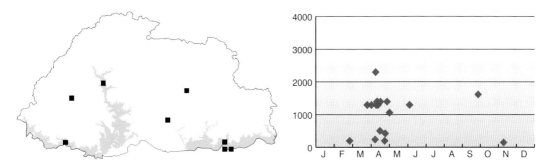

Punakha and Wangdue Phodrang. Elsewhere, there are isolated records in the western[19] and central valleys[22,14]. Its overall altitudinal range spans 200–1,600 m, with presence beyond the foothills probably seasonal. The highest record is from 2,300 m[19]. In the Punakha/Wangdue Phodrang area it probably breeds, as suggested by the observation of birds in song-flight in April[19] and June[52]. Numbers are invariably small, with a max. 3 at a site, which is in surprising contrast to its abundance elsewhere in the Himalayas.

# Tawny Pipit
## Anthus campestris
N=1(1)

The Tawny Pipit breeds from Europe east to Mongolia. In the Indian subcontinent it is a winter visitor, being common in the north-west but uncommon elsewhere. It inhabits open, dry habitats.

In the Tawny Pipit has been recorded once in Bhutan: on 26 November 1968 it was collected in Samtse, at 300 m[1].

# Blyth's Pipit
## Anthus godlewskii
N=9(7)

Blyth's Pipit breeds in east Asia, from southern Siberia to Mongolia and northern China. In the Indian subcontinent it is a widespread but probably under-recorded winter visitor. Habitat is open grassland and cultivation.

In Bhutan Blyth's Pipit is rare on migration. Between mid-September and early November it has been found around 2,400 m in the Thimphu Valley[22,52], at Phuntsholing at 250 m[22] and at 3,800 m in the Bumthang Valley[1]. The latter concerned a dead bird found during a sudden cold spell in October. In spring, passage appears to occur in the second half of April, with records at Bajo, Thimphu district, at c.1,300 m[27] and in the Deothang/Samdrup Jongkha area[28]. Possible wintering birds were recorded near Bongde, Paro district, at 2,300 m on 16 February [1]. The maximum number found at a site is three[52].

# Tree Pipit
## Anthus trivialis
N=3(3)

The Tree Pipit breeds from Europe east to Yakutia. It occurs in the Indian subcontinent as a winter visitor, found commonly east to Darjeeling but rarely further east to Assam. Habitat is open country with scattered trees.

In Bhutan the Tree Pipit is a rare passage migrant, with three records all from spring. On 21 March 1967 one was collected near Zhemgang at 1,100 m[1]. In 2001 singles were found in the eastern valleys on 19 April[28] and 27 April, the latter at 1,800 m[27].

# Olive-backed Pipit
*Anthus hodgsoni*

N=799(110). S 2000-3600 (mid-May-mid-Sep); W 600-3400

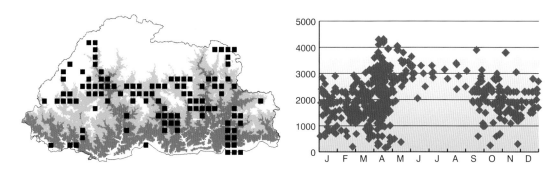

The Olive-backed Pipit breeds in Siberia, from the Urals east to Japan, with a separate population in the Himalayas, montane western China, southern China and northern Myanmar. In the Himalayas it breeds from Himachal Pradesh to Arunachal Pradesh, and is a winter visitor elsewhere. It frequents forest edge and clearings in open forest as well as scrub above the treeline. In winter it is, more than Tree Pipit, associated with forested habitat.

In Bhutan the Olive-backed Pipit is abundant throughout the alpine and temperate zones and the foothills. It summers at 2,000–3,600 m, with territorial birds observed singing in March–July. Ludlow reported numerous nests at 2,400–3,600 m[31]. Its presence is more occasional to 4,300 m, although it may have been under-recorded at higher levels. Singing birds have been noted to 4,100 m[52,53]. Wintering birds are present from September to early May at 600–3,400 m, occasionally to 200 m. In winter it occurs in small flocks, sometimes of up to 20. At the onset of the breeding season at higher elevations, wintering birds are still present at lower altitudes and remain until early May. These latter largely concern *yunnanensis*, which migrates to the Indian subcontinent from across the Himalayas and has been identified on a few occasions in spring[52]. The onset of winter is marked by individuals or small flocks of migrants appearing in September in early mornings and evenings[52].

# Red-throated Pipit
*Anthus cervinus*

N=1(1)

Red-throated Pipit breeds in the tundra of northern Europe and Asia, reaching westernmost Alaska. It is a scarce winter visitor to the Indian subcontinent, preferring moist grassland and marshes.

In Bhutan the Red-throated Pipit is a vagrant with one record. On 26 October 1991 a single was sighted at Jakar, Bumthang Valley[22].

# Rosy Pipit
*Anthus roseatus*

N=180(49). S 3600-4400 (mid-May-Sep); W 1200-4000

The Rosy Pipit inhabits the high Himalayas from western Pakistan to Arunachal Pradesh, and continuing north-east to western China. It breeds above the treeline, particularly in marshy meadows. In winter it descends to the foothills and adjacent plains where it frequents marshes, cultivation and riverbanks.

In Bhutan the Rosy Pipit is a common altitudinal migrant throughout the alpine and temperate zones, with single records from the western[52,53] and central foothills[52], where it appears to have been largely overlooked. It breeds from late May to September, when it has been reported at 3,600–4,400 m. The highest records are from 4,600 m[1], although it may occur even higher. In October–November it moves downslope, with passage migrants being recorded at 1,200–4,000 m. From mid-November to January it largely vacates this zone, with only few records of singles. Its winter range is unclear, but these data suggest that a large percentage of the

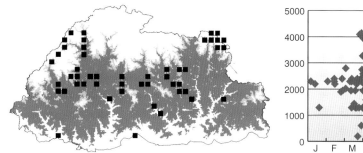

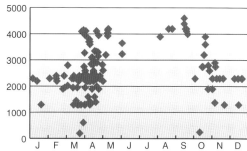

population winters in the Indian plains, as records from the foothills are rare. However, in Nepal wintering in the plains only occurs occasionally, with the majority staying at 750–1,500 m. Further exploration of the Bhutanese foothills is thus required. The paucity of suitable winter habitat, i.e. marshes and irrigated farmland, in the foothills could be a factor. It reappears in numbers in the passage zone in February, when spring migration commences. By mid-May all have reached the breeding areas. Interestingly, habitat choice on migration seems to differ from that in the summer and winter quarters, as it is found particularly along rivers and streams where it forages between the boulders. Spring migration is evident from small numbers of active migrants, observed particularly in early morning. The first are seen over Zhemgang in late February and over Thimphu in late March[52]. During spring migration important concentrations occur, with up to 50 foraging at the sewage ponds at Babesa, Thimphu district, by the end of March[52], which appears to be the peak passage period at this altitude. Autumn migration, however, is much less noticeable, with mostly singles and no records of active migration.

# Buff-bellied Pipit
## *Anthus rubescens*

N=2(2)

The Buff-bellied Pipit breeds in eastern Siberia and North America. It is a rare winter visitor to the northern Indian subcontinent. Habitat is marshes and irrigated land.

In Bhutan the Buff-bellied Pipit is a vagrant that has been recorded twice. On 29 October 1991 a single was at Jakar, Bumthang district[22], and on 18 November 2001 two were at the sewage ponds at Babesa, Thimphu district, at 2,300 m[52].

Alpine Accentor
Jan Wilczur

# Alpine Accentor
*Prunella collaris*

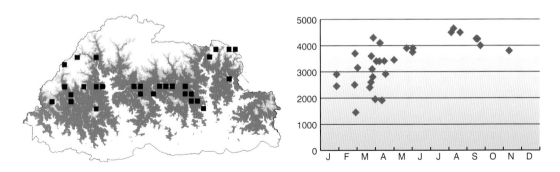

The Alpine Accentor is a bird of high mountains from Europe through Central Asia to China and Japan. In the Himalayas its range spans Pakistan to Arunachal Pradesh, thence north to western China. Habitat consists of rocky slopes and cliffs in the alpine zone.

In Bhutan the Alpine Accentor is frequent in the alpine and temperate zones. Like other accentors, there are relatively few records from its high-elevation breeding grounds due to insufficient surveys. Based on the limited data, its summer range appears to be located at 3,800–4,600 m, but probably reaches higher. In winter it remains present to at least 4,200 m, but spreads lower to 2,000 m, with one record at 1,500 m in late February[57]. Occurrence at lower elevations is limited to January–March and is largely related to heavy snowfall in the mountains. During this period flocks of up to 20 reach lower elevations. Ludlow collected juveniles at *c*.4,500 m in August, providing some evidence of breeding in Bhutan.

# Altai Accentor
*Prunella himalayana*

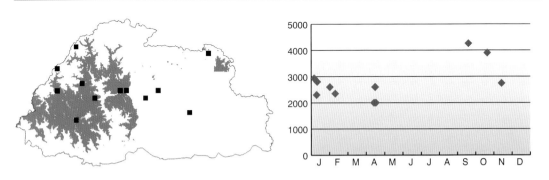

The Altai Accentor breeds in Turkestan north to Lake Baikal and in a narrow band east to south-east Tibet. It occurs in the Indian subcontinent as a winter visitor to the Himalayas, from Pakistan to Bhutan. Winter habitat consists of grassy and rocky slopes, where it may gather in large flocks.

In Bhutan this accentor is an uncommon winter visitor to the alpine zone and in the western and Sunkosh valleys, with isolated records in the central and eastern valleys. It appears to arrive in Bhutan in September/October, when it is first noted at higher elevations, e.g. a flock of more than 100 at 3,900 m along the Snowman trail around 20 October[51]. From November to mid-April wintering flocks are present at 2,000–3,000 m. Mean flock size is 35, with a max. 200 reported[28]. The latest spring record is from 16 April at 2,000 m[5].

338

# Robin Accentor
## *Prunella rubeculoides*

N=19(14). W 2000-4200

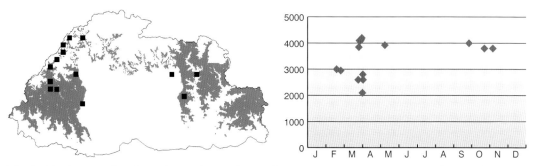

The Robin Accentor breeds in the southern Tibetan Plateau east to montane western China, and extending locally to the southern Himalayas, from Pakistan to Bhutan. It summers in dwarf willow and other scrub vegetation above the treeline, descending to winter on stony slopes and around cultivated areas.

In Bhutan the Robin Accentor is primarily an uncommon winter visitor, found in the high west and in the western and eastern valleys, with isolated records from the Sunkosh and central valleys. There are no confirmed summer records and it is thus unclear whether it breeds in Bhutan. The species has been found in mid-October to March, with the earliest record on 25 September[43] and the latest on 1 April[5]. In this period it occurs in small flocks of up to five at 2,000–4,200 m. Altitudes from 3,800 m to 4,200 appear to constitute its normal range. Only in periods with heavy snowfall, e.g. February/March 1996 and 1998, does it appear between 2,000 m and 3,000 m.

# Rufous-breasted Accentor
## *Prunella strophiata*

N=415(81). S 3600-4400 (mid-May-mid-Oct); W 1600-3200

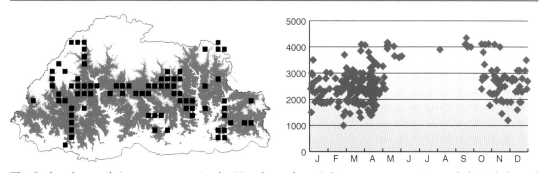

The Rufous-breasted Accentor occurs in the Himalayas from Pakistan to western Arunachal Pradesh, and thence north-east to montane western China. It breeds in the alpine and subalpine zones, affecting scrub. In winter it occurs in scrub in cultivated areas.

In Bhutan the Rufous-breasted Accentor is an abundant altitudinal migrant throughout the alpine and temperate zones. It is primarily known from winter, with relatively few summer records, reflecting insufficient coverage of high elevations outside the trekking seasons. From the limited records, the zone 3,600–4,400 m appears to be its summer range. The only evidence of breeding is a juvenile collected by Ludlow at 3,900 m on 6 August[31]. In winter it is found at 1,600–3,200 m, with records from intermediate altitudes on migration and the lowest from 1,000 m in February[52]. Birds reach the winter range from mid-October, with the earliest record on 13 October at 2,400 m[52]. They rapidly spread throughout the range, reaching lower levels by mid-November. Return movement is noted through gradually decreasing numbers from mid-March. The lower range is vacated by mid-April, with the last leaving the winter range in early May. In winter (November to mid-March) flocks of up to 20 are regular with the largest concentrations at mid-elevations, in January–March 1995 and 1998, probably relating to heavy snowfall in higher areas. In its winter habitat of scrub in cultivated areas it is frequently found with Little Bunting.

# Maroon-backed Accentor
## *Prunella immaculata*

N=59(30). W 1800-3200

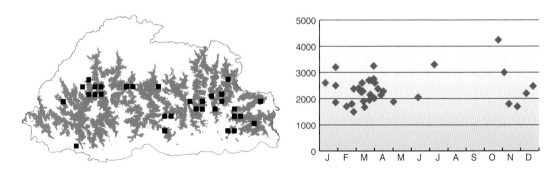

Among accentors in the Himalayas, Maroon-backed Accentor is most associated with forest habitat. It is principally known as a winter visitor from central Nepal to Arunachal Pradesh, with few data on its whereabouts in summer. Its range continues north-east to montane western China.

In Bhutan this accentor is uncommon throughout the temperate zone, primarily in winter, where it occurs in warm and cool broadleaf forests at 1,800–3,200 m, with the lowest record from 1,500 m[31], the highest 4,200 m in October[1]. The latter might concern a passage bird, although there are four records in June–July[31,49], which suggests regular summer presence in Bhutan. These latter are from temperate forest at 2,000–3,300 m, which would imply that the species is largely resident. There is no evidence of breeding and further surveys are needed to confirm its status at this season. In winter it occurs singly or in small flocks, feeding inconspicuously on the ground at forest edge. The maximum number reported is 20. January–March 1995 and 1998 witnessed relatively large numbers, indicating that birds move lower in response to heavy snowfall, although it is possible that the large numbers were also related to the Dark-throated Thrush irruptions in those years. However, the largest thrush irruption, which occurred in 1999/2000, failed to produce larger numbers of Maroon-backed or other accentors.

# Black-breasted Weaver
## *Ploceus benghalensis*

N=2(1)

The Black-breasted Weaver is endemic to the Indian subcontinent and is mostly found in the Ganges and Indus river systems, reaching locally to the Himalayan foothills. Habitat consists of tall grassland and marshes along rivers and canals.

In Bhutan this weaver is a vagrant, collected once in the 19th century with one recent record: on 7 February 1995 three were present in the Kuri Chhu valley at 700 m[29].

# Baya Weaver
## *Ploceus philippinus*

N=9(3)

The Baya Weaver is a common resident over most of the Indian subcontinent except parts of the north-west, north-east and the Himalayas. It is equally widespread further east in south-east Asia, reaching south to parts of Indonesia. It occurs particularly in the vicinity of cultivated areas.

In Bhutan the Baya Weaver is a rare resident, found locally in the eastern valleys and foothills, between Narphung and Deothang, Samdrup Jongkha district, at 200–1,700 m. Up to 20 have been noted there[28]. It has been found breeding at Samdrup Jongkha, with a minimum of nine nests in a palm tree in mid-May 1999[5]. All records are from late April to mid-May, coinciding with the (later) bird-tour groups. However, the possibility cannot be excluded that the species is only a seasonal visitor to Bhutan.

# White-rumped Munia
## *Lonchura striata*

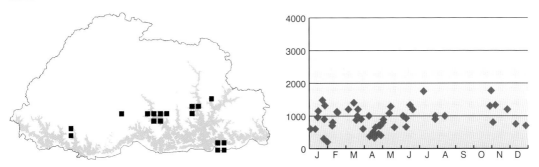

The White-rumped Munia is widespread in south-east Asia, from Taiwan in the east to Sumatra in the south. In the Indian subcontinent it has a scattered distribution, mostly in hill areas, including the Himalayan foothills. Habitat is scrub and open forest, generally around settlements.

In Bhutan the White-rumped Munia is an uncommon resident, being found primarily in the central and eastern valleys and foothills, with only a few records from the western and Sunkosh valleys, the former all from the 1960s and 1970s[1,36]. Its altitudinal range spans 400–1,400 m, occasionally to 200 m, with the highest records from 1,800 m in the western valleys[1]. It occurs in flocks of up to 20 most of the year. Only in May–June are sightings of individuals and pairs more frequent. By August larger flocks are again in evidence, probably indicating fledging of young birds. Thus, the appearance of fledged young seems to be timed to coincide with the ripening of grass seeds and crops in autumn. However, there are no confirmed breeding records for Bhutan. It is less associated with cultivation than Scaly-breasted Munia and also exploits seeding bamboo in open forest[5,52].

# Scaly-breasted Munia
## *Lonchura punctulata*

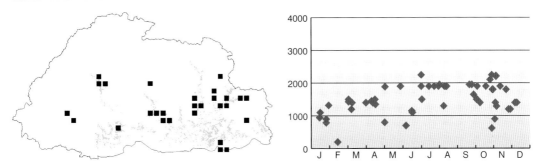

The Scaly-breasted Munia occurs over most of the Indian subcontinent, except the north-west. Elsewhere it is widespread in south-east Asia, reaching the Philippines and parts of Indonesia. Habitat consists of secondary forest with open areas and scrub near settlements.

In Bhutan this munia is only occasionally reported, from the eastern foothills and the temperate zone from the Sunkosh Valley east, with isolated records from the western valleys. It occupies a slightly higher range than White-rumped Munia, from 800 m to 2,200 m in summer. It exhibits some altitudinal movements, with birds retreating below 1,400 m in winter and gradually ascending to the upper part of the summer range from May. The lowest record in winter is at 200 m[29]. Descent to the winter range occurs from October and appears to follow, to some extent, the rice-harvesting season, which is subsequently later at lower elevations. The species generally occurs in smaller flocks than White-rumped Munia, with up to ten birds together. The largest concentration noted is 30[14]. In May–September it is invariably encountered singly or in pairs, with flocks appearing in October, these presumably family groups. There are no confirmed breeding records.

# Chaffinch
## *Fringilla coelebs*

N=1(1)

The Chaffinch breeds from Western Europe to western Siberia. In the Indian subcontinent it is an irregular winter visitor to Pakistan, with occasional records further east.

In Bhutan the Chaffinch is a vagrant recorded once in spring: on 29 March 1995 a male was observed at Tashithang, Punakha district[5].

# Brambling
## *Fringilla montifringilla*

N=1(1)

The Brambling breeds in the boreal zone of Eurasia, from Scandinavia to Kamchatka and south to the Altai. In the Indian subcontinent it is a regular winter visitor to Pakistan, with occasional records further east.

In Bhutan the Brambling is a vagrant recorded once in spring: on 6 May 1990 a single was observed in the Tang Valley, Bumthang district[10].

# Yellow-breasted Greenfinch
## *Carduelis spinoides*

N=288(66). S 1200-3200 (Apr-Oct); W 1000-2800

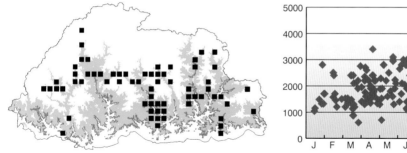
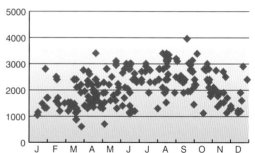

The Yellow-breasted Greenfinch occurs in the Himalayas from Pakistan to western Arunachal Pradesh, thence east to south-east Tibet and Myanmar. It is a bird of open forest and forest edge, often near cultivation.

In Bhutan the Yellow-breasted Greenfinch is common throughout the temperate zone, with single records from the high west and eastern foothills. It shows some altitudinal movements, with its summer range spanning 1,200–3,200 m and in winter retreating slightly lower to 1,000–2,800 m, occasionally reaching 600 m. Despite this apparently small difference in summer and winter ranges, like some other seedeaters it shows a pattern of overall gradual ascent to higher altitudes during spring and a relatively swift descent in autumn. Highest altitudes are reached in August–October, during which period it has been recorded once as high as 4,000 m[1]. Probably its movements are primarily nomadic. It appears to breed in May–June, when observations of pairs or singles predominate and are followed by the appearance of small flocks in July–August, presumably family groups. Larger flocks of in excess of 20 appear from September. In December–March these may aggregate in large flocks of more than 200.

# Tibetan Siskin
## *Carduelis thibetana*

N=52(28). W 1400-2600

The Tibetan Siskin has a small breeding range comprising south-east Tibet and western Sichuan. Its breeding status in the Himalayas is unclear and it is primarily a winter visitor to this region, in Nepal, Sikkim and Bhutan.

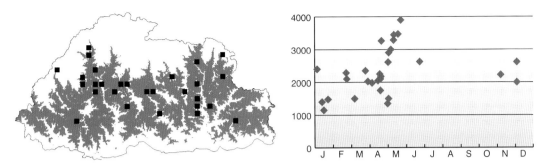

In Bhutan the Tibetan Siskin is uncommon and primarily a winter visitor, found throughout the temperate belt. Arrivals commence early November, after which birds are noted until late May. The absence of records in June–October makes the presence of a breeding population questionable, although it may have been overlooked in this season due to its unobtrusive habits. In November–April the regular altitudinal range of wintering flocks is 1,400–2,600 m, where they exploit particularly the seeds of *Alnus*. The lowest record is at 1,200 m in the Kuri Chhu valley in January[22,49]. In this period birds occur in flocks, typically of 10–40, with a max. 200 reported[13]. In May the birds move higher, to 2,600–3,600 m, with the highest record at *c*.3,900 m[44]. Here they occur in hemlock and fir forests. The reason for this is unclear and could relate to return migration to the breeding grounds or to a search for a seasonally available food source. Alternatively, it is possible that a breeding population has thus far gone unnoticed in the hemlock and fir forests.

# Plain Mountain Finch
## *Leucosticte nemoricola*

N = 146(42). S 2600-4000 (Jun-Nov); W 2000-4200

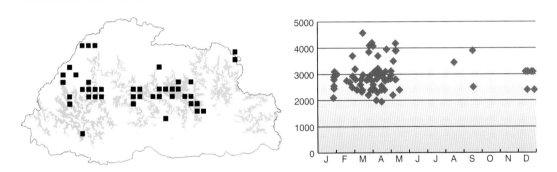

The core range of the Plain Mountain Finch is the Tibetan Plateau, from where it extends to montane western China and the southern Himalayas. It breeds above the treeline on the high alpine slopes, and in winter descends to forest clearings and cultivated areas.

In Bhutan the Plain Mountain Finch is a frequently recorded altitudinal migrant, noted mostly at its wintering sites at lower elevations, as its high-elevation breeding sites have been insufficiently explored. It occurs throughout the alpine and temperate zones, and is relatively more common in the west. Like other finches, it is a late breeder and therefore only records in June–September and possibly October can be ascribed to its summer range. As there are only a few records from this period, its summer range is unclear. Although records range from 2,600 m to 4,000 m, most probably in summer it remains above 3,600 m and may reach above 4,000 m. The highest record is from 4,600 m in March[1]. Breeding is unconfirmed and it is possible that wintering birds originate from the Tibetan Plateau. In winter birds are present to at least 4,200 m, while some reach down to 2,000 m. The first birds at lower elevations arrive in late December and are present until mid-May. Throughout winter it is regularly found in large flocks of several tens to several hundreds, the largest concentration being 1,000[5]. Larger flocks frequent cultivated areas of upland valleys, e.g. the Paro, Thimphu, Bumthang and Phobjikha valleys. Heavy snowfall at higher elevations drives larger numbers lower, with the largest flocks reported in the snow-rich winters of 1994/1995, 1997/1998 and 1999/2000.

# Blanford's Rosefinch
## *Carpodacus rubescens*

N=15(8). R 3200-3400

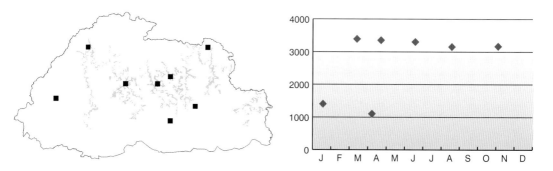

Blanford's Rosefinch is a rare rosefinch, which has been found in central Nepal, Sikkim, Bhutan and Yunnan. Habitat consists of glades in high-altitude conifer/birch forest. Possible altitudinal movements are unclear.

In Bhutan this rosefinch is uncommon, with scattered records throughout the temperate zone and the high east. In the western valleys there is only one record[31] and elsewhere it is also very thinly spread. Records are concentrated at 3,200–3,400 m, which appears to be its regular range. It has been found there in March–November. In January–April there are three records below 2,000 m[28,29,52], indicating some altitudinal movement. However, due to the paucity of records, these movements are poorly understood at present (one record is not included on the graph as the altitude is not precisely known).

Blanford's Rosefinch
*Dan Cole*

# Dark-breasted Rosefinch
## *Carpodacus nipalensis*

N=89(37). S 2400-4000 (May-Oct); W 1200-3000

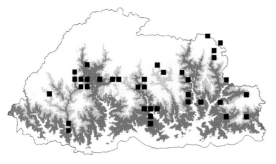

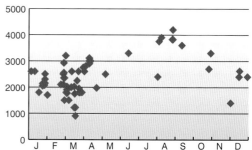

The Dark-breasted Rosefinch occurs in the Himalayas, from Kashmir east to Arunachal Pradesh, thence north-east into western China and northern Vietnam. It summers in open forest and scrub near the treeline. In winter it occurs in open patches in forest at lower elevations.

In Bhutan the Dark-breasted Rosefinch is a frequently recorded altitudinal migrant throughout the temperate belt and in the high east. In May–October it occurs at 2,400–4,000 m, albeit with most records above 3,600 m, where its breeding range may lie. The highest record is from 4,200 m[31]. From November it occurs in its winter range, at 1,200–3,000 m, with the lowest record from 900 m[10]. In winters with heavy snowfall it is regular and appears in larger numbers, such as in 1999/2000 and 2001/2002. Winter flocks commonly number up to 20, with particularly spring 2002 seeing larger concentrations, the largest totalling c.100[19]. In milder winters there are only occasional records of flocks, numbering just a few birds, suggesting that most of the population is resident in the breeding areas in these years. Once in the winter quarters, flocks remain in the same area over long periods, usually frequenting open patches in broadleaf forest. During April the winter range is vacated again.

# Common Rosefinch
## *Carpodacus erythrinus*

N = 131(50). S 2800-3600 (Jun-Sep); W 800-3200

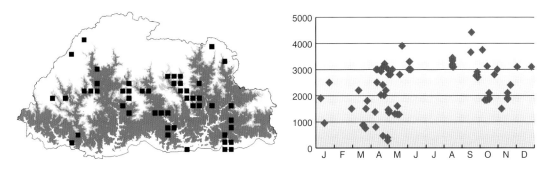

The Common Rosefinch occurs over large parts of Eurasia in various subspecies. It breeds throughout the Himalayas, where the subspecies *roseatus* occurs in the east. The winter quarters of the various subspecies extend from Iran through India to mainland south-east Asia. The subspecies *erythrinus*, which breeds from Eastern Europe to central Siberia, comprises a large percentage of wintering flocks in India. In the Himalayas summer habitat consists of shrubs and open forest at the treeline, while it winters in flocks in open forest and cultivated areas.

In Bhutan the Common Rosefinch is frequently recorded. Both subspecies, *roseatus* and *erythrinus*, occur[1,52]. The species is widespread throughout the alpine and temperate zones and the central and eastern foothills. Given the presence of two subspecies with different migration patterns, the distribution pattern appears complex. Records above 2,800 m from mid-April most likely concern breeders (*roseatus*). Until late September records are from 2,800 m and 3,600 m, i.e. its summer range. More occasionally it is found over 4,000 m, with the highest record at 4,400 m[1]. While July is reportedly the main breeding season in the Himalayas, there are no records for this month in Bhutan. However, the species is known to be rather inconspicuous in the breeding season, with only a short period of vocal activity, and is thus easily missed. A singing bird was noted on 13 April[5], which is the only evidence of breeding in Bhutan. Considering the lack of clarity in the status of the two subspecies, confirmation of breeding is an urgent gap to be filled. In October–November there appears to be a gradual movement to lower elevations, with numbers probably augmented by migrant *erythrinus* (records in November and January[52]). Subsequently, there are records at 800–3,200 m in winter until late May, with occasional presence at 200 m. In particular, those records in April–May should concern *erythrinus*, which only arrives in its breeding areas north of the Himalayas in late May, by which period *roseatus* may already have occupied its breeding areas at higher elevations. The period mid-April to mid-May witnesses a peak in numbers, which also suggests passage of *erythrinus* from wintering areas south of Bhutan. Throughout winter, flocks number fewer than five, but in this period concentrations of 10–40 are reported, with a max. of 200 at Kori La, Mongar district, on 11 May[5]. These numbers are noted particularly in the eastern valleys, where passage appears concentrated.

# Beautiful Rosefinch
*Carpodacus pulcherrimus*                    N=51(15). S 3600-4200 (May-Sep); W 2800-3400

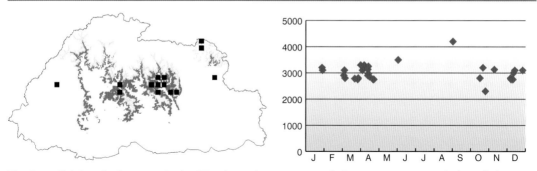

The Beautiful Rosefinch occurs in the Himalayas from Uttar Pradesh to western Arunachal Pradesh. From there, it is distributed further north-east on the Tibetan Plateau and to Mongolia. It breeds above the treeline in rhododendron scrub, and winters in scrub and cultivated land in upland valleys.

In Bhutan the Beautiful Rosefinch is uncommon and primarily a winter visitor. It has been found in the upland Sunkosh and central valleys, with isolated records from the western and eastern valleys. Its winter range spans 2,800–3,400 m, with the lowest record from 2,300 m[25]. It is particularly common and regular in the Bumthang region, where flocks of up to 20 are noted. It arrives in the winter areas by mid-October, departing late March. Its summer distribution appears limited in Bhutan, with records only from the high east, in the upper reaches of the Kuri Chhu valley at 3,500 m[49] and 4,200 m[31]. It therefore appears to be primarily a breeding bird of the Tibetan Plateau, with no confirmed records in Bhutan.

# Dark-rumped Rosefinch
*Carpodacus edwardsii*                    N=68(23). S 3000-3800 (May-Oct); W 2600-3400

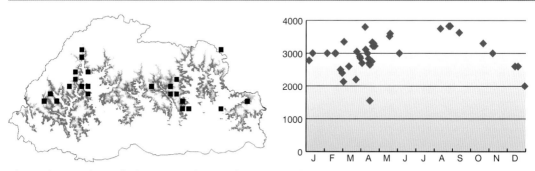

The Dark-rumped Rosefinch occurs in the Himalayas mainly from Sikkim west to Arunachal Pradesh, as well as in adjacent northern Myanmar. It extends further north-east through China reaching Sichuan. Summer habitat is rhododendron scrub at high elevations, descending to open forests and scrub at lower elevations in winter.

In Bhutan this rosefinch is a frequently recorded altitudinal migrant, found throughout the temperate zone and in the high east. Its breeding quarters appear to be situated at 3,000–3,800 m, where it arrives from mid-April. From October it gradually descends lower, wintering mainly at 2,600–3,400 m and occasionally down to 2,000 m, with the lowest record from 1,600 m[5]. In its winter quarters it is mostly found in small flocks of up to seven, particularly in January–April. In autumn sight records are remarkably few, with almost all records concerning specimens taken during the ornithological surveys. This might be explained by the birds frequenting more closed habitat than in spring, e.g. a bird observed in November fed on the ground in dense hemlock forest[52]. In late April spring migration to higher elevations is marked by the birds gathering in larger flocks, e.g. of 40 at Koina, Gasa district, at c.3,300 m[39], and birds observed at Chilai La, Paro district, around 3,800 m[5].

# Three-banded Rosefinch
## Carpodacus trifasciatus

N=1(1)

The Three-banded Rosefinch breeds in cultivated areas in western China and winters in south-east Tibet.

Three-banded Rosefinch is a vagrant to Bhutan, recorded on 13 March 1986, when two males and a female were observed near Jakar at 2,800 m[10]. This is the only confirmed record for the Indian subcontinent.

# White-browed Rosefinch
## Carpodacus thura

N=99(42). S 3000-4200 (mid-Mar-mid-Nov); W 2600-3800

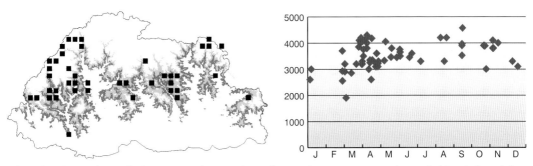

The White-browed Rosefinch occurs in the Himalayas from Pakistan to western Arunachal Pradesh and thence north-east to Yunnan and Sichuan. It is a bird of scrub around the treeline that is mostly resident and one of the highest wintering rosefinches.

In Bhutan the White-browed Rosefinch is a common altitudinal migrant throughout the alpine and temperate zones, but becomes gradually scarcer further east where it approaches its westernmost limits in the Himalayas. In April–September it occurs in its breeding quarters at 3,000–4,200 m, with the highest record at 4,600 m[1]. In winter it remains present to at least 3,800 m, but also moving lower, down to 2,600 m, with the lowest record from 1,900 m[44]. In winter birds form small flocks of up to 15. In its summer range it is the most regular of the rosefinches, with up to 15 encountered in a day.

# Streaked Rosefinch
## Carpodacus rubicilloides

N=2(1)

The Streaked Rosefinch inhabits open rocky country well above the treeline. Its range includes the Caucasus, the mountains of Turkestan, the Altai and the Tibetan Plateau. It occurs in the Indian subcontinent from Ladakh to central Nepal and is a vagrant east to Bhutan.

In Bhutan the Streaked Rosefinch has been recorded twice: during the 1989 Naturetrek tour (Inskipp 2001) and in June 2000, when it was found in the high east, in the upper reaches of the Kuri Chhu valley at 4,100 m[49].

# Red-fronted Rosefinch
## Carpodacus puniceus

N=5(3)

The Red-fronted Rosefinch occurs on the Tibetan Plateau, reaching the southern Himalayas locally from Pakistan to Bhutan. It is a bird of steep rocky slopes well above the treeline and is mostly resident, with only limited movements to lower altitudes in winter.

In Bhutan the Red-fronted Rosefinch is an uncommon resident found only in the high east at the head of the Kuri Chhu valley, near Singye Dzong, Lhuntse district[31,49], in the breeding season (May–August) at altitudes between 4,400 m and 4,500 m.

# Crimson-browed Finch
*Propyrrhula subhimachala*  N=44(13). S 3200-3800 (May-Oct); W 1800-3200

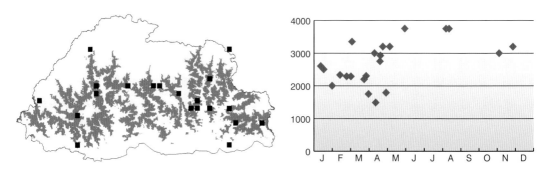

The Crimson-browed Finch breeds in the Himalayas from central Nepal to Arunachal Pradesh, spreading in winter to north-east India. Further east its range extends to northern Myanmar and western China. It summers in scrub near the treeline, particularly juniper. In winter it occurs in forest with dense undergrowth, feeding on seeds and berries.

In Bhutan the Crimson-browed Finch is widespread but uncommon throughout the temperate zone and in the high east. The only site where it is recorded annually is between Sengor and Yonkhola, Mongar district. Elsewhere it is more erratic and probably frequently overlooked. The species shows marked altitudinal movements, summering in scrub at 3,200–3,800 m, and wintering at 1,800–3,200 m, with the lowest record from c.1,600 m[28]. Most records concern singles, although in January–April it is also found in small flocks of up to five. The maximum single-day total is 12[28].

# Scarlet Finch
*Haematospiza sipahi*  N=172(43). S 1400-2800 (mid-May-Sep); W 1000-2200

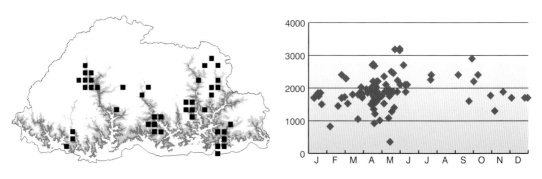

The Scarlet Finch ranges in the Himalayas from central Nepal to Arunachal Pradesh and north-east India. In the east its range extends to Yunnan and northern Vietnam. Habitat comprises forest edge and clearings in broadleaf forest.

In Bhutan the Scarlet Finch is frequently recorded throughout the temperate zone and in the eastern foothills. Its summer range spans 1,400–2,800 m, occasionally to 3,200 m. In winter it is found at 1,000–2,200 m, with the lowest record from 400 m[6]. In mid-May to November it is encountered in pairs or singly. Flocks form in December, when up to 40 visit seeding trees. From April these disband as smaller flocks or pairs. It is a late breeder, vacating the lower part of its range only in mid-May. Singing birds have been noted late May and early June at 1,900 m[52], and a pair with juveniles was seen at 2,900 m on 29 September[43,52]. It is closely associated with broadleaf forest year-round.

# Red Crossbill (Common Crossbill)
## *Loxia curvirostra*

N=116(31). R 2400-3600

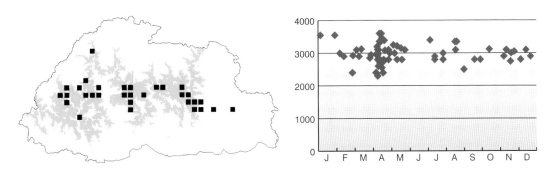

The Red Crossbil occurs across a broad swathe of Eurasia and North America in coniferous forest zones. A separate population exists in the Himalayas from Pakistan to Bhutan, montane western China and east to northern Vietnam. It is a specialist feeder on conifer seeds, its occurrence and breeding erratic according to variations in the availability of this food source.

In Bhutan the Red Crossbill is frequently recorded throughout the temperate zone, becoming gradually scarcer further east and reaching its easternmost limits in the Himalayas in the eastern valleys. There are only two records east of the Kuri Chhu valley, both from April 2001[19]. It is found year-round at 2,400–3,600 m, but with marked differences in annual abundance. Peak numbers occurred in 1995, 1998 and 2001, suggesting a three-year cycle in seed production of one the conifer species. Which conifer species is preferred is unclear; it has been found in Blue Pine, fir and hemlock/mixed forests, with more or less equal preference for the latter two. The largest peak appeared to be in 1995, with large numbers both in the west and centre of the country. However, irruptions in the west and centre appear not to be synchronised in all years, although the limited data do not permit firm conclusions. The 1998 irruption was noted particularly in the west, while highest numbers in the centre appeared to follow in the subsequent year. In 2001 peak numbers were noted in the centre, but 2000 was the better year in the west. The season of peak numbers is roughly April–September, possibly with some variation between years. In irruption

Red Crossbills
*Mike Langman*

years flocks of up to 60 are noted, whereas in years of low abundance birds are seen mostly singly or in small flocks of up to five. 1997 was definitely the most meagre in the period 1995–2002, with just a single record[5].

# Brown Bullfinch
## *Pyrrhula nipalensis*

N=87(39). R 1800-3000

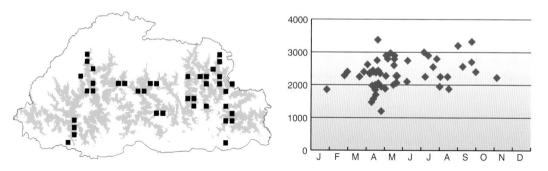

The Brown Bullfinch is patchily distributed in the Himalayas from Himachal Pradesh to Arunachal Pradesh and in north-east India. Its range extends east to Taiwan, and it also occurs in Vietnam and the Malay Peninsula. It inhabits dense, moist forest in the temperate zone.

In Bhutan the Brown Bullfinch is a frequently recorded resident throughout the temperate zone, at altitudes of 1,800–3,000 m, with occasional records at 1,400 m and 3,400 m. Year-round it is mostly found singly or in pairs, although concentrations of up to 20 have been noted in March–April[28]. Small flocks of up to five are noted until early June, after which observations of singles and pairs dominate throughout summer and autumn. The breeding season is somewhat unclear and the only indication of timing is the observation of a singing bird at 2,600 m in May[52].

# Red-headed Bullfinch
## *Pyrrhula erythrocephala*

N=203(56). S 2800-3800 (May-Sep); W 1800-3400

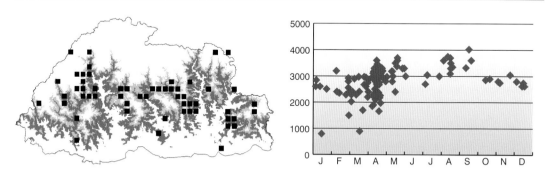

The Red-headed Bullfinch's core range is formed by the Himalayas from Himachal Pradesh to western Arunachal Pradesh, extending east only to south-east Tibet. Its breeding habitat is deciduous forest at higher elevations, particularly birch. It winters in rhododendron scrub in various forest types.

In Bhutan the Red-headed Bullfinch is a common altitudinal migrant throughout the alpine and temperate zones, with isolated records from the central and eastern foothills. Its summer range spans 2,800–3,800 m, with the highest record at 4,000 m[1]. In winter it is found at 1,800–3,400 m, with occasional records at 800 m[44]. From January to late April it is mostly found in flocks of ten, sometimes more, e.g. a flock of 60 at 3,200 m on 24 April[5]. Only by May do observations of pairs and singles start to dominate, and birds vacate the lower part of the range. Not until January is the species again noted in its winter range and in larger flocks. An observation of a singing bird on 18 August at 3,400 m on 18 August[52] points to a relatively late breeding season.

# Grey-headed Bullfinch
## *Pyrrhula erythaca*

N=10(10). R 2000-3000

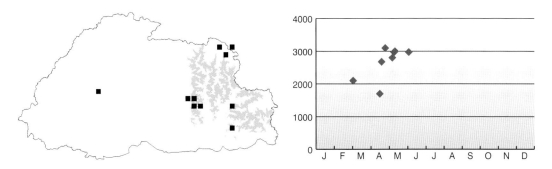

The main range of the Grey-headed Bullfinch is in western and northern China, Taiwan and Yunnan. It penetrates the Indian subcontinent in the Eastern Himalayas from Darjeeling to Arunachal Pradesh, where it is generally scarce. Habitat consists of conifer–rhododendron forest and scrub.

In Bhutan the Grey-headed Bullfinch is rare and found mostly in the eastern valleys and the high east, with single records of flocks in the Sunkosh[10] and central valleys[5]. Records fall between 2,000 m and 3,000 m, with one from 1,700 m[5]. Almost all concern flocks of 4–12, in fir, hemlock and broadleaf forests. It has been recorded in the spring season from March to early June, but without any evidence of breeding. Thus, occurrence in Bhutan could be seasonal and remains poorly understood.

# Collared Grosbeak
## *Mycerobas affinis*

N=102(31). S 2400-3600 (Apr-Oct); W 2200-2800

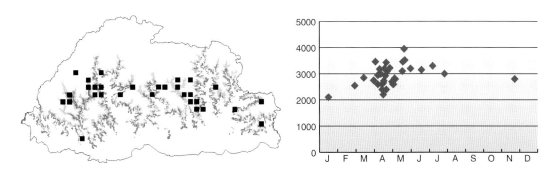

The Collared Grosbeak occurs in the Himalayas from Himachal Pradesh to Arunachal Pradesh, as well as north-east into western China. It is a bird of coniferous and mixed forests at higher elevations.

In Bhutan this grosbeak is frequently recorded throughout the temperate zone and in the high east. Its summer altitudinal range spans 2,400–3,600 m, with the highest record at 4,000 m[22]. In winter it appears to descend to 2,200–2,800 m, with the lowest record 2,100 m in January[1]. However, as records are relatively few, particularly in autumn/winter, its altitudinal movements are not entirely clear. It is most readily found in March–May, when there appears to be a gradual movement to the higher-elevation breeding areas. Birds have largely vacated the lower part of the range by mid-May. During this period it is found in flocks of 5–20, with the largest concentrations noted in the Paro Valley, where up to 60 have been found. The reason for the abundance of spring records could lie in its regular occurrence in Blue Pine forest, where it is located relatively easily. In the breeding season and in autumn it appears to affect denser fir and hemlock forests, and is found singly or in pairs. As elsewhere in its range, no nest has been found and, thus far, breeding evidence is lacking for Bhutan.

# Spot-winged Grosbeak
## Mycerobas melanozanthos

N=82(26). S 1000-3200 (Apr-Oct); W 600-2000

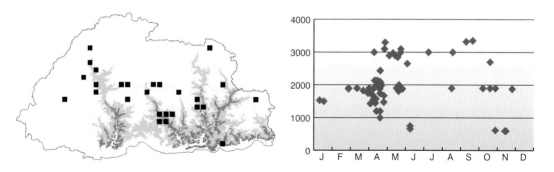

The Spot-winged Grosbeak has a scattered distribution in the Himalayas from Pakistan to Arunachal Pradesh and in north-east India. Its range extends to northern Vietnam and Sichuan. Summer habitat consists of mixed coniferous–broadleaf forest, and it winters in broadleaf forest.

In Bhutan the Spot-winged Grosbeak is frequently recorded in the Sunkosh, central and eastern valleys and in the eastern foothills. There is a single record from the western valleys[1]. It shows marked altitudinal movements and occupies the lowest range of the three grosbeaks. The summer range is situated at 1,000–3,200 m, with the core probably above 2,000 m in cool broadleaf and mixed forests. In winter it withdraws to the warm broadleaf zone, at 600–2,000 m. It only moves higher in mid-April–May, with birds still present at low elevations in early June[52]. Return movement to lower elevations is noted in October–November. In the warm broadleaf zone it is encountered in small flocks of 5–20, feeding in the top canopy on *Acer* and other seeding trees. The largest flocks occur in late March–April. In early April, a flock of *c*.100 birds has been noted at 1,700 m[5]. There are no confirmed breeding records.

# White-winged Grosbeak
## Mycerobas carnipes

N=182(51). S 2600-4000 (Apr-Oct); W 2200-3600

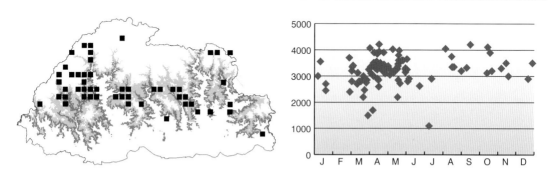

The White-winged Grosbeak is found in the Himalayas from Pakistan to western Arunachal Pradesh, its range continuing west to Iran and the Central Asian republics, and north-east to western China. Habitat is conifer forest and shrub with juniper.

The White-winged Grosbeak is a common altitudinal migrant and the commonest grosbeak in Bhutan. It is found throughout the alpine and temperate zones, and is strongly attached to dry juniper-covered slopes and patches of juniper in forest. It becomes gradually scarcer further east where it approaches its easternmost limits. Its summer altitudinal range spans 2,600–4,000 m and occasionally reaches above the treeline to 4,200 m. In winter it remains present to at least 3,600 m, although some disperse to 2,200 m, particularly in late February to early April. There are occasional records to 1,600 m, of which the most notable is the observation of *c*.40 at

1,700 m in early April, together with a large flock of Spot-winged Grosbeaks[5]. The lowest record is from 1,100 m in July[43]. In November–April it is frequently found in flocks of up to ten, with the largest concentration being of 90 in the Phajoding area near Thimphu on 27 February[57]. From May it is mostly found singly or in pairs, and withdraws from lower elevations. There is no evidence for breeding in Bhutan as yet.

# Gold-naped Finch
## *Pyrrhoplectes epauletta*   N=93(32). S 3000-3600 (mid-Apr-mid-Oct); W 1800-2800

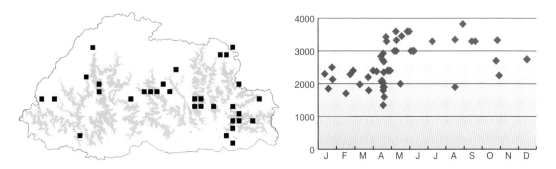

The Gold-naped Finch is found in the Himalayas from central Nepal to Arunachal Pradesh, from where its range continues east to south-west China and northern Myanmar. Habitat consists of dense undergrowth in oak–rhododendron forest and rhododendron scrub.

In Bhutan the Gold-naped Finch is frequently recorded throughout the alpine and temperate zones, with most records from the east. In summer it occurs in high-altitude forest at 3,000–3,600 m, with one record from 3,800 m[31]. It winters in cool broadleaf forest at 1,800–2,800 m, occasionally reaching 1,300 m[19]. Birds move towards the breeding areas in the second half of April, as evidenced by records throughout the altitudinal range in this period. Descent in autumn is much less obvious, but may take place in October–November. In fact, birds appear to shift gradually lower during the winter, with the highest altitudes noted in early season and the lowest elevations reached in March–April. The species is mostly observed singly or in small flocks of up to five. The concentration of *c*.20 observed in late April 2000, on Kori La[5], is exceptional. Four males distributed along 1 km of road on Yotong La in August[52] suggest that the species may reach considerable densities in parts of its summer breeding range.

Gold-naped Finch
*Ren Hathway*

# Crested Bunting
## *Melophus lathami*

N=248(45). S 800-2000 (mid-Mar-Aug); W 800-1600

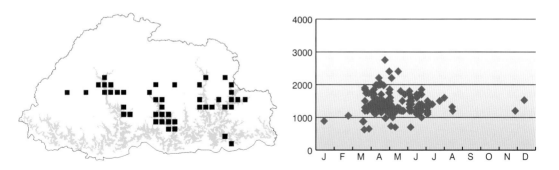

In the Indian subcontinent the Crested Bunting occurs in central India, the Himalayan foothills from Himachal Pradesh to Arunachal Pradesh, and in north-east India. Its range reaches further east to southern China and northern Vietnam. It is a bird of dry hillsides with grass and shrubs.

In Bhutan the Crested Bunting is common throughout the temperate zone, but with only a few records in the western valleys. It is localised, occurring in areas with large continuous stretches of cultivated land in the warm broadleaf forest zone. In summer it ranges at 800–2,000 m, more occasionally to 600 m and 2,400 m, and has been found once at *c*.2,800 m[5]. There are few records outside the breeding season, when it appears to occupy a lower range at 800–1,600 m. It is mostly noted from mid-March to mid-July, when it is more conspicuous as singing males defend territories. However, records in August–February are so few that migration could be involved, possibly with part of the population wintering in the Indian plains. In suitable habitat it can be quite common, with probably tens of pairs present in large agricultural areas such as around Shali, Trashi Yangtse district, and Samchhoeling, Trongsa district.

# Grey-necked Bunting
## *Emberiza buchanani*

N=1(1)

The Grey-necked Bunting breeds in Central Asia, from Turkey south to Iran, Afghanistan and occasionally Pakistan. It is a winter visitor to the north-west Indian subcontinent.

It is a vagrant to Bhutan. It has been observed once in the Tang Valley, Bumthang district, at 2,700 m on 7 May 1990[10], when a single was present. As spring migration from its main winter quarters is reported to be in March to mid-April, this record is relatively late.

# Little Bunting
## *Emberiza pusilla*

N=277(60). W 1000-2800

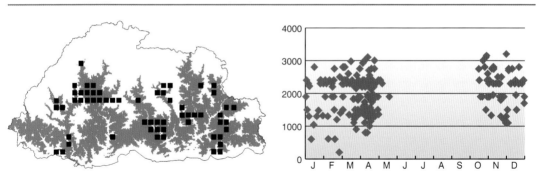

The Little Bunting breeds in the tundra and taiga zone, from Finland to the Sea of Okhotsk. It winters mostly in south-east Asia, reaching the Indian subcontinent in the Himalayas west to central Nepal and in north-east India. Winter habitat comprises cultivated areas with scrub.

The Little Bunting is a common winter visitor throughout the temperate zone and in the eastern and western foothills. Its regular altitudinal range is 1,000–2,800 m, and it is usually encountered in small flocks of up to 20. In autumn it arrives around 15 October[22,52], being initially noted in the higher part of its range, spreading gradually down to 1,000 m, which is reached in December. In this period there are also several records from higher elevations, the highest being at 3,200 m[1]. At 2,400 m numbers peak in December–January, when up to 40 have been noted at the sewage ponds at Babesa, Thimphu district[52]. During spring the gradual movement to lower elevations appears to continue, as evidenced by occasional records down to 200 m[19] in the first months of the year. Around mid-April a decline in numbers is evident, indicating migration to the breeding quarters. By late April most have left and there few May records, the latest being on 18 May[52]. As high-altitude records during migration periods are lacking, the birds probably move along an east–west axis, circumventing the main Himalayan range either to the east or to the west.

# Black-faced Bunting
## *Emberiza spodocephala*

N=1(1)

The Black-faced Bunting breeds in eastern Siberia to Japan and south to western China, wintering in mainland south-east Asia. It is a winter visitor to the Indian subcontinent, mainly the north-east. Habitat is tall grass and scrub, where it may be easily overlooked through its habit of feeding in cover on the ground.

The Black-faced Bunting is a vagrant to Bhutan. It has been found once at Subrang, Zhemgang district, in the Mangde Chhu valley at *c.*1,400 m[22], on 30 April 1993. This date is rather late, as birds are reported to leave their winter quarters in north-east India by early April.

# 9. Update to 2004

New information on birds in Bhutan becomes available on almost any birding trip to the country. Species will be confirmed from new squares, and more data will be discovered on status and association with particular habitats. The species accounts are up to date until June 2002. This section highlights some notable records in the period up to the end of 2004, in particular new additions to the country's bird list, breeding records of threatened species, significant range extensions and records of vagrants. While this update is not exhaustive, it illustrates that there is still a lot to be learned about the avifauna of the country.

Since June 2002 five new species have been confirmed for Bhutan. These are **Great Thick-knee**[49] (p.120), **Yellow-wattled Lapwing**[49] (p.124), **Egyptian Vulture**[14] (p.132), **Stripe-breasted Woodpecker** *Dendrocopos atratus*[19] and **Common Moorhen**[42] *Gallinula chloropus*. Stripe-breasted Woodpecker was already included in Inskipp *et al.* (1999), but the record was later withdrawn. On 30 March 2003 a male was found near Tingtibi, Zhemgary district, at an approximate altitude of 600 m. The Common Moorhen was found at Babesa, Thimphu district, in April 2004. Details of Stripe-breasted Woodpecker and Common Moorhen were received too late for them to be included in the species accounts.

The breeding of **White-bellied Heron** in Bhutan was further confirmed by the sighting of a pair building a nest in a Chir Pine tree, at an unspecified location in the Punakha/Wangdue Phodrang area[47]. The pair was first observed at the nest site in mid-April 2003. Later in the season a young bird was photographed on the nest. In 2003 and 2004 there were regular sightings of 1-3 White-bellied Herons in the Punakha area in April and May, possibly in relation to the presence of another breeding pair[5,28,42]. In the Zhemgang area indication of probable breeding of **Beautiful Nuthatch** was obtained when a pair was observed transporting lichen nest material on 19 April 2003 at 1,600 m[19]. Breeding in Bhutan has been further substantiated for a few other species: **Mountain Imperial Pigeon** (pair at a nest at 1,100 m on 30 March 2003)[19], **Fire-tailed Myzornis** (nest-building pair in April 2004)[5], **Red-wattled Lapwing** (pair with chick in early August 2003 at 2,300 m)[14] and **Black-tailed Crake** (nest found on 14 August 2003 at 2,400 m)[14]. After the discovery of **Wedge-billed Wren Babbler** and **Long-billed Wren Babbler** in the forests of Thrumshingla National Park in 2001 and 2002 respectively, both species have been recorded here annually[5,14,19,28]. Up to three singing birds of each species were noted in this area.

Range extensions were noted for some uncommon or rare species. **Spot-breasted Scimitar Babbler** was found in the central valleys, near Tingtibi, Zhemgang district, in April 2003[19]. It appears to occupy an altitudinal range from 1,200 m to 1,600 m here. **Ashy Wood Pigeon** was newly recorded in the Sunkosh valley in April[5] and August 2003[14]. A **Spot-winged Starling** was observed in the Sunkosh valley at around 1,100 m near Kamechu, Wangdue Phodrang district, on 20 May 2004[42]. This also represents a range extension, and considering the season and habitat this could concern a breeding site. **Black-headed Shrike Babbler** was recorded at an exceptionally high altitude of 2,600 m in the eastern valleys in April 2003[19].

A flock of 30 **Grandala** was noted at the low elevation of 2,450 m near Pele La on 30 March 2003[5]. This species has not been found to straggle outside its normal altitude range in this season before. The same goes for **Indian Pond Heron,** observed near Punakha at 1,300 m on 27 March 2003[19]. Observations of **Eurasian Marsh Harrier**[5] and **Streak-throated Woodpecker**[5] in 2003 represented the second records for each species for the country. **Blyth's Pipit** is a rare passage migrant and was noted on 29 April 2003 at 3,400 m[19].

# 10. Birding sites in Bhutan

The sites listed are all easily accessible and provide excellent birdwatching opportunities. A good cross-section of the avifauna of Bhutan can be observed by visiting most of the places listed below.

## Phuntsholing

**Habitats:** Subtropical forest; river with shingle and sand banks.
**Altitude range:** 150-1,000 m.
**Planning a visit:** Best season is November-April. Birding along the road is not always comfortable due to heavy traffic, but the river bed can easily be visited.
**Birds of interest:**
A good variety of birds characteristic of the Indian plains and rivers, many of which are difficult to find elsewhere in Bhutan. *Coppersmith Barbet, Small Pratincole, Little Cormorant, Golden-fronted Leafbird, White-rumped Shama, White-crowned Forktail, Plain Flowerpecker.*
A good site for observing migrants, including waterbirds, birds of prey and songbirds: *Black Kite, Steppe Eagle, Dusky Warbler.*

## Chilai La

**Habitats:** Alpine scrub and pasture; high altitude fir forest.
**Altitude range:** 3,800-4,100 m.
**Planning a visit:** Best season is April-May; largely unexplored in summer. Easiest site in Bhutan to reach above the tree-line. Suitable for a morning excursion from Paro. From the 4,000 m pass short walks can be made.
**Birds of interest:**
A selection of high-altitude species including rosefinches and accentors: *Blood Pheasant, Himalayan Monal, Rufous-vented Tit, Buff-barred Warbler, Alpine Accentor, Dark-breasted Rosefinch.*

## Thimphu Valley

**Habitats:** River; Blue Pine and cool broadleaf forest.
**Altitude range:** 2,300-2,600 m.
**Planning a visit:** Easy accessibility throughout the year. Various sites of interest throughout the valley, all suitable for short trips from Thimphu.
**Birds of interest:**
Migrant waterbirds, swallows, pipits and wagtails along the river in the Babesa area: *Ruddy Shelduck, Common Merganser, Black-tailed Crake, Red-rumped Swallow, Citrine Wagtail, Rosy Pipit, Little Bunting.*

A variety of forest birds in the scenic Tango/Cheri area at the top of the valley: *Yellow-rumped Honeyguide, Long-billed Thrush, Ultramarine Flycatcher, Yellow-browed Tit, Spotted Laughingthrush, Mrs Gould's Sunbird.*

## Tashithang

**Habitats:** Warm broadleaf forest; river gorge.
**Altitude range:** 1,300-1,600 m.
**Planning a visit:** Best season is November–March. The rough road from Rimchu to Tashithang provides good opportunities for the observation of forest birds. Easy accessibility from Punakha.
**Birds of interest:**
Rare species associated with forested rivers: *Crested Kingfisher, Tawny Fish Owl, Pallas's Fish Eagle, White-bellied Heron, three species of forktails.*
A wide variety of forest birds, with the presence of mixed bird flocks in winter: *Red-headed Trogon, Large Niltava, Yellow-vented Warbler, Spotted Wren Babbler, Scarlet Finch.*

## Puna Sang Chhu

**Habitats:** A river in a broad glacial valley with adjacent scrub and agricultural fields.
**Altitude range:** 1,300 m.
**Planning a visit:** Best season is November and March-April. Easy accessibility from Wangdue Phodrang and Punakha. Best visited in the morning, before the winds start to blow.
**Birds of interest:**
A high-concentration site for migrant waterbirds, with a good daily turnover in species and numbers: *Ruddy Shelduck, Spot-billed Duck, Red-crested Pochard, Little Ringed Plover, Long-billed Plover, Greenshank, Pallas's Gull.*
A good site for migrant warblers. *Common Stonechat, Wallcreeper, Dusky Warbler.*
Other specialities: *Ibisbill, Osprey, Pallas's Fish Eagle, Paddyfield Pipit, Crested Bunting.*

## Phobjikha Valley

**Habitats:** High altitude marsh and agricultural fields.
**Altitude range:** 2,800-3,000 m.
**Planning a visit:** Best season is December-February. Opportunities to stay overnight in the area.

Bhutan: protected areas and birding sites

**Legend:**

protected areas

birding sites

roads

**Labels on map:**

Sakteng Wildlife Sanctuary

Khaling Wildlife Sanctuary

Bumdeling Wildlife Sanctuary

Wamrong

Deothang

Samdrup Jongkha

Trashigang

Bumdeling

Lingmethang

Mongar

Yonkhola

Sengor-Namling-Yonkhola

Thrumshingla NP

Sengor

Ura

Jakar

Zhemgang

Zhemgang

Royal Manas NP

Yotong La

Tingtibi

Trongsa

Jigme Singye Wangchuck NP

Celephu

Phobjikha

Phobjikha Valley

Jigme Dorji NP

Wangdue Phodrang

Puna Sang Chhu

Punakha

Laya

Gasa

Phibsoo Wildlife Sanctuary

Tashithang

Thimphu Valley

Thimphu

Paro

Gedu

Chilai La

Torsa Strict Nature Reserve

Phuntsholing

Phuntsholing

359

**Birds of interest:**
Winter population of *Black-necked Cranes*.
Other specialities: *Japanese Quail (summer), Hen Harrier, Oriental Skylark*.

# Yotong La

**Habitats:** Cool broadleaf forest; fir forest with extensive bamboo stands.
**Altitude range:** 2,600-3,500 m.
**Planning a visit:** Best season is April-August. Can be visited in a day trip from Trongsa.
**Birds of interest:**
Birds associated with bamboo stands: *Slender-billed Scimitar Babbler, Great Parrotbill, Fulvous Parrotbill*.
A variety of high altitude species: *Satyr Tragopan, Himalayan Griffon, Red-headed Bullfinch, White-winged Grosbeak, Gold-naped Finch*.

# Sengor-Namling-Yonkhola

**Habitats:** Fir and hemlock forest; cool and warm broadleaf forest.
**Altitude range:** 1,500-3,800 m.
**Planning a visit:** Best season is April-May. Far from any major town; preferably plan to camp in the area. The quiet road passes through the heart of Thrumshingla National Park and provides perfect viewing conditions. The site offers great opportunities for exploring a unique unbroken stretch of well-developed forests covering a wide altitude range. Probably the most diverse bird community at an accessible site in Bhutan.
**Birds of interest:**
Thrumshing La-Sengor: *Blood Pheasant, Himalayan Monal, Orange-flanked Bush Robin, Slender-billed Scimitar Babbler*.
Sengor-Namling: *Satyr Tragopan, Bar-winged Wren Babbler, Fire-tailed Myzornis*.
Namling-Yonkhola: *Rufous-necked Hornbill, Ward's Trogon, Blue-bearded Bee-eater, Blue-fronted Robin, Grey-sided Laughingthrush, Scaly Laughingthrush, Coral-billed Scimitar Babbler, Rufous-throated Wren Babbler, Wedge-billed Wren Babbler, Cutia, Yellow-throated Fulvetta, Black-throated Parrotbill, Greater Rufous-headed Parrotbill*.

# Zhemgang

**Habitats:** Warm broadleaf and subtropical forest.
**Altitude range:** 600-1,900 m.
**Planning a visit:** Best season is November-April. Far from major towns; preferably plan to camp in the area. The quiet road provides perfect viewing conditions. The site offers great opportunities for exploring well-developed forests covering a wide altitude range, complementary to the Sengor-Namling area.
**Birds of interest:**
A good variety of forest birds: *Great Hornbill, Rufous-necked Hornbill, Red-headed Trogon, Pin-tailed Green Pigeon, Long-tailed Broadbill, White-tailed Robin, Beautiful Nuthatch, Sultan Tit, White-throated Bulbul, Yellow-vented Warbler, Rufous-faced Warbler, White-crested Laughingthrush, Lesser Necklaced Laughingthrush, Greater Necklaced Laughingthrush, Spotted Wren Babbler, Cutia, Greater Rufous-headed Parrotbill*.
In winter, a variety of mixed bird flocks with resident birds and altitudinal migrants.

# Bumdeling

**Habitats:** A river in a broad valley; warm broadleaf forest.
**Altitude range:** 1,900-2,000 m.
**Planning a visit:** Best season is November-April. A day's hike from Chhorten Kora/Trashigang.
**Birds of interest:**
Species associated with wetland habitats: *Ferruginous Pochard, Little Ringed Plover, Black-necked Crane, Wood Snipe, Little Forktail, Spotted Forktail*
A variety of forest birds: *Ward's Trogon, White-tailed Robin, Golden-breasted Fulvetta, Maroon-backed Accentor*.

# 11. References

## 11.1 Literature sources

Ali, S. (1977) *Field guide to the birds of the eastern Himalayas*. New Delhi: Oxford University Press.

Ali, S. and Ripley, S. D. (1983) *Handbook of the birds of India and Pakistan*. Compact edition. New Delhi: Oxford University Press.

Ali, S., Biswas, B. and Ripley, S. D. (1996) The birds of Bhutan. *Rec. Zool. Survey India, Occ. Pap*. 136.

Alström, P. and Olsson, U. (1999) The Golden-spectacled Warbler: a complex of sibling species, including a previously undescribed species. *Ibis* 141: 545–568.

Aris, M. (1995) *The Raven crown: the origins of Buddhist monarchy in Bhutan*. Weatherhill.

Aste, C. (1995) *Forestry integrated wildlife management, Wangthangla-Thrumsingla, Bhutan. Integrated forest management project. Final report*. Vienna: Institute for Wildlife Biology & Game Management.

BirdLife International (2001) *Threatened birds of Asia: the BirdLife International Red Data Book*. Cambridge: BirdLife International.

Bishop, K. D. (1999a) Preliminary notes on some birds in Bhutan. *Forktail* 15: 87–91.

Bishop, K. D. (1999b) The road between Ura and Lingmethang in eastern Bhutan. *Bull. Oriental Bird Club* 29: 44–47.

Bijlsma, R. G. (1991) Migration of raptors and Demoiselle Cranes over central Nepal. *Birds of Prey Bull*. 4: 73–80.

Choudhury, A. (1998) Some new elevation records of birds from Mehao Wildlife Sanctuary, Arunachal Pradesh, India. *Forktail* 14: 71.

Choudhury, A. (2001) Some bird records from Nagaland, north-east India. *Forktail* 17: 91–104.

Clements, F. A. (1992) Recent records of birds from Bhutan. *Forktail* 7: 57–73.

Dorji, P. J. (1987) Bhutan's Black-necked Cranes. *Oryx* 21: 71–72.

Dorji, S. (2000) Avifauna survey in Ura Valley. *Druk Bja Yigsel* 3: 1–6.

Farrow, D. and Spierenburg. P. J. (2000) Golden-spectacled and Whistler's Warbler. *Druk Bja Yigsel* 3: 15–19.

Fletcher, B. (2001) A record of Slender-billed Gull, *Larus genei*, in Bhutan. *Druk Bja Yigsel* 4: 11.

Gaston, A. J. (1989) Black-necked Cranes and other birds in Bhutan in winter. *Bull. Oriental Bird Club* 9: 9–12.

Grimmett, R., Inskipp C. and Inskipp, T. (1998) *Birds of the Indian subcontinent*. London: Christopher Helm.

Grierson, A. J. C. and Long, D. G. (1983) *Flora of Bhutan*. Vol. 1, part 1. Edinburgh: Royal Botanic Garden.

Hagemeijer, E. J. M. and Blair, M. J., eds. (1997) *The EBCC atlas of European breeding birds: their distribution and abundance*. London: T. & A. D. Poyser.

Hussain, S. A. and Ali, S. (1979) Beehive predation by wasps (genus *Vespa*) and its possible benefit to honeyguides (Indicatoridae) in Bhutan. *J. Bombay Nat. Hist. Soc*. 76: 159.

Hussain, S. A. and Ali, S. (1984) Some notes on the ecology and status of the Orange-rumped Honeyguide *Indicator xanthonotus* in the Himalayas. *J. Bombay Nat. Hist. Soc*. 80: 564–574.

Inskipp, C. (2001) Globally threatened birds of Bhutan. *Druk Bja Yigsel* 4: 1–10.

Inskipp, C. and Inskipp, T. (1985) *A guide to the birds of Nepal*. London: Christopher Helm.

Inskipp, C. and Inskipp, T. (1993a) Birds recorded during a visit to Bhutan in autumn 1991. *Forktail* 8: 97–112.

Inskipp, C. and Inskipp, T. (1993b) Birds recorded during a visit to Bhutan in spring 1993. *Forktail* 9: 121–142.

Inskipp, C. and Inskipp, T. (1995) *Introduction to birdwatching in Bhutan*. WWF Bhutan Programme.

Inskipp, C. and Inskipp, T. (2000) Single species bird flocks. *Druk Bja Yigsel* 2: 1–3.

Inskipp, C., Inskipp, T. and Grimmett, R. (1999) *Birds of Bhutan*. London: Christopher Helm.

Inskipp, C., Inskipp, T. and Sherub (2000a) The ornithological importance of Thrumshingla National Park, Bhutan. *Forktail* 16: 147–162.

Inskipp, T. (2001) Annotated checklist and bibliography of the birds of Bhutan. Unpublished.

Inskipp, T., Inskipp, C. and Sherub (2000b) Wedge-billed Wren-babbler—a new species for Bhutan. *Druk Bja Yigsel* 3: 7–9.

Inskipp, T., Lindsey, N. and Duckworth, W. (1996) *An annotated checklist of the birds of the Oriental region.* Sandy: Oriental Bird Club.

Kazmierczak, K. (2000) Sunbird Bhutan tour—April 2000. *Druk Bja Yigsel* 3: 10–14.

Kaul, R. and Shakya, S. (2001) Spring call counts of some Galliformes in the Pipar Reserve, Nepal. *Forktail* 17: 75–80.

King, B., Buck, H., Ferguson, R., Fisher, T., Goblet, C., Nickel, H. and Suter, W. (2001) Birds recorded during two expeditions to north Myanmar (Burma). *Forktail* 17: 29–40.

King, D. I. and Rappole, J. H. (2001) Kleptoparasitism of laughingthrushes *Garrulax* by Greater Racket-tailed Drongos *Dicrurus paradiseus* in Myanmar. *Forktail* 17: 121–122.

Ludlow, F. and Kinnear, N. B. (1937) The birds of Bhutan and adjacent territories of Sikkim and Tibet. *Ibis* (14) 1: 1–46, 249–293, 467–504.

Ludlow, F. and Kinnear, N. B. (1944) The birds of south-eastern Tibet. *Ibis* 86: 43–86, 176–208, 348–389.

MacKinnon, J. (1991) *National conservation plan Bhutan (draft).* Thimphu: Dept. Forestry, Bhutan.

Mauro, I. and Vercruysse, E. (2000) Rusty-bellied Shortwing *Brachypteryx hyperythra* at Lava, Darjeeling, India in April and June 1996. *Forktail* 16: 176–178.

McClure, H. E. and Leelavit, O. (1972) Birds banded in Asia during the MAPS program, by locality, from 1963 through 1971. *US Army Res. & Development Group, Far East, Rep.* No. FE-315–7.

Meine, C. D. and Archibald, G. W. (1996) *The cranes: status survey and conservation action plan.* IUCN, Gland and Cambridge: International Union for Conservation of Nature.

Miehe, G. and Miehe, S. (1998) *Plant formations in central Bhutan and the challenges of conserving biodiversity. Reflections after a short-term visit in October 1998.* Eschborn: Deutsche Gesellschaft für Technische Zusammenarbeit (GTZ).

Ministry of Agriculture (1997) *Atlas of Bhutan. Land cover & area statistics of 20 dzongkhags.* Thimphu: Ministry of Agriculture, Royal Government of Bhutan.

Ministry of Agriculture (2002) *Biodiversity action plan for Bhutan.* Thimphu: Ministry of Agriculture, Royal Government of Bhutan.

Moet, F. I. (1996) Some notes on the birds of Bhutan. *J. Bombay Nat. Hist. Soc.* 93: 299–300.

Negi, G. S. (1983) *Forestry development in Bhutan. Report on remote sensing, land use and vegetation mapping.* Rome: UNDP/FAO.

Oaks, J. L., Meteyer, C. U., Rideout, B. A., Shivaprasad, H. L., Gilbert, M., Virani, M. Z., Watson, R. T. and Khan, A. A. (2004) Diagnostic investigation of vulture mortality: the anti-inflammatory drug Diclofenac is associated with visceral gout. *Falco* 24: 13-14.

Pelgen, U. and Rigden, T. (1999) *Khengrig Namsum: a historical profile of Zhemgang Dzongkhag.* Zhemgang: Integrated Sustainable Development Project.

Pradhan R. and Wangdi, T. (1999) *Threatened birds in Bhutan.* Privately published, Kathmandu, Nepal.

Pradhan, R. (2000) Linkages between Bhutan's hornbills and broadleaf forest ecosystem. *Habitat Himalaya* 7 (2).

Robson, C. (2000) *A field guide to the birds of South-East Asia.* London: New Holland.

Roder, F, de (1989) The migration of raptors south of Annapurna, Nepal autumn 1985. *Forktail* 4: 9–17.

Schultz, S., Sagar Baral, H., Charman, S., Cunningham, A. A., Das, D., Ghalsasi, G. R., Goudar, M. S., Green, R. E., Jones, A., Nighot, P., Pain, D. J. and Prakash, V. (2004). Diclofenac poisoning is widespread in declining vulture populations across the Indian subcontinent. *Proceedings of the Royal Society of London.* Series B271: S458–460.

Sherub (2000a) Cinnamon Bittern: new to Bhutan. *Druk Bja Yigsel* 1: 5–6.

Sherub (2000b) Avifaunal survey in Bhutan. *Druk Bja Yigsel* 1: 11–16.

Sherub (2000c) Wetlands of Bhutan. *Druk Bja Yigsel* 2: 12–22.

Spierenburg, P. J. (2000a) The Eurasian Hobby in Bhutan. *Druk Bja Yigsel* 1: 2–4.

Spierenburg, P. J. (2000b) Honeyguides and rock bees. *Druk Bja Yigsel* 2: 4–11.

Spierenburg, P. J. (2000c) Waterfowl counts. *Druk Bja Yigsel* 2: 25–28.

Spierenburg, P. J. (2001) Migrating birds of prey. *Druk Bja Yigsel* 4: 19–24.

Spierenburg, P. J. and Sherub (2000a) Waterbirds in west Bhutan, winter 2000. *Druk Bja Yigsel* 1: 7–10.

Spierenburg, P. J. and Sherub (2000b) *Wetland sites and water birds in west Bhutan.* Thimphu: Nature Conservation Division, Bhutan.

Tymstra, R., Connop, S. and Tshering, C. (1997) Some bird observations from central Bhutan, May 1994. *Forktail* 12: 47–60.

Wetlands International (2002) *Waterbird population estimates.* Third edition. Wageningen: Wetlands International (Global Series No. 12).

# 11.2 Primary data

1.  **Ali, S., Biswas, B. and Ripley, S. D.**

    Ali, S., Biswas, B. and Ripley, S. D. (1996) The birds of Bhutan. *Rec. Zool. Survey India, Occ. Pap.* 136.

    Abdulali, H. (1969–1992) record on museum specimen of Kashmir Flycatcher in: BirdLife International (2001) *Threatened birds of Asia: the BirdLife International Red Data Book.* Cambridge: BirdLife International.

2.  **Armstrong, R. and Armstrong, S.**

    Armstrong, R. and Armstrong, S. (2001) Bhutan: The Laya Trek (March–April 2001). Unpublished.

3.  **Aste, C.**

    Aste, C. (1995) *Forestry integrated wildlife management, Wangthangla–Thrumsingla, Bhutan. Integrated forest management project. Final report.* Vienna: Institute for Wildlife Biology & Game Management.

4.  **Bevanger, K. and Gjershaug, J. O.**

    Bevanger, K. and Gjershaug, J. O. (1998) Wildlife report EIA—Mangde Chu. Unpublished.

5.  **Bishop, K. D./Victor Emanuel Nature Tours**

    Bishop, K. D. (1994) The list of birds and mammals observed on the VENT Bhutan and Assam tour, February 26–April 5, 1994. Unpublished.

    Bishop, K. D. (1995) Assam & Bhutan, March 14–April 13, 1995. Victor Emanuel Nature Tours. Unpublished.

    Bishop, K. D. (1996) Notes on birds seen in Bhutan in 1996. Unpublished.

    Bishop, K. D. (1997) The birds and mammals recorded on the VENT Bhutan tour, April 12–May 2, 1997. Unpublished.

    Bishop, K. D. (1998) The birds and mammals recorded on the 1998 VENT Bhutan tour. Unpublished.

    Bishop, K. D. (1999) The birds and mammals recorded on the 1999 VENT Bhutan tour. Unpublished.

    Bishop, K. D. (1999a) Preliminary notes on some birds in Bhutan. *Forktail* 15: 87–91.

    Bishop, K. D. (1999b) The road between Ura and Limithang in eastern Bhutan. *Oriental Bird Club Bull.* 29: 44–47.

    Bishop, K. D. (2000) The checklist of birds, other vertebrates and flowering plants recorded on the VENT Bhutan tour 24 April–18 May 2000. Unpublished.

    Bishop, K. D. and Kennerley, P. (2001) The list of birds recorded on the VENT tour of Bhutan 2001. Unpublished.

Bishop, K. D. (2002) The birds and mammals recorded on the 2002 VENT Bhutan tour. Unpublished.

Bishop, K. D. Pers. comm. Records after 2002.

6. **Bishop, M. A.**

Records in: BirdLife International (2001) *Threatened birds of Asia: the BirdLife International Red Data Book*. Cambridge: BirdLife International.

7. **Chacko, R. T.**

Chacko, R. T. (1991) Black-necked Cranes in Bhutan, winter study, February–March 1991. Unpublished.

Chacko, R. T. (1992) Birds seen in Bhutan during winter Oct. 91–Apr. 92. Unpublished.

8. **Caron, C.**

Records in: BirdLife International (2001) *Threatened birds of Asia: the BirdLife International Red Data Book*. Cambridge: BirdLife International.

9. **Carrick, B.**

Records in: BirdLife International (2001) *Threatened birds of Asia: the BirdLife International Red Data Book*. Cambridge: BirdLife International.

10. **Clements, F. A.**

Clements, F. A. (1992) Recent records of birds from Bhutan. *Forktail* 7: 57–73.

11. **Dorji, T.**

Dorji, T. (1994) Notes on birds seen in Bhutan. Unpublished.

12. **Dorji, L. and Wangchuk, S./Jigme Singye Wangchuck National Park**

Bird survey March/April 2002. Unpublished.

13. **Dreyer, N. P.**

Dreyer, N. P. (1995) Trip report: Bhutan, January 8–27 1995. Unpublished.

14. **Farrow, D./Birdquest**

Farrow, D. Pers. comm. on July 1994 tour.

Farrow, D. (1995) Bhutan & Assam, 28 Oct–18 Nov 95. Explore Worldwide Tour. Unpublished.

Farrow, D. (1997) Birdquest Bhutan 1997, 9–27 April. Unpublished.

Farrow, D. (1998) Birdquest Bhutan 1998, 8–26 April. Unpublished.

Farrow, D. (1999) Birdquest Bhutan 1999, 9–25 April. Unpublished.

Farrow, D. (2000a) Birdquest Bhutan 2000, 10 March–4 April. Unpublished.

Farrow, D. (2000b) Birdquest Bhutan 2000, 11–29 April. Unpublished.

Farrow, D. and Spierenburg, P. J. (2000) Golden-spectacled and Whistler's Warbler. *Druk Bja Yigsel* 3: 15–19.

Farrow, D. (2001) Birdquest Bhutan 2001, 7–25 April. Unpublished.

Farrow, D. (2002) Birdquest Bhutan 2002, 7–25 April. Unpublished.

Farrow, D. Pers. comm. Records after 2002.

15. **Fletcher, B.**

Fletcher, B. (2001) A record of Slender-billed Gull, *Larus genei*, in Bhutan. *Druk Bja Yigsel* 4: 11.

Fletcher, B. Bird records 2000/2001.

16. **Gaston, A. J.**

Gaston, A. J. (1989) Black-necked Cranes and other birds in Bhutan in winter. *Bull. Oriental Bird Club* 9: 9–12.

17. **Geest, G. M. van der**

Geest, G. M. van der. Records October 2001.

18. Gole, P.

Records in: BirdLife International (2001) *Threatened birds of Asia: the BirdLife International Red Data Book*. Cambridge: BirdLife International.

19. Holt, P./Sunbird

Holt, P. (1995) Bhutan, 24 February–9 March 1995. Unpublished.

Holt, P. (1996) Bhutan, 8–21 April 1996. Unpublished.

Holt, P. (1998) Bhutan, 5–22 April 1998. Unpublished.

Holt, P. (1999) Bhutan, 4–21 April 1999. Unpublished.

Holt, P. (2001) Sunbird tour of Bhutan, 25 March–11 April 2001. Unpublished.

Holt, P. (2002) Sunbird tour of Bhutan, 7–25 April 2002. Unpublished.

Holt, P. Pers. comm. Records after 2002.

20. Holmes, J. R. S.

Ali, S., Biswas, B. and Ripley, S. D. (1996) The birds of Bhutan. *Rec. Zool. Survey. India, Occ. Pap.* 136.

21 Hussain, S. A.

Hussain, S. A. and Ali, S. (1979) Beehive predation by wasps (genus *Vespa*) and its possible benefit to honeyguides (Indicatoridae) in Bhutan. *J. Bombay Nat. Hist. Soc.* 76: 159.

Hussain, S. A. and Ali, S. (1984) Some notes on the ecology and status of the Orange-rumped Honeyguide *Indicator xanthonotus* in the Himalayas. *J. Bombay Nat. Hist. Soc.* 80: 564–574.

22. Inskipp, C. and Inskipp, T.

Inskipp, C. and Inskipp, T. (1993a) Birds recorded during a visit to Bhutan in autumn 1991. *Forktail* 8: 97–112.

Inskipp, C. and Inskipp, T. (1993b) Birds recorded during a visit to Bhutan in spring 1993. *Forktail* 9: 121–142.

Inskipp, C. and Inskipp, T. (1995) *Introduction to birdwatching in Bhutan*. WWF-Bhutan Programme.

Inskipp, C. and Inskipp, T. (1996) Avifauna survey-cum-training programme in Jigme Dorji National Park, April–May 1996. Unpublished.

Inskipp, C., Inskipp, T. and Sherub (2000a) The ornithological importance of Thrumshingla National Park, Bhutan. *Forktail* 16: 147–162.

Inskipp, T, Inskipp, C. and Sherub (2000b) Wedge-billed Wren-babbler—a new species for Bhutan. *Druk Bja Yigsel* 3: 7–9.

Inskipp, C. and Inskipp, T. (2000) Single species bird flocks. *Druk Bja Yigsel* 2: 1–3.

Inskipp, C. and Inskipp, T. Pers. comm. Additional records 1996–2000.

23. Jannes, H.

Records in: Inskipp, C., Inskipp, T. and Sherub (2000a) The ornithological importance of Thrumshingla National Park, Bhutan. *Forktail* 16: 147–162.

24. Jensen, B. O.

Jensen, B. O. Pers. comm.  Records March 2000.

25. Jepson, P.

Jepson, P. (1988) Naturetrek. Bhutan bird list, 17th October to 1st November 1988. Unpublished.

Jepson, P. (1989) Naturetrek Bhutan bird list. Unpublished.

26. Johnson, D. L.

Johnson, D. L. (1993) Birds recorded in Bhutan, 17 March to 3 April 1993. Unpublished.

27. Kazmierczak, K.

Kazmierczak, K. (2000) Sunbird Bhutan tour—April 2000. *Druk Bja Yigsel* 3: 10–14.

Kazmierczak, K. and Fisher, D. (2000) Bhutan 9–26 April 2000. Unpublished.

Kazmierczak, K. (2001) Bhutan, The Hidden Kingdom 14–30 April 2001. Peregrine Holidays trip report. Unpublished.

28. **King, B.**

King, B. (1995) KingBird tour, Bhutan, 8–27 January 1995. Unpublished.

King, B. (1996) 1996 KingBird tour, Bhutan, 28 April–18 May. Unpublished.

King, B. (1997) 1997 KingBird tour, Bhutan, 6–26 April. Unpublished.

King, B. (1998) 1998 KingBird tour, Bhutan, 28 March–17 April. Unpublished.

King, B. (1999) 1999 KingBird tour, Bhutan, 11 April–1 May. Unpublished.

King, B. (2000) 2000 KingBird tour, Bhutan, 9–21 April. Unpublished.

King, B. (2001) 2001 KingBird tour, Bhutan, 8–28 April. Unpublished.

King, B. (2002) 2002 KingBird tour, Bhutan, 7–27 April. Unpublished.

King, B. Pers. comm. Records after 2002.

29. **Kovacs, J.-C.**

Kovacs, J.-C. (1995a) Bhutan et Inde du Nord (janvier–février 1995). Comptes rendu d'observations ornithologiques. Unpublished.

Kovacs, J.-C. (1995b) Bhutan et Népal (septembre–octobre 1995). Comptes rendu d'observations ornithologiques. Unpublished.

30. **Leahey, C.**

Records in: Inskipp, C., Inskipp, T. and Sherub (2000a) The ornithological importance of Thrumshingla National Park, Bhutan. *Forktail* 16: 147–162.

31. **Ludlow, F.**

Ludlow, F. and Kinnear, N. B. (1937) The birds of Bhutan and adjacent territories of Sikkim and Tibet. *Ibis* (14) 1: 1–46, 249–293, 467–504.

Ludlow, F. and Kinnear, N. B. (1944) The birds of south-eastern Tibet. *Ibis* 86: 43–86, 176–208, 348–389.

32. **Madge, S. C.**

Madge, S. C. (2001) Birds recorded in Bhutan, 17 March–2 April 2001. Unpublished.

33. **Mair, L.**

Mair, L. (2001) Bhutan birding trip report, April 2001. Unpublished.

34. **Martins, R.**

Martins, R. (1994) Ornitholidays, Bhutan and Assam, 18 November–5 December 1994. Unpublished.

35. **Matthijsen, H.**

Matthijsen, H. Pers. comm. Records March 2002.

36. **McClure, H. E. and Leelavit, P.**

McClure, H. E. and Leelavit, P. (1972) Birds banded in Asia during the MAPS program, by locality, from 1963 through 1971. *US Army Res. & Development Group, Far East, Rep.* No. FE-315–7.

37. **Mills, D. G. H.**

Mills, D. G. H. (1989) Bhutan's Bumthang Valley—April/May 1989: a list of birds and mammals recorded, Naturetrek. Unpublished.

38. **Moet, F. I.**

Moet, F. I. (1996) Some notes on the birds of Bhutan. *J. Bombay Nat. Hist. Soc.* 93: 299–300.

39. **Murphy, C.**

Murphy, C. (1994) Birds recorded in Bhutan, April–May 1994. Unpublished.

40. **Pain, A.**

Pain, A. Pers. comm. Records February–March 2000.

41. **Pemberton, R. B.**

Records in: Ludlow, F. and Kinnear, N. B. (1944) The birds of south-eastern Tibet. *Ibis* 86: 43–86, 176–208, 348–389.

Records in: Inskipp, T. (2001) Annotated checklist and bibliography of the birds of Bhutan. Unpublished.

42. **Phuntsho, T.**

Phuntsho, T. Pers. comm.  Records January–June 2002; spring 2004.

43. **Pickering, R.**

Bird records January 1998–December 2001. Unpublished.

44. **Pradhan, R.**

Pradhan R. Bird species occurring in FMUs and their conservation status, including occurrence in adjacent protected areas. Unpublished.

Pradhan R. Overview bird records per locality and quarter—early nineties.

Pradhan R. Selected field notes 1994–1996.

Pradhan R. Field notes January–February 2000.

Pradhan R. and Wangdi, T. (1999) *Threatened birds in Bhutan*. Privately published, Kathmandu, Nepal.

Pradhan, R. (2000) Linkages between Bhutan's hornbills and broadleaf forest ecosystem. *Habitat Himalaya* 7 (2).

Records in: Inskipp, C., Inskipp, T. and Sherub (2000a) The ornithological importance of Thrumshingla National Park, Bhutan. *Forktail* 16: 147–162.

Records in: BirdLife International (2001) *Threatened birds of Asia: the BirdLife International Red Data Book*. Cambridge: BirdLife International.

45. **Riessen, A. van**

Riessen, A. van. Pers. comm. Records November 1999.

46. **Redman, N. J.**

Redman, N. J. (1998) Bhutan, 11–28 March 1997: checklist. Unpublished.

47. **Royal Society for Protection of Nature**

Records in: BirdLife International (2001) *Threatened birds of Asia: the BirdLife International Red Data Book*. Cambridge: BirdLife International.

Dago Tshering. Pers. comm. Records November 1999–March 2001.

Tshewang Norbu. White-bellied Heron project 2003 *www.rspn-bhutan.org*

48. **Sharma, D. D.**

Sharma, D. D. (1998) Notes on birds recorded in Bhutan. Unpublished.

49. **Sherub**

Sherub (2000a) Cinnamon Bittern: new to Bhutan. *Druk Bja Yigsel* 1: 5–6.

Sherub (2000) Report of avifauna survey of Bumdeling Wildlife Sanctuary May–June and September 2000. Unpublished.

Sherub (2001) Bird list Dakpai–Buli road area. Unpublished.

Spierenburg, P. J. and Sherub (2000) Wetland sites and waterbirds in west Bhutan. Results of a survey conducted 13–20 February 2000. Unpublished.

Sherub. Pers. comm. Records after 2002.

50. **Singye, R. and Dorji, S./Thrumshingla National Park**

Dorji, S. (2000) Avifauna survey in Ura Valley. *Druk Bja Yigsel* 3: 1–6.

Singye, R. (2002) Field notes birds Ura/Thrumshingla NP. Unpublished.

51. **Sparks, J. and Lang, D.**

Sparks, J. and Lang, D. (2000) Birds seen in Bhutan, Lunana–Snowman trek, October/November 2000. Unpublished.

**52. Spierenburg, P. J.**

Spierenburg, P. J. Field notes, February 1997–June 2002. Unpublished.

**53. Steenvoorden, A.**

Steenvoorden, A. (2000) Reisverslag Bhutan, December 2000. Unpublished.

Steenvoorden, A. (2002) Overzicht waargenomen vogelsoorten Bhutan 2002. Unpublished.

**54. Sutherland, T. and Sutherland, M.**

Sutherland, T. and Sutherland, M. (2000) Trip report: western Bhutan, March 13–18, 2000. Unpublished.

**55. Tymstra, R., Connop, S. and Tshering, C,**

Tymstra, R., Connop, S. and Tshering, C. (1997) Some bird observations from central Bhutan, May 1994. *Forktail* 12: 47–60.

**56. Urban, R.**

Urban, R. Pers. comm.  Records January 2000.

**57. Westrienen, R. van**

Westrienen, R. van (2000) Birdlist Bhutan, Feb–Mar 2000. Unpublished.

# Index of scientific names

Abroscopus albogularis 278
    schisticeps 279
    superciliaris 279
Accipiter badius 137
    gentilis 139
    nisus 138
    trivirgatus 136
    virgatus 138
Aceros nipalensis 67
    undulatus 68
Acridotheres fuscus 232
    ginginianus 232
    grandis 232
    tristis 231
Acrocephalus aedon 265
    dumetorum 264
Actinodura egertoni 304
    nipalensis 304
Actitis hypoleucos 118
Aegithalos concinnus 244
    iouschistos 244
Aegithina tiphia 184
Aegolius funereus 98
Aegypius monachus 134
Aethopyga gouldiae 325
    ignicauda 327
    nipalensis 326
    saturata 326
    siparaja 327
Aix galericulata 45
Alauda gulgula 322
Alcedo atthis 72
    hercules 72
Alcippe castaneceps 308
    chrysotis 307
    cinerea 307
    dubia 310
    ludlowi 309
    nipalensis 310
    rufogularis 309
    vinipectus 308
Alophoixus flaveolus 252
Amaurornis phoenicurus 111
Anas acuta 48
    clypeata 47
    crecca 49
    falcata 45

Anas (cont.)
    formosa 49
    penelope 46
    platyrhynchos 46
    poecilorhyncha 47
    querquedula 48
    strepera 45
Anser anser 43
    indicus 43
Anthracoceros albirostris 68
Anthreptes singalensis 325
Anthus campestris 335
    cervinus 336
    godlewskii 335
    hodgsoni 336
    richardi 334
    roseatus 336
    rubescens 337
    rufulus 334
    trivialis 335
Apus acuticauda 92
    affinis 92
    pacificus 91
Aquila chrysaetos 144
    clanga 142
    heliaca 143
    nipalensis 143
Arachnothera longirostra 328
    magna 328
Arborophila mandellii 37
    rufogularis 36
    torqueola 36
Ardea cinerea 153
    insignis 154
Ardeola grayii 155
Artamus fuscus 170
Asio flammeus 99
    otus 99
Athene brama 98
Aythya baeri 51
    ferina 50
    fuligula 52
    nyroca 51
Blythipicus pyrrhotis 62
Brachypteryx hyperythra 197
    leucophrys 197
    montana 198

*Brachypteryx* (cont.)
    *stellata* 196
*Bradypterus luteoventris* 263
    *seebohmi* 263
    *thoracicus* 263
*Bubo nipalensis* 94
*Bubulcus ibis* 155
*Buceros bicornis* 66
*Burhinus oedicnemus* 120
*Buteo buteo* 140
    *hemilasius* 141
    *rufinus* 141
*Butorides striata* 156
*Cacomantis merulinus* 83
    *passerinus* 83
    *sonneratii* 82
*Calandrella acutirostris* 321
    *brachydactyla* 321
    *raytal* 322
*Calidris ferruginea* 119
    *temminckii* 119
*Caprimulgus affinis* 100
    *indicus* 99
    *macrurus* 100
*Carduelis spinoides* 342
    *thibetana* 342
*Carpodacus edwardsii* 346
    *erythrinus* 345
    *nipalensis* 344
    *pulcherrimus* 346
    *puniceus* 347
    *rubescens* 344
    *rubicilloides* 347
    *thura* 347
    *trifasciatus* 347
*Casmerodius albus* 154
*Celeus brachyurus* 59
*Centropus bengalensis* 87
    *sinensis* 87
*Cephalopyrus flammiceps* 238
*Certhia discolor* 237
    *familiaris* 236
    *nipalensis* 237
*Ceryle rudis* 75
*Cettia acanthizoides* 262
    *brunnifrons* 262
    *flavolivacea* 261
    *fortipes* 260
    *major* 261

*Cettia* (cont.)
    *pallidipes* 260
*Ceyx erithacus* 73
*Chaimarrornis leucocephalus* 220
*Chalcophaps indica* 106
*Charadrius alexandrinus* 123
    *dubius* 122
    *mongolus* 123
    *placidus* 122
*Chloropsis aurifrons* 160
    *hardwickii* 160
*Chrysococcyx maculatus* 84
    *xanthorhynchus* 84
*Chrysocolaptes lucidus* 61
*Ciconia episcopus* 157
    *nigra* 156
*Cinclidium frontale* 223
*Cinclus cinclus* 185
    *pallasii* 185
*Circaetus gallicus* 135
*Circus aeruginosus* 135
    *cyaneus* 136
    *melanoleucos* 136
*Cissa chinensis* 164
*Clamator coromandus* 77
*Cochoa purpurea* 227
    *viridis* 227
*Collocalia brevirostris* 89
*Columba hodgsonii* 102
    *leuconota* 101
    *livia* 100
    *pulchricollis* 102
    *rupestris* 101
*Conostoma oemodium* 317
*Copsychus malabaricus* 217
    *saularis* 216
*Coracias benghalensis* 71
*Coracina macei* 172
    *melaschistos* 173
*Corvus corax* 170
    *macrorhynchos* 169
    *splendens* 168
*Coturnix coturnix* 34
    *japonica* 35
*Cuculus canorus* 80
    *micropterus* 80
    *poliocephalus* 82
    *saturatus* 81
*Culicicapa ceylonensis* 211

*Cutia nipalensis*  300
*Cyornis poliogenys*  209
    *rubeculoides*  210
    *unicolor*  210
*Cypsiurus balasiensis*  90
*Delichon dasypus*  248
    *nipalensis*  248
*Dendrocitta formosae*  165
    *frontalis*  165
    *vagabunda*  164
*Dendrocopos atratus*  356
    *canicapillus*  56
    *cathpharius*  58
    *darjellensis*  58
    *hyperythrus*  57
    *macei*  57
*Dendrocygna bicolor*  43
*Dendronanthus indicus*  330
*Dicaeum chrysorrheum*  322
    *concolor*  323
    *cruentatum*  324
    *ignipectus*  324
    *melanoxanthum*  323
*Dicrurus aeneus*  180
    *annectans*  180
    *hottentottus*  182
    *leucophaeus*  179
    *macrocercus*  178
    *paradiseus*  182
    *remifer*  181
*Dinopium shorii*  61
*Ducula aenea*  108
    *badia*  109
*Egretta garzetta*  153
*Elanus caeruleus*  129
*Emberiza buchanani*  354
    *pusilla*  354
    *spodocephala*  355
*Enicurus immaculatus*  225
    *leschenaulti*  226
    *maculatus*  226
*Enicurus schistaceus*  225
    *scouleri*  224
*Esacus recurvirostris*  120
*Eudynamys scolopacea*  85
*Eumyias thalassina*  206
*Eurystomus orientalis*  71
*Falco amurensis*  148
    *columbarius*  149

*Falco* (cont.)
    *peregrinus*  150
    *severus*  150
    *subbuteo*  149
    *tinnunculus*  148
*Ficedula hodgsonii*  200
    *hyperythra*  203
    *monileger*  202
    *parva*  202
    *sapphira*  206
    *strophiata*  201
    *subrubra*  202
    *superciliaris*  204
    *tricolor*  205
    *westermanni*  204
*Francolinus francolinus*  34
*Fringilla coelebs*  342
    *montifringilla*  342
*Fulica atra*  112
*Gallinago gallinago*  116
    *nemoricola*  114
    *solitaria*  114
    *stenura*  115
*Gallinula chloropus*  356
*Gallirallus striatus*  111
*Gallus gallus*  40
*Gampsorhynchus rufulus*  303
*Garrulax affinis*  287
    *albogularis*  280
    *caerulatus*  285
    *erythrocephalus*  287
    *gularis*  283
    *leucolophus*  281
    *lineatus*  285
    *monileger*  281
    *ocellatus*  284
    *pectoralis*  282
    *ruficollis*  282
    *rufogularis*  284
    *squamatus*  286
    *striatus*  283
    *subunicolor*  286
*Garrulus glandarius*  163
*Gecinulus grantia*  62
*Glareola lactea*  125
*Glaucidium brodiei*  96
    *cuculoides*  97
    *radiatum*  97
*Gracula religiosa*  233

*Grandala coelicolo* 224

*Grus grus* 109
    *nigricollis* 110
    *virgo* 109

*Gypaetus barbatus* 132

*Gyps bengalensis* 132
    *himalayensis* 133

*Haematospiza sipahi* 348

*Halcyon coromanda* 73
    *pileata* 74
    *smyrnensis* 74

*Haliaeetus albicilla* 131
    *leucoryphus* 130

*Haliastur indus* 130

*Harpactes erythrocephalus* 69

*Harpactes wardi* 70

*Hemiprocne coronata* 93

*Hemipus picatus* 176

*Hemixos flavala* 253

*Heterophasia annectans* 310
    *capistrata* 311
    *picaoides* 312

*Hieraaetus fasciatus* 145
    *kienerii* 146
    *pennatus* 145

*Hierococcyx fugax* 79
    *sparverioides* 78
    *varius* 78

*Hippolais caligata* 265

*Hirundapus caudacutus* 90

*Hirundo daurica* 247
    *rupestris* 246
    *rustica* 246

*Hodgsonius phaenicuroides* 222

*Hypothymis azurea* 183

*Hypsipetes leucocephalus* 254
    *mcclellandii* 253

*Ibidorhyncha struthersii* 120

*Ichthyophaga humilis* 131

*Ictinaetus malayensis* 142

*Indicator xanthonotus* 54

*Irena puella* 159

*Ithaginis cruentus* 38

*Ixobrychus cinnamomeus* 156

*Jynx torquilla* 55

*Ketupa flavipes* 95

*Lanius cristatus* 161
    *schach* 162
    *tephronotus* 162

*Lanius* (cont.)
    *vittatus* 161

*Larus brunnicephalus* 126
    *genei* 127
    *ichthyaetus* 126

*Leiothrix argentauris* 299
    *lutea* 300

*Lerwa lerwa* 33

*Leucosticte nemoricola* 343

*Liocichla phoenicea* 288

*Lonchura punctulata* 341
    *striata* 341

*Lophophorus impejanus* 40

*Lophura leucomelanos* 41

*Loxia curvirostra* 349

*Luscinia brunnea* 213
    *calliope* 212
    *pectoralis* 213
    *svecica* 213

*Lymnocryptes minimus* 116

*Macronous gularis* 298

*Macropygia unchall* 105

*Malacocincla abbotti* 288

*Megaceryle lugubris* 74

*Megalaima asiatica* 64
    *australis* 65
    *franklinii* 64
    *haemacephala* 65
    *lineata* 63
    *virens* 63

*Megalurus palustris* 280

*Melanochlora sultanea* 243

*Melophus lathami* 354

*Mergus merganser* 52

*Merops leschenaulti* 77
    *orientalis* 76

*Mesophoyx intermedia* 154

*Metopidius indicus* 120

*Microhierax caerulescens* 147
    *melanoleucos* 147

*Milvus migrans* 129

*Minla cyanouroptera* 305
    *ignotincta* 306
    *strigula* 306

*Mirafra assamica* 321

*Monticola cinclorhynchus* 186
    *rufiventris* 186
    *solitarius* 187

*Motacilla alba* 330

Motacilla (cont.)
   *cinerea* 334
   *citreola* 332
   *flava* 333
   *maderaspatensis* 332
*Mulleripicus pulverulentus* 62
*Muscicapa dauurica* 199
   *ferruginea* 200
   *muttui* 199
   *sibirica* 198
*Muscicapella hodgsoni* 211
*Mycerobas affinis* 351
   *carnipes* 352
*Mycerobas melanozanthos* 352
*Myiomela leucura* 222
*Myophonus caeruleus* 188
*Myzornis pyrrhoura* 317
*Napothera epilepidota* 292
*Nectarinia asiatica* 325
*Neophron percnopterus* 132
*Niltava grandis* 207
   *macgrigoriae* 208
   *sundara* 208
   *vivida* 209
*Ninox scutulata* 98
*Nucifraga caryocatactes* 166
*Numenius arquata* 117
   *phaeopus* 116
*Nycticorax nycticorax* 156
*Nyctyornis athertoni* 76
*Oenanthe isabellina* 229
   *pleschanka* 229
*Oriolus oriolus* 171
   *tenuirostris* 171
   *traillii* 172
   *xanthornus* 172
*Orthotomus cuculatus* 265
   *sutorius* 266
*Otus bakkamoena* 94
   *spilocephalus* 93
   *sunia* 94
*Pandion haliaetus* 128
*Paradoxornis atrosuperciliaris* 320
   *fulvifrons* 319
   *gularis* 318
   *nipalensis* 319
   *ruficeps* 320
   *unicolor* 318
*Parus ater* 240

Parus (cont.)
   *dichrous* 240
   *major* 241
   *monticolus* 241
   *rubidiventris* 239
   *spilonotus* 242
*Passer domesticus* 329
   *montanus* 330
   *rutilans* 329
*Pavo cristatus* 42
*Pellorneum albiventre* 289
   *ruficeps* 289
*Perdix hodgsoniae* 34
*Pericrocotus brevirostris* 175
   *ethologus* 174
   *flammeus* 176
   *roseus* 173
   *solaris* 174
*Pernis ptilorhyncus* 128
*Phaenicophaeus tristis* 85
*Phalacrocorax carbo* 152
   *fuscicollis* 152
   *niger* 151
*Philomachus pugnax* 120
*Phoenicurus auroreus* 219
   *caeruleocephalus* 217
   *erythrogaster* 220
   *frontalis* 220
   *hodgsoni* 218
   *ochruros* 218
   *schisticeps* 219
*Phylloscopus affinis* 268
   *cantator* 274
   *chloronotus* 270
   *collybita* 266
   *fuligiventer* 267
   *fuscatus* 267
   *humei* 271
   *inornatus* 270
   *maculipennis* 269
   *magnirostris* 272
   *pulcher* 268
   *reguloides* 273
   *trochiloides* 272
*Pica pica* 166
*Picumnus innominatus* 55
*Picus canus* 60
   *chlorolophus* 59
   *flavinucha* 60

*Picus* (cont.)
   *xanthopygaeus* 60
*Pitta nipalensis* 157
   *sordida* 158
*Ploceus benghalensis* 340
   *philippinus* 340
*Pnoepyga albiventer* 292
   *pusilla* 293
*Podiceps cristatus* 151
*Polyplectron bicalcaratum* 42
*Pomatorhinus erythrocnemis* 289
   *erythrogenys* 290
   *ferruginosus* 291
   *ruficollis* 291
   *schisticeps* 290
*Porphyrio porphyrio* 112
*Porzana bicolor* 111
   *fusca* 112
*Prinia atrogularis* 255
   *cinereocapilla* 255
   *criniger* 254
   *hodgsonii* 256
   *inornata* 257
   *rufescens* 256
   *sylvatica* 257
*Propyrrhula subhimachala* 348
*Prunella collaris* 338
   *himalayana* 338
   *immaculata* 340
   *rubeculoides* 339
   *strophiata* 339
*Psarisomus dalhousiae* 158
*Psittacula alexandri* 89
   *eupatria* 88
   *himalayana* 89
   *krameri* 88
*Pteruthius flaviscapis* 302
   *melanotis* 303
   *rufiventer* 301
   *xanthochlorus* 302
*Pycnonotus cafer* 252
   *jocosus* 251
   *leucogenys* 251
   *melanicterus* 250
   *striatus* 250
*Pyrrhocorax graculus* 168
   *pyrrhocorax* 167
*Pyrrhoplectes epauletta* 353
*Pyrrhula erythaca* 351

*Pyrrhula* (cont.)
   *erythrocephala* 350
   *nipalensis* 350
*Recurvirostra avosetta* 121
*Regulus regulus* 249
*Rhipidura albicollis* 178
   *hypoxantha* 177
*Rhodonessa rufina* 50
*Rhyacornis fuliginosus* 221
*Rimator malacoptilus* 292
*Riparia diluta* 245
   *paludicola* 246
   *riparia* 245
*Sarcogyps calvus* 134
*Saroglossa spiloptera* 230
*Sasia ochracea* 56
*Saxicola caprata* 228
   *ferreus* 229
   *insignis* 227
   *torquatus* 228
*Saxicoloides fulicata* 217
*Scolopax rusticola* 113
*Seicercus affinis* 276
   *burkii* 274
   *castaniceps* 277
   *poliogenys* 277
   *whistleri* 274
   *xanthoschistos* 276
*Serilophus lunatus* 158
*Sitta castanea* 233
   *formosa* 234
   *frontalis* 234
   *himalayensis* 234
*Spelaeornis caudatus* 294
   *formosus* 295
   *troglodytoides* 294
*Sphenocichla humei* 296
*Spilornis cheela* 135
*Spizaetus nipalensis* 146
*Stachyris chrysaea* 297
   *nigriceps* 298
   *ruficeps* 297
   *rufifrons* 296
*Sterna aurantia* 127
   *hirundo* 127
*Streptopelia chinensis* 104
   *decaocto* 105
   *orientalis* 103
   *senegalensis* 103

*Streptopelia* (cont.)
    *tranquebarica* 104
*Strix aluco* 96
    *leptogrammica* 95
*Sturnus contra* 231
    *malabaricus* 230
    *vulgaris* 230
*Surniculus lugubris* 86
*Sylvia curruca* 321
*Sylviparus modestus* 242
*Tachybaptus ruficollis* 151
*Tachymarptis melba* 91
*Tadorna ferruginea* 44
    *tadorna* 44
*Tarsiger chrysaeus* 214
    *cyanurus* 214
    *hyperythrus* 216
    *indicus* 215
*Tephrodornis gularis* 184
*Terpsiphone paradisi* 183
*Tesia castaneocoronata* 258
    *cyaniventer* 259
    *olivea* 258
*Tetraogallus tibetanus* 33
*Tichodroma muraria* 236
*Tickellia hodgsoni* 278
*Tragopan blythii* 39
    *satyra* 38
*Treron apicauda* 107
    *bicincta* 106
    *curvirostra* 106
    *phoenicoptera* 107
    *pompadora* 106
    *sphenura* 108
*Tringa glareola* 118
    *nebularia* 117
    *ochropus* 118
    *totanus* 117
*Troglodytes troglodytes* 238
*Turdoides striatus* 299
*Turdus albocinctus* 192
    *boulboul* 192
    *kessleri* 194
    *merula* 193
    *naumanni* 196
    *obscurus* 194
    *rubrocanus* 193
    *ruficollis* 195
    *unicolor* 191

*Turnix suscitator* 53
    *tanki* 53
*Upupa epops* 69
*Urocissa flavirostris* 163
*Vanellus duvaucelii* 124
    *indicus* 125
    *malarbaricus* 124
    *vanellus* 123
*Xiphirhynchus superciliaris* 292
*Yuhina bakeri* 313
    *castaniceps* 312
    *flavicollis* 314
    *gularis* 314
    *nigrimenta* 316
    *occipitalis* 315
    *zantholeuca* 316
*Zoothera citrina* 188
    *dauma* 190
    *dixoni* 190
    *mollissima* 189
    *monticola* 191
*Zosterops palpebrosus* 257

# Index of English names

Accentor, Alpine  338
  Altai  338
  Maroon-backed  340
  Robin  339
  Rufous-breasted  339
Avocet, Pied  121
Babbler, Abbott's  288
  Bar-winged Wren  294
  Black-eared Shrike  303
  Black-headed Shrike  301
  Coral-billed Scimitar  291
  Eyebrowed Wren  292
  Golden  297
  Green Shrike  302
  Grey-throated  298
  Jungle  299
  Long-billed Wren  292
  Puff-throated  289
  Pygmy Wren  293
  Rufous-capped  297
  Rufous-fronted  296
  Rufous-throated Wren  294
  Rusty-cheeked Scimitar  290
  Scaly-breasted Wren  292
  Slender-billed Scimitar  292
  Spot-breasted Scimitar  289
  Spot-throated  289
  Spotted Wren  295
  Streak-breasted Scimitar  291
  Striped Tit  298
  Wedge-billed Wren  296
  White-browed Scimitar  290
  White-browed Shrike  302
  White-hooded  303
Barbet, Blue-eared  65
  Blue-throated  64
  Coppersmith  65
  Golden-throated  64
  Great  63
  Lineated  63
Barwing, Hoary-throated  304
  Rusty-fronted  304
Bee-eater, Blue-bearded  76
  Chestnut-headed  77
  Green  76
Besra  138
Bittern, Cinnamon  156

Blackbird, Eurasian  193
  Grey-winged  192
  White-collared  192
Bluebird, Asian Fairy  159
Bluetail, Red-flanked  214
Bluethroat  213
Brambling  342
Broadbill, Long-tailed  158
  Silver-breasted  158
Bulbul, Ashy  253
  Black  254
  Black-crested  250
  Himalayan  251
  Mountain  253
  Red-vented  252
  Red-whiskered  251
  Striated  250
  White-throated  252
Bullfinch, Brown  350
  Grey-headed  351
  Red-headed  350
Bunting, Black-faced  355
  Crested  354
  Grey-necked  354
  Little  354
Bushchat, Grey  229
  Hodgson's  227
  Pied  228
Bushlark, Rufous-winged  321
Buttonquail, Barred  53
  Yellow-legged  53
Buzzard, Common  140
  Long-legged  141
  Upland  141
Chaffinch  342
Chat, River  220
Chiffchaff, Common  266
Chough, Red-billed  167
  Yellow-billed  168
Cochoa, Green  227
  Purple  227
Coot, Common  112
Cormorant, Great  152
  Indian  152
  Little  151
Coucal, Greater  87
  Lesser  87

Crake, Black-tailed  111
    Ruddy-breasted  112
Crane, Black-necked  110
    Common  109
    Demoiselle  109
Crossbill, Common  349
    Red  349
Crow, House  168
    Large-billed  169
Cuckoo, Asian Emerald  84
    Banded Bay  82
    Chestnut-winged  77
    Common Hawk  78
    Drongo  86
    Eurasian  80
    Grey-bellied  83
    Hodgson's Hawk  79
    Indian  80
    Large Hawk  78
    Lesser  82
    Oriental  81
    Plaintive  83
    Violet  84
Cuckooshrike, Black-winged  173
    Large  172
Curlew, Eurasian  117
Cutia  300
Dipper, Brown  185
    White-throated  185
Dollarbird  71
Dove, Barred Cuckoo  105
    Emerald  106
    Eurasian Collared  105
    Laughing  103
    Oriental Turtle  103
    Red Collared  104
    Spotted  104
Drongo, Ashy  179
    Black  178
    Bronzed  180
    Crow-billed  180
    Greater Racket-tailed  182
    Lesser Racket-tailed  181
    Spangled  182
Duck, Falcated  45
    Mandarin  45
    Spot-billed  47
    Tufted  52
Eagle, Black  142

Eagle (cont.)
    Bonelli's  145
    Booted  145
    Crested Serpent  135
    Golden  144
    Greater Spotted  142
    Imperial  143
    Lesser Fish  131
    Mountain Hawk  146
    Pallas's Fish  130
    Rufous-bellied  146
    Short-toed Snake  135
    Steppe  143
    White-tailed  131
Egret, Cattle  155
    Great  154
    Intermediate  154
    Little  153
Falcon, Amur  148
    Peregrine  150
Falconet, Collared  147
    Pied  147
Fantail, White-throated  178
    Yellow-bellied  177
Finch, Crimson-browed  348
    Gold-naped  353
    Plain Mountain  343
    Scarlet  348
Flameback, Greater  61
    Himalayan  61
Flowerpecker, Fire-breasted  324
    Plain  323
    Scarlet-backed  324
    Yellow-bellied  323
    Yellow-vented  322
Flycatcher, Asian Brown  199
    Blue-throated  210
    Brown-breasted  199
    Dark-sided  198
    Ferruginous  200
    Grey-headed Canary  211
    Kashmir  202
    Little Pied  204
    Pale-chinned  209
    Pale Blue  210
    Pygmy Blue  211
    Red-throated  202
    Rufous-gorgeted  201
    Sapphire  206

Flycatcher (cont.)
  Slaty-backed  200
  Slaty-blue  205
  Snowy-browed  203
  Ultramarine  204
  Verditer  206
  White-gorgeted  202
Flycatcher-shrike, Bar-winged  176
Forktail, Black-backed  225
  Little  224
  Slaty-backed  225
  Spotted  226
  White-crowned  226
Francolin, Black  34
Fulvetta, Brown-throated  309
  Golden-breasted  307
  Ludlow's  309
  Nepal  310
  Rufous-throated  309
  Rufous-winged  308
  Rusty-capped  310
  White-browed  308
  Yellow-throated  307
Gadwall  45
Garganey  48
Goldcrest  249
Goosander  52
Goose, Bar-headed  43
  Greylag  43
Goshawk, Crested  136
  Northern  139
Grandala  224
Grassbird, Striated  280
Grebe, Great Crested  151
  Little  151
Greenfinch, Yellow-breasted  342
Greenshank, Common  117
Griffon, Himalayan  133
Grosbeak, Collared  351
  Spot-winged  352
  White-winged  352
Gull, Brown-headed  126
  Great Black-headed  126
  Pallas's  126
  Slender-billed  127
Harrier, Eurasian Marsh  135
  Hen  136
  Pied  136
Heron, Black-crowned Night  156

Heron (cont.)
  Grey  153
  Indian Pond  155
  Little  156
  White-bellied  154
Hobby, Eurasian  149
  Oriental  150
Honey-buzzard, Oriental  128
Honeyguide, Yellow-rumped  54
Hoopoe, Common  69
Hornbill, Great  66
  Oriental Pied  68
  Rufous-necked  67
  Wreathed  68
Ibisbill  120
Iora, Common  184
Jacana, Bronze-winged  120
Jay, Eurasian  163
Junglefowl, Red  40
Kestrel, Common  148
Kingfisher, Black-capped  74
  Blyth's  72
  Common  72
  Crested  74
  Oriental Dwarf  73
  Pied  75
  Ruddy  73
  White-throated  74
Kite, Black  129
  Black-shouldered  129
  Brahminy  130
Koel, Asian  85
Lammergeier  132
Lapwing, Northern  123
  Red-wattled  125
  River  124
  Yellow-wattled  124
Lark, Greater Short-toed  321
  Hume's Short-toed  321
  Sand  322
Laughingthrush, Black-faced  287
  Blue-winged  286
  Chestnut-crowned  287
  Greater Necklaced  282
  Grey-sided  285
  Lesser Necklaced  281
  Rufous-chinned  284
  Rufous-necked  282
  Rufous-vented  283

Laughingthrush (cont.)
Scaly 286
Spotted 284
Streaked 285
Striated 283
White-crested 281
White-throated 280
Leafbird, Golden-fronted 160
Orange-bellied 160
Leiothrix, Red-billed 300
Liocichla, Red-faced 288
Magpie, Black-billed 166
Common Green 164
Yellow-billed Blue 163
Malkoha, Green-billed 85
Mallard 46
Martin, Asian House 248
Eurasian Crag 246
Nepal House 248
Pale 245
Plain 246
Sand 245
Merganser, Common 52
Merlin 149
Mesia, Silver-eared 299
Minivet, Grey-chinned 174
Long-tailed 174
Rosy 173
Scarlet 176
Short-billed 175
Minla, Blue-winged 305
Chestnut-tailed 306
Red-tailed 306
Monal, Himalayan 40
Monarch, Black-naped 183
Moorhen, Common 356
Munia, Scaly-breasted 341
White-rumped 341
Myna, Bank 232
Common 231
Hill 233
Jungle 232
White-vented 232
Myzornis, Fire-tailed 317
Needletail, White-throated 90
Nightjar, Grey 99
Large-tailed 100
Savanna 100
Niltava, Large 207

Niltava (cont.)
Rufous-bellied 208
Small 208
Vivid 209
Nutcracker, Spotted 166
Nuthatch, Beautiful 234
Chestnut-bellied 233
Velvet-fronted 234
White-tailed 234
Oriole, Black-hooded 172
Eurasian Golden 171
Maroon 172
Slender-billed 171
Osprey 128
Owl, Boreal 98
Brown Hawk 98
Brown Wood 95
Collared Scops 94
Long-eared 99
Mountain Scops 93
Oriental Scops 94
Short-eared 99
Spot-bellied Eagle 94
Tawny 96
Tawny Fish 95
Tengmalm's 98
Owlet, Asian Barred 97
Collared 96
Jungle 97
Spotted 98
Paradise-flycatcher, Asian 183
Parakeet, Alexandrine 88
Red-breasted 89
Rose-ringed 88
Slaty-headed 89
Parrotbill, Black-throated 319
Brown 318
Fulvous 319
Great 317
Greater Rufous-headed 320
Grey-headed 318
Lesser Rufous-headed 320
Partridge, Chestnut-breasted 37
Common Hill 36
Rufous-throated 36
Snow 33
Tibetan 34
Peafowl, Indian 42
Pheasant, Blood 38

Pheasant (cont.)
   Grey Peacock 42
   Kalij 41
Piculet, Speckled 55
   White-browed 56
Pigeon, Ashy Wood 102
   Green Imperial 108
   Hill 101
   Mountain Imperial 109
   Orange-breasted Green 106
   Pin-tailed Green 107
   Pompadour Green 106
   Rock 100
   Snow 101
   Speckled Wood 102
   Thick-billed Green 106
   Wedge-tailed Green 108
   Yellow-footed Green 107
Pintail, Northern 48
Pipit, Blyth's 335
   Buff-bellied 337
   Olive-backed 336
   Paddyfield 334
   Red-throated 336
   Richard's 334
   Rosy 336
   Tawny 335
   Tree 335
Pitta, Blue-naped 157
   Hooded 158
Plover, Kentish 123
   Lesser Sand 123
   Little Ringed 122
   Long-billed 122
Pochard, Baer's 51
   Common 50
   Ferruginous 51
   Red-crested 50
Pratincole, Small 125
Prinia, Grey-breasted 256
   Grey-crowned 255
   Hill 255
   Jungle 257
   Plain 257
   Rufescent 256
   Striated 254
Quail, Common 34
   Japanese 35
Rail, Slaty-breasted 111

Raven, Common 170
Redshank, Common 117
Redstart, Black 218
   Blue-capped 217
   Blue-fronted 220
   Daurian 219
   Güldenstädt's 220
   Hodgson's 218
   Plumbeous Water 221
   White-bellied 222
   White-capped Water 220
   White-throated 219
   White-winged 220
Robin, Blue-fronted 223
   Golden Bush 214
   Indian 217
   Indian Blue 213
   Orange-flanked Bush 214
   Oriental Magpie 216
   Rufous-breasted Bush 216
   White-browed Bush 215
   White-tailed 222
Roller, Indian 71
Rosefinch, Beautiful 346
   Blanford's 344
   Common 345
   Dark-breasted 344
   Dark-rumped 346
   Red-fronted 347
   Streaked 347
   Three-banded 347
   White-browed 347
Rubythroat, Siberian 212
   White-tailed 213
Ruff 120
Sandpiper, Common 118
   Curlew 119
   Green 118
   Wood 118
Shama, White-rumped 217
Shelduck, Common 44
   Ruddy 44
Shikra 137
Shortwing, Gould's 196
   Lesser 197
   Rusty-bellied 197
   White-browed 198
Shoveler, Northern 47
Shrike, Bay-backed 161

Shrike (cont.)
    Brown  161
    Grey-backed  162
    Long-tailed  162
Sibia, Long-tailed  312
    Rufous  311
    Rufous-backed  310
Siskin, Tibetan  342
Skylark, Oriental  322
Snipe, Common  116
    Jack  116
    Pintail  115
    Solitary  114
    Wood  114
Snowcock, Tibetan  33
Sparrow, Eurasian Tree  330
    House  329
    Russet  329
Sparrowhawk, Eurasian  138
Spiderhunter, Little  328
    Streaked  328
Starling, Asian Pied  231
    Chestnut-tailed  230
    Common  230
    Spot-winged  230
Stint, Temminck's  119
Stonechat, Common  228
Stork, Black  156
    Woolly-necked  157
Sunbird, Black-throated  326
    Crimson  327
    Fire-tailed  327
    Green-tailed  326
    Mrs Gould's  325
    Purple  325
    Ruby-cheeked  325
Swallow, Barn  246
    Red-rumped  247
Swamphen, Purple  112
Swift, Alpine  91
    Asian Palm  90
    Dark-rumped  92
    Fork-tailed  91
    House  92
    Little  92
Swiftlet, Himalayan  89
Tailorbird, Common  266
    Mountain  265
Teal, Baikal  49

Teal (cont.)
    Common  49
Tern, Common  127
    River  127
Tesia, Chestnut-headed  258
    Grey-bellied  259
    Slaty-bellied  258
Thick-knee, Eurasian  120
    Great  120
Thrush, Blue-capped Rock  186
    Blue Rock  187
    Blue Whistling  188
    Chestnut  193
    Chestnut-bellied Rock  186
    Dark-throated  195
    Dusky  196
    Eyebrowed  194
    Kessler's  194
    Long-billed  191
    Long-tailed  190
    Orange-headed  188
    Plain-backed  189
    Scaly  190
    Tickell's  191
Tit, Black-throated  244
    Coal  240
    Fire-capped  238
    Great  241
    Green-backed  241
    Grey-crested  240
    Rufous-fronted  244
    Rufous-vented  239
    Sultan  243
    Yellow-browed  242
    Yellow-cheeked  242
Tragopan, Blyth's  39
    Satyr  38
Treecreeper, Brown-throated  237
    Eurasian  236
    Rusty-flanked  237
Treepie, Collared  165
    Grey  165
    Rufous  164
Treeswift, Crested  93
Trogon, Red-headed  69
    Ward's  70
Vulture, Cinereous  134
    Egyptian  132
    Eurasian Black  134

Red-headed  134
White-rumped  132
Wagtail, Citrine  332
Forest  330
Grey  334
White  330
White-browed  332
Yellow  333
Wallcreeper  236
Warbler, Aberrant Bush  261
Ashy-throated  269
Black-faced  279
Blyth's Leaf  273
Blyth's Reed  264
Booted  265
Broad-billed  278
Brownish-flanked Bush  260
Brown Bush  263
Buff-barred  268
Chestnut-crowned  277
Chestnut-crowned Bush  261
Dusky  267
Golden-spectacled  274
Greenish  272
Grey-cheeked  277
Grey-hooded  276
Grey-sided Bush  262
Hume's Leaf  271
Large-billed Leaf  272
Lemon-rumped  270
Pale-footed Bush  260
Rufous-faced  278
Russet Bush  263
Smoky  267
Spotted Bush  263
Thick-billed  265
Tickell's Leaf  268
Whistler's  274
White-spectacled  276
Yellow-bellied  279
Yellow-browed  270
Yellow-vented  274
Yellowish-bellied Bush  262
Waterhen, White-breasted  111
Weaver, Baya  340
Black-breasted  340
Wheatear, Isabelline  229
Pied  229
Whimbrel  116

Whistling-duck, Fulvous  43
White-eye, Oriental  257
Whitethroat, Lesser  321
Wigeon, Eurasian  46
Woodcock, Eurasian  113
Woodpecker, Bay  62
Crimson-breasted  58
Darjeeling  58
Fulvous-breasted  57
Great Slaty  62
Grey-capped Pygmy  56
Grey-headed  60
Pale-headed  62
Rufous  59
Rufous-bellied  57
Streak-throated  60
Stripe-breasted  356
Woodshrike, Large  184
Woodswallow, Ashy  170
Wren, Winter  238
Wryneck, Eurasian  55
Yellownape, Greater  60
Lesser  59
Yuhina, Black-chinned  316
Rufous-vented  315
Striated  312
Stripe-throated  314
Whiskered  314
White-bellied  316
White-naped  313

# The Author

**Peter Spierenburg** has lived and worked in Bhutan for more than five years. He has assisted the Nature Conservation Division of the Royal Government of Bhutan on conservation and development programmes in their national parks. He has travelled the country extensively and in all seasons, including treks to some of the remotest villages. His main base was the Zhemgang area in the south of the Jigme Singye Wangchuck National Park, one of the most bird-rich areas of the country and until recently off-limits for visiting birders.

# The Publisher

The **Oriental Bird Club** is a UK registered charity, founded in 1984, with the principal objectives of promoting an interest in the birds of the Oriental region and their conservation, liaising with and encouraging the work of existing regional organisations, and collating and publishing material on the birds of the region. Each year the Club publishes two issues of the topical bulletin *BirdingASIA* and one issue of *Forktail – Journal of Asian Ornithology*. The Club now has a membership approaching 2,000 and spans almost 60 countries worldwide.

The Club also operates a conservation fund and through the small grant award scheme supports the work of nationals of the region in conservation and conservation awareness projects. In 1999 the Club set up the Bertram Smythies Memorial Fund, following the bequest of a share in the estate of the late Bertram Smythies, the pioneering ornithologist of Borneo and Burma. It is thanks to this fund that *Birds in Bhutan: Status and Distribution* has been published, a project that the Club believes the benefactor would have warmly approved.

For further information about the Club, please write to OBC, P.O. Box 324, Bedford, MK42 0WG, UK. Email: mail@orientalbirdclub.org or visit the website www.orientalbirdclub.org. The website also gives access to the 'OBC Image Database' which includes photographs of many of the birds that feature in this book.